Architectural Construction

THE CHOICE OF STRUCTURAL DESIGN

THEODORE CRANE, C.E., M.A.
Consulting Engineer; Professor of Architectural Engineering, Yale University

1947

New York · JOHN WILEY & SONS, *Inc.*
London · CHAPMAN & HALL, *Limited*

PRINTED IN THE UNITED STATES OF AMERICA

Preface

This book deals with the problem of making an appropriate choice for the structural portions of a building, as governed by the geographical location, site conditions, type of occupancy, equipment, and architectural design. It presents a procedure for determining the type of building frame, foundation, floor, roof, and wall construction most suitable to meet the requirements of any particular structure.

Such a selection is a prerequisite of all quantitative design. Upon it depend the economy and often both the service and the appearance of a structure. No refinement in future computations can correct a serious error in the arrangement of the framing or in the choice of floor or roof construction. Inadvertence in planning foundations or failure to investigate soil conditions has too often proved disastrous.

The text is written for students in architecture, architectural engineering, and building construction, and for practicing architects and architectural engineers who desire a comprehensive résumé of all the better types of construction now available in the American market, with recommendations concerning their specific applications. Portions of the text should be of value to mechanical and electrical engineers who require a knowledge of modern building assemblies as influencing their own work.

To verify many statements made in this text, it has been necessary to consult or correspond with architects, engineers, builders, trade associations, and manufacturers of building materials throughout the United States. In some instances actual inspections have been made to determine the present condition of structures in which particular systems or assemblies were used. It is impossible to mention the names of all who have been of assistance. The author apologizes for the brevity of the following list, which includes the names of only those individuals and corporations which have been particularly helpful.

Mr. Fred N. Severud, Consulting Engineer, New York City.

Mr. Henry D. Dewell, Dewell & Dewell, Consulting Engineers, San Francisco, California.

Mr. J. E. Sirrine, J. E. Sirrine Company, Consulting Engineers, Greenville, South Carolina.

Mr. L. H. Boase, Manager Structural Bureau, Portland Cement Association, Chicago, Illinois.

Mr. Joseph Di Stasio, Joseph Di Stasio Company, Consulting Engineers, New York City.

Turner Construction Company, Builders, New York City.

The Austin Company, Engineers and Builders, Cleveland, Ohio.

Mr. W. Joshua Barney, W. J. Barney Corporation, Builders, New York City.

Mr. Verne Ketchum, Chief Engineer, Timber Structures, Inc., Seattle, Washington.

Roberts & Schaefer, Engineers, Chicago, Illinois.

The author is especially indebted to the following individuals for their kindness in reading portions of the text in manuscript.

Mr. Clinton T. Bissell, Consulting Engineer, National Board of Fire Underwriters.

Mr. A. E. Cummings, Raymond Concrete Pile Company, New York City.

Mr. H. M. Eastman, Consulting Engineer, East Orange, New Jersey.

Mr. Henry A. Pfisterer, Wilcox, Erickson, & Pfisterer, Consulting Engineers, New Haven, Connecticut.

Mr. R. H. Gloss, Structural Engineer, Timber Engineering Company, Washington, D. C.

Mr. Harold D. Hauf, Professor of Architectural Engineering, Yale University

Mr. T. R. Higgins, Director of Engineering, American Institute of Steel Construction.

Mr. Dimitri P. Krynine, Associate Professor of Soil Mechanics, Yale University.

Mr. Harry C. Plummer, Director of Engineering and Research, Structural Clay Products Institute, Washington, D. C.

Mr. Walter Weiskopf, Weiskopf & Pickworth, Consulting Engineers, New York City.

Mr. Lazarus White, Spencer, White, & Prentis, Engineers & Contractors, New York City.

THEODORE CRANE

January, 1947

Contents

Chapter One · BUILDING CODES AND DESIGN STANDARDS

Chapter Two · CHOOSING THE FRAMING MATERIAL

Chapter Three · PLANNING THE FRAMING OF A BUILDING

Chapter Four · CHOOSING THE STRUCTURAL FLOOR SYSTEM

Chapter Five · CHOOSING THE STRUCTURAL ROOF SYSTEM

Chapter Six · WIDE-SPAN DESIGNS

Chapter Seven · CHOOSING THE WALL ASSEMBLY

Chapter Eight · MASONRY WALLS

Chapter Nine · CHOOSING THE TYPE OF FOUNDATION

Chapter One

BUILDING CODES AND DESIGN STANDARDS

Fundamental to all practical considerations are the requirements of building codes or the standards chosen by the designer in the absence of mandatory regulations. These requirements or standards apply to both the architectural planning of a building and the choice of structural design.

Article 1. Codes Controlling the Design of Buildings

FEDERAL STANDARDS. There is no national building code in the United States. Several excellent texts, embodying recommendations on subjects such as are usually covered by building ordinances, have been prepared by the National Bureau of Standards and the Building Code Committees of the Department of Commerce, but their use is in no way mandatory unless they are adopted by a specific authority. Work executed for a department or agency of the federal government is designed according to the standards of that department. Buildings constructed on federal property are not subject to the requirements of local codes. This statement applies to those erected by the army, navy, and other federal agencies such as the Public Buildings Administration, which supervises the design and erection of post offices, court houses, custom houses, and government office buildings.

STATE CODES. A few states have building codes, and many states have existing statutes, not identified as codes, applying to the design of buildings erected for particular uses or types of occupancy. These state regulations affect particularly the design of multifamily dwellings, factories, or other buildings where labor is employed and places of public assembly. Some state authorities have issued sanitary standards applying to buildings which are occasionally mandatory but more often in the form of recommendations.

State regulations controlling the design of multifamily dwellings may be expanded, as in the State Housing Act of California (1942), to include hotels and some other residential types. Such regulations apply within their jurisdiction to all grades of buildings erected for these purposes, but the standards which they impose have particular significance in the design of low-cost housing. These standards generally include minimum spatial and hygienic requirements, sanitary regulations, and a reasonable degree of security against dangers incident to fire.

State legislation, incorporated in a labor law or industrial code, may affect the design of industrial buildings. Such legislation often includes ventilation and sanitary requirements, as well as standards to safeguard employees from danger due to manufacturing processes or the fire hazard. It applies not only to factories but also, with certain exceptions, to any other type of occupancy where wage earners are employed.

State regulations pertaining to places of public assembly, such as theaters and dance halls, do not ordinarily impose restrictions more severe than a modern municipal building code. They have particular significance for the designer of buildings of this class erected in the smaller towns or rural districts. In such localities the minimum requirements demanded by the state may control the design.

MUNICIPAL CODES. Many cities have building ordinances, referred to as building codes, applying to the design of new buildings and to alterations in or additions to existing buildings. In this case the codes control all types of occupancy, not being limited in their application to special categories, as are most state regulations. When checking the content of a municipal code, the designer should remember that important revisions may have been made since the publication of the current edition. These revisions can be obtained from the Building Department. Supplementing the city ordinances identified as the building code, there are usually regulations affecting building design promulgated by various city departments, such as those for fire and health.

COUNTY AND TOWNSHIP CODES. There are only a few county building codes, but the designer should check the possibility of their existence in rural districts. Many townships and some villages have building ordinances. These usually cover, much more briefly, the same subjects as the municipal codes in so far as they are appropriate for the locality. If the designer follows a standard of good practice, they have little significance except in the matter of zoning.

Article 2. Classification of Buildings

INTRODUCTION. Building codes generally contain a classification of buildings, with respect to both type of construction and class of occupancy or use. Because of the fact that one of the primary objects is to protect life and property from dangers incident to fire, the specific requirements differentiating the construction classifications pertain primarily to fire risk and are actually classifications on the basis of fire hazard. For this reason it became necessary to establish a uniform procedure for determining the relative fire resistance of various building materials and types of construction. This was done under the joint sponsorship of the American Society for Testing Materials, the National Bureau of Standards, and the Fire Protection group of the American Standards Association.

THE STANDARD FIRE TEST. The following procedure is given in more detail in Appendix B of the Building Code Recommended by the National Board of Fire Underwriters. It prescribes a standard of exposure to fire of controlled extent and severity, in some cases followed immediately by subjecting the sample, or assembly, to a fire-hose stream. Performance is defined as the period of resistance to such exposure elapsing before the first critical point in behavior is observed. If this period is 2 hours, the material or assembly, such as a partition or floor system, is given a "2-hour rating." These ratings, which vary from 1 to 4 hours, have considerable significance for the designer. They appear as requirements for the more fire-resistant construction classifications. It is consequently often necessary to limit the choice of structural assemblies to those having the ratings necessary to meet the desired classification.

CLASSIFICATION ACCORDING TO CONSTRUCTION. These classifications are recommended by the National Board of Fire Underwriters; they are more complete than those in most codes.

1. Fireproof construction.
2. Semifireproof construction.
3. Heavy-timber construction.
4. Ordinary construction.
5. Light noncombustible construction.
6. Frame construction.
7. Unprotected metal construction.

These classes are defined in the Fire Underwriters' Recommended Building Code as follows:

1. Fireproof construction is that in which the structural members are of approved noncombustible construction having the necessary strength and stability and having fire-resistance ratings of not less than 4 hours for exterior nonbearing walls and for wall panels, for columns, and for wall-supporting girders and trusses; and not less than 3 hours for floors, for roofs, and for floor- and roof-supporting beams, girders, and trusses, and in which exterior bearing walls and interior bearing walls, if any, are of approved masonry or of reinforced concrete. This type of construction corresponds generally with that sometimes called "fully protected" or "fire-resistive" construction. Because of the long, well-established and almost universal use of the term "fireproof," it is thought best to retain that term for the type of construction here defined.

2. Semifireproof construction is that in which the structural members are of approved noncombustible construction having the necessary strength and stability and having fire-resistance ratings of not less than 4 hours for exterior nonbearing walls and for wall panels; not less than 3 hours for columns, and for

wall-supporting girders and trusses; not less than 2 hours for floors, for roofs, and for floor- and roof-supporting beams, girders, and trusses; and in which exterior bearing walls and interior bearing walls, if any, are of approved masonry or reinforced concrete. This type of construction corresponds generally with that sometimes called "protected" or "fire safe."

3. HEAVY-TIMBER CONSTRUCTION is that in which walls are of approved masonry or reinforced concrete; and in which the interior structural elements, including columns, floors, and roof construction, consist of heavy timbers with smooth flat surfaces assembled to avoid thin sections, sharp projections, and concealed or inaccessible spaces; and in which all structural members which support masonry walls shall have a fire-resistance rating of not less than 3 hours; and other structural members of steel or reinforced concrete, if used in lieu of timber construction, shall have a fire resistance rating of not less than 1 hour. This type of construction is the same as that called "mill" construction or "slow-burning" construction.

4. ORDINARY CONSTRUCTION is that in which exterior walls and bearing walls are of approved masonry, or reinforced concrete, and in which the structural elements are wholly or partly of wood of smaller dimensions than required for heavy-timber construction, or of steel or iron not protected as required for fireproof construction or semifireproof construction. The term "ordinary" construction corresponds generally with that variously called "nonfireproof," "masonry walls and wooden joists," or "ordinary masonry" construction.

5. LIGHT NONCOMBUSTIBLE CONSTRUCTION is that in which all structural members, including walls, floors, roofs, and their supports, are of steel, iron, concrete, or of other noncombustible materials, and in which the exterior enclosure walls are of masonry or concrete, or are of other fire-resistive materials or assemblies of materials which have not less than 2-hour fire-resistance ratings. Structures similar to all-metal gasoline service stations would be included under this classification.[1]

6. FRAME CONSTRUCTION is that in which walls and interior construction are wholly or partly of wood. Buildings of exterior masonry veneer, metal or stucco on wooden frame, constituting, wholly or in part, the structural supports of the building or its loads, are frame buildings within the meaning of this definition.

7. UNPROTECTED METAL CONSTRUCTION is that in which the structural supports are unprotected metal and in which the roofing and walls or other enclosures are of sheet metal, or of other noncombustible materials, or of masonry deficient in thickness or otherwise not conforming to approved masonry.

RELATION BETWEEN COMBUSTIBLE CONTENTS, FIRE SEVERITY, AND FIRE-RESISTANCE RATINGS. For a number of years this subject has received consideration in documents concerned with fire-protection engineering. In the Appendix of the report entitled "Recommended Minimum Requirements for Fire Resistance in Buildings," published in 1931 by the Building Code Committee, Department of Commerce, the weight of combustible contents, on a basis of pounds per square foot of

[1] Light-gage steel-stud construction, surfaced on the exterior with a 4-in. brick veneer, insulated with noncombustible material and finished on the interior with a sanded gypsum plaster carried by metal or wire lath, would also be included under this classification.

floor area, was related to the probable severity of a potential fire. This discussion was based on tests sponsored by the National Bureau of Standards. It showed the effect of combustible contents, including combustible materials incorporated in the structure, upon fire duration in terms of the Standard Fire Test.

In "Fire-Resistance Classifications of Building Constructions," *Building Materials and Structures Report BMS* 92, National Bureau of Standards (1942), the subject was further developed to the extent that the total fuel content of a building was identified as one of the more important criteria to be considered in determining the minimum fire-resistance ratings that should be required for various structural and occupancy conditions. The following table, abstracted from this publication, gives the relationship between the amount of combustible contents and potential fire severity.

RELATION OF AMOUNT OF COMBUSTIBLES TO FIRE SEVERITY

COMBUSTIBLE CONTENTS Average Weight of Furniture, Wood Flooring, Wood Trim, etc., as Well as Stored Materials in Pounds per Square Foot of Floor Area	FIRE SEVERITY Duration in Hours
5	½
7½	¾
10	1
15	1½
20	2
30	3
40	4½
50	6
60	7½

In regard to the use of this table, the report states:

It is considered sufficiently accurate in computing combustible contents to take wood, paper, cotton, wool, silk, straw, grain, sugar, and similar organic materials at their actual weights and to take animal and vegetable oils, fats, and waxes, petroleum products, asphalt, bitumen, paraffin, pitch, alcohol, and naphthalene at twice their actual weights.

As mentioned above, the periods in the table identify the potential fire severity for varying amounts of combustible contents and correspond to the destructive effect which would be produced by exposure to the Standard Fire Test for the duration noted. For example, 10 lb per sq ft of burning contents might be capable of producing the same effect as a 1-hour Standard Fire Test and would imply the necessity for a somewhat greater fire resistance in the structure, even if a lower rating were permitted by the building code.

These data should be more seriously considered and reflected to a greater extent than at present in the fire-resistance ratings demanded by codes. During the past few years the subject has become particularly important because of the development of several new types of construction which do not conform with conventional building assemblies. At the present time these newer constructions may be required to meet demands out of proportion to the fire risk involved by the types of occupancy for which they are built. Although only one of several considerations, a more thorough appreciation of this relationship between combustible contents and potential fire severity would be a helpful step toward more economical design.

Additional information on this subject will be found in the references which have been mentioned and in *Fire Protection through Modern Building Codes* by B. L. Wood, published by the American Iron and Steel Institute, 1945.

CLASSIFICATION ACCORDING TO OCCUPANCY. These classifications are those recommended by the National Board of Fire Underwriters; they are typical of many codes.

1. Public buildings.
2. Institutional buildings.
3. Residence buildings.
4. Business buildings.
5. Storage buildings.

These classes are defined in the Fire Underwriters' Recommended Building Code as follows:

1. PUBLIC BUILDINGS are those in which persons congregate for political, educational, religious, social, or recreational purposes. This class includes, among others, court houses, schools, colleges, libraries, museums, exhibition buildings, lecture halls, churches, assembly halls, lodge rooms, dance halls, theaters, bath houses, armories, recreation piers, stadiums, passenger stations, bowling alleys, skating rinks, gymnasiums, city halls, grandstands, motion picture theaters, auditoriums, clubs, restaurants.

2. INSTITUTIONAL BUILDINGS are those in which persons are harbored to receive medical, charitable, or other care or treatment, or in which persons are held or detained by reason of public or civic duty, or for correctional purposes. This class includes, among others, hospitals, asylums, sanitariums, fire houses, police stations, jails, penal institutions, orphanages, infirmaries, homes for the aged, reformatories, nurseries, houses of correction.

3. RESIDENCE BUILDINGS, except when classed as institutional buildings, are those in which sleeping accommodations are provided. This class includes, among others, dwellings, tenements, multifamily houses, hotels, lodging houses, dormitories, convents, studios, club houses, apartments, old people's homes.

4. BUSINESS BUILDINGS are those occupied for the transaction of business, for the rendering of professional services, for the display, sale of goods, wares, or merchandise, or for the performance of work or labor. This class includes, among

others, office buildings, stores, markets, factories, workshops, laboratories, gasoline service stations, smoke houses, central power plants, electric substations, bakeries, laundries, chemical laboratories, telephone exchanges, barber shops, open stores,[2] creameries, radio stations, ice plants, paint shops, dry cleaning plants, varnish and lacquer plants, mattress factories, box factories.

5. STORAGE BUILDINGS are those used, except for purely display purposes, to house airplanes, automobiles, railway cars, or other vehicles of transportation; for the sheltering of horses, livestock, or other animals; or exclusively for the storage of goods, wares, or merchandise, not excluding, in any case, offices incidental to such uses; and including among other buildings, garages, barns, hangars, storage warehouses, freight depots, grain elevators, coal storage, and gasoline bulk stations.

If a building is occupied for two or more purposes not included in the same class, it is customary to enforce code requirements applying to each class of occupancy to the parts of the building within that class. If there are conflicting provisions, the requirements securing the greater safety apply. If there is any doubt in regard to the classification applying to a specific building, its status should be definitely fixed by the appropriate authority.

Article 3. Fire Limits and Building-Height and Area Limitations

FIRE LIMITS. In order to reduce the fire hazard, city building codes generally require more fire-resistant construction within the more congested areas. Boundaries of such areas are designated as "fire limits." They usually include all closely built mercantile and adjoining manufacturing districts, together with surrounding areas which constitute an exposure to the district or within which new construction of a mercantile or a manufacturing character is developing. Within these limits wood-frame structures are normally prohibited or restricted to small private garages, greenhouses, and sheds. Unprotected metal construction is prohibited or restricted to such small buildings as gasoline service stations of a very limited area. Figure 1 shows fire limits and other information pertaining to fire control for a small city, together with recommendations made by the National Board of Fire Underwriters for additional installations.

BUILDING HEIGHT AND AREA LIMITATIONS. City codes generally prescribe height and area limitations applying to all classes of construction, other than fireproof, built within fire limits. There is considerable variation in these requirements, and the designer should check the local authority, as such regulations may influence the choice of structure. The tables on pages 9 and 10, abstracted from the Building Code Recommended by the National Board of Fire Underwriters, represent a standard of good practice. Although thoroughly justified by experience, they are somewhat more restrictive than the regulations of most small cities.

[2] An "open store" is a small, low building with the front or front and sides open, used generally for the display and sale of fruit or farm produce.

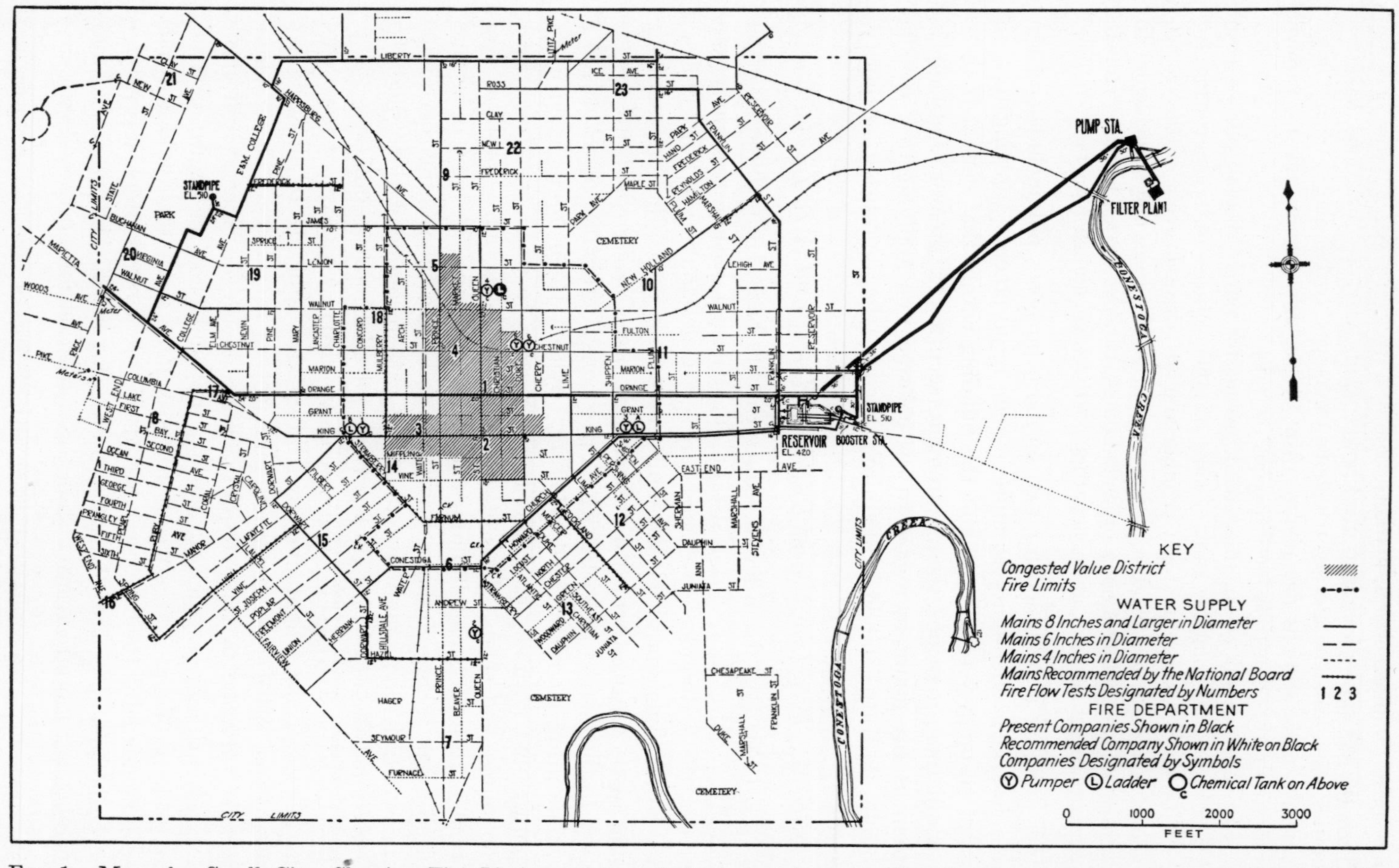

FIG. 1. Map of a Small City, Showing Fire Limits and Installations Pertaining to Fire Control. Courtesy, National Board of Fire Underwriters.

ALLOWABLE HEIGHTS OF BUILDINGS

(From the Building Code Recommended by the National Board of Fire Underwriters)

<table>
<tr><th rowspan="3">Classes of Occupancy</th><th colspan="7">Classes of Construction</th></tr>
<tr><th rowspan="2">Fire-proof</th><th rowspan="2">Semi-fireproof</th><th rowspan="2">Heavy Timber</th><th rowspan="2">Ordinary</th><th rowspan="2">Light Noncom-bustible</th><th>Frame</th><th>Unpro-tected Metal</th></tr>
<tr><th colspan="2">Not permitted within fire limits</th></tr>
<tr><td>Public* buildings</td><td>No limit</td><td>75 ft</td><td colspan="3">Three stories nor more than 35 ft
Churches: Two stories nor more than 45 ft
Schools: Two stories
Theatres: See Note † below</td><td>Two stories nor more than 30 ft</td><td>One story</td></tr>
<tr><td>Institutional buildings</td><td>No limit</td><td>75 ft</td><td colspan="3">Two stories nor more than 35 ft
See Note † below</td><td>One story nor more than 35 ft
See Note † below</td><td>One story</td></tr>
<tr><td>Residence buildings</td><td>No limit</td><td>75 ft</td><td>75 ft</td><td>Three stories nor more than 45 ft
See Note ‡ below</td><td>Three stories nor more than 45 ft</td><td>Two stories nor more than 35 ft
Dwellings not to exceed three stories</td><td>One story</td></tr>
<tr><td>Business* buildings</td><td>No limit</td><td>75 ft</td><td>75 ft</td><td colspan="2">Four stories nor more than 50 ft</td><td>25 ft</td><td>One story</td></tr>
<tr><td>Storage* buildings</td><td>No limit</td><td>50 ft
See Note § below</td><td>35 ft
See Note § below</td><td colspan="2">35 ft
See Note § below</td><td>One story nor more than 25 ft</td><td>One story</td></tr>
</table>

* Outside the fire limits public buildings, business buildings, or storage buildings may be erected to greater heights in the discretion of a board.

† Special occupancies: Asylums, detention buildings, hospitals, penal institutions, orphanages, nurseries, and theaters hereafter erected shall be of fireproof construction or semifireproof construction; except that hospitals where occupants are not involuntarily detained or bedridden (sanatoriums), may be of nonfireproof construction provided such buildings do not exceed two stories in height and the floors and partitions have fire-resistance ratings of not less than 1 hour, with fire-retardant ceilings under roofs. One-story theaters not over 30 ft in height may have wood or steel trusses and wood, steel, or gypsum roof decks if protected by fire-retardant ceilings.

‡ With a 2-hour first floor, height may be four stories or 55 ft; in multifamily houses with a 2-hour first floor and other floors 1-hour, with fire partitions subdividing floors into areas not exceeding 2,500 sq ft, the height may be five stories or 65 ft.

§ Buildings which are sprinklered of semifireproof or heavy-timber construction may be 75 ft, and ordinary construction and light noncombustible may be 50 ft.

Author's Note: Sprinklers are required by this code for certain types of occupancy.

ALLOWABLE AREAS OF BUILDINGS

(From the Building Code Recommended by the National Board of Fire Underwriters)

Maximum areas in square feet permitted in new buildings not protected by automatic sprinklers and without suitable subdivisions by fire walls for heavy timber, ordinary, light noncombustible, and frame construction or by fire partitions in fireproof and semifireproof construction.

Classes of Occupancy	Classes of Construction							
	Fireproof	Semi-Fireproof		Heavy Timber	Ordinary and Light Noncombustible		Frame	Unprotected Metal
			Street Fronts *		One Story	More Than One Story	Not permitted within fire limits	
Not a Factor	Unlimited except as restricted by combustible occupancy		One street Two streets Three streets Four streets	6,500 8,000 10,000 10,000	6,000 7,500 9,000 10,500	5,000 6,000 7,500 9,000	5,000	Not restricted

Area Modification.

a. The limiting areas may be increased by 100 per cent when the building is sprinklered, and by 200 per cent when the building is sprinklered and does not exceed one story or an average of 25 ft in height to the roof, or to a fire-retardant ceiling through which there are no openings unless they open into shafts or ducts to the roof, the enclosing walls of which have the same construction as the ceiling.

b. Outside the congested areas of the city, when a hazardous condition is not created thereby, the area of a public building, a business building, or a storage building, not over two stories high, may be increased in excess of the areas fixed by this section, in the discretion of a board consisting of the chief executive officer of the municipality, the building official, and the chief of the fire department; provided that a building of combustible occupancy, or involving considerable combustible material in its structural parts, shall be sprinklered.

* *c.* Under this section a street shall be deemed to include any avenue, boulevard, street, alley, or lane, 20 ft or greater in width, or any court, parking space, or yard, with direct connection to a street, and not less than 20 ft wide. Such court, parking space, or yard shall be the property of the owner of the building and shall not be enclosed or roofed over.

Author's Note: Sprinklers are required and further area restrictions established by this code for certain types of occupancy.

The table entitled Allowable Heights of Buildings will be helpful to the designer as a standard for determining the probable type or types of construction permitted for a building of known height and class of occupancy. On the basis of the standards given in the table, it will be seen that frame construction should not be used within fire limits nor for other than low structures outside the fire limits. A business building located within fire limits should not be designed of ordinary or light noncombustible construction if over 50 ft in height or more than four stories.

It should be noted that, in applying the height limitations as given in the Underwriters' Code, the following appurtenances are not deemed parts of the building: church spires, tanks and their supports, roof structures, chimneys, signs attached to the building, radio masts, water-cooling towers for air conditioning, and other apparatus and parapets that do not extend more than 4 ft above the roof surface at their point of contact. Each part of a building included within fire walls, required to conform to the area limitations prescribed for its type of construction, is limited in height as though such part were a separate building.

The table entitled Allowable Areas of Buildings will be helpful to the designer as a standard for determining the probable type or types of construction permitted for a building of known area and class of occupancy when located within the "congested areas" of a municipality. It will be seen that heavy-timber, ordinary, and light noncombustible designs are very definitely restricted in area. Fireproof and semifireproof constructions are not limited in area, but sprinkler systems are required under certain conditions where the type of occupancy or the contents of the building present a particular fire hazard.

City codes do not in general permit buildings to cover the entire lot area. Restrictions vary for different classes of occupancy, for various districts, and in relation to the height of the structure. As the primary object of such regulations is to provide light and air for the occupants of the building in question and for those of adjoining buildings, the proportion of the lot area which must remain uncovered is usually reduced for corner locations and increased with the height of the structure. Some city codes also set a definite height limitation for even fireproof buildings. For example, the Los Angeles, California, Code (1944), permits no building over 150 ft.

NEW YORK CITY "SET-BACK LAW." In addition to the limitations of height and area applying to other than fireproof or semifireproof construction, some of our larger municipalities have regulations, similar to the New York City ordinance, which control the profile of a building in relation to the width of the street or streets upon which it fronts. The city is divided into eight districts. The vertical height of the street wall, with certain exceptions, is limited as a ratio of the street width, varying in the different districts from one-quarter times the street width to two times the street width.

Above this level the building walls must be set back a distance which is proportional to the next increment of height and varies for the different districts. In the so-called "one-quarter district," where the street front may rise vertically only a quarter of the street width, the added height can

FIG. 2. The Tishman Building, New York City. *Arch.:* Kahn and Jacobs; *Engr.:* Fred N Severud.

MINIMUM DESIGN DEAD LOADS (*Continued*)

Floor Finish and Fill	Finish Floor to Top of Slab, Inches	Pounds per Square Foot
Double $\frac{7}{8}$ wood on sleepers, light-concrete fill	4	19
Single $\frac{7}{8}$ wood on sleepers, light-concrete fill	4	23
Floor Finish	**Thickness, Inches**	
$1\frac{1}{2}$-in. asphalt mastic flooring	$1\frac{1}{2}$	18
3-in. wood block on $\frac{1}{2}$-in. mortar base	$3\frac{1}{2}$	16
Solid flat clay tile on 1-in. mortar base	2	23
2-in. asphalt block, $\frac{1}{2}$-in. mortar	$2\frac{1}{2}$	30
1-in. terrazzo, 2-in. stone concrete	3	38
Floor Fill		
Cinder concrete, per inch		9
Light-weight concrete, per inch		7
Ceilings		
Plaster on tile or concrete		5
Suspended metal lath and gypsum plaster		10
Suspended metal lath and cement plaster		15
Plaster on wooden lath		8
Roof Coverings		
Asbestos shingles		4
Asphalt shingles		6
4-ply felt and gravel composition		$5\frac{1}{2}$

Roof Coverings (*Cont.*)	Pounds per Square Foot
Sheathing, per 1-in. thickness	3
Slate, $\frac{3}{16}$-in.	7
Slate, $\frac{1}{4}$-in.	10
Wood shingles	3

Weights of Materials	Pounds per Cubic Foot
Cast-stone masonry (cement, stone, sand)	144
Cinder fill	57
Concrete, plain	
Stone (including gravel)	144
Slag	132
Cinder	108
Haydite (burned-clay aggregate)	90
Expanded-slag aggregate	100
Concrete, reinforced	
Stone (including gravel)	150
Slag	138
Cinder	111
Masonry, brick	
Hard (low absorption)	130
Medium (medium absorption)	115
Soft (high absorption)	100
Masonry, ashlar	
Granite	165
Limestone, crystalline	165
Limestone, oolitic	135
Marble	173
Sandstone	144
Timber, seasoned	
Cypress, southern	32
Fir, Douglas, coast region	34
Oak, commercial reds and whites	45
Pine, southern yellow	39
Redwood	28
Spruce, red, white, and Sitka	28

Weights of masonry include mortar but not plaster. For plaster, add 5 lb per sq ft for each face plastered. Values given represent averages. In some cases there is a considerable range of weight for the same construction. These variations are given in the authority from which this table is abstracted.

The table on page 17 shows the minimum live loads required by representative authorities. This table is included because the live-load requirement affects the choice of structural design, since certain types of construction have been developed for light or medium loads, whereas others are particularly suitable for heavier loads. It should be remembered that these loads do not include any permanent parts of the structure; for example, in determining the total load to be carried by a structural assembly such as a floor system, the weight of nonstructural portions, such as fill, floor finish, and plaster on the ceiling beneath, must be added to the weight of the structural system plus the live load given in the code for the corresponding type of occupancy.

The report of the Building Code Committee of the Department of Commerce, entitled "Minimum Live Loads Allowable for Use in Design of Buildings," was issued over 20 years ago and has had considerable influence on building codes. It was appropriate for the time it was issued, but during the past 20 years there has been a tendency to use much heavier office equipment and heavier trucks. This tendency is reflected in the corresponding minimum live loads given in the recommendation of the American Standards Association.

The code prepared by the Pacific Coast Building Officials Conference, known as the Uniform Building Code, has been accepted by approximately three hundred cities and may be considered typical of good practice in that locality. The Canadian Code was prepared for the purpose of offering an authoritative document that would commend itself for adoption to local authorities. Although the function of a dominion government agency can be no more than advisory, the text presents a very praiseworthy effort, which might well be emulated in the United States.[3]

Our own Underwriters' Code is too well known to need comment. The requirements of Philadelphia are included as representing one of our larger cities. The report of the American Standards Association, identified on page 13, presents recommendations applying to the partial loading of floors, partition loads, impact loads, and the reduction of live loads, as well as a discussion of wind loads and earthquake loads.

It should be clearly understood that the loads shown in the table on page 17 are merely minimum live-load requirements and do not relieve the designer from providing adequate structural strength to support safely the actual loads due to the type of occupancy for which the structure is intended. This is particularly important in regard to manufacturing and storage buildings. For clarity, the requirements to provide safety against injury due to concentrations have been omitted, except for garages. These requirements appear in most codes as supplementing the uniformly dis-

[3] The Building Officials Conference of America has recently undertaken the preparation of a basic building code.

MINIMUM LIVE LOADS OF REPRESENTATIVE CODES

Type of Occupancy	Minimum Live Loads per Square Foot of Floor Area					
	Department of Commerce, 1925	Pacific Coast Building Officials Conference, 1946	National Building Code of Canada, 1941	National Board of Fire Underwriters' Recommendations, 1943	Philadelphia Code, 1941	American Standards Association, 1945
Dwellings	40	40	40	40	40	40
Hotels * Lodging houses, tenements Apartments, hospitals (private rooms and wards)	40	40	40	40	40	40
Office buildings:						
Offices and private corridors	50	50	50	50	60	80
Lobbies and public spaces †	100	100	100	100	100	100
Schools: Classrooms	50	40	50	50	50	40
Buildings for public assembly:						
With fixed seats ‡	50	50	60	75	60	60
Without fixed seats	100	100	100	100	100	100
Aisles and corridors	100	100	100	100	100	100 §
Stores:						
Wholesale	100	100	125	100	110	125
Retail	75	75	100		110	
Garages:						
All types of vehicles	100	100 ‖	150 ¶	175	100 **	100–200 ††
Passenger cars only	80		75 ‡‡		100	
Warehouses §§	100–250	125–250	125	120	150	125–250
Manufacturing:						
Heavy §§	100	125	125	120	200	125
Light §§	75	75			120	
Stairways	100	100	100	100	100	100 ‖‖
Sidewalks	250	250	250	300	120	250 ¶¶

* Does not apply to hotel lobbies, stairways, or any portion used for public assembly. Such spaces same as for office buildings.

† This requirement is often applied to the entire first floor irrespective of expected use.

‡ This requirement is usually applied to aisles between rows of seats.

§ Corridors, upper floors.

‖ Additional provision required for loaded trucks.

¶ Limited to 20,000 lb gross weight; minimum concentrated load, 8000 lb on an area 2 ft 6 in. square.

** Minimum concentrated load "at any point" 8000 lb.

†† One hundred for cars with loads less than 3 tons; 150 for trucks with loads 3 to 10 tons; 200 for trucks with loads above 10 tons; each classification also subject to maximum wheel concentrations.

‡‡ Any type of vehicle not exceeding 6000 lb gross weight; minimum concentrated load 4000 lb on an area 2 ft 6 in. square.

§§ These figures have significance only as minimums. Such structures should be designed for the actual loads due to the type of materials stored or manufacturing equipment.

‖‖ Or a series of concentrated loads of 300 lb each, spaced 3 ft 0 in. center to center, each occupying an area 1 ft wide by the depth of the tread, whichever will produce the greater stresses.

¶¶ Or a concentrated load of 8000 lb on an area 2½ ft square placed in any position, whichever will produce the greater stresses.

tributed loads. For example, the floors of office or storage buildings are often required to support a concentrated weight of 2000 lb, without other live load, on any area 2½ or 3 ft square, and sidewalks a concentrated load of 800 lb (8000 lb recommended by the American Standards Association). Such regulations affect the design only if the stresses produced are greater than those due to the uniform load.

Roofs that are intended for human occupancy or other use should be designed to sustain the same loads as corresponding floor areas. The live loads specified by building codes for roofs that are not so used vary from 20 to 40 lb per sq ft of horizontal projection for flat roofs and those of moderate slope. Flat roofs should also be checked for wind suction. Steeper roofs are designed for dead load, snow load appropriate for their slope and locality, and wind load. Recommendations are given on page 20.

When computing the load carried by a column, pier, wall, foundation, truss, girder, or beam, some codes permit a reduction in the specified live loads of from 5 to 15 per cent, depending on the size of the tributary floor area. As there is a tendency in many types of occupancy to place furniture or stored materials adjacent to partitions, which often correspond to beam or girder locations, the advisability of making such reductions, even when allowed by code, should be checked by comparing the proposed design with the actually expected loads. Such reductions should not be confused with those customarily allowed for multistory buildings, as shown in the table on this page.

LIVE-LOAD REDUCTIONS. As the probability of all floors being simultaneously loaded to capacity decreases as the number of floors increases, certain reductions are permissible in computing the live loads carried by supporting members, such as columns. In no case, however, should the total reduction be over 50 per cent. The following standard is abstracted from the Building Code Recommended by the National Board of Fire Underwriters. The same reductions are allowed by many cities, but the designer should check the local code, as considerable variation exists.

MAXIMUM PERMISSIBLE LIVE-LOAD REDUCTIONS

	Per Cent Reduction
Carrying the roof	0
Carrying one floor and roof	0
Carrying two floors and roof	10
Carrying three floors and roof	20
Carrying four floors and roof	30
Carrying five floors and roof	40
Carrying six floors (or more) and roof	50

These percentages represent allowable reductions in the live loads carried by columns, girders, trusses, walls, piers, or foundations. They apply to the live loads of the floors dependent for support upon the structural member being designed. The Underwriters' Code allows these reductions for all buildings except those intended for storage purposes, for which type of occupancy no reduction is permitted. Some codes permit lesser reductions for storage and manufacturing buildings.

MOVING LOADS. The dynamic effect of all moving loads should be considered. For example, in designing the beams and girders to support elevator machinery the static loads may be increased or the working stresses reduced to allow for this effect. Some building codes, such as that of Philadelphia, require a 100 per cent increase in the static load on beams, girders, and the first tier of supporting columns.

LATERAL LOADS. Wind load is the allowance for the effect of wind pressure or suction against exposed surfaces of a building. A minimum is specified by all building codes. The Report of the Building Code Committee, Department of Commerce, 1925, contains the following recommendations:

For purposes of design the wind pressure upon all vertical plane surfaces of all buildings and structures shall be taken at not less than 10 lb per sq ft for those portions less than 40 ft above ground, and at not less than 20 lb per sq ft for those portions more than 40 ft above ground. Where it shall appear that a building or structure will be exposed to the full force of the wind throughout its entire height and width, the pressure upon all vertical surfaces thus exposed shall be taken at not less than 20 lb per sq ft.[4]

Much more thoroughly studied requirements are recommended in "Wind Bracing in Steel Buildings," Final Report of Subcommittee No. 31, Committee on Steel of the Structural Division, American Society of Civil Engineers, published in the society's *Transactions*, 1940, page 1713. These requirements read in part as follows:

1. As a standard wind load for the United States and Canada the Subcommittee recommends a uniformly distributed force of 20 lb per sq ft for the first 300 ft, above ground level, increased above this level by 2.5 lb per sq ft for each additional 100 ft of height, no omission of wind force being permitted for the lower parts of the building by reason of alleged shelter. Special wind-force specifications should be formulated locally for areas that are definitely known to be subject to hurricanes or tornadoes.

2. For proportioning the wind bracing of tall buildings it is not necessary to divide the wind force into pressure and suction effects, although this should generally be done for structures with rounded roofs, for mill or other buildings with large open interiors, and for walls in which large openings may occur. The effects of possible high local suction should be investigated in relation to secondary members and the attachment of roofing or siding.

[4] Special recommendations apply to sprinkler tanks, sky signs, etc.

3. For plane surfaces inclined to the wind and not more than 300 ft above the ground, the external wind force may be pressure or suction, depending on the exposure and the slope. For a windward slope inclined at not more than 20° to the horizontal, a suction of 12 lb per sq ft is recommended; for slopes between 20° and 30° a suction uniformly diminishing from 12 lb per sq ft to zero; and for slopes between 30° and 60° a pressure increasing uniformly from zero to 9 lb per sq ft. For the leeward slope, for all inclinations in excess of zero, a suction of 9 lb per sq ft is recommended.

4. For roofs that are rounded, or may be represented roughly by a circular arc passing through the two springings and the eaves, the wind force will depend not only upon the exposure and the ratio of rise to span of the equivalent circular arc, but also upon whether the springings are elevated above the ground or are on the ground. Where the surfaces considered are not more than 300 ft above ground level, the recommended external wind force is as follows:

a. On windward quarter of the roof arc, when the roof rests on elevated vertical supports and where the rise ratio is less than 0.20, a suction of 12 lb per sq ft is recommended; and for a rise ratio varying from 0.20 to 0.60, a pressure increasing uniformly from zero to 12 lb per sq ft, or, alternatively, for rise ratios between 0.20 and 0.35, a suction varying uniformly between these limits from 12 lb per sq ft to zero is recommended. For roofs springing from the ground level a pressure, for rise ratios varying from zero to 0.60, uniformly increasing from zero to 11.4 lb per sq ft, is recommended.

b. For the central half of the roof arc, where the roof rests on elevated vertical supports, with rise ratios varying from zero to 0.60, a suction uniformly varying from 11 lb per sq ft to 20 lb per sq ft is recommended; for roofs starting from ground level, a suction of 11 lb per sq ft, regardless of the rise ratio, is recommended.

c. For the leeward quarter of the roof arc, for all values of the rise ratio greater than zero, a suction of 9 lb per sq ft is recommended.

5. It is recommended that for a flat roof a normal external suction of not less than 12 lb per sq ft should be considered as applied to the entire roof surface.

6. On walls parallel to the wind it is recommended that an external suction of 9 lb per sq ft should be considered.

7. Even for buildings that are nominally airtight, internal wind forces of either pressure or suction may exist, varying from 3 to 6 lb per sq ft, and depending on whether the openings are generally in the windward or in the leeward surfaces. Large internal pressure may arise due to the breaking of windows in the windward side of buildings by reason of flying gravel from the roof or other objects carried by the wind. Still larger internal forces of pressure or suction may arise when the windward or leeward side of a building is completely open. The subcommittee recommends that for buildings that are nominally airtight an internal pressure or suction of 4.5 lb per sq ft should be considered as acting normal to the walls and the roof. For buildings with 30 per cent or more of the wall surfaces open, or subject to being open, an internal pressure of 12 lb per sq ft, or an internal suction of 9 lb per sq ft, is recommended; for buildings that have percentages of wall openings varying from zero to 30 per cent of the wall space, the recommendation is an internal pressure varying uniformly from 4.5 to 12 lb per sq ft, or an internal suction varying uniformly from 4.5 to 9 lb per sq ft.

8. The Subcommittee recommends that the design wind force applied to any surface of a building be a combination of (*a*) the aforementioned appropriate external wind force, and (*b*) the appropriate indicated internal wind force.

9. Where a series of roofs exists in one building, one roof being nominally masked by another, the structure as a whole should be designed for the full wind load on the first roof and for 80 per cent of the wind load on the other roofs. Any one roof should be designed for the full wind load.

10. When wind surfaces are more than 300 ft above the ground, the external and internal wind forces should be scaled up in the proportion that the prescribed wind force on plane surfaces normal to the wind fixed by recommendation (1) at the level under consideration bears to 20 lb per sq ft.

Although the preceding recommendations apply more specifically to the quantitative structural design than to the choice of structural assemblies, they have been quoted for the purpose of emphasizing the magnitude and character of wind forces. These forces should often be considered in the selection of building assemblies, particularly roofs, for which the potential effect of suction may disqualify certain designs.

Special provision for wind bracing is very important for high buildings and for narrow buildings of even medium height. In tower-like structures wind bracing should be planned in the early stages of design. It may also be necessary for low buildings having prefabricated panels or unusually light-weight framing members. Except where foundations are securely anchored, the overturning moment due to wind pressure should not exceed 66⅔ per cent of the moment of stability disregarding live loads. There may also be a possibility of the structure sliding on its foundation bed.

The evaluation of lateral forces due to earth or water pressure is not usually a matter for specific code control. Designs are accepted if good practice is followed in evaluating horizontal pressures and uplift due to hydrostatic head.

Requirements pertaining to earthquake resistance are found only in the codes of localities likely to be subjected to appreciable seismic disturbance. Within such areas these requirements may materially affect the choice of structural assemblies as well as the actual structural design. The reference to this subject in the American Standards Association report should be supplemented by the regulations given in the Uniform Building Code, Pacific Coast Building Officials Conference, and the Los Angeles City Building Code.

Article 5. Interpreting and Analyzing Code Requirements

INTRODUCTION. As the regulations of building codes are mandatory, it is imperative that the designer be familiar with their influence on both the architectural and structural aspects of his work. Unfortunately, there is such a wide and unjustifiable variation in the approximately two thousand building codes now in effect in the United States that it is impossible to present any average of their specific requirements. There is, however, sufficient uniformity in the subjects which they control to permit standardization in their analysis.

From the viewpoint of the designer, buildings must be structurally adequate to meet the conditions of locality and occupancy. The design must provide, from danger incident to fire, a degree of protection which is appropriate to the size, location, and use of the building. This requirement applies to property as well as to the occupants of the building and the public. Minimum hygienic and safety standards are established. Adding to these three broad requirements the subject of zoning, we have a substantially inclusive résumé of the topics covered by building codes, in so far as their regulations affect the work of the architectural or structural engineer.

The following outline is based upon the content of the more complete ordinances. It identifies the features of both architectural and structural design which will probably be affected by code. It is arranged in the form of a procedure to facilitate the application of code regulations to specific projects. The terms "architectural" and "structural" are not subject to precise definition. The requirements of structure often effect the desired esthetic, which is surely an architectural quality. The utilitarian demands of the architectural design may often dictate the choice of structural forms. The two expressions are used because they help in an analysis of building design, although the work which they connote should always be considered as merged into a single procedure. In a broad sense, the word "architectural" is used in this text to identify all matters pertaining to the spatial requirements of a building, together with those concerned with appearance. "Structural" implies the considerations necessary to resist applied forces, such as caused by floor loads or wind, and all other purely utilitarian demands of the building components, such as durability and fire resistance.

DETERMINE THE REQUIRED OCCUPANCY AND CONSTRUCTION CLASSIFICATION. The first step is to identify the classification according to occupancy, such as public building or residence building. Most codes have from five to seven classifications. The one appropriate for the structure being designed is usually obvious and has particular significance in determining the allowable types of construction and in relation to zoning laws.

The class or classes of construction that would be permitted can then be determined as controlled by the type of occupancy, the location in reference to fire limits or zoning laws, and the height and ground area. By use of the standards given in the preceding discussion for exemplifying the procedure, it will be seen from the tables on pages 9 and 10 that asylums and penal institutions should be of fireproof or semifireproof construction irrespective of location or size. Within the fire limits of a city, a high office building would have to be fireproof, whereas one under 75 ft in height could be designed in a lower classification. A storage building, "unsprinkled," could be of heavy-timber construction if 35 ft or less in height, and semifireproof if between 35 and 50 ft; over 50 ft fireproof construction would be required with no limiting height. Likewise, there would be no restrictions as to the ground area of the building for a fireproof or semifireproof design, but a building of heavy-timber construction or a classification with a lower fire resistance would probably be subject to such a limitation.

The identification of the construction classification provides the designer with a standard of minimum requirements which apply particularly to structural design and all features pertaining to fire resistance.

CHECK CODE REGULATIONS IDENTIFIED BY THE FOLLOWING CAPTIONS. Although there is a wide variation in both the content and arrangement of building codes, the following topical analysis will serve as a frame upon which to build a résumé of the local code requirements for any particular project.

ZONING LAWS. These laws may prohibit especially hazardous or objectionable types of occupancy, even within industrial districts. They often contain restrictions applying to the ground area of a building in relation to the lot area, or a limiting ratio of total floor area to lot area. They also restrict the type of occupancy permitted in certain zones. Many of our larger cities have code requirements relating the permissible perpendicular height of a building to the width of the street or streets upon which it fronts, as described on page 11. Some smaller cities have definite height limitations for even fireproof structures. These are important, as they affect the architectural design by controlling the envelope of the building.

HEIGHT AND AREA LIMITATIONS. Most municipal codes limit the heights and ground areas of buildings in the more combustible classifications. This limitation has already been considered. Some municipal and state codes or other state statutes specify minimum dimensions for habitable rooms in regard to both floor area and ceiling height. These specifications are particularly important in the design of low-cost housing.

MEANS OF EGRESS. The following matters are usually controlled by definite regulations applying to other than single- and two-family dwellings: minimum hallway widths; the location and design of stairs when serving as a required exit; the location and design of fire towers and fire escapes; the number, location, size, construction, and operation of doors serving as required exits; the slope of ramps. In places of public assembly, such as theaters, the width of aisles and the arrangement of seats are likewise specified.

LIGHT AND VENTILATION. Minimum requirements apply to the areas of windows and skylights, vent shafts and the width of courts, the design of alcoves, and provision for mechanical ventilation. Zoning laws may further limit the size of courts or the ground area of the building in relation to the size of the lot.

Permitted Encroachments. Certain structural elements and ornamental features are usually allowed to project under or over a public sidewalk or street. Such projections are definitely limited in building codes. For example, a column or wall footing may be allowed to project 12 in. outside the building line, provided that the upper surface of the projection is 8 ft below curb level. A cornice is often allowed to project as much as 3 ft beyond the building line provided that its lower surface is at least 12 ft above curb level. Such provisions may, however, be modified by zoning laws.

Illumination, Wiring, and Electrical Equipment. The light levels required upon working surfaces may be specified in state codes or state legislation applying to the employment of labor. They may be controlled by a state board of education for classrooms or workshops within school buildings. Adequate lighting from the viewpoint of safety, particularly in connection with exit facilities, is a general requirement of most municipal codes. The standards of the National Electrical Code and the National Board of Fire Underwriters are usually incorporated in building ordinances to insure the safety of electrical wiring and electrical appliances.

Plumbing, Heating, Gas Piping. State codes or state statutes often contain minimum sanitary requirements applying to factories or other places of employment and to multifamily dwellings. City codes cover all kinds of occupancy. The designer will be concerned principally with the number and type of fixtures required; location and size of toilets or bathrooms, water tanks, and stand-pipes; regulations regarding sprinkler systems; fire-fighting equipment and automatic fire-alarm systems for high buildings. Heating installations and heat appliances of all kinds are controlled by the better codes in so far as they are related, directly or indirectly, to danger incident to fire. The design of fireplaces and chimneys is included. Provisions for safety in the use of gas are customary.

Elevators, Escalators, and Dumbwaiters. The requirements cover design, construction, inspection, operation, and maintenance, but only a few matters concern the architect or architectural engineer. Most important are the regulations regarding the design of shafts and elevator machinery compartments, the size of elevator pits and penthouses, equipment loads, and the maximum permissible slope of escalators. Much of this information may usually be obtained more easily from the manufacturers of the equipment than from the local building code.

Quality of Materials. The regulations regarding materials often reflect local practice. Most large cities, however, follow the standards of our national organizations, such as the American Society for Testing

Materials, supplemented by those of the National Board of Fire Underwriters on all materials or appliances related to fire risk.

WEIGHTS OF MATERIALS. These specifications are necessary for the computation of dead loads.

LIVE LOADS. These include floor, roof, sidewalk, and courtyard loads. Wind loads, permitted reduction in live loads, requirements for moving loads, and maximum soil loads should also be recorded.

WORKING STRESSES AND STRUCTURAL LIMITATIONS. These are the stresses to be used in the future design. They also have some significance in the choice of construction. All specific limitations, such as minimum thicknesses for walls and structural floor slabs and maximum heights for partitions of certain type and thickness, should be recorded. Some codes give many of these requirements under the caption "Construction."

METHODS OF COMPUTATION. Although most modern building codes follow the more recent standards recommended by our national engineering associations, others do not, and the designer should check the formulas and computation methods applying to structural design, as their specific requirements may penalize certain types of construction.

CONSTRUCTION DETAILS AND STANDARDS OF WORKMANSHIP. These standards apply principally to two aspects of the work: structural adequacy and fire resistance. The first type of regulation is concerned with such matters as the bonding of masonry walls, application of metal lath, and riveting or welding structural-steel assemblies. The second group of standards, often covered under the title "Fire-Resistive Construction," gives detailed requirements for the different construction classifications on all structural matters affecting fire hazard. It includes such subjects as minimum thicknesses for fire walls, partitions, and shaft enclosures; limitations in the use of combustible materials in fireproof or semifireproof construction, firestopping; thicknesses of fireproofing surrounding structural-steel or concrete reinforcement. Particular attention is given to buildings intended for public assembly. The designer should carefully check the regulations for this type of occupancy. For example, in a theater the design of the stage, proscenium wall, and projection booth, as well as the exit facilities, lighting, and ventilation mentioned above, may be affected by specific requirements.

Article 6. Design Standards

In many localities the regulations of building codes do not provide an adequate basis for design purposes, and there is often a need to choose standards representing good practice. The following brief list gives a few useful references.

For those who seek a standard in the form of a building code, that furnished gratuitously by the National Board of Fire Underwriters and identified as their Recommended Building Code (1943 Edition) will be of help. The city codes of New York, Philadelphia, Boston, Chicago, and Los Angeles will be useful as indicating current practice. The Uniform Building Code adopted by the Pacific Coast Building Officials Conference and the Southern Standard Building Code, prepared by the Southern Building Code Congress in 1946, illustrate a movement to standardize code requirements. The state codes of Wisconsin and Ohio, supplemented by the Multiple-Dwelling Law of New York State and the State Housing Act of California, should be of interest from the viewpoint of state control.

Much valuable information bearing upon structural design and related subjects will be found in the publications sponsored by the United States Department of Commerce and published by the National Bureau of Standards. These are obtainable from the Superintendent of Documents, United States Government Printing Office, Washington, D. C. The following titles identify some of the more pertinent texts which apply to the contents of this chapter.

"Recommended Minimum Requirements for Fire Resistance in Buildings," 1931.
"Preparation and Revision of Building Codes," *Report BMS* 19, 1939.
"Recommended Building Code Requirements for New Dwelling Construction," *Report BMS* 88, 1942.
"Fire-Resistance Classifications of Building Constructions," *Report BMS* 92, 1942.
"A Glossary of Housing Terms," *Report BMS* 91, 1942.
"American Standard Building Code Requirements for Masonry," *Misc. Pub.* M-174. (Developed under the American Standards Association Project A41 and approved by the association in 1944.)

A full list of the publications sponsored or published by the National Bureau of Standards will reveal other texts valuable as references applying to structural design. Important among these is the standard entitled "Minimum Design Loads in Buildings and Other Structures," sponsored by the National Bureau of Standards, approved and published by the American Standards Association, 1945. Sponsored by the United States Department of Commerce and the Forest Service of the United States Department of Agriculture, in cooperation with the National Committee on Wood Utilization, are several texts applying to timber construction.

Various federal authorities, such as the Federal Emergency Administration of Public Works, Housing Division, have also sponsored publications applying to particular aspects of building. The minimum construction standards and special requirements of the Federal Housing Authority furnish helpful criteria for residential occupancies. These requirements become mandatory when mortgages are to be insured by that authority.

The Standards of the American Society for Testing Materials are accepted authorities for the specification of materials and tests concerned with the quality of materials. The publications of the American Standards Association apply to many aspects of building construction. Copies of all such documents may be obtained at a small cost from the secretary of the society or association.

The publications of the American Concrete Institute, in particular "Building Regulations for Reinforced Concrete," 1941, present widely accepted standards for the design of concrete. These Regulations were prepared by Committee 318 of the Institute and published as a part of *Proceedings*, Vol. 41, in the June, 1945, issue of the *Journal of the American Concrete Institute.* They are obtainable in separate pamphlet form. Committee 315 of the Institute issued in 1946 "A Proposed Manual of Standard Practice for Detailing Reinforced-Concrete Structures," which is also available in separate pamphlet form. The Report of the Joint Committee, entitled "Recommended Practice and Standard Specifications for Concrete and Reinforced Concrete," 1940, furnishes a basis for both design and specification. This was published by the American Society of Civil Engineers in *Proceedings,* Part II, June, 1940, and is likewise available in pamphlet form.

The design and specification of structural steel can be based upon the publications of the American Institute of Steel Construction and those of the American Iron and Steel Institute. In locations where there is no mandatory control of structural design such standards may be used as representing the best current American practice, but the designer should remember that some building codes do not as yet permit the stress levels recommended for reinforced concrete by the American Concrete Institute nor those recommended for structural steel by the American Institute of Steel Construction.

In addition to the building code mentioned above, the standards of the National Board of Fire Underwriters represent good practice in regard to all materials, appliances, or building assemblies in so far as they are related directly or indirectly to fire risk.

In the field of heating and ventilating the publications of the American Society of Heating and Ventilating Engineers exemplify current practice. For many years the National Electrical Code, which contains the standards of the National Board of Fire Underwriters for electrical wiring and apparatus, has been the authority in this field. The American Standards Association has sponsored the American Standard Safety Code for Elevators, Dumbwaiters, and Escalators; the American Gas Association has promulgated rules defining good practice for house piping and the installation of gas appliances. Many other technical organizations have standards available which will be helpful to the designer within their specific fields.

Supplementing the work of the more professional groups, there are a large number of trade associations and individual firms which have contributed greatly in providing the designer with a knowledge of good practice in the use of their products. Prominent among these is the Portland Cement Association, which for many years has published and furnished gratuitously to the public a current library pertaining to practically every aspect of the design and construction of concrete work. The National Lumber Manufacturers' Association and Forest Products Laboratories, Inc., have contributed valuable information on the structural design of wood. The Structural Clay Products Institute has made easily available the result of much research in its field.

The foregoing list includes only the more widely accepted standards and the more useful texts. Many other sources of information that will be helpful to the designer are mentioned in the following chapters. This list should be expanded by obtaining the publications of a trade association or a leading manufacturer in every field of the industry. For example, certain prominent producers of electrical equipment have issued publications on the subject of illumination, and much useful information on vertical transportation is available from the larger manufacturers of elevator equipment.

Chapter Two

CHOOSING THE FRAMING MATERIAL

Structural steel or reinforced concrete, in skeleton construction, present the two broad options for other than comparatively low structures. Buildings of only a few stories may be supported by bearing walls supplemented by an interior framing of structural steel, concrete, wood, or light-weight cold-formed steel sections. Entire frames of cold-formed steel sections are also appropriate for low buildings. Complete wood framing is very widely used in rural, suburban, and often urban districts for smaller residential and commercial buildings, notwithstanding the fire risk. Wood has also a structural application for wide-span construction, as discussed in Chapter Six.

INTRODUCTION. The difficulty of making definite recommendations will be apparent to any experienced designer. The choice between structural steel and reinforced concrete for the framing of a building is obviously influenced by architectural and structural requirements, prices of materials, and conditions in the building trades at a particular time and place. Furthermore, many years ago the practice of some districts began to favor either steel or concrete design for reasons which were not always based on structural or economic analysis. Over a period of time, however, this preference resulted in a preponderance of either one or the other type of construction and a corresponding development in efficiency on the part of the builders, which may be reflected today in their contract prices. Generalizations are consequently subject to error and should be taken only as a guide.

The mandatory or accepted design standards may also have an influence on the selection of material for the structural frame. This influence is largely due to a lack of uniformity not only in the stress levels prescribed by various building codes, but also in the methods of computation and the more or less arbitrary limitations, such as minimum thicknesses, which they often require. It is apparent that, if the use of structural steel were permitted at comparatively high stresses and reinforced concrete controlled by overconservative standards, the concrete would be at a distinct economic disadvantage. Some small cities such as New Haven, Connecticut, do not permit as economical design of short-span cinder-concrete slabs (see page 130) as does New York City. If this floor system were the most desirable for structural-steel framing, which might be the case under some conditions, the choice between a steel and a concrete frame would, obviously, be influenced.

At this stage of design the concept of the building should have been developed sufficiently to identify the height, bulk, and general spatial requirements. Information regarding the structural demands, the site conditions, and the utilities or other building equipment should also be available. The designer should have studied the previous chapter of this text and recorded the code regulations applying to his particular type of occupancy, location, building height, and area. With these data at hand he is ready to proceed.

Article 1. Structural Steel Framing

HEIGHT CONSIDERATIONS. From the viewpoint of height, structural steel is almost invariably the better choice for buildings of twenty stories or more, but there may be exceptions. The Master Printers' Building in New York City appears to be an example of a well-considered design in reinforced concrete, and it is twenty stories high. A concrete frame was used for the purpose of employing a flat-slab floor system (see page 72). This choice resulted in a very appreciable saving in story height, as compared with steel framing.

About twenty other concrete-framed buildings, varying in height from twenty to twenty-three stories, have been erected in the United States. There is another of twenty-six stories in Toronto, Canada. Most of these were constructed during the late 1920's, and about one-half of the group are apartments built within the Chicago metropolitan area. In a number of cases the choice was based upon a cost comparison which was reported to have indicated the economy of reinforced-concrete as compared to structural-steel framing.

For buildings between fifteen and twenty stories, the acceptance of a reinforced-concrete frame increases considerably. The best available record would indicate that about one hundred have been built in this group within the United States. Structural steel, however, will probably prove more desirable except when architectural or structual requirements or the economic conditions of the locality are particularly favorable to concrete. In such cases each type of design should be checked. Most buildings of this height, often subject to set-back requirements, present practical problems of form work and concrete placement. The column size through the lower stories, often mentioned as an objection, can be greatly reduced by the use of steel cores.

For buildings up to fifteen stories in height, particularly those not over ten stories, structural steel and reinforced concrete compete so closely that any one of several factors may determine the choice. For example, concrete may be chosen to effect an architectural treatment impracticable

Fig. 1. Mercantile National Bank Building, Dallas, Texas. *Contr.:* Henger Construction Company. Courtesy, American Institute of Steel Construction.

with steel, or either steel or concrete may be selected for the purpose of using a particularly favorable system of floor construction not suitable for the other type of framing. In districts subject to earthquakes building-code regulations may restrict the height of reinforced-concrete construction, leaving no option for the designer. Examples are the San Francisco

Fig. 2. Finished Exterior of Dallas Bank Building. *Arch.:* W. W. Ahlschlager; *Engr.:* R. O. Jameson.

City Ordinance (1939), which limits reinforced-concrete buildings to ten stories, and the proposed revision of 1946, which sets a limit of 135 ft without reference to stories.

For structures of considerable height, steel has the advantage of greater speed in construction. For example, steel erection through the entire mid-section of the Chrysler Building, built in New York City in 1929, required an average of a little less than 3 calendar days per story. The steel frame for portions of some buildings has been erected at the rate of less than 2 days per story. The placing of structural floors normally follows about four stories below the steel erection, and because of the support furnished by the spandrel beams work upon the exterior walls can proceed simultaneously from several levels. The building of interior partitions, furring, and many of the supplementary trades, such as plumbing and heating, can also be carried on through the lower portions of the structure long before erection has been completed in the higher zones. The building shown in Figs. 1 and 2 is typical of this type. When a reinforced-concrete frame is used, there is not the same opportunity for synchronizing these operations.

TYPE OF OCCUPANCY. From the viewpoint of occupancy, steel is particularly suited to the lighter live loads and normal interior arrangements of city office buildings, hotels, and apartments. Structural-steel framing lends itself more easily to alterations than monolithic concrete. In addition to its use in multistory commercial or residential buildings, it may be the best choice in some districts for even comparatively low multistory factories. This fact is illustrated by designs popular in the industrial South, where steel frames with heavy wood-plank or concrete floors are used for textile mills which require comparatively light live loads. If, however, the live load is 200 lb or more per sq ft, a reinforced-concrete frame with a flat-slab floor system (see page 72) will probably be more economical unless local conditions are unfavorable to concrete.

INDUSTRIAL DESIGNS.[1] For the one-story building extending over a large area, such as is shown in Fig. 3, structural steel is the usual choice. Typical exceptions are the one-story factories built for the Wright Aeronautical Company in New Jersey and the Dodge plant of the Chrysler Corporation in Chicago. Although the choice of concrete rather than structural steel for these buildings was largely due to war conditions, the designer should remember that, where the architectural plan permits simple form construction, many uses of the same forms, and their movement from section to section, concrete should be considered in districts where materials and labor costs are favorable. Furthermore, there may be specific reasons, either structural or due to the type of manufacture, for choosing a concrete rigid-frame (see page 192) or a concrete shell-roof (see page 197) design for a one-story industrial building.

As the multistory factory can usually be built more cheaply with rein-

[1] Detailed information on the planning of industrial buildings will be found in *Planning Industrial Structures*, by Clarence W. Dunham, McGraw-Hill Book Company.

forced concrete than with steel framing, the selection of the framing material is often related, in the broader aspects of industrial work, to the option between a one-story or multistory building. The former has a definite advantage for many types of industry, but no valid generalization can be made, as each project demands individual study. On the basis of gross floor area, the single-story building generally costs less. There is also a very appreciable saving in the loss between gross area and usable area. The single-story structure is more flexible from the viewpoint of future changes and more easily day-lighted. Except where gravity systems of distribution can be employed advantageously, it is often better suited to manufacturing operations.

Fig. 3. Single-Story Factory with Structural-Steel Framing. Design and Construction by the Austin Company.

On the other hand, high land value obviously favors a multistory design, such as that shown in Fig. 4. This particular concrete-framed industrial building was selected for comparison with the one-story steel-framed factory in Fig. 3 because the gross floor area, 51,000 sq ft, is the same. The floors are of flat-slab design with flared column capitals similar to those shown on page 40. The heating load in cold climates and the heat gain in hot climates are also less for the multistory building. The maintenance of the roof areas again favors this type. Furthermore, in any comparison between steel and concrete framing for the roofs of industrial buildings, the designer should consider the required fire resistance, as the cost of fireproofing steel trusses may well be an important factor. This has been one of the reasons for employing the concrete shell-roof designs, described on page 197, for one-story industrial buildings.

MISCELLANEOUS USES. Another type of structure for which a steel frame is often more economical than reinforced concrete is the comparatively small one-story machine shop or garage, particularly where large exterior glass areas are required. Such buildings are susceptible to a high degree of prefabrication and can usually be erected more cheaply of steel than of concrete or bearing-wall construction. Structural steel is also appropriate today for buildings such as university dormitories four stories in height, which some years ago would have been designed with bearing walls. The masonry required for the exterior may be only a little less than that which would be needed if a more traditional design were followed, but there is often an appreciable saving in time.

Steel framing is usually an appropriate choice for the structural members of pitched roofs. Such framing may be part of a skeleton design or sup-

FIG. 4. Multistory Factory with Reinforced-Concrete Framing. Design and Construction by the Austin Company.

ported by bearing walls. Various types of steel trusses are used in building construction for spans from 40 to 200 ft. Comparatively recent developments in steel fabrication now make available to the designer many forms of steel arches and rigid frames having a particular application to wide-span roof construction. As these differ so materially from the common skeleton designs used for the conventional multistory building, they are discussed in Chapter Six.

SPECIFICATION REFERENCES. For specification of structural steel the designer is referred to "Structural Steel (Riveted, Bolted, or Welded Construction)." Sponsored by the American Institute of Steel Construction and the American Society of Civil Engineers, this code was approved in 1943 by the American Standards Association as *Standard* A57.1. For additional information on design, detailing, and specification, refer to "Steel Construction," published by the American Institute of Steel Construction.

Article 2. Reinforced-Concrete Framing

ARCHITECTURAL AND ECONOMIC CONSIDERATIONS. Reinforced concrete is an architectural as well as a structural material and lends itself to a wide range of architectural expression. If concrete surfaces and forms appropriate to concrete are desired, it is logical to use this material for framing purposes. Steel can provide an adequate frame, often at less expense, but concrete can furnish not only the frame but the walls and ornament as well. The designer should bear this fact in mind and choose the material which best expresses the esthetic character of his building and meets most economically the utilitarian requirements of load, span, and fire resistance.

The monolithic character of reinforced concrete and the ease with which structural elements can be built with varying cross-section make this material extremely adaptable to designs such as the rigid frame and the shell arch. With the exception of the flat-plate rigid frame, mentioned later in this article, such types have particular application to wide-span roof construction and are described in Chapter Six.

For designs in which the form or expression of the structural materials, either as exposed surfaces or through their functionalism, plays little or no part, such as the office building or apartment house faced with stone, brick or terra cotta, the choice between a structural-steel or reinforced-concrete frame is largely one of relative cost. The only exception is the instance where one or the other may be preferred as offering a specific structural advantage, such as greater resistance to seismic disturbance. For example, some authorities on the Pacific Coast consider that from this viewpoint an all-concrete structure is at least equal to the same building designed with a structural-steel frame and brick walls, but somewhat inferior to a structural-steel frame with reinforced-concrete walls. If there are no such considerations or specific building code restrictions, as mentioned on page 11, the decision can be based on relative economy, considering all the matters identified in this chapter, such as speed of erection and effect on contiguous or related work.

The fact that erection is considerably slower for buildings framed in reinforced concrete than for those of steel design is important for high structures but of little moment for low buildings, where the time required to fill an order for fabricated steel may cancel any time gained in construction. Provided that good curing conditions for the concrete are maintained, it is usually practicable to build the structural work at the rate of one story a week after the first deck is poured. If two sets of forms are employed, greater speed can be obtained, but the additional cost is seldom warranted. When comparing a reinforced-concrete frame with a wall-bearing design, it should also be remembered that reinforced concrete is far preferable from the viewpoint of job coordination and speed in construction.

FIG. 5. Clinton Hill Apartments, Built for the Equitable Life Assurance Society of the United States. *Arch.:* Harrison, Fouilloux, and Abramavitz; *Engr.:* J. Di Stasio Company.

MULTIFAMILY DWELLINGS. An interesting use of reinforced-concrete framing for buildings from two to four stories high is exemplified by designs for low-cost housing units constructed in several different localities. Many earlier buildings of this type were wall-bearing brick masonry with reinforced-concrete interior framing and flat concrete roofs. Volumetric changes occurring in the roof slabs, probably augmented by the restraint of the foundations, which were not subject to the same atmospheric exposure as the superstructure, caused considerable cracking of parapets, roof copings, and exterior walls adjacent to corners. This led to the study of various reinforced-concrete framed designs as possible alternates. The two-span frame used on the buildings of the Ida B. Wells low-

Fig. 6. Clinton Hill Apartments under Construction. *Gen. Contr.:* Starrett Brothers and Eken. Courtesy, J. Di Stasio Company, Engrs.

cost housing project in Chicago [2] and the flat-plate rigid-frame design of the Newark and Atlantic City [3] low-cost housing projects demonstrate the

[2] See article entitled "The Ida B. Wells Low-Cost Housing Project in Chicago," *Journal of the American Concrete Institute*, February, 1941.

[3] See article entitled "Flat-Plate Rigid-Frame Design of Low-Cost Housing Projects in Newark and Atlantic City, New Jersey," *Journal of the American Concrete Institute*, February, 1941.

advantages of such construction over the old wall-bearing types. The cracking of walls was practically eliminated, and savings were made in exterior wall construction. There was also better coordination of the different trades and greater speed in erection. The Chicago design is typical of that commonly used for multistory concrete-framed buildings of greater height. The Atlantic City and Newark design, applying a rigid-frame analysis, is shown in cross-section on page 78. Figures 5 and 6 illustrate a more recent application of the reinforced-concrete frame to housing requirements where the same structural analysis was used by the engineers.

INDUSTRIAL DESIGNS. A reinforced-concrete frame is particularly suitable for a building supporting heavy floor loads, such as factories, warehouses, and garages. If the plan of the building and column spacing does not meet the requirements, given on page 75, which permit a conventional flat-slab floor design (see Fig. 7) with standard moment coefficients, or if it is desired either to eliminate column capitals or to cantilever the floor slabs beyond exterior columns, as shown in the illustration on page 75, a flat-plate, rigid-frame analysis may be used. This was recently done successfully for a laboratory in New Jersey where interior bays were as large as 25 × 26 ft and supported comparatively heavy floor loads.

Although the choice of the framing material should be the first step in developing the structural design, its selection should be considered in relation to the probable floor system and wall assembly. There are several types of structural floors that cannot be used with concrete framing. From the viewpoint of construction it is not practicable to pour cinder concrete, chemically expanded concrete, or gypsum between stone-concrete beams, even if the design could be adapted to such a purpose. The appropriate use of the structural floor systems in relation to the type of framing material is described in Chapter Four.

DEAD-LOAD CONSIDERATIONS. When comparing the relative advantages of reinforced concrete and structural steel, the respective dead loads of competing designs may be a factor for structures of considerable height (ten to fifteen stories) if soil conditions were such as to require piles. By combining a steel cellular floor (see page 134) with a structural-steel frame enclosed with one of the lighter wall assemblies, the weight of a building can be considerably reduced, but this type of floor is not appropriate for concrete framing.

If a concrete frame is desired, there is the possibility of using a lightweight aggregate for all structural work or for that above a certain level. This procedure may prove an economical means of reducing dead load in localities where materials like Haydite are available at a comparatively low price. Haydite is manufactured by burning shale or clay in a rotary kiln, grinding, and screening from ⅛- to ¾-in. size. It produces a strong concrete weighing about one-third less than sand-stone concrete of equal strength. Its principal value is for precast units such as the concrete joist, slabs, and channel sections described in the chapters on floor and roof construction, but the saving in weight may effect economies warranting a more extensive use. On several large buildings in the Kansas City district for which additional stories were required, Haydite permitted appreciably higher additions than would have been possible with a heavier aggregate.

Fig. 7. Reinforced-Concrete Flat-Slab Design. Courtesy, Turner Construction Company.

SOUTH AMERICAN PRACTICE. Tradition in the United States, combined with building code restrictions, has contributed to conservatism in concrete design. As long ago as 1928 a twenty-two-story residential building was constructed of reinforced concrete in Rio de Janeiro, and more recently an office building 325 ft above grade was erected in Buenos Aires. In both Brazil and the Argentine concrete frames are comparatively more popular than in this country. Although the difference in economic conditions largely accounts for this preference, design practice based upon German precedent has favored economy in accepting structural sections much lighter than our own.

Recent inspection [4] indicates that South American buildings of this type are generally satisfactory for their required use and exposure. With certain

[4] "South American Building Is Challenging," by Arthur T. Boase, published in *Engineering News-Record*, October 19, 1944. Supplementary articles by the same author: "Building Codes Explain the Slenderness of South American Structures," *Engineering News-Record*, April 19, 1945; "Brazilian Concrete Building Design Compared with United States Practice," *Engineering News-Record*, June 28, 1945; "Construction Practices in South America," *Engineering News-Record*, September 6, 1945.

obvious modifications, such as those dictated by climate, these designs might well form a basis for important modifications of our own practice. The articles identified in the footnote present an extremely interesting analysis of this subject.

SPECIFICATION REFERENCES. For the specification of concrete the designer is referred to the Report of the Joint Committee identified on page 27. Current developments in this field are described in the publications of the American Concrete Institute. Special attention should be given to the reports of the various committees, which cover subjects applying to design, specification, and construction.

Article 3. Wall-Bearing Construction

EXTERIOR WALLS. In this country wall-bearing designs are economical only for low buildings. Seldom are they an appropriate choice for those over three, or at most four, stories in height, and the present tendency, as previously mentioned, is toward the use of steel or reinforced-concrete frames for even lower structures. Wall-bearing construction, however, can often be used to advantage for many types of buildings, from residential to industrial, in localities where suitable masonry materials are available at comparatively low prices and the cost of placement is not excessive. It is particularly applicable to single-family dwellings above the 9000-dollar class and to commercial buildings of from one to three stories in height. Where any doubt exists in regard to such a choice, alternate designs should be made and priced by a competent builder. Such estimates should include consideration of all contiguous or related work, with particular attention to the time element.

Architectural features and the size of the operation are important considerations. If extensive fenestration is required, demanding considerable steel in the form of lintels, it will probably be cheaper to use a complete frame and eliminate masonry piers. On the other hand, if there are large expanses of wall area and deep reveals are required at windows, as in many traditional designs, the masonry must be built in any case, and it is logical to use its bearing capacity. Where a portion of the building is of considerable height, such as a tower, for which framed construction is the only reasonable choice, it may be desirable to use the same for all portions. On large operations there should be no question of the competence of the contractor to erect structural steel or reinforced concrete. There is an opportunity for synchronizing the steel erection with other trades or obtaining many uses of the highly standardized concrete forms, but on the small or isolated jobs conditions are far different. Simply built masonry bearing walls do not present the more serious construction problems of erecting either a structural-concrete or structural-steel assembly.

For this reason and similar ones wall-bearing designs in stone, brick, concrete-masonry units, and structural clay tile still have a broad application for many types of low buildings. In comparison to wood-framed construction, these are ordinarily more expensive in first cost but may be desired for reason of appearance or cheaper maintenance. Greater protection is also afforded from the external fire hazard, even if the interior construction is combustible. Furthermore, provided that the exterior walls conform with standard requirements, the interior framing may be designed to meet any desired degree of fire resistance.

FIG. 8. School in Eustis, Florida, Showing Wall-Bearing Design in Reinforced Concrete. *Arch.:* Richard B. Rogers.

The specification for masonry covers so broad a field that no single reference is adequate. This fact, as well as the necessity for considering conventional limitations in wall thicknesses, bonding, or anchorage, before making the actual design analysis, has led to the inclusion of a fairly comprehensive treatment of the subject in Chapter Eight, where sufficient material for specification purposes will be found.

Wall-bearing designs in reinforced concrete are also economical for low buildings similar to the two-story school house shown in Fig. 8. Although there is no reason why such buildings should not be entirely satisfactory in any locality if well designed and carefully erected, it is suggested that greater confidence can be placed in concrete-framed construction except in the more moderate climates like that of Florida or Southern California. Extreme temperature variations and heavy rains, occasionally followed by freezing weather, present the possibility of cracks in exterior walls or surface disintegration, which places a heavy responsibility upon both designer and builder.

INTERIOR FRAMING. The material used for columns, girders, and beams, comprising the interior framing which supports floors and roof, may be structural steel, reinforced concrete, light-weight, cold-formed steel sections (see page 45), heavy timber, or the lighter wood sections. Bearing walls or bearing partitions of masonry may be used alone or in combination with any one of these possibilities. It is generally customary, particularly for residential buildings, to permit wall-bearing designs, with ordinary interior wood framing, to be higher than otherwise allowed, provided that floors immediately over basements or cellars and supporting columns are of incombustible materials or assemblies having a fire-resistance rating of not less than 2 hours. This practice results from the fact that a large proportion of fires start in basements or cellars.

Structural-Steel or Reinforced-Concrete Interior Framing. If we include the cold-formed, light-weight steel designs described on page 45, one of these two materials must be used if a fireproof or semifireproof rating is necessary. The choice is largely governed by structural considerations, checked on the probable cost. Long spans or complicated framing, such as auditorium balconies, favor structural steel; if exterior walls are to be of concrete, the same material is appropriate for the interior structural work. It is often impossible to make more than a tentative decision at this stage of the design, as the choice of the structural floor system, spanning between the beams, may influence the selection. If local conditions seem to favor steel, it may be chosen with the reservation that an estimate will be obtained on an alternate design in concrete. If concrete is the preliminary choice, the final selection may be held subject to the possible use of a structural floor system which will require steel framing.

Where brick bearing walls are used as a support for flat concrete roofs, special provision in the form of deep, reinforced-concrete spandrel beams should be made to prevent cracking of the walls caused by distortion of the roof slab. Such designs, however, are inferior to the completely framed construction described on page 78.

Heavy-Timber Interior Framing. Heavy-timber or mill construction, as described on page 91, is one of the specific construction classifications of most building codes. Its particular application, as its name implies, is for factories and storage buildings, but in some sections, such as the Pacific Northwest, it has been used for commercial and even multifamily occupancy. Until about 1917 such designs were very popular throughout the industrial districts of the United States. Since that time reinforced concrete and structural steel have developed to the extent that wall-bearing designs with typical heavy-timber interior framing are seldom a desirable choice for even industrial work, except in localities where the cost of masonry and timber framing is low in comparison with that of concrete or steel construction. In such districts heavy-timber designs may offer an economy in first cost or facility in alteration for plans permitting the close column spacing described on page 92. There are also certain modifications of the conventional design, which have been used considerably on the Pacific Coast. The great future for timber framing, however, would appear to be in the adaptation of laminated sections to wide-span construction.

ORDINARY WOOD INTERIOR FRAMING. When interior framing of a wall-bearing structure is composed wholly or partly of wood, designed to carry the required loads but without regard to fire resistance, it is identified in most building codes as "ordinary construction" or merely "nonfireproof construction." In such designs the framing consists of wood beams or girders, occasionally supplemented by unprotected structural steel, which may be used for girders carrying the longer or more heavily loaded spans. Wood posts, unprotected steel sections, or pipe columns serve as supports. Masonry bearing partitions are often used, particularly in basements. Wood bearing partitions are customary above the first floor. The particular application of such designs is for residential and commercial buildings from one to three stories in height in districts where the fire risk can be accepted.

From the viewpoint of the designer who is concerned with identifying the types of interior framing that are permitted by the local code for a particular building of known location, size, and type of occupancy, the problem is simple. If the tables on pages 9 and 10 are used as representing code restrictions, it appears that a church facing on only one street could be of ordinary or nonfireproof design if not over two stories or 45 ft in height nor having a ground area over 5000 sq ft. If the church were three stories high, but under 75 ft, it would be necessary to obtain a semifireproof rating, which would result in choosing a steel or reinforced-concrete interior framing. If over 75 ft in height, the same materials, with the exception of the lighter-weight steel assemblies, would be used, but the specification would call for additional fireproofing.

Article 4. Wood-Frame Construction

The traditional use of wood for the complete frame of all types of low structures where the fire risk can be accepted is too well known to need more than brief mention. It has the advantage of simplicity and the fact that standardization over a period of many years has acquainted the designer, the builder, and the carpenter with the practice of their locality. The particular application of the conventional wood frame, as shown on pages 97 and 98, is for single- and two-family dwellings, barns, small stores, and similar structures not over three stories in height. For such buildings wood is usually popular except in districts where the absence of suitable timber, an excessively high cost of importation, or other local conditions favor other material. In parts of the Southwest the availability of a suitable soil, climate, and traditional trade practice have resulted in the fairly extensive use of adobe (see page 348). Similarly, certain localities in the East favor brick or other types of masonry, wood being employed only for interior framing.

The requirements of good practice, as well as the better building codes, apply severe limitations to completely wood-framed structures, as shown in the tables on pages 9 and 10. These limitations should be considered when comparing the advantages of timber with those of other designs. Comparatively recent developments in the manufacture of glued laminated sections and the use of metal connectors have made wood beams, trusses, arches, and rigid frames appropriate for many types of wide-span construction. These differ so materially from the common wood framing typical of the small structure that they are described in Chapter Six.

For the specification of lumber the designer is referred to *National Design Specification for Stress-Grade Lumber and Its Fastenings*, 1944, published by the National Lumber Manufacturers' Association. An excellent bibliography on the structural use of timber has been prepared by the Committee of the Structural Division on Timber Structures of the American Society of Civil Engineers. It appears in the *Proceedings* of the society for March, 1944, under the title, "Classified Bibliography of the Physical and Mechanical Properties of Wood and the Design and Construction of Timber Structures."

Article 5. Light-Weight Steel and Prefabricated Framing

Within recent years the wood frame has come into competition with light-weight steel assemblies, composed usually of cold-formed rather than hot-rolled sections. Complete steel frames of this type, illustrated in Fig. 9, are appropriate for buildings not over three stories in height provided that the occupancy does not demand heavy floor loads. Where standardization is practicable, the first cost may closely approach that of wood-framed construction, with the advantage of using an incombustible material and the elimination of shrinkage. Figure 10 shows the completed building. The exterior walls were finished with three coats of portland-cement stucco applied over metal lath carried by 4-in. or 2-in. steel studs spaced 23½ in. on centers.

Designs in this same group proved an economical choice for machine shops, one-story warehouses, hutments, and service buildings required for the armed forces during World War II. Any kind of exterior and interior finish may be applied with practically the same facility as over wood. Combined with insulated, cellular steel wall panels, light-weight steel frames are appropriate for some types of industrial buildings; surfaced with

FIG. 9. Construction View of a Texas Dwelling with Steel-Stud Framing. *Contr.:* J. R. Condron. Courtesy, Milcor Steel Company.

FIG. 10. Finished Exterior of Texas Dwelling. *Arch.:* Fred W. Murphree. Courtesy, Milcor Steel Company.

porcelain-enamelled steel sheets, they are used for commercial work. Figure 11 shows a design in which wall panels are composed of "latisteel" sections with a 2-in. thickness of concrete. These panels are cast in a horizontal position. After a 24-hour curing period they are erected by a crane and bolted in place. The roof is of more conventional design, being a steel deck of welded sections, supported by steel trusses. It is surfaced with insulation and waterproofing.

FIG. 11. One-Story Industrial Building with Light-Steel Framing. Courtesy, Latisteel Inc., Pasadena, Cal.

The Stran-Steel System offers a practicable solution for pitched-roof framing over bearing-wall, structural-steel, or even reinforced-concrete construction. Figure 12 shows a typical design. If an incombustible material is desired, the cost may be considerably less than for hot-rolled sections. Many of the light-weight steel assemblies serving as structural frames are more or less prefabricated. In most cases framing members are cut to length in the shop, and trusses are shop-welded.

In the concrete field, prefabricated structural members have been used, as shown in Fig. 13. During World War II prefabricated concrete columns, girders, and slabs were erected at the Norfolk Navy Yard. In 1945 two large single-story warehouses were built for the navy of thin shell, precast concrete elements. These structures are in Mechanicsburg, Pa. The framing comprises a system of bents supporting precast roof panels. These bents are of hollow section, and reinforcement is welded to obtain conti-

FIG. 12. Stran-Steel Framing Applied to Small Dwelling Construction. Courtesy, Great Lakes Steel Corporation.

FIG. 13. Precast Concrete Framing for an Industrial Building. Courtesy, Cemenstone Company.

nuity where adjacent segments join.[5] Other prefabricated designs are described in Article 12 of Chapter Three; with few exceptions they have their principal application in comparatively low structures, such as housing units, service buildings, and single- and two-family dwellings, sufficiently standardized to take advantage of shop manufacture.

[5] For a detailed description of these buildings see articles entitled "Precast Concrete Storehouses," by Arshom Amirikian, and "Precast Concrete Warehouse Construction," by Louis P. Corbetta, *Journal of the American Concrete Institute*, June, 1947.

Chapter Three

PLANNING THE FRAMING OF A BUILDING

The composition of a building frame offers many possibilities in the choice of type and location of structural elements. The solution is derived from the requirements of architectural design, occupancy, and locality, supplemented by a knowledge of the equipment which the building must contain. Each step is conditioned by the need for structural adequacy and economy.

INTRODUCTION. The construction of a modern building is a complicated operation with many interlocking elements manufactured and erected by diverse trades. Only through painstaking forethought combined with very careful planning on the part of architect, engineers, contractor, and subcontractors can coordination be obtained. The framing is developed primarily from the viewpoint of structural adequacy and structural economy, but economy should be studied in relation to all the dependent or related work. Conditions at the site and the geographical location may also be important, as well as the design standards imposed by mandatory ordinance or assumed by the designer.

Although the purpose of this chapter is to identify the essential steps constituting the procedure in determining the location and type of the structural members, a number of subjects are mentioned which have little significance in the arrangement of the framing. This is done for the purpose of laying a comprehensive foundation for subsequent work and of assisting the less experienced designer in obtaining what might be called a philosophical view of his entire problem.

At this stage the preliminary architectural drawings should have been developed to the extent that they show the complete spatial requirements of the building. There should also be a memorandum identifying the mechanical and electrical equipment to be installed, heat insulation, acoustical work, natural or artificial lighting levels, surface finishes, and other architectural features not shown on the drawings. The designer should then carefully check and note the structural significance of all such information.

Starting with the subjects which more obviously affect structure, he should consider the influence of the site and local conditions. The next step may well be an analysis of the mandatory or accepted design standards and special structural requirements. Lastly, but not by any means least important, should be considered the provisions for elevators, plumbing, heating, illumination, and other mechanical or electrical equipment. It is clearly impossible to give a list of subjects that will have significance for all types of buildings. It is hoped, however, that the following articles may suggest the matters which should be considered at this time in order to obtain a thorough coordination of the work.

Article 1. Framing in Relation to Locality and Structural Standards; Modular Design

LOCALITY. All characteristics of the site or geographical location which may directly or indirectly affect structure should be studied and reduced to the form of simple notes. Subsurface conditions are the most obvious; they may be investigated by any of the means described in Chapter Nine. The probable severity of seismic disturbance and the character of the material upon which the building foundations are to rest should be studied in localities subject to earthquakes. In particularly exposed positions and in districts where exceedingly strong winds may be expected, the probable wind loads should be compared with the minimums required by the local building ordinance.

Because of the expansion and contraction of building materials caused by temperature variation, it is necessary to consider the effect of the probable temperature range upon the structure. Long, concrete buildings erected in the colder climates require particular attention (see page 83). Joints are also necessary in some types of steel and masonry assemblies. The designer should compute the probable amount of movement for the structural elements and, where such movement would be likely to cause buckling or cracking, joints should be planned as part of the future design.

In districts subject to extreme temperatures the building walls and roof should, obviously, be more thoroughly insulated than in moderate climates. Various methods are described on page 173. When the radiant heat of the sun's rays is an important element of the cooling load of air-conditioned buildings, special provision may be required to reduce its effect. Such necessity may influence the design of exterior walls or roof. It may be desirable to provide actual separation or introduce nonhomogeneous materials between elements of the foundation assembly to isolate the building frame from a source of external vibration. This subject is discussed on page 145.

On the economic side, the effect of locality has its principal significance in the relative prices for the various building materials, labor rates, and union restrictions for the different trades. Such considerations are more important in regard to the choice of material for the structural framing, floor, roof, and wall design than for the arrangement of the framing but should be noted at this time. There is the possibility, mentioned in the introduction to Chapter Two, that the practice of the locality may favor certain types of construction and that local organizations may be better trained to perform certain classes of work. There is also the very important need of checking the availability of materials.

STRUCTURAL STANDARDS. In Chapter Two it was mentioned that the mandatory or accepted stress levels and methods of computation may influence the choice between structural steel or reinforced concrete as a framing material. Design standards may also affect the arrangement of the framing. For example, some building codes allow a less favorable distribution than others in the proportionment of the load carried on a reinforced-concrete floor system having a two-way reinforcement. This situation may penalize such systems in comparison with those in which the entire load is carried in one direction (see page 115). Again, some city ordinances favor certain types of floor construction which may be unapproved by others. As the various systems, like the long- and short-span designs, discussed on page 65, require different framing for their support, the arrangement of beams may be considerably influenced.

When high buildings are designed for large cities, there may very likely be a "set-back law," such as that described on page 11, or the architect may desire to follow a similar form even if it is not demanded by the local code. The envelope of the building, conforming with such requirement, would of course be shown on the preliminary drawings, but the subject is mentioned here because set-backs obviously affect the framing and may sometimes be adjusted for greater structural economy.

MODULAR DESIGN. Although the application of modular design pertains rather to architectural than structural planning, it seems desirable that the subject should be very briefly outlined in this text, as it is an important movement toward greater economy in building construction.

The modular theory, as developed by Albert F. Bemis and his associates, was described some 20 years ago in their publication entitled, *The Evolving House.* It proposes a method by which site assembly of buildings can be effected without excessive alteration of cutting of component parts. This objective requires dimensional coordination upon the part of architects or other designers, fabricators, and manufacturers of building materials.

The active interest in dimensional coordination dates from 1938, when a meeting representing all branches of the building industry was initiated by the American Standards Association. The purpose was to coordinate manufacture and assembly of building units. The American Institute of Architects and the Producers' Council were joint sponsors with the American Standards Association in carrying on the work which was presented in a report approved in October, 1945, and issued as *American Standards*

A62.1 and A62.2. The former applies to building materials and equipment; the latter, to the coordination of masonry. *Standard* A62.3, approved in

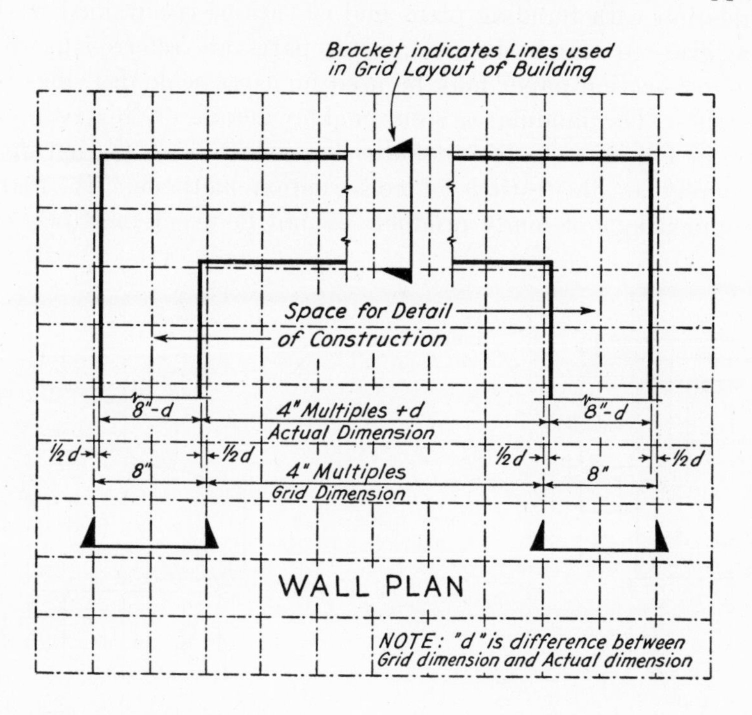

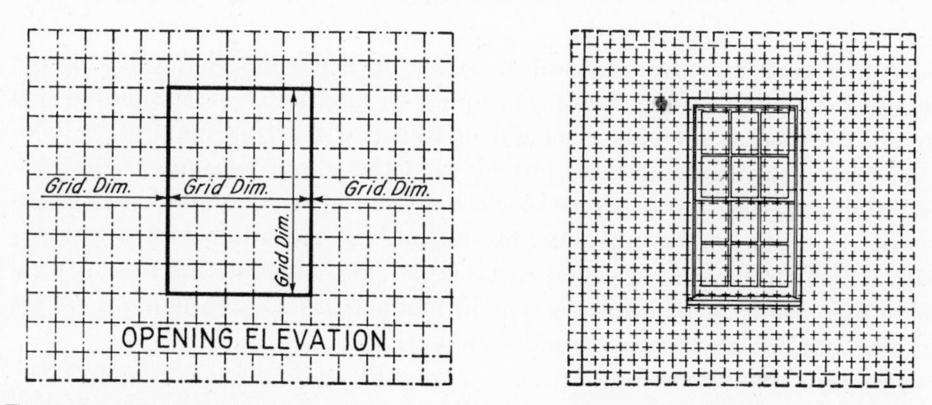

FIG. 1. Application of Grid Dimensions to Modular Design. From "Modular Coordination as Related to Building Design," Issued by Committee A62, American Standards Association.

1946, is entitled, "American Standard Sizes of Clay and Concrete Modular Masonry Units."

After considerable study the committee agreed upon a 4-in. module as a basis for dimensions of both building materials and the layout of the building. This basis results in making horizontal and vertical dimensions multiples of 4 in. but does not necessarily apply to floor or wall thicknesses. The correlation with building plans and elevations is obtained by the use of a 4-in. grid, to which the component parts are referred as shown in Fig. 1. Cross-section paper may be used for large-scale drawings, such as ¾-in. details. The modular system enables details of this type, such as are shown in Fig. 2, to convey definite dimensional information instead of serving merely as illustrations of construction methods. It is apparent that the dimensions of many products cannot be exact multiples of 4 in.,

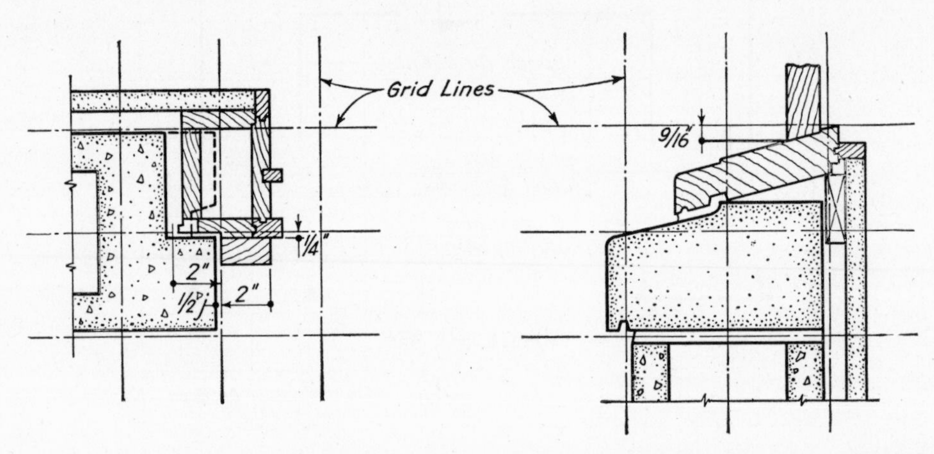

Fig. 2. Application of Grid Lines to Window Jam and Sill Details. From "Modular Coordination as Related to Building Design," Issued by Committee A62, American Standards Association.

but the actual sizes are determined by the modular detail referred to the grid lines, and the same detail will apply to all similar assemblies, which should increase or decrease in height or width by multiples of 4 in.

Modular masonry standards provide that the size of masonry units, such as brick, clay tile, and concrete block, be based upon a nominal size, which is the actual size of the unit plus the thickness of the standard mortar joint with which the unit is designed to be laid. This thickness is added to all three dimensions, which means that in modular design the joint thickness is fixed and not optional with the architect.

The principle of modular design is rapidly spreading throughout the country. Many manufacturers of building materials, including both steel and wood windows, have adopted sizes which correspond to multiples of 4 in. Such standardization offers the advantage of eliminating much cutting and fitting upon the job, as well as an appreciable reduction in the number of sizes of building products which must be manufactured and carried in inventory. These economies should be encouraged by the designer through the application of the modular system wherever practicable.

A brief explanation for the use of architects and engineers is contained in "Modular Coordination as Related to Building Design" (1945), which may be obtained from the Secretary, Committee A62, American Standards Association, Boston, Massachusetts. A much more complete exposition of the subject, in book form, is published by the Modular Service Association, Boston, Massachusetts, under the title *A62 Guide for Modular Coordination*, by Myron W. Adams and Prentice Bradley.

Article 2. Special Structural Requirements and Mechanical and Electrical Equipment

SPECIAL STRUCTURAL REQUIREMENTS. There are often certain requirements not shown on the preliminary architectural drawings, such as a provision for very heavy equipment loads, a future horizontal extension of the building, or additional stories. Such possibilities should not be forgotten. A decision should also be made in regard to the type of foundations. Whether the footings are placed on soil, rock, piles, or concrete piers sunk by pneumatic or open caissons may affect the planning of the framing. For example, in steel mill-building construction it is common practice to favor longer spans when the columns beneath trusses must be supported by piles, in order to reduce the number of pile clusters. Where there is any probability of unequal settlement, the more rigid types of framing would be inappropriate.

The height and bulk of the building, with due regard for exposure, determine whether wind bracing is needed. Typical requirements for wind load, or pressure, are given on page 19. Such provisions do not ordinarily affect the disposition of the principal members of the frame except in tower-like buildings, for which the placement of adequate bracing should be studied in preliminary design. It should be remembered, however, that a computation for wind load may be required for even comparatively low structures, and this fact may demand special connections between structural members or the addition of diagonal bracing.

The exterior framing should be considered in relation to the panel or spandrel-wall design, as certain types may need special provision. If waterproofing or dampproofing is required below grade, the method to be used should be studied, as slight modifications of the structural work may facilitate such installations. If the location and type of partitions are known, an approximate estimate should be made of the load which they contribute. As the weights of various designs are quite different, this procedure is preferable to using an arbitrary allowance per square foot of floor area, as often required by building codes.

The provision for heat insulation and vapor seal will probably influence the design of walls and roof. This subject is discussed on pages 173 and

184. Acoustical considerations, in so far as they affect the structural assemblies, are given on page 142. The amount of day-lighting, or the character of artificial light, demanded by the particular type of occupancy may have an important effect upon the choice of exterior wall design. If skylights are required, the roof construction is obviously affected. Surface finishes to be applied upon walls, partitions, ceilings, and floors have only an indirect influence on the arrangement of the framing but should be noted at this time, as the information will be needed later in connection with floor and wall construction.

MECHANICAL AND ELECTRICAL EQUIPMENT. The requirements mentioned in the following paragraphs should be checked:

(a) Number, size, location, and height of rise for elevators, with particular attention to penthouse dimensions and equipment loads.

(b) General requirements for plumbing, with particular attention to the location of soil stacks, stand-pipes, mains, pumps, water-storage tanks, and sprinkler systems.

(c) If steam is to be produced within the building, requirements of the boiler room and accessories, such as fuel storage. The distribution of heat by the piped systems has little significance in the preliminary design except for high buildings which might be zoned in about twenty-story sections, requiring increased story heights at those levels. The distribution of air, however, either for heating or ventilating, requires ducts of comparatively large size in order that air velocities may be held to permissible levels. This requirement makes it necessary for the designer to consider the probable location of ducts and their approximate sizes in order that interference with structural members or other utilities may be avoided.

(d) Typical lighting demands, with particular attention to ceiling outlets. Their proper spacing may influence the framing, and the necessary provision for running conduit often affects the floor design. For many types of occupancy the lighting levels should be checked in relation to natural light, particularly where glass blocks of plain or directional design are used. If extensive power or telephone facilities are required, such as a close spacing of outlets over extensive floor areas, this fact may affect the choice of floor construction and influence the disposition of the framing members.

(e) The mechanical and electrical equipment, which deserves particular attention in buildings designed for industry. Interior clearances and the specific demands of the manufacturing process should be identified in so far as they affect the structural plan.

STRUCTURAL-STEEL OR REINFORCED-CONCRETE FRAMING

There is an old saying that should always be remembered: "A good design is easy to build." This implies a thorough coordination of archi-

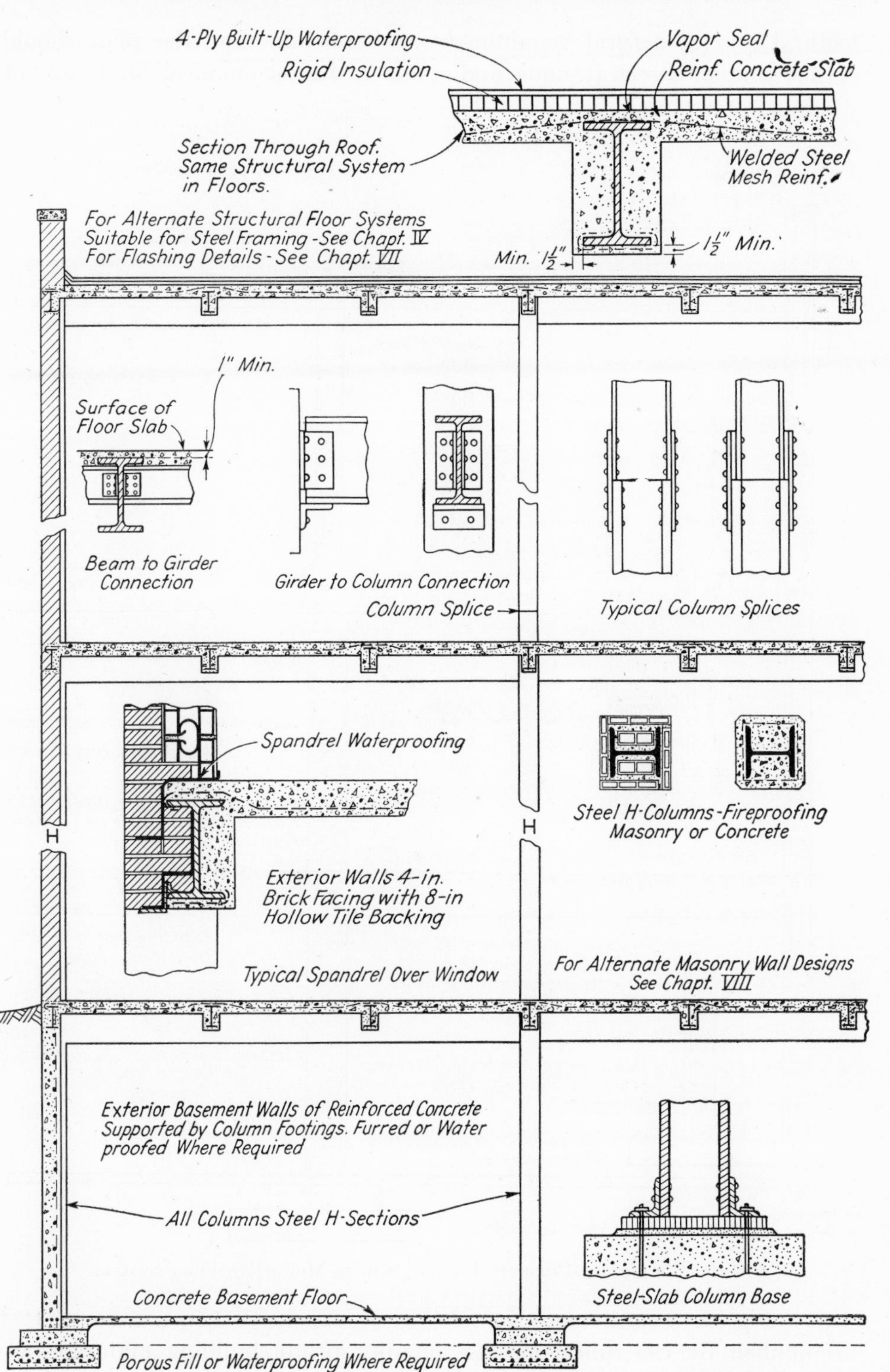

FIG. 3. Structural-Steel Framing with Short-Span Reinforced-Concrete Slabs.

tectural and structural requirements. It means that the plan should permit simple, direct framing and spans within economical limits except

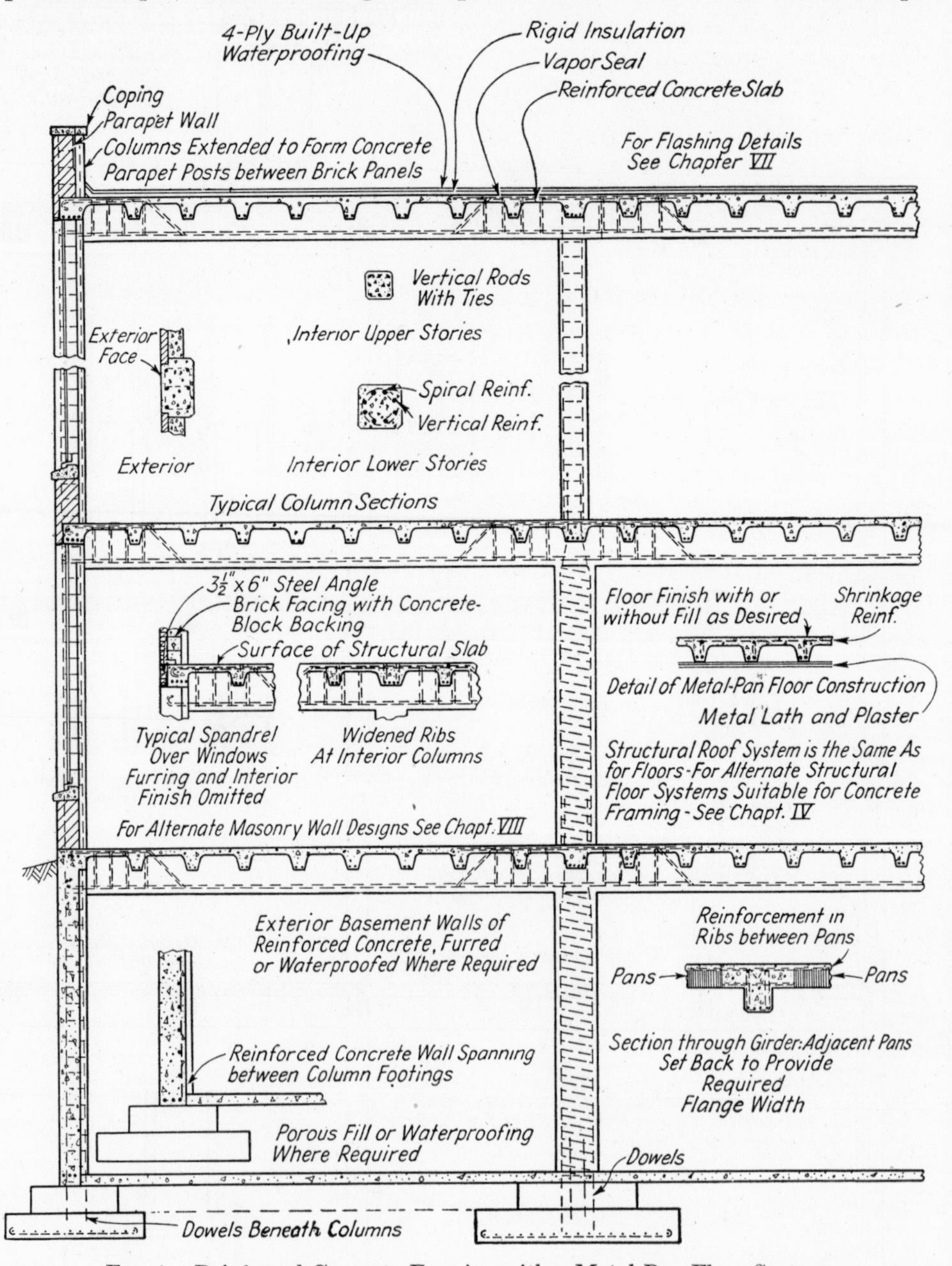

Fig. 4. Reinforced-Concrete Framing with a Metal-Pan Floor System.

where a prime requirement justifies more expensive construction. It is exemplified by the functional use of appropriate building materials and assemblies.

As the arrangement of both structural-steel and reinforced-concrete framing, except for the flat-slab (page 73) and flat-plate, rigid-frame (page 76) designs have many principles in common, discussion of the two types is combined in the following articles. Figure 3 shows the principal structural elements of a steel-framed building, and Fig. 4 a corresponding section designed in reinforced concrete.

Article 3. Locating Columns

PROCEDURE AND RECOMMENDATIONS. The first step is to determine the location of all columns and, in wall-bearing designs, the other structural elements, bearing walls, and bearing partitions that are available to help support the floor and roof construction. The position of each column or tier of columns should be determined and marked on copies of the architectural floor plans. Each tier should be concentric as far as architectural considerations permit. Obvious exceptions are set-backs where offsets less than the column spacing are required in the exterior building walls or where large interior areas, such as a ballroom, must be clear of obstructions. The location of exterior columns is largely controlled by windows or other exterior openings; that of interior columns, by partitions. It is often impossible to obtain an ideal structural arrangement, but there are a few considerations which should be borne in mind.

The best column spacing usually results from dividing the supported area into squares or rectangles of approximately equal size. For example, a building 125 ft long and 65 ft wide would suggest a longitudinal spacing of columns at 25 ft and a spacing of about 22 ft across the building. In reinforced-concrete designs a modification of uniform spacing may be helpful to reduce the maximum bending moments. For example, if it were desired to reduce the negative bending moment in a continuous girder, beam, or slab, over the first interior line of supports, this could be done by shortening the end spans. As the typical connections employed at the present time for structural steel, whether riveted or welded,[1] are not usually considered to furnish continuity over supports, this procedure would have no significance for steel-framed structures.

A column spacing of less than 20 ft is seldom desirable unless there are unusual conditions, such as very heavy industrial loads or concentrations which may require very short spans to conserve headroom beneath the connecting girders. Another exception is found in the concrete design illustrated on page 79, where spans from 12 to 18 ft have been found economical. A maximum span of 25 ft where reinforced-concrete girder framing is used and 40 ft for rolled-steel girders is generally desirable from the viewpoint of structural economy, but either limit may be extended

[1] This subject should be followed in the publications of the American Welding Society.

considerably to meet special conditions. The heaviest of the standard wide-flange steel girders, 36 in. deep, may occasionally be used to advantage on spans up to as much as 65 ft.

Column spacing may be affected by the presence of concentrated loads such as water tanks or mechanical equipment. It should be checked for coordination with elevator shafts and stairways or special basement facilities such as boiler rooms. Institutional buildings such as hospitals often require much more duct space for the distribution of utilities than other types of occupancy. Such needs should be studied even in this preliminary phase of the design, so that basic changes will not later be necessary to accommodate the installations. For example, it might be desirable to shorten the spans between two adjacent lines of columns for the purpose of lessening the depth of the connecting beams or floor construction, thereby obtaining more duct space.

Exterior steel columns are placed sufficiently back from the building line to allow for the enclosing masonry, which serves as fire and moisture proofing. A minimum is 5 in., and the usual maximum is 9 in. This allows sufficient depth to accommodate 8-in. bond stones, or a nominal 4-in. stone facing with one course of brick backing. Exterior reinforced-concrete columns, if covered by masonry or other architectural surfacing, are set back the distance which such surface treatment requires. Where uncovered, their outer faces often coincide with the building line, as the reinforcement is placed a sufficient distance within the face of the column to obtain the necessary fireproofing thickness. The possibility of additional space being required between the face of the column and the building or property line for exterior waterproofing of basement walls should be checked.

All columns rest upon some type of footing, and it is desirable to place the footing concentrically with the column. The proximity of a property line often makes this impossible, as noted on page 368, but the matter should be considered when locating columns, as a set-back of even 2 or 3 ft, carrying the enclosing walls or glass on cantilever construction, may obtain this advantage. Reinforced concrete is particularly appropriate for such a treatment. A cantilever design extending beyond the exterior line of columns is shown on page 75. This design has become popular to permit continuous glazing.

SPECIAL CONSIDERATIONS APPLYING TO WALL-BEARING CONSTRUCTION. In wall-bearing construction, as the name implies, the exterior walls serve as end support for beams and girders carrying the weight of floors and roof. The location of interior columns follows the same principles as are given for skeleton designs, except that partitions may be constructed as bearing partitions or as interior bearing walls when their position is such as to provide support along lines that divide the floor area into spans suitable for the floor system. In such cases, the partitions or walls eliminate the necessity for girders with their supporting columns, and their positions should be shown on the structural floor plans.

The designer should remember, however, that a bearing partition is dependent for its load-carrying capacity upon the strength of the framing or floor system upon which it rests. If such partitions are required as fire stops, identified as "fire partitions," the necessary fire rating of the floor or other supporting elements, as well as the design of the partition itself, will probably be covered by building code. The construction of fire walls, which extend throughout the entire building height, from a footing to the underside of a fire-resistant roof or a few feet above a combustible roof, is closely controlled by good practice and building codes both in regard to design and the permitted openings.

In most structures of this type there are a few interior bearing walls, particularly in the basements, and all additional support is furnished by steel or reinforced-concrete framing. Occasionally, a section such as a gymnasium may be designed with exterior columns built into the exterior walls for the support of roof trusses which would otherwise require rather heavy masonry piers. Sometimes this same idea is carried to the extent that parts of a structure are designed as wall-bearing and other higher sections of skeleton construction. This is particularly satisfactory in reinforced concrete, as the same trades execute both types of work.

Article 4. Column Types

STRUCTURAL-STEEL COLUMNS. Most steel columns used today are of standard H-section; other types are occasionally employed to meet special conditions. Typical designs are shown in Fig. 5. When selecting

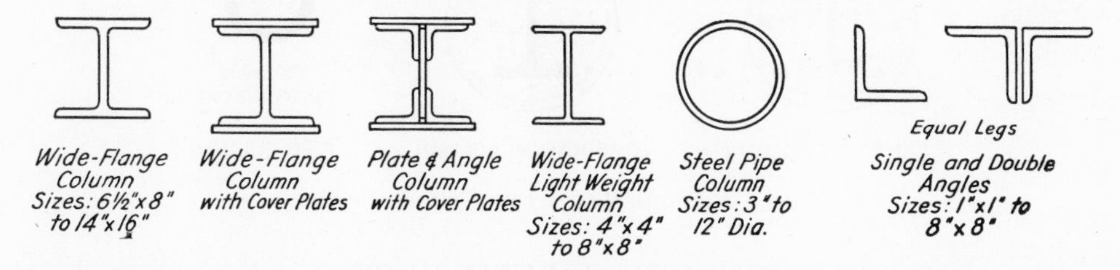

FIG. 5. Steel Column Sections.

steel-column sizes, it should be remembered that the section is usually made the same throughout two stories. This results in somewhat understressing the portion above the intermediate floor but costs less than changing the column section at each floor level, because of the added expense of splices and erection. The use of cover plates to increase the carrying capacity of the lower portion of a two-story tier is also uneconomical because of fabrication cost; but, where loads are in excess of that which can be carried by the maximum available or acceptable standard section, cover plates are often used to increase the thickness of the flanges. When computing sizes and estimating the weight of structural-steel columns, it should be remembered that fireproofing is an essential of all fire-resistant construction.

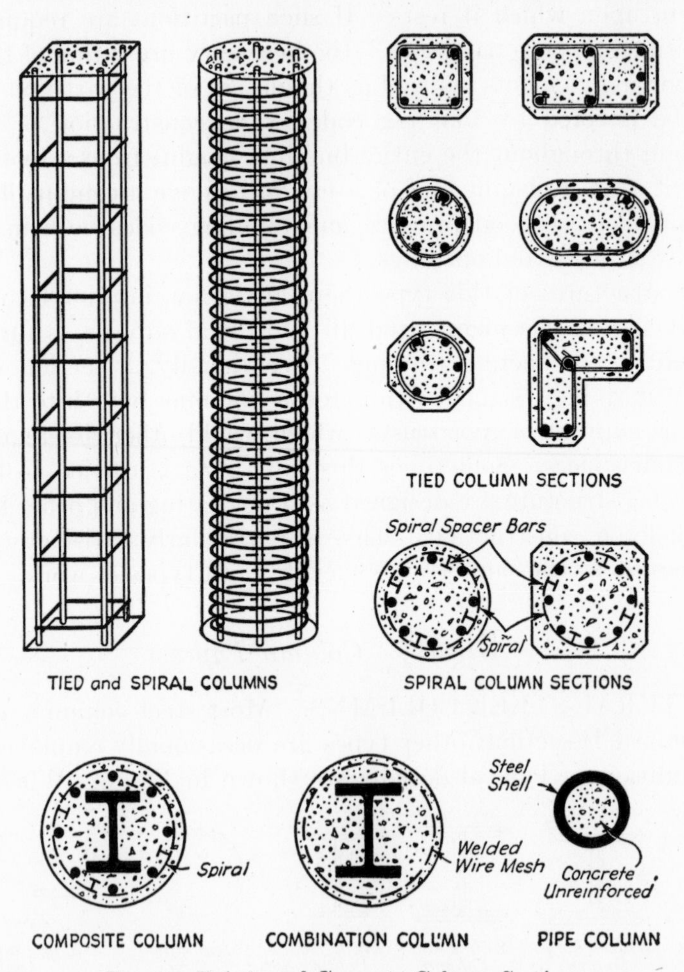

FIG. 6. Reinforced-Concrete Column Sections.

REINFORCED-CONCRETE COLUMNS. These columns may be of practically any cross-section that the architect desires, provided that design requirements are met. The only other restrictions are the practicability of constructing, filling, and stripping the forms, and the appropriateness of the section to receive the beams, girders, or other structural elements which they support. The common sections are square, oblong, round, oval, or as shown in Fig. 6. Forms are usually constructed of either wood or plywood except for round columns, those having curved surfaces or the conical heads so widely used with flat-slab designs, which are built of thin sheet steel.

The types of columns appropriate for reinforced-concrete assemblies are described in the following paragraphs. The classification is based on the Report of the Joint Committee on Standard Specifications for Concrete and Reinforced Concrete (1940), but it should be noted that some building codes use different terms. For example, the tied column is sometimes called a "hooped column," and a spirally reinforced column a "laterally reinforced column."

1. THE TIED COLUMN is reinforced with longitudinal bars or rods and separate lateral steel ties. This is the simplest design and is widely used; but, as its carrying capacity for a given cross-section is less than any of the following designs, it should be discarded in favor of another type when the required size becomes too large for either economy or appearance.

2. THE SPIRALLY REINFORCED COLUMN is reinforced with longitudinal bars or rods enclosed by a closely spaced steel spiral. This design is particularly applicable to heavily loaded buildings such as factories, warehouses, and garages. In such structures a tied column is often appropriate for the top story, below which the spiralled design would be used.

3. THE COMPOSITE COLUMN consists of a structural-steel or cast-iron section encased in concrete reinforced with both longitudinal and spiral steel. A hollow metal core can be used if filled with concrete. Loads are transferred to the metal core by bearing members such as billets, brackets, or other positive connections; these are placed at the top of the metal core and at intermediate floor levels where required. This design permits a much smaller cross-section for any given load than does even the spiralled column. Structural-steel H-sections are the usual choice for the column cores. They can be economically erected in one piece through a height of about six normal stories and are often helpful in reducing the size of heavily loaded columns through the lower stories of a comparatively high concrete-framed building.

4. THE COMBINATION COLUMN is a structural-steel section encased in concrete 2½ in. thick over all metal (except rivet heads), reinforced with a welded-wire mesh. Special brackets are used to receive the entire floor load at each floor level. This design has the same application as the composite column but is not as widely used.

5. THE PIPE COLUMN is a steel pipe section filled with concrete. This type is similar to the Lally column. Its particular application is in low buildings and in localities where fire-resistive standards are not severe. It may often be used to take the place of the interior wood column in wall-bearing construction and as a support for the lighter types of structural work.

STANDARDIZATION. From the viewpoint of design, reinforced-concrete columns are more flexible than structural-steel, as there is the opportunity of changing the concrete section, the concrete mixture, and the steel reinforcement at any floor level. Standardization of the form work, by avoiding all changes that are not obviously justified by a reduction in material quantities or other economic advantage, is a basic principle of concrete design. This fact should be remembered. On the other hand, oversized columns waste floor space and those of minimum size, requiring the maximum percentages of reinforcement allowed by code, are often uneconomical. The form material should also be considered. Sheet-steel cylinders, commonly used for round columns, are easily altered to suit varying column diameters, whereas a change in a wood form may require a round trip to the job form-building shop.

The best plan is to make the most economical design, from a structural viewpoint, for the typical columns of each story, using the concrete mixture and percentage of vertical steel or, for spiralled columns, the percentages of vertical and spiral steel, that give the greatest load-carrying capacity for the least cost under the governing code or standard. Only for extremely heavy loads would the composite or combination column designs be used. The next step is to prepare a few alternate designs to check the relative economy of obtaining either a higher degree of standardization or smaller sections wherever possible.

Article 5. Locating Girders and Beams

Having located all columns and, in the case of wall-bearing construction, lines of support such as walls or bearing partitions, the designer is ready to complete the framing diagram. At this stage he should consider the appearance of the structural beams and girders where their soffits project below ceiling surfaces. In large rooms of monumental buildings, the centering of columns between windows and the alignment of girders at exact column centers are not only good construction but also add a feeling of functionalism to the entire assembly. Few will deny the esthetic value gained by a frank expression of structure, but in practice there is often a tendency to consider the exposure of the framing as almost immodest.

DEFINITIONS OF GIRDERS, BEAMS, AND JOISTS. To avoid ambiguity in the use of terms applying to structural framing, it should be noted that the word "girder" identifies a relatively heavy member spanning between walls, piers, or columns. Girders are usually horizontal or practically horizontal and normally support walls, beams, or joists. A beam is a somewhat lighter member spanning between girders, walls, piers, or columns. Beams are usually horizontal but may occasionally be inclined or even curved. They normally furnish the direct support for a floor or flat-roof system, including partitions and other minor concentrated loads.

The term "joist" is generally applied to the lightest of all horizontal members, which are used at a comparatively close spacing, seldom more than 30 in., on centers and spanning between beams, girders, or walls. Where joists are used, they are integral elements of the floor, roof or ceiling design and in this text are considered a part of the floor or roof system as distinguished from the general framing of the building. Examples are the open-truss steel joist (page 123), and the precast concrete joist (page 119).

LIVE LOAD AND SUPERIMPOSED LOAD. Another matter that often causes trouble is confusion of the terms "live load" and "superimposed load." This statement applies particularly to "safe-load" tables distributed by certain manufacturers. In the choice of structural systems, as affected by load considerations, we are concerned with the superimposed load, which is the live load plus all dead load carried by the structural floor in excess of its own weight. For example, for a floor system spanning between two beams, we might have the following data in pounds per square foot of floor surface.

	Pounds per Square Foot
Live load (as required for the type of occupancy)	50
Weight of finish floor construction (including under floor and fill)	15
Weight of ceiling (comprising metal lath and plaster)	7
Total superimposed load	72
Weight of structural floor	60
Total design load (exclusive of partitions)	132

In addition to the uniform loads there are often concentrations to be carried by the structural system, particularly the loads due to partitions. If partitions are placed over beams or girders, their weight is included in that carried by these members. When they are supported by the floor system, however, the floor must be designed for such additional concentrations.

SHORT-SPAN VERSUS LONG-SPAN DESIGNS. The next step in this procedure is to decide between a short-span and a long-span system for the floor construction. The term "short-span" identifies a group of structural floor designs which are used on spans varying from about 6 to 10 ft and consequently require one or more intermediate beams between each line of columns, as shown in Fig. 7(*b*). "Long-span" systems are those capable of spanning, under varying loads within the usual range, from 20 to about 30 ft, thus eliminating the need for intermediate beams, as shown in Fig. 7(*a*). As this decision affects the design of the framing, it should be made at this time before the final choice of the particular type of floor construction.

Avoiding beams except along column axes, particularly where the columns and the connecting beams can be concealed by partitions, improves the general appearance of a room and facilitates the lighting arrangement.

To obtain a flat ceiling with a short-span design, by attaching metal lath or other plaster base to the intermediate beam soffits, referred to as a "hung ceiling," is usually more expensive than to choose a long-span system. Sometimes, however, the space above a hung ceiling is wanted for duct or pipe installation, or there may be other reasons for preferring short spans.

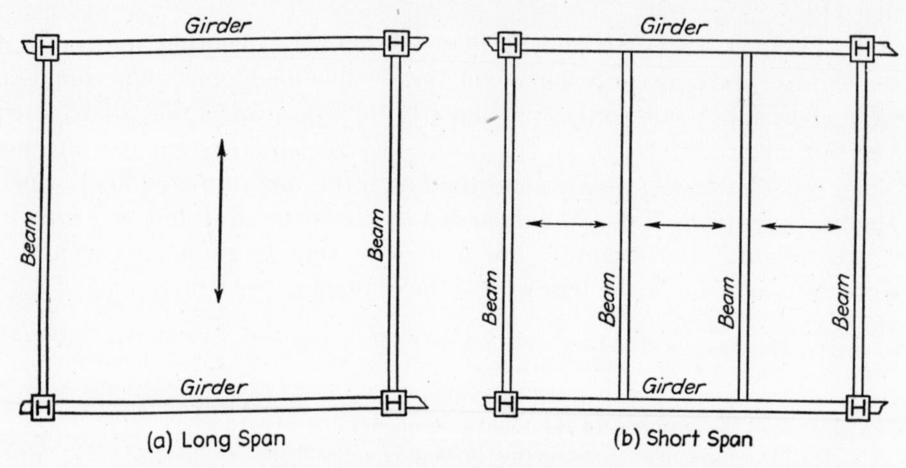

FIG. 7. Comparison of Long- and Short-Span Designs.

Long-span designs are particularly suitable for light and medium loads where there are no heavy concentrations. They are an appropriate choice for many types of occupancy where the superimposed load on the typical floors, exclusive of hallways, is not over about 75 lb per sq ft. If spans are not more than 20 ft, this limit may be raised to about 100 lb. Before a

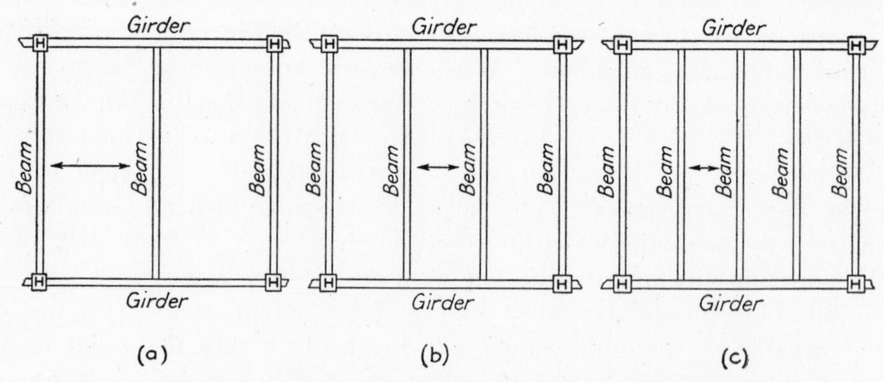

FIG. 8. Alternate Arrangements for Short-Span Beam and Girder Designs.

final decision is made, the designer should compare the relative advantages of the various systems given in Chapter Four on floor construction, as the framing of a building and the choice of the structural floor are closely related.

If a long-span system is chosen, the only beams required for the typical bays are those framing into the columns. If a short-span system is selected, there are three alternate beam arrangements, as shown in Fig. 8. Of these, *b*, employing two intermediate beams, is usually the most economical; to use one beam causes an appreciable increase in the size of the girder because of concentrating one-half the load of the floor panel at the mid-point of the girder span; to use three beams not only adds unnecessarily to the number of beams but, except for very wide panels, results in shortening the slab spans to such an extent that the minimum thickness demanded by most building codes would not be fully developed except under severe loading conditions.

THE DIRECTION IN WHICH TO RUN THE GIRDERS OR DEEPER BEAMS. The designer should now determine whether to run the deeper beams or girders across the building or parallel to its longer dimension. If windows extend as high as possible to facilitate the natural lighting of the interior, the girders should run across the building, permitting spandrel beams of lesser depth. This arrangement also favors structural rigidity, particularly desirable for high, narrow buildings. On the other hand, the exterior columns supporting the ends of deep beams or girders are subjected to a correspondingly heavy eccentric load, reflected in design requirements. This is especially true in the upper stories of buildings where the concentric loads are low. Designing the girders to span across the building obviously results in the necessity of making such a provision for a larger number of columns.

Another consideration, often the most important where the spacing of columns results in oblong bays, is the desirability of using the girders or heavier beams on the shorter spans for the sake of conserving headroom or improving the appearance of an open floor area. Although these considerations are somewhat contradictory, the designer will find that the special conditions of his particular building usually result in certain factors of prime importance governing his choice.

RELATIVE HEIGHT OF BEAMS AND GIRDERS. This subject has no significance in reinforced-concrete framing, but in structural-steel design the beams and girders may be framed with their top surfaces flush, or the beams may be dropped sufficiently to avoid the expense of coping their upper flanges. When precast concrete, gypsum plank, or similar units are used as a floor or roof deck, a flush surface is required. For long-span designs a flush assembly is also the usual choice, as the principal beams frame into the columns and are not supported by girders.

For short-span designs with poured-concrete slabs, either type of assembly may be preferable. If panels are square or nearly square, the girders determine the clear height, and it may be advantageous to drop the beams as shown in the detail of Fig. 3 (beam-to-girder connection). This saves the expense of coping the upper flanges of the beams and may have other advantages. If panels are definitely oblong in plan, the girders will normally be run in the shorter direction to conserve height. This often results in choosing beams and girders of about the same depth, which is not economical from the viewpoint of steel tonnage, but may be economical in relation to the building as a whole. In this case the beams are coped and placed with their top surfaces flush with the girders. The illustration on page 129 shows such an arrangement.

ROOFS. The framing of "flat roofs," which are horizontal, or only slightly sloped in one or more directions for the purpose of drainage, may follow that of the typical floor as far as the types and general arrangement of structural members are concerned, or it may be desirable to employ a different arrangement to meet the requirements of a lighter-weight construction. The same framing should usually be retained for multistory buildings unless special features of the roof design or obvious economy justifies a change. In this case the final design of the girders, beams, and roof deck will naturally reflect the difference between the load requirements.

Where no change is made, it is more satisfactory, except possibly for structures only one span in width, to build the structural roof without slope, obtaining the necessary grade by means of a cinder fill or other light-weight material which also provides insulation. If puddles of water after a rain are not considered objectionable, the fill is often omitted, as the same guarantee can be obtained upon a built-up roofing laid over a level surface. In some cases provision is made to retain water for the purpose of cooling. This is done by slightly raising the level of the roof drains. When one of the light-weight roof systems is chosen, the structural surface is sloped or not sloped as desired, and no fill is used.

The framing of pitched roofs is normally of steel or wood because of the obvious difficulty of pouring concrete on steep slopes. Various designs have been developed employing precast concrete framing, but these have not been found very practicable.

Article 6. Girder and Beam Types

STRUCTURAL STEEL. A variety of structural-steel shapes, shown in Fig. 9, can be used for framing, but the present practice favors the wide-flange H-sections for the principal beams and girders unless the span or load requirements demand built-up units, such as the plate girder or truss, which are discussed in Chapter Six. Around openings, such as stair wells, the steel section is chosen to facilitate the stair erection, and for roof construction several light-weight types have their particular application. Spandrel assemblies are shown in connection with flashings on page 279; typical stair arrangements, in Fig. 10.

When employing a floor system which does not provide lateral support for the beams or girders, a designer should be careful to use the "safe loads" corresponding to this condition or to introduce additional structural members. Solid reinforced-concrete slabs or one of the ribbed designs (page 108) are ordinarily adequate to resist the lateral deflection of the beam or girder which supports them. Where open-truss steel joists (page 123) or another light-weight floor system is chosen, it is necessary to consider the beam or girder as unsupported laterally unless additional steel framing is placed at the third points of the span or lateral deflection otherwise prevented. When computing sizes and estimating the weight of structural-steel framing, the fireproofing should be included.

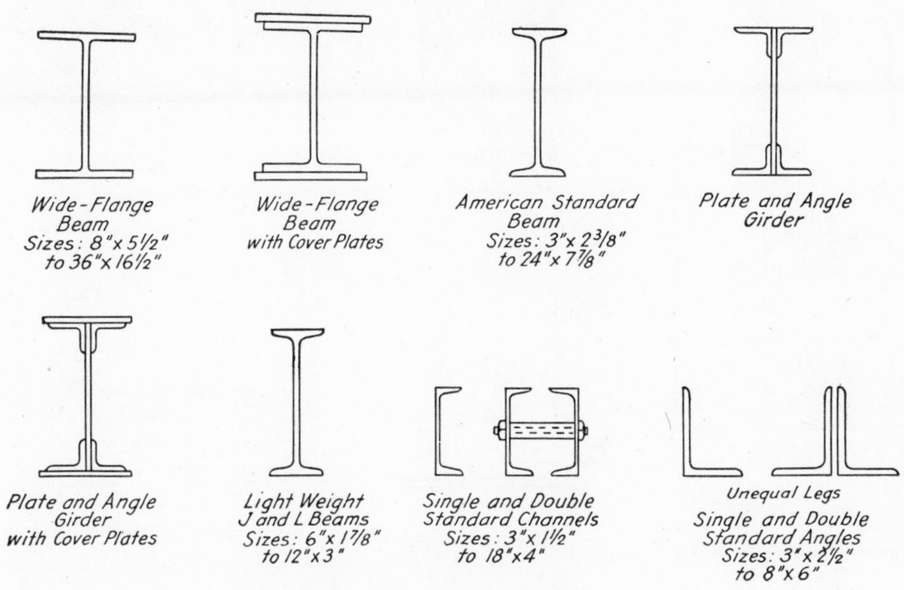

FIG. 9. Steel Beam Sections.

REINFORCED CONCRETE. Typical designs for two framing plans in reinforced concrete are shown in Figs. 11 and 12. Figure 11 shows a beam-and-girder system with short-span slabs. Figure 12 shows a long-span system with very shallow beams on column centers only. The usual reinforced-concrete beam or girder is of T-section, as shown in Fig. 13(*a*), the flange of the T being supplied by the contiguous floor construction which is placed monolithically with the beam or girder.

Around openings, such as stair and elevator wells, where the slab occurs only on one side of the beam, the section takes the form of an inverted L, sketch (*b*). In an exterior beam spanning between wall columns, past an open well, such as an elevator shaft, the section becomes rectangular, sketch (*c*). The shallow beams, shown in Fig. 12 and in sketch (*d*) of Fig. 13, require more reinforcement because of their reduced effective depth. On the other hand, there is the obvious advantage of facilitating ceiling installations, which applies particularly to industrial buildings, and of somewhat better light reflection.

Because of the tendency of concrete floor slabs to crack near the corners, as shown in sketch (*a*) of Fig. 14, it is desirable to place additional reinforcement in such locations. This is indicated in (*b*) of the same illustration.

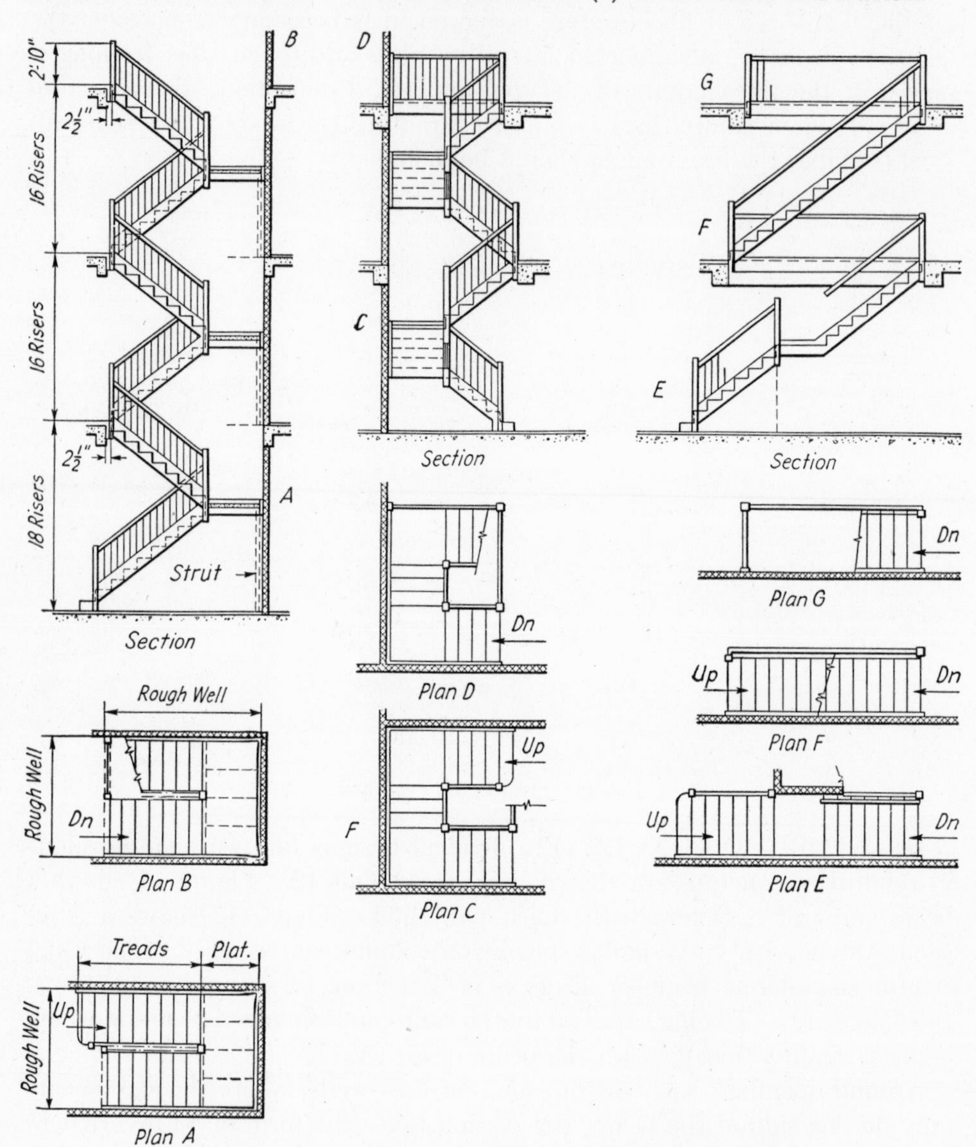

Fig. 10. Steel Stair Designs. Courtesy, Stanley Iron Works, Inc.

Where it is desired to extend windows as nearly as possible to the ceiling line, reinforced-concrete spandrel beams may be constructed above, rather than below, the structural floor. On the other hand, where several feet of wall is needed above the window head, the entire depth may be formed as a deep spandrel beam, thereby eliminating the necessity for any other type

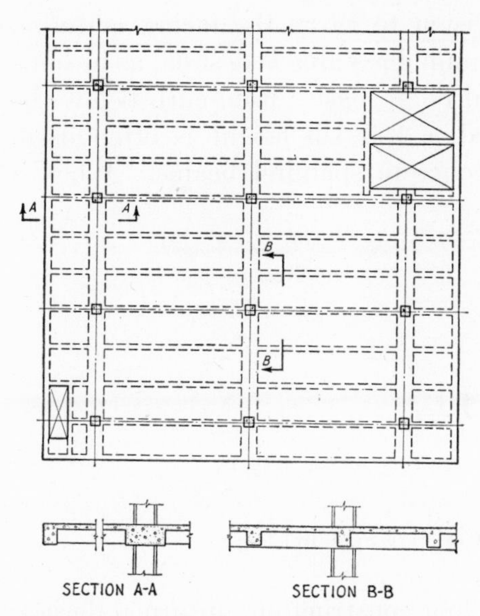

FIG. 11. Short-Span, Reinforced-Concrete, Beam-and-Girder Framing Plan.

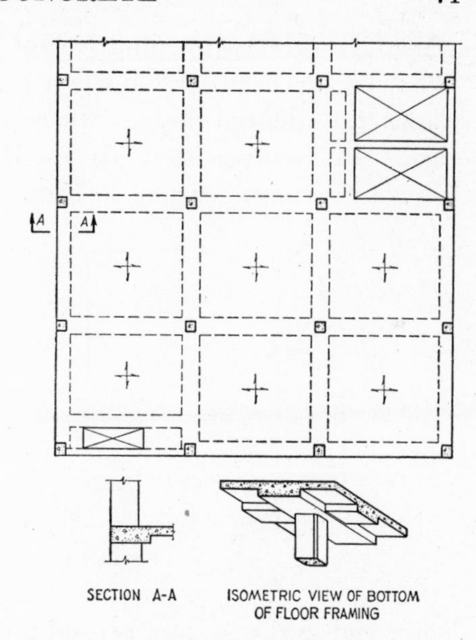

FIG. 12. Long-Span, Reinforced-Concrete Framing Plan with Shallow Beams.

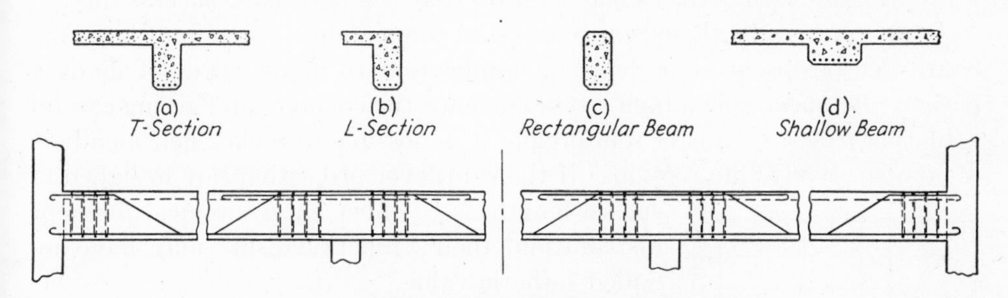

FIG. 13. Types of Reinforced-Concrete Beams.

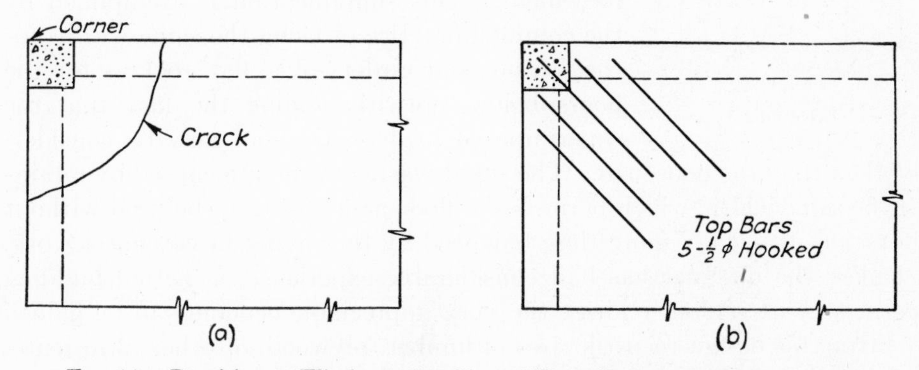

FIG. 14. Provision to Eliminate Cracking of Floor Slabs at Exterior Corners.

of lintel over the opening except provision to carry the facing material, where such is used. Even when a maximum glass area is desired, as in some modern residential designs, there should be at least a 6-in. curb below the sash. In factories that are day-lighted, a 3-ft sill height is often used. Figure 15 shows various designs for concrete spandrel beams. When a

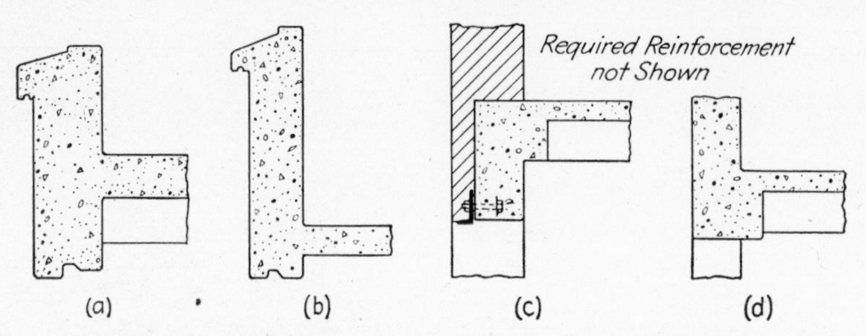

FIG. 15. Typical Designs for Concrete Spandrel Beams.

beam-and-girder system is used for the floor construction, upturned designs such as (*b*) should be studied in regard to beam arrangement, as it is apparent that such a spandrel cannot furnish support for beams below the floor level. Figure 16 illustrates one solution that has been used successfully.

As previously mentioned on page 60 in connection with column location, cantilever beams or slabs have an application to many types of modern design. By specifying a high stress value for the concrete and giving careful attention to the details of reinforcing, it is possible to make such members of comparatively thin section. If the cantilever projections are designed of such a length as to effect an economical moment distribution, their "functionalism" may have an added esthetic value.

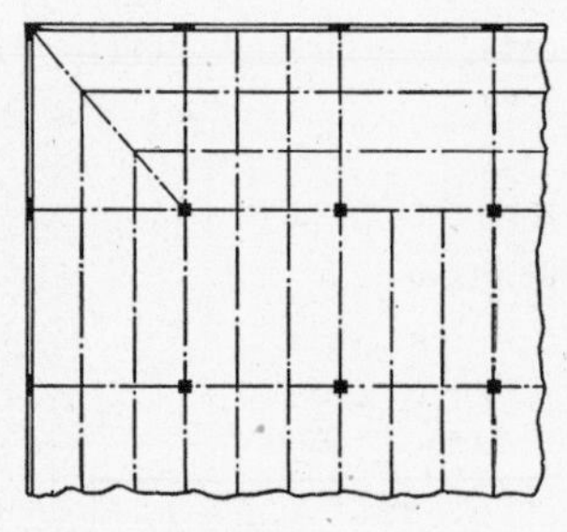

FIG. 16. Diagonal Corner Framing.

All structural members should be studied to minimize the alteration of forms and simplify the cutting, bending, and assembling of the reinforcement. This simplification is exemplified by the common practice of using the same widths for the beams and girders of a flat roof as for the floors below, notwithstanding the fact that the superimposed load on the roof may be considerably less than the floor load. The slight waste of concrete caused by retaining the same width, which permits the floor-panel forms to be used without alteration, is usually more than balanced by the saving in carpenter work.

Unless the designer has had considerable experience on actual building operations, he seldom realizes the very appreciable economy to be gained by fitting his design to stock sizes of lumber, plywood, or other form materials. Neither will he be able to visualize the methods used for form assembly and adjust the dimensions of beam, girder, and column to facilitate fabrication, erection, stripping, alteration, and re-erection. In concrete construction these matters are so important that the advice of an experienced builder should be sought. The phenomenal achievements of the building industry during World War II would have been impossible except for the fact that large operations were handled by a staff of experts who coordinated every phase of design with shop fabrication and erection.

For many types of buildings, the flat-slab or flat-plate designs, discussed in Article 7, often offer more advantages than beam-and-girder construction.

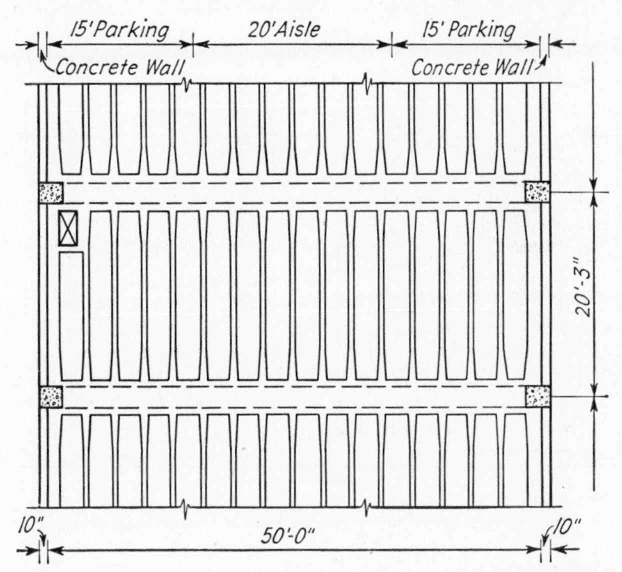

Fig. 17. Single-Span, Rigid-Frame Design with a Metal-Pan Floor System.

Obvious exceptions are where interior requirements demand many openings, changes in floor level, concentrated loads, offset columns, or other structural variations which interrupt continuity between adjacent panels. In some cases the beams or girders may also be a definite asset in resisting lateral forces. Furthermore, it may be practicable to apply a rigid-frame analysis to vertical bents formed by the supporting columns and girders spanning one or more continuous bays. Such designs are similar to the larger rigid frames of reinforced concrete discussed in Chapter Six and implement the same principle of continuity. Figure 17 shows such a type with the slab load lightened by metal pans.

Article 7. Flat-Slab and Flat-Plate, Rigid-Frame Designs

FLAT SLABS DESIGNED WITH SPECIFIED MOMENT COEFFICIENTS. The flat-slab design (Fig. 18) is particularly suitable for heavy floor loads in multistory concrete-framed structures. It has a wide application for industrial buildings. If columns may be placed without reference to interior requirements, which is usual for factories and warehouses, a spacing of about 20 or 22 ft is economical for uniformly distributed superimposed loads up to 300 lb per sq ft. Garages are often designed with columns about 25 × 22 ft on centers. A 30-ft spacing is nearly the practicable maximum for a uniformly distributed superimposed load of 200 lb

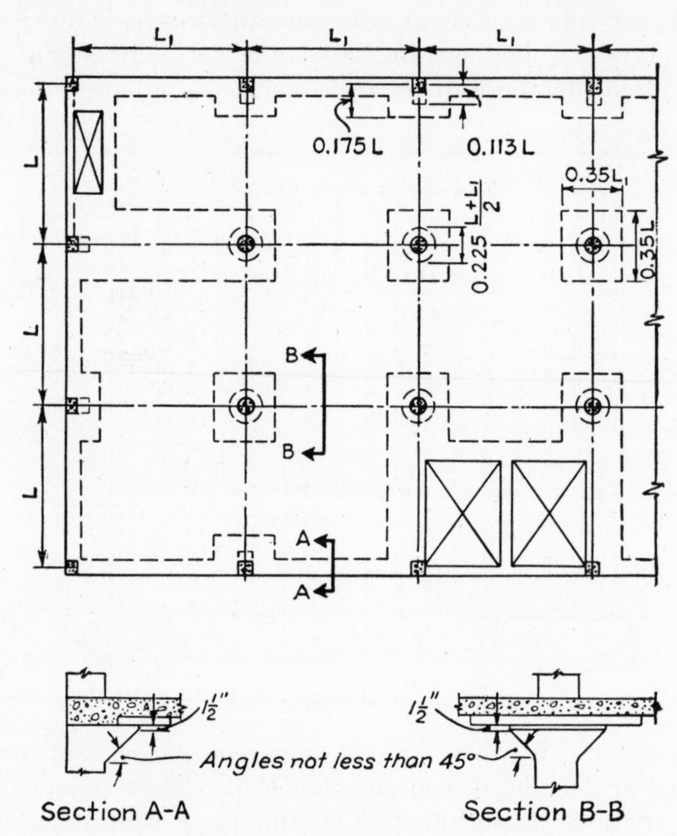

Fig. 18. Typical Reinforced-Concrete Flat-Slab Design.

per sq ft, except where the dead load of the construction is decreased by fillers of voids, as shown in the illustration on the preceding page.

In the design shown in Fig. 18, wide shallow sections of the same depth as the drop panels may be used along all discontinuous edges of the slab. Narrower and deeper beams, such as that shown in Fig. 19, section *B-B*, offer an alternate which is often desirable, particularly around stairs or elevator wells or elsewhere above partitions. It should be noted that openings of any size may be cut through a flat slab if provision is made for the stress requirements. Except in the case of small openings, the limiting dimensions of which are dependent upon location, framing is necessary upon all sides.

The design employing specified moment coefficients, such as given in "Building Regulations for Reinforced Concrete," American Concrete Institute, 1941, is limited in its application. The ratio of length to width of panel must not exceed 1.33: there must be at least three continuous panels

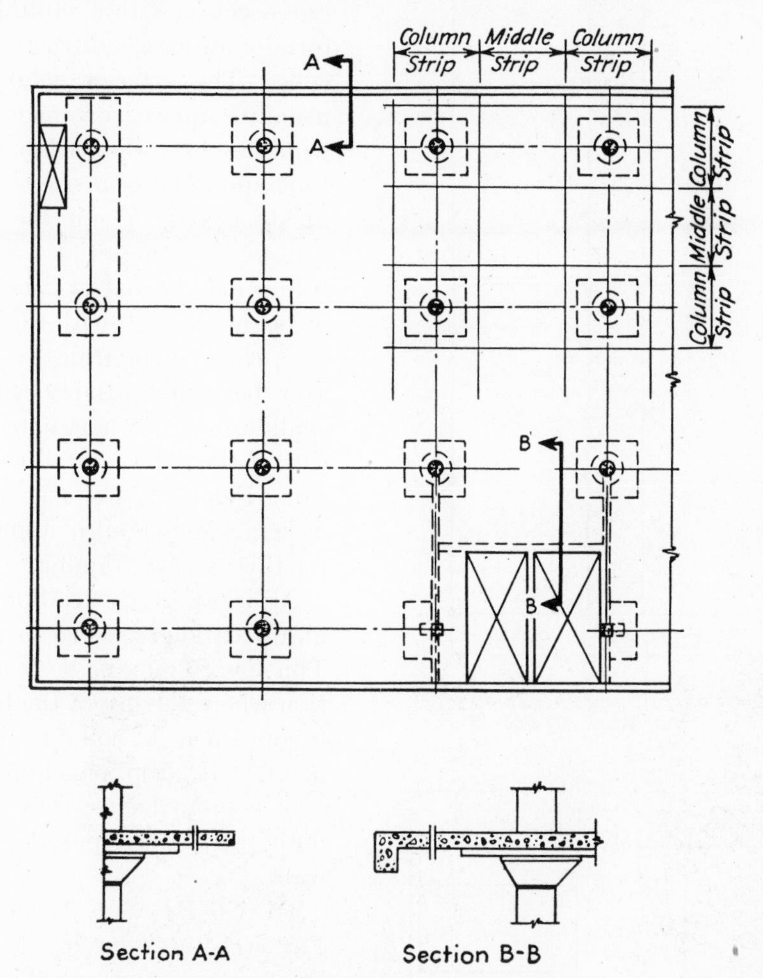

FIG. 19. Reinforced-Concrete Flat-Slab Design with Cantilever Projections at Exterior Walls.

in each direction. Successive span lengths in each direction must not differ by more than 20 per cent [2] of the shorter span.

Interior columns have flared capitals; brackets are used for exterior columns. Drop panels, as shown, are usually placed over columns, as they are structurally economical, but can be omitted if the slab is thick enough

[2] This is the requirement of the American Concrete Institute. The Report of the Joint Committee on Standard Specifications for Concrete and Reinforced Concrete, 1940, allows only 15 per cent variation.

to satisfy stress requirements. When drop panels are used over interior columns, they should also be used over exterior columns. Interior columns are usually of circular cross-section with a capital in the form of an inverted frustrum of a cone. The exterior columns are usually square or rectangular, windows extending from column to column and of a size chosen to fit stock sash or suit the dimensions of other materials. Spandrel beams may be placed either above or below the slab with which they are cast monolithically. They may be comparatively wide and shallow or of any adequate section to suit the exterior-wall construction. Figure 19 shows a cantilever design which is also appropriate for this type of framing.

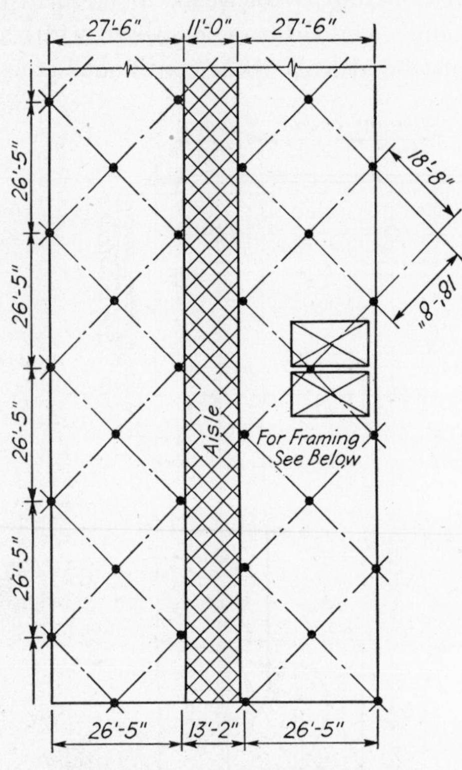

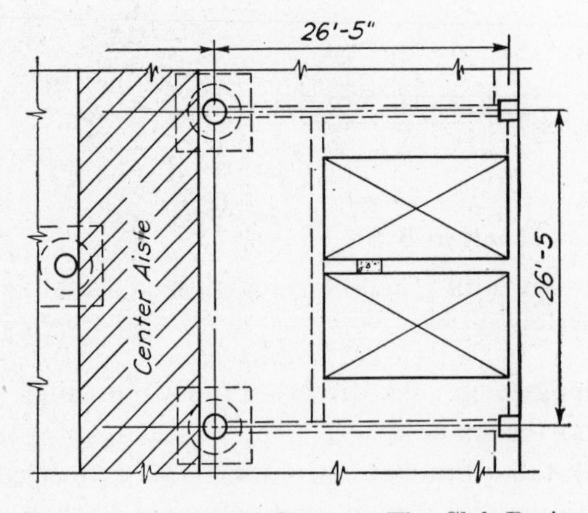

Fig. 20. Reinforced-Concrete Flat-Slab Design with Staggered Columns.

An interesting variation in column location is shown in Fig. 20. This design may have an application where the use of the building favors such a column arrangement. If drop panels are used over column heads, they may be built with sides parallel to the walls.

FLAT-PLATE DESIGNS. For structures having less than three consecutive panels in each direction or those where the size or shape of panels does not fall within the specified limits, or where it is desired to eliminate column capitals, standard moment coefficients are inapplicable, and the structural designer will apply the method of elastic analysis. An appropriate procedure is given in "Building Regulations for Reinforced Concrete," American Concrete Institute, 1941. In this connection it should be noted that the use of specified moment coefficients for flat-slab designs, meeting the requirements mentioned on page 75, is merely a special case for which it is possible, within these limits, to use a definite moment distribution and simplify the computations. Similarly, the moment coefficients commonly used in designing a series of continuous concrete beams or girders having spans of approximately the same length are special cases of continuity for which it is possible to use a standard moment distribution.

The broader application of continuity in concrete design is exemplified by the work of Fred N. Severud, consulting engineer of New York City, in

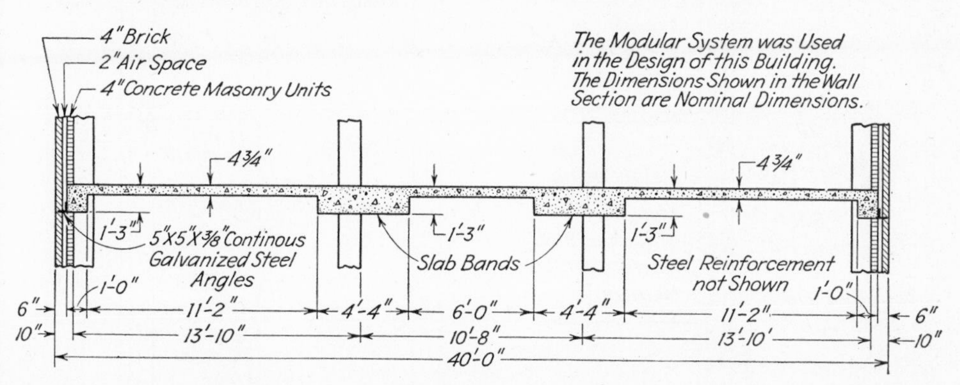

FIG. 21. Concrete-Slab Construction Adapted to Special Requirements of the Architectural Plan. Residence and School for Nurses, Bellevue Hospital, New York City. *Engr.:* Fred N. Severud.

which column capitals are omitted, and shallow reinforced-concrete beams called "slab bands" are the only projections below the concrete slab except for spandrels or where special conditions demand deeper framing. The typical floor construction of the nurses' home planned for Bellevue Hospital in New York City (Fig. 21) is an excellent example of adapting structural design to architectural plan. By this system it was possible to obtain economically a uniform thickness of floor slab except for the depressed bands which are placed over lavatories and closets where the slight reduction in ceiling height is negligible. This same type of design was used for the Tripler General Hospital, built in Hawaii in 1945, and for several large housing projects. It is also appropriate for industrial buildings.

Figure 22 shows a cross-section of the housing units mentioned on page 37. These structures were designed by Joseph Di Stasio & Company, consulting engineers of New York City, in 1939. Drop panels were omitted, and the column capitals reduced to small splays. About 5 years later the same firm developed the design illustrated in Fig. 23 for the Clinton Hill housing project in Brooklyn, New York. In these structures the column capitals were entirely omitted. The uniformly thick 6-in. slab was reinforced with bands of rods crossing over the column heads in a two-way system, similar to the typical flat-slab arrangement, but the entire assembly was designed as a continuous frame. Photographs of this same group

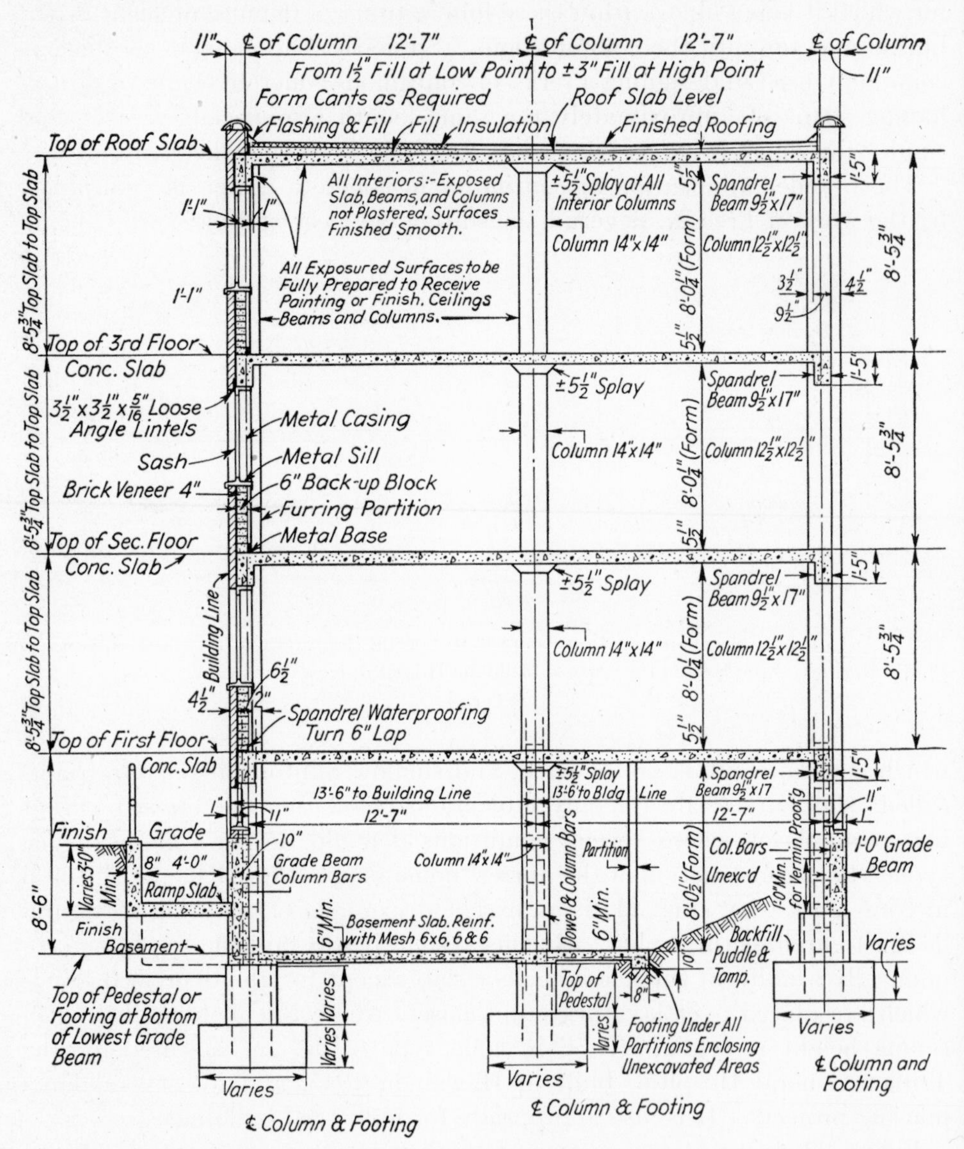

FIG. 22. Concrete-Slab Construction for Multifamily Housing Units. *Engr.:* Joseph di Stasio and Company.

are shown on pages 38 and 39, as they illustrate a very appropriate use of reinforced concrete.

The stress analysis of these structures was based on "Building Regulations for Reinforced Concrete," American Concrete Institute, 1941. Although the desired column locations caused a considerable variation in the size and shape of panels, spans were comparatively short, varying for the most part from 12 to 17 ft. The 6-in. slab thickness facilitated the embedment of crossing conduit and other pipes. Openings such as stair wells required particular attention in regard to adequacy of reinforcement. There has been no suggestion of weakness around column heads. Such designs are very appropriate for the comparatively light loads and moderate spans of apartment houses. Furthermore, where ceilings are not

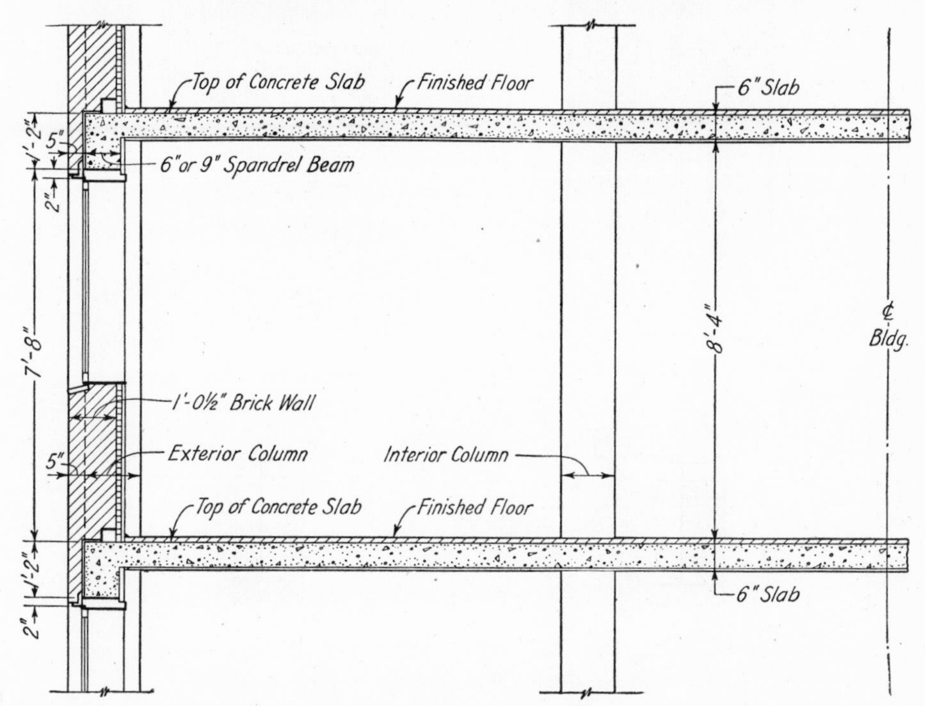

Fig. 23. Concrete Slab of Uniform Thickness for Multifamily Housing Units. *Engr.:* Joseph di Stasio and Company.

required to be plastered, and there is no reason for plastering in most cases, the solid concrete slab has a definite economic advantage.

Article 8. Fireproofing Structural Members; Moisture Protection

STRUCTURAL STEEL. The capacity of structural steel to support load is considerably reduced at temperatures such as may easily occur in any serious fire. Figure 24 shows the usual means of protection for columns, girders, and beams. A specified thickness of fireproofing is required for a certain rating, corresponding to the construction classification (see page 3). Typical requirements, abstracted from the New York City Building Code, are shown in the table on page 81. For example, a 3-hour rating would be accorded under this ordinance if all structural-steel beams were protected by a 2-in. thickness of any one of the following materials: grade I cement concrete, hollow or solid burned-clay tile, solid gypsum block, hollow or solid cinder-aggregate block, or the other materials with corresponding thicknesses as noted.

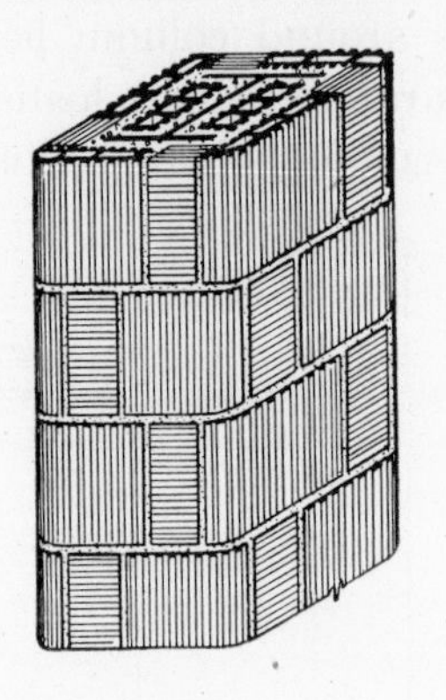

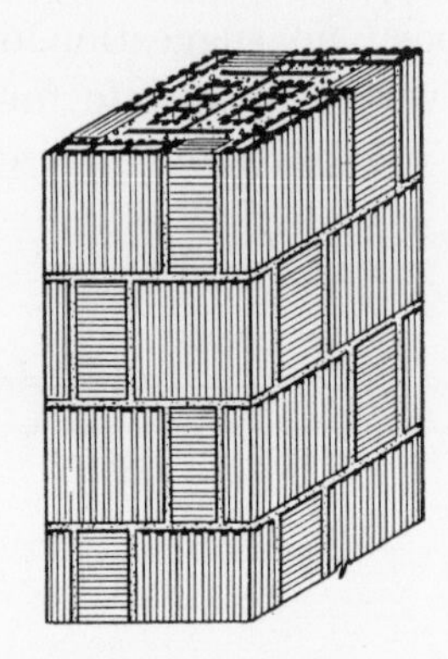

Columns Protected by Clay Tile

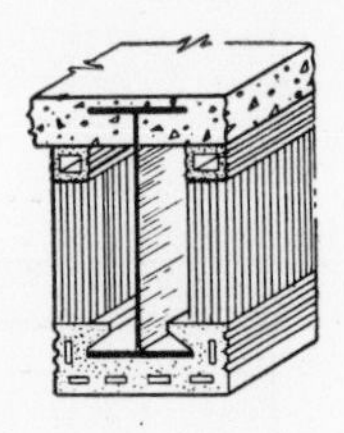

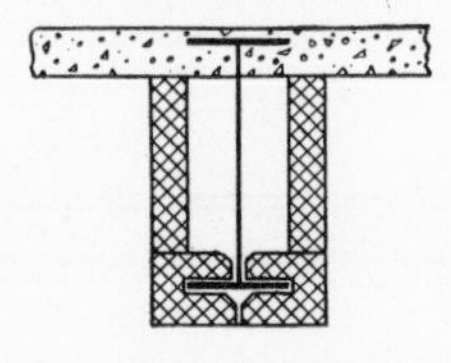

Deep Beams or Girders Protected by Clay Tile or Gypsum

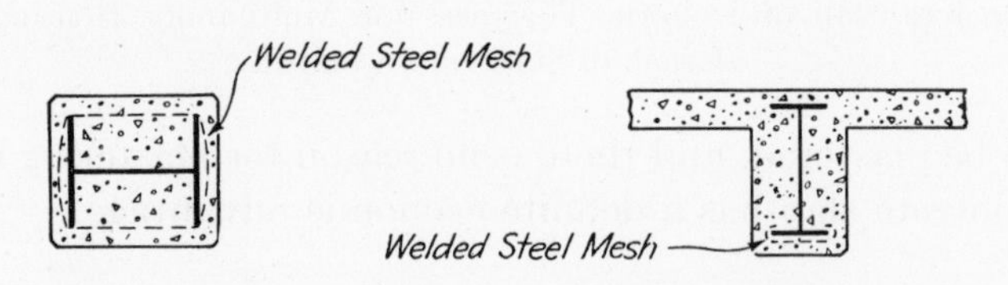

Concrete Fireproofing for Columns and Beams

Fig. 24. Methods of Fireproofing Structural-Steel Columns, Girders, and Beams.

When concrete poured-in-place is used for the structural floor system, it is usually economical to fireproof the supporting beams and girders with the same material, provided that the haunches below the floor slab are not over about 16 in. deep. This statement also applies to gypsum cast-in-place. The concrete or gypsum is poured into trough-like forms, hung by wires from the steel members. Clay tile, gypsum tile, or light-weight

THICKNESS OF FIREPROOFING TO PROTECT STRUCTURAL STEEL
REQUIREMENTS FOR VARIOUS FIRE-RESISTANCE RATINGS

(From the Building Code of New York City, Amended to 1942)

Fire-Resistive Materials	Minimum Thickness in Inches			
	4-Hour	3-Hour	2-Hour	1-Hour
Brick, burned clay or shale	3¾	3¾	2¼	2¼
Brick, sand-lime	3¾	3¾	2¼	2¼
Concrete brick, block or tile, except cinder-concrete units	3¾	3¾	2¼	2¼
Hollow or solid cinder-concrete block and tile having a compressive strength of at least 700 lb per sq in of gross area	2½	2	2	1½
Solid gypsum block (to obtain 4-hour rating must be plastered with ½-in. gypsum plaster)	2	2	1½	1
Gypsum poured in place and reinforced	2	1½	1½	1
Hollow or solid burned-clay tile or combinations of tile and concrete	2½	2	2	1½
Metal lath and gypsum plaster	2½	2	1½	⅞
Cement concrete, grade I *	2	2	1½	1
Cement concrete, grade II †	4	3	2	1½
Cement concrete, grade II, with wire mesh	3	2	2	1½
Hollow gypsum block (to obtain 4-hour rating must be plastered with ½-in. gypsum plaster on outer side)	3	3	3	3

* Grade I concrete is defined in this code as that in which the aggregate consists of limestone, traprock, blast-furnace slag, cinders, or calcareous gravel.

† Grade II concrete is defined as that in which the aggregate consists of granite or silicious gravel.

cement-aggregate blocks have a general application for fireproofing purposes in types of construction where a poured-in-place material is not used for the floor design and in all cases for the deeper beams, girders, and trusses. If masonry is used for deep beams and girders, it is desirable to place it before the pouring of the floor system. This procedure complicates the form support but saves considerable time on the part of the masons by avoiding the necessity of building up to the soffit of the slab.

Interior columns are sometimes fireproofed with cinder concrete or other light-weight concretes poured into forms, when such material is being employed for the floor system, but the masonry units mentioned above are often cheaper because of the cost of formwork. Exterior columns are usually fireproofed with a combination of the materials used for the exterior wall construction and furring, such as brick and clay tile, or any type of masonry other than gypsum, which should never be used where there is any possibility of moisture.

Adequate moisture protection will often be provided by the fireproofing requirements, but where a 4-in. thickness of masonry is used to fireproof exterior columns, it is desirable to apply first a moisture-proof paint to the steel surfaces. This application is required by the New York City Code. If column bases or other elements will be exposed to water or ground moisture, special provision may be necessary.

REINFORCED CONCRETE. Fireproofing of reinforced concrete is obtained by requiring a minimum thickness outside the metal reinforcement. The following table is taken from the Report of the Joint Committee on Standard Specifications for Concrete and Reinforced Concrete. Like the New York City Code, it recognizes the difference in fire resistance between aggregates which change a relatively small amount in volume when subjected to high temperature and those which change appreciably. The two classes are identified as follows:

Group 1: Blast-furnace slag, limestone, calcareous gravel, traprock, burnt clay or shale, cinders containing not more than 25 per cent of combustible material and not more than 5 per cent of volatile material, and other aggregates meeting the Committee's specifications and containing not more than 30 per cent of quartz, chert, flint, and similar materials.

Group 2: Granite, quartzite, siliceous gravel, sandstone, gneiss, cinders containing more than 25 per cent, but not more than 40 per cent, of combustible material and not more than 5 per cent of volatile material, and other aggregates meeting the Committee's specification and containing more than 30 per cent of quartz, chert, flint, and similar materials.

THICKNESS OF CONCRETE FIREPROOFING TO PROTECT METAL REINFORCEMENT. REQUIREMENTS FOR VARIOUS FIRE-RESISTANCE RATINGS

(From the Report of the Joint Committee on Recommended Practice and Standard Specifications for Concrete and Reinforced Concrete, 1940)

Structural Member	Minimum Thickness of Concrete in Inches			
	4-Hour	3-Hour	2-Hour	1-Hour
Columns, beams, girders and unprotected ribbed slabs				
Group 1, aggregate	1½	1½	1½	1
Group 2, aggregate	2	1½	1½	1
Solid slabs				
Group 1, aggregate	¾	¾	¾	¾
Group 2, aggregate	1	¾	¾	¾

In a ribbed-floor construction, such as that shown on page 109, where ribs are protected by plaster and spaced not more than 30 in. face to face and formed between permanent masonry filler blocks, or between permanent or removable forms, the fire-protection requirement for the ribs may be reduced to that indicated in the table for solid slabs. The plaster protection can be in the form of ¾ in. of portland-cement mortar or gypsum plaster, applied directly to the ribs and masonry fillers or to metal lath attached to or suspended below the ribbed construction.

MOISTURE PROTECTION. This requirement is covered in the Report of the Joint Committee as follows:

At those surfaces of footings and other principal structural members in which concrete is deposited directly against the ground, metal reinforcement should have a minimum covering of 3 in. of concrete. At other surfaces exposed to the ground or to severe weathering conditions, metal reinforcement should be protected by not less than 2 in. of concrete. At undersides of slabs exposed to weather 1 in. should be provided. Where metal fabric in the form of wire mesh or expanded metal is used as reinforcement for protective coatings on columns, beams, or girders, the minimum covering should be 1½ in. for structures exposed to water, ground. or weather and ¾ in. for structures not so exposed.

Article 9. Expansion or Contraction Joints

It is not within the scope of this text to give complete details of such joints, which should be carefully adapted to the general shape of the building, framing, floor, roof, and wall construction. The designer should, however, be able to determine when and where they are necessary. For that purpose the following paragraphs on the subject are quoted from the same Report of the Joint Committee.

PURPOSE AND LOCATION. a. If a reinforced concrete structure is free to expand and contract with variations in temperature or moisture conditions (uniform over the section), no stresses of any importance will be developed. When the movement of the structure is restrained, however, or when temperature or moisture variations are not uniform over the section, stresses are introduced which should be provided for in the design.

b. Points requiring special consideration are located where large changes in cross-section occur or at corners in long members where expansions or contractions may result in rupture of the side members. No amount of reinforcement will prevent the formation of cracks in a restrained structure in which the required change in length exceeds the extensibility of the concrete, but reinforcement properly designed will serve to distribute the cracks.

c. Joints providing a complete separation in the structure, when properly located, can relieve the restraint and prevent or greatly minimize the development of cracks. Such joints should be carefully designed with respect to the type of structure and should provide for the full expected movements without introducing local stresses severe enough to rupture the concrete. They should be located at predetermined points and fully detailed on the drawings. They may or may not be designed to carry load or distribute stress across the joint. Frequently this type of joint requires some form of protection to keep out extraneous material.

EXPANSION JOINTS IN LONG BUILDINGS. a. Expansion joints are expensive and in some cases difficult to maintain. They are, therefore, to be avoided if possible. In relatively short buildings, expansion and contraction can be provided for by additional reinforcement. No arbitrary spacing for joints in long buildings can be generally applicable. In heated buildings joints can be spaced

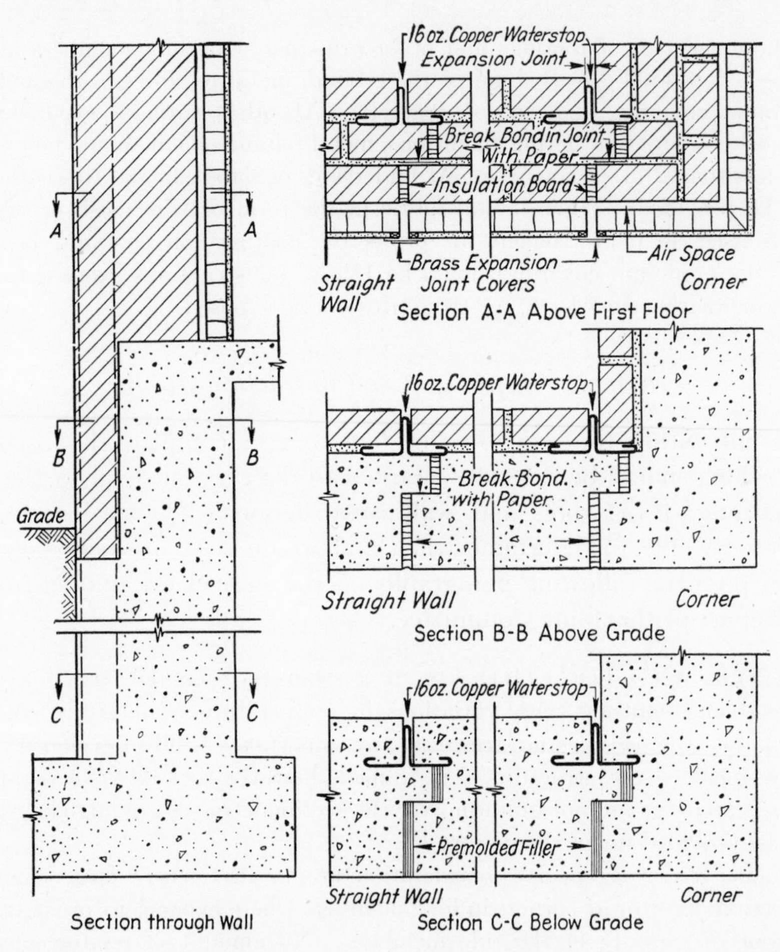

FIG. 25. Expansion Joints in Exterior Masonry Walls. Courtesy, Revere Copper Company.

farther apart than in unheated buildings. Also, where the outside walls are of brick or of stone ashlar backed with brick, or where otherwise insulated, the joints can be farther apart than with exterior walls of lower insulating value.

b. In localities with large temperature ranges, the spacing of joints for the most severe conditions of exposure (uninsulated walls and unheated buildings) should not exceed 200 ft. Under favorable conditions buildings 400 to 500 ft long have been built without joints even in localities with large temperature ranges.

c. In localities with small temperature ranges, the spacing of joints for unheated buildings or with uninsulated walls should not exceed 300 ft. In such localities buildings up to 700 ft long have been successfully built without joints where other conditions were favorable.

d. In roof construction, provision for expansion is an important factor. The joints in the roof may be required at more frequent intervals than in the other portions of the building because of more severe exposure. In some cases expansion joints spaced 100 ft apart have been provided in roofs and not in walls or floors.[3]

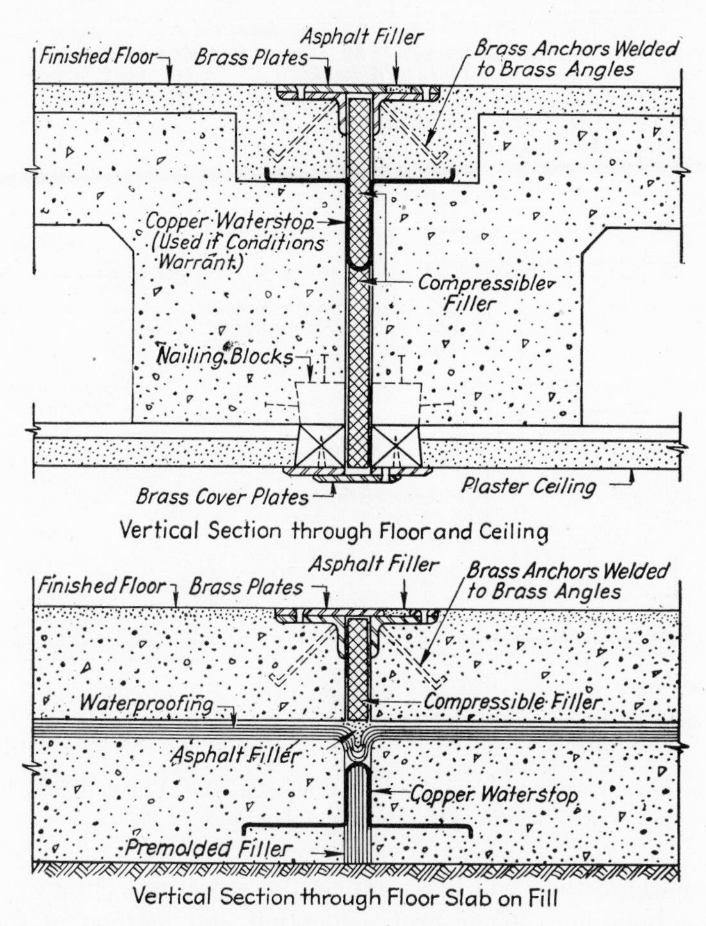

FIG. 26. Expansion Joints in Reinforced-Concrete Floor Slabs. Courtesy, Revere Copper Company.

e. Joints should be located at junctions in L-, T-, or U-shaped buildings and at points where the building is weakened by large openings in the floor construction, such as at light wells, stairs, or elevators. Joints should provide for a complete separation from the top of the footings to the roof, preferably by separate columns and girders.

[3] In regard to paragraph d above, it is the author's opinion that, if a joint across a roof slab is expected to function, the slab should not be rigidly connected to the supporting structure, unless corresponding joints are provided in this structure.

Joints of this type, shown in Figs. 25 and 26, provide for either contraction or expansion of the concrete by an actual separation of structural members and are not to be confused with construction joints, which are merely horizontal or vertical planes along which it is necessary to interrupt the continuous placing of the concrete as the work progresses from day to day. Construction joints should be planned in advance with the builder

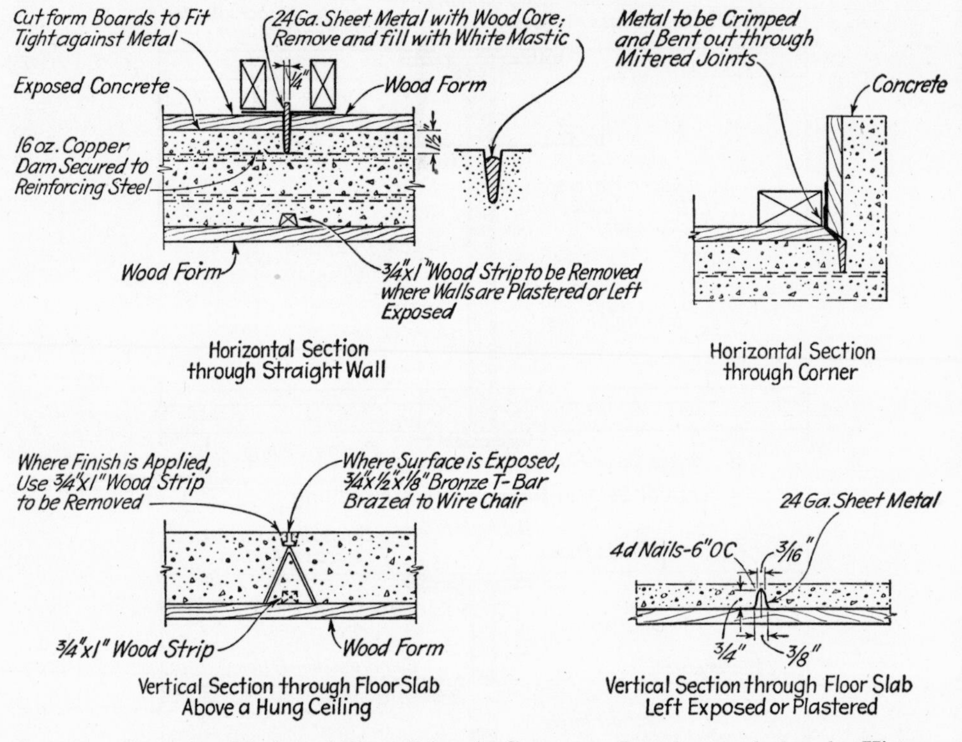

Fig. 27. Control or Weakened-Plane Joints in Concrete. Based upon designs by Kistner, Curtis, and Wright, Architects, Los Angeles, Calif.

and located where they will least impair the structural design or appearance of the building. Their proper location and method of forming is described in the specification included as part of the report previously quoted (page 83).

CONTROL JOINTS. A modification of the conventional contraction or expansion joint is known as the "control" or "weakened-plane" joint. Typical designs are shown in Fig. 27. They are obviously of no value to prevent buckling in case of expansion but may often be effectively used, as most cracking of concrete is due to shrinkage occurring either during the early stages of hydration or subsequently by reason of drying and chilling. Such joints may offer an appropriate means of controlling the location of potential cracks. They should be seriously considered where a change in the concrete cross-section, or extensive unbroken areas of walls or floors, present the probability of developing secondary stresses due to volumetric change. Other critical locations are those where wall panels join pilasters (see definition on page 291), where steel columns are cast into concrete walls, and where openings occur adjacent to long or thick wall sections.

Some experienced designers even favor the practice of placing joints of this type in both walls and floors at a spacing of from 15 to 25 ft. If the floor slabs are left exposed, those in the floor should be in line with the joints in walls. Although the exact location and frequency of jointing depend upon the architectural and structural design as well as the exposure, a reasonable degree of articulation is recommended as a means of eliminating unsightly cracks. Each situation, however, requires individual study, and it must be realized that shrinkage in a floor assembly occurs in both directions. Recent inspection of several large concrete buildings constructed on the Pacific Coast during World War II indicates that this type of joint, although often very effective for localizing cracks in the positions mentioned above, is not adaptable to all framing systems.

WOOD FRAMING AND PREFABRICATION

Article 10. Interior Wood Framing with Masonry Bearing Walls

Except for the newer types of laminated sections and other designs particularly applicable to wide-span requirements, wood framing is so well standardized and universally understood that the subject is covered only briefly in this text. Since the acceptance of wood as a framing material ordinarily implies its use for the entire structural floor, the typical wood-joist and heavy-timber designs are described in this article and the following one instead of in Chapter Four.

ORDINARY CONSTRUCTION. This term is used to identify buildings having exterior walls of masonry or reinforced concrete and in which the interior framing is wholly or partly of wood of smaller dimensions than that required for heavy-timber construction. Interior bearing walls are often used, and occasionally steel beams or girders or steel or iron columns, not protected as required for fireproof or semifireproof construction. Most building codes have such a classification,[4] which is associated with exterior brick-, stone-, or concrete-block masonry walls and interior floors of conventional wood-joist design carried by wood or steel girders, supported in turn by wood columns, light structural-steel sections, or pipe columns.

EXTERIOR WALLS. The general requirements for wall construction are given in Chapter Seven. For pitched-roof designs, such as that shown in Fig. 28, a wood plate is placed at the top of the exterior wall. This plate is

[4] See underwriters' definition, page 4.

ordinarily of 2-in. nominal thickness and of width equal to the wall and is anchored by means of bolts. For flat-roof designs the exterior wall is often extended above the roof to form a parapet, usually 32 or 36 in. high. The

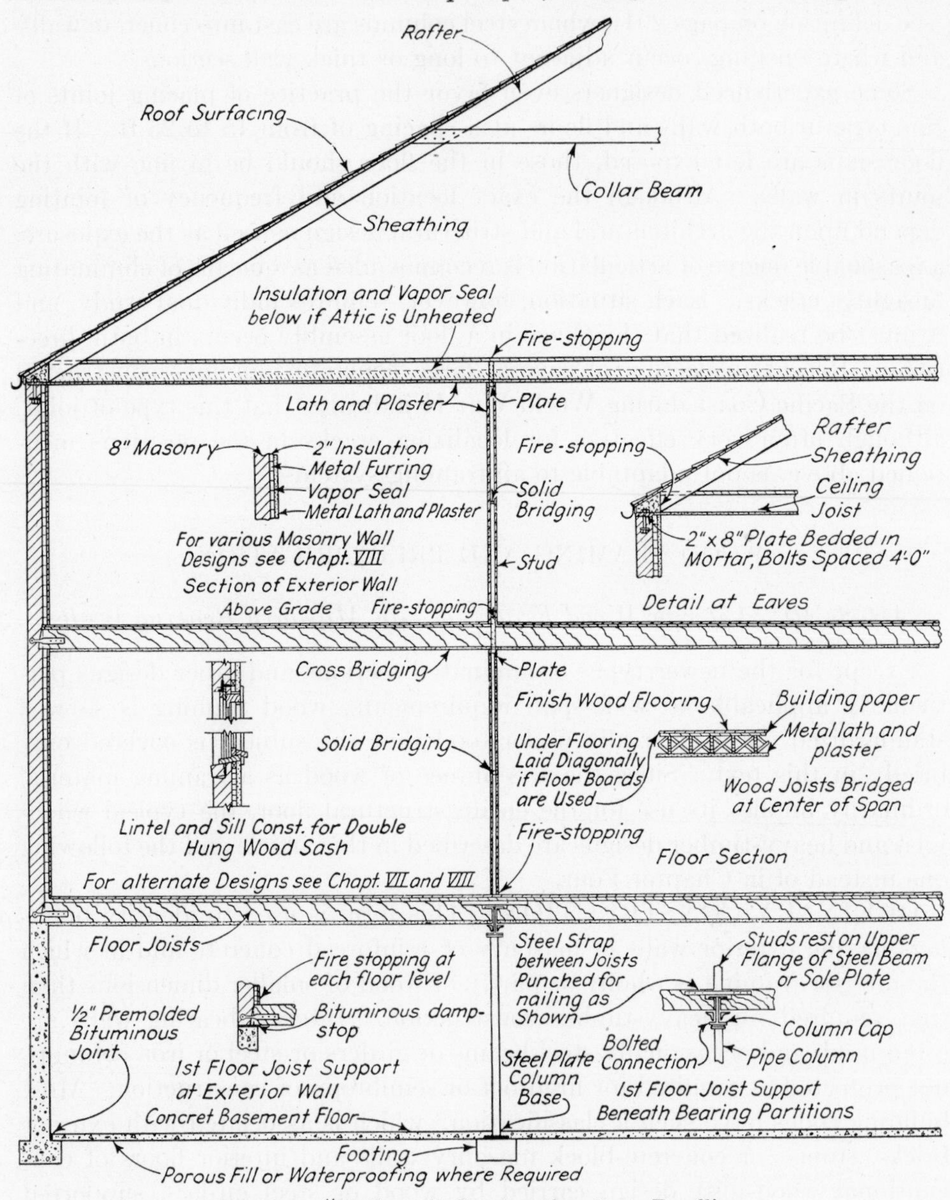

FIG. 28. "Ordinary" Construction for a Dwelling.

exact height is generally specified in local codes; good practice in regard to thickness of parapets is given on page 355 of this text. An alternate treatment, popular in recent years, is to eliminate the parapet and finish the junction of roof and walls as shown on page 172.

Floors and Roofs. The typical floor construction is of wood joists, usually 2 × 10 or 2 × 12 in. in nominal size, spaced 12 to 16 in. on centers. A 3-in. minimum thickness may be demanded by a municipal code within fire limits. As noted on page 43, the first structural floor is often of a more fire-resistant design. When wood joists are used, bridging is placed at a maximum spacing of 8 ft. A subflooring composed of matched boards $\frac{7}{8}$ × 6 or 8 in. is laid diagonally over the wood joists, or plywood may be used. A finished wood flooring or other desired surface treatment is then applied. Building paper is laid between the two floors; it is desirable to use a waterproof building paper for this purpose, particularly for floors laid over a basement or in other locations where dampness might be present beneath the floor. A finished flooring of wood is usually laid at right angles to the joists and should be securely nailed through the subfloor and into the joists. Other classes of finished flooring are laid in a manner appropriate for their type.

Ceiling material is applied to the soffits of the wood joists. Metal lath, occasionally wood lath, or gypsum lath serves as a base for plaster. Metal lath well nailed, lapped and wired where sheets intersect, is the best from the viewpoint of insurance against plaster cracks. Gypsum lath, often called "rock lath," requires less plaster and gives slightly better heat insulation. Many types of fiber and composition boards, finished to present a suitable ceiling surface or adapted to the application of paint, are available. If the roof surface is comparatively flat, the construction is similar to that of the floors. If pitched, the rafters forming the skeleton-like frame carry shingle lath, solid boarding, or other desired material serving as a base for the roof surface and providing rigidity for the entire roof assembly. Where attic spaces are heated, an appropriate type of insulation (see page 175) can be used between the roof rafters instead of between the floor joists.

Framing Details. Most building codes have specific regulations applying to the manner in which structural members are supported. For example, wood girders carried by a masonry wall are usually either held by a metal wall hanger or built into a recess of the wall and supported by a metal plate, as shown in Fig. 29. The recess is made large enough to provide ventilation against dry rot. Firestopping is important. It is shown in Fig. 28.

Wood joists should have a 4-in. bearing on exterior walls and be secured by metal anchors placed on at least one joist in every 6 ft. The ends of joists are also bevelled to permit release in case of fire without dislodging the masonry. Figure 29 shows typical details. Where supported by interior masonry walls, joists in small dwelling-house construction are merely lapped across the wall and spiked together, but special methods of support may be required for larger structures. Where supported by wood partitions which, in two-story dwellings, would normally require 2-in. × 4-in. studs, the floor joists are similarly lapped across the partition plate and spiked.

Where supported by steel girders, the designs shown in Fig. 30 have been found satisfactory. Solid bridging should be used at the mid-height of all wood-stud partitions. Where lateral stiffness is essential, partition

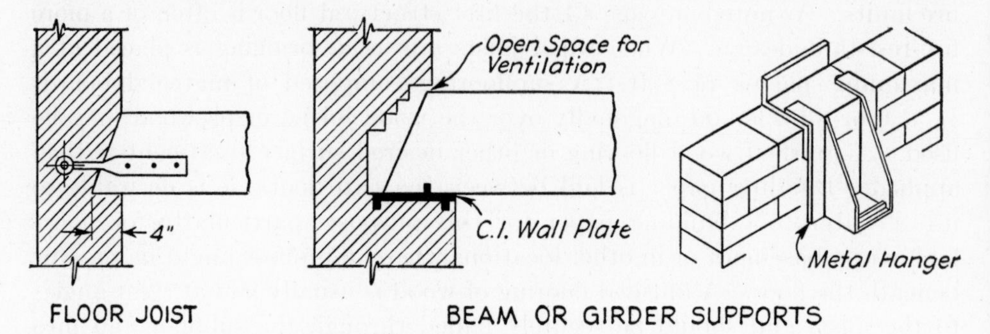

FIG. 29. End Support of Wood Framing on Masonry Walls.

bridging is inclined. Studs are doubled at sides of openings with wood lintels or trusses across the heads.

When wood framing is used with exterior masonry bearing walls, there is an obvious tendency for the shrinkage of the wood to cause settlement of the interior assembly. Timber shrinks only slightly in direction parallel to the grain, but the cross-grain shrinkage may be considerable. For this reason the framing should be arranged to eliminate such effect as far as

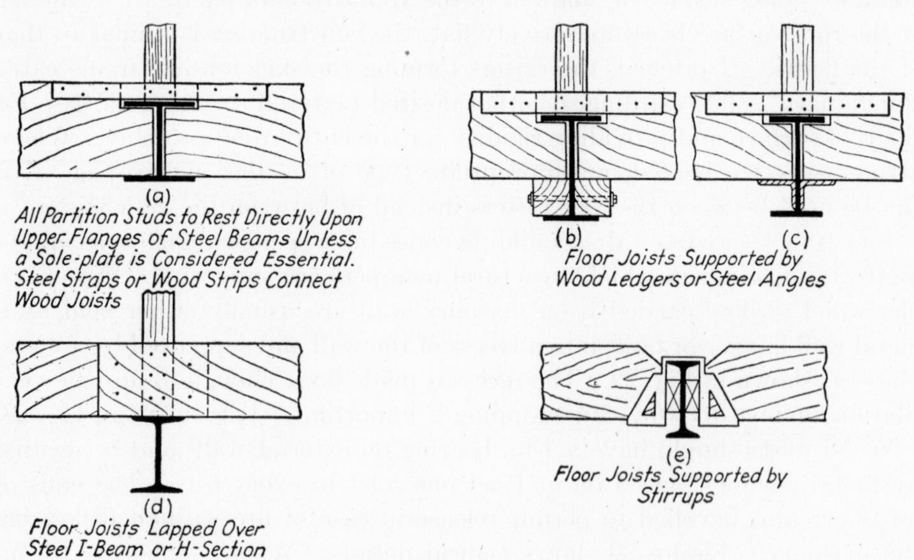

FIG. 30. Steel Girders Supporting Wood Joists.

practicable. Although it is common experience that serious plaster cracking generally develops in such structures during the first year of occupancy, this cracking can be almost entirely avoided by proper design. The studs of wood bearing partitions should rest directly upon the plate below when supported by a partition and directly upon the wood girder where such a girder furnishes the support. If carried by a steel girder this arrangement is also desirable unless a sole plate is considered necessary to permit nailing the lower ends of the studs. It is preferable to use pipe columns and steel girders instead of wood, even for small one-family dwellings.

If wood posts are used in a basement, they should rest upon cast-iron bases for protection against moisture. Any type of post or column should be supported by a small concrete footing, rather than merely resting upon a concrete cellar floor unless this floor is laid over rock.

HEAVY-TIMBER OR MILL CONSTRUCTION. This term is used to identify buildings which have exterior walls of masonry or reinforced concrete and in which the interior structural framing, including the roof, is of heavy timbers designed to resist the effect of fire. For this reason it is sometimes called slow-burning construction.[5] Interior bearing walls are often used, particularly in buildings of large area where they may be designed as fire walls.

WALLS AND PARTITIONS. The exterior bearing walls are of thickness and design to meet structural and fire-resistive demands. Other requirements are described in Chapter Eight. If the walls are of brick, 12 in. are a minimum; beneath concentrations, such as roof trusses, in buildings over 50 ft wide this thickness would be increased to form a pier at least 16 in. deep. If an automatic sprinkler system is to be installed, as is quite often the case in buildings of this type, scuppers are provided. As the flooring should be kept back from inner faces of exterior walls a distance of ½ in. to allow for swelling, walls are often corbelled to cover the joint and provide support for the flooring. Steel lintels are generally used to span openings. If such lintels are more than 6 ft wide, the steel is protected to meet a semifireproof classification (see page 3).

Inner court walls are often of the same material as exterior walls, but laminated wood construction 4 in. thick may be used if protected on the weather side by incombustible material. Interior partitions usually require a 1-hour fire-resistance rating and may be of solid wood construction formed of two layers of matched boards, each of 1-in. nominal thickness, or of solid wood laminated design not less than 3⅝ in. thick. Walls enclosing stair wells, elevator shafts, vent shafts, or other vertical openings should have a 2-hour rating except for structures not over three stories in height where sprinklers are installed.

In districts subject to earthquakes, the roof trusses of one-story buildings are often supported on the exterior by columns, the walls serving merely as enclosures or "filler walls," as they are called. Such enclosures are not actually wall bearing but are included in this article, as they are a modifi-

[5] See underwriters' definition, page 4.

cation of such construction, used particularly in the Pacific Northwest, and may have their application in any locality where land and timber are cheap and the possibility of earthquakes is a factor in the design.

Floors and Roofs. In typical mill construction, wood girders span from an exterior wall to an interior column and then from column to column in one direction only. The girder spans between columns vary from 12 to 18 ft. No beams are used at right angles to the girders. The distance between the girders, which usually varies from 7 to 10 ft, is spanned by heavy plank flooring. The smooth undersurface of the floor plank helps to lessen the inflammability of the construction. Lath and plaster are not

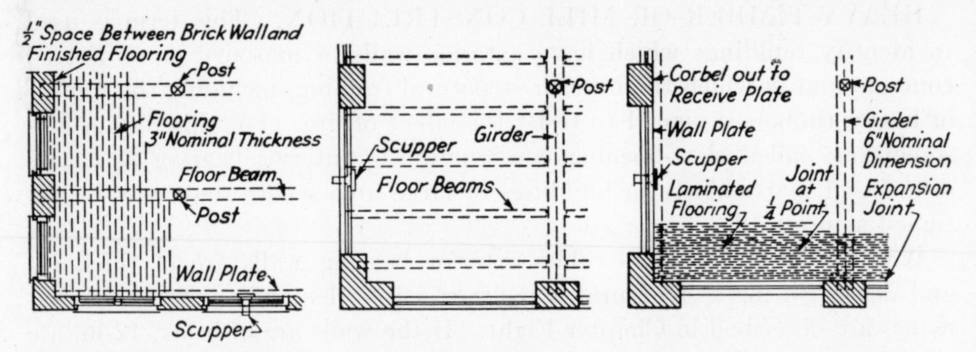

Fig. 31. Plans of Corner Bays for Three Types of Mill Flour Construction. Courtesy, National Lumber Manufacturers' Association.

used on typical designs. Most building codes, and good practice as well, provide severe regulations in regard to the protection of shafts or other vertical openings which might act as flues in case of fire.

Wood columns are of a minimum 8-in. nominal thickness in any dimension, and all corners are rounded or chamfered. Steel or cast-iron columns are generally permitted, if protected to furnish a fire-resistance rating of at least 1 hour. Wood beams and girders used for the support of floors have a minimum nominal thickness of 6 in. and a minimum nominal depth of 10 in. Floors are usually composed of wood plank, tongued and grooved or preferably splined, not less than 3-in. nominal thickness, laid across the timber framing. Planks set on edge and spiked together are also used to form a laminated floor. The minimum nominal thickness of this design is 4 in., but wider planks which permit a spacing of girders up to 12 or 18 ft are sometimes used. Over the structural floor is laid a finished flooring of nominal 1-in. thickness to take wear and improve the appearance.

An alternate framing design is similar to that described above, except for wood beams spaced 4 to 10 ft apart between the girders. Beams are either placed on top of the girders, ends of contiguous members being joined by a steel strap, or are supported by metal stirrups attached to the girders. Plank floors rest upon the beams. Typical designs, including the application of laminated flooring, are shown in Fig. 31.

Construction of roofs is similar to that of floors except that the requirements are somewhat less severe. For example, plank used for the roof deck may be of 2½-in. nominal thickness or, if a laminated design is used, a minimum plank width of 3 in. laid on edge and spiked together as required

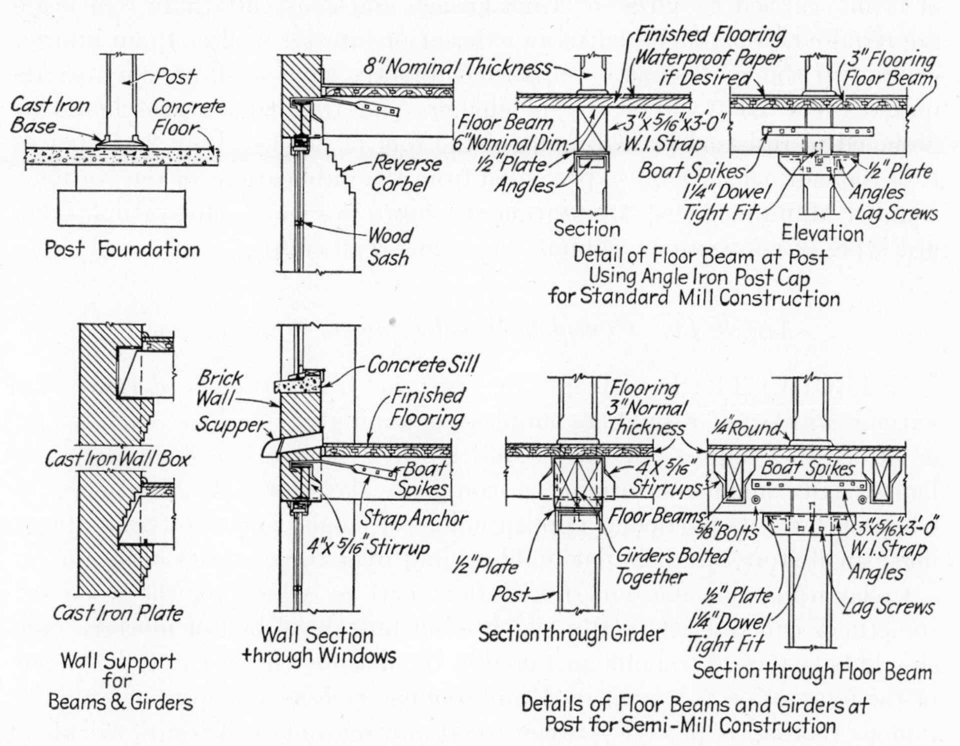

FIG. 32. Typical Details of Mill Construction. Courtesy, National Lumber Manufacturers' Association.

for floors. Wood beams and girders, however, even when supporting only roof loads, are required by the Underwriters' Recommended Code to have a nominal depth of at least 6 in. The roof covering should be incombustible or of a fire-retardant type.

FRAMING DETAILS. All columns should be superimposed throughout all stories and provided with reinforced-concrete or metal post caps with brackets, or connected by steel or iron caps, pintles, and base plates or by timber splice blocks affixed to the columns by means of devices or connectors housed within the contact faces. Columns are not permitted to rest on floor timbers, and stone, cast-iron, or steel bases are used to transmit the load to masonry foundations. Wall plates, boxes of self-releasing type, or an appropriate hanger is required where beams or girders rest on walls.

There should be at least 8 in. of masonry between the ends of beams or girders and the outside face of the wall, and where beams enter walls from opposite sides there should be the same thickness of masonry between faces of adjacent beams.

Most building codes give specific regulations for the connections between beams or girders and the supporting columns or walls and for the support of beams carried by girders. Roof girders and every alternate roof beam are required to be anchored to an exterior or interior wall or to an interior column; if the roof plank is supported directly by a wall, anchors are required every 20 ft. The size of anchors and their anchorage should be designed to resist a vertical uplift of the roof of not less than 20 lb per sq ft of roof surface. Details abstracted from the publications of the National Lumber Manufacturers' Association are shown in Fig. 32, illustrating standard types of connections, column bases, and wall support.

Article 11. Complete Wood-Framed Construction

INTRODUCTION. Except for certain heavy-timber designs and various wide-span assemblies employing laminated sections, such as are described in Chapter Six, the wood-framed structure is a combination of light-weight members forming a complete skeleton. As mentioned in Chapter Two, its particular application is for single- and two-family dwellings, small stores, and similar buildings not over three stories in height.

Cellar walls or a masonry foundation serve as a base for the wood sill, sometimes called a sole plate, which is set on a level bed of mortar. Sills should be attached to bolts anchored in the masonry or cast in the concrete of the foundation. A layer of dampproofing, such as a strip of heavy bituminous roofing, is placed between wood and masonry. Termite shields of noncorrodible metal are advisable in many localities. The interior framing comprises corner posts and vertical studs carrying a horizontal top plate. These are braced as shown in the illustrations and strengthened around openings.

The outer ends of the first-floor joists or beams rest upon the sill and, except in structures not over about 20 ft wide, which can be spanned without intermediate support, the inner ends rest upon a bearing wall, stud partition, or girder. The second- and third-story joists are supported on the exterior by girts or ribbons which are horizontal members carried by the corner posts and studs. Their inner ends may be supported in the same manner as the first-floor joists, but stud bearing partitions are the usual practice, as interior masonry walls are seldom necessary above the basement and partitions which can be used for bearing are generally available.

Cross-bridging is placed between all floor joists at a maximum spacing of 8 ft. This stiffens the floor assembly and distributes concentrated loads.

The boards comprising the underflooring should be laid diagonally for the purpose of bracing the building, as well as for the reason that such an arrangement permits laying a finished wood floor either parallel to or across

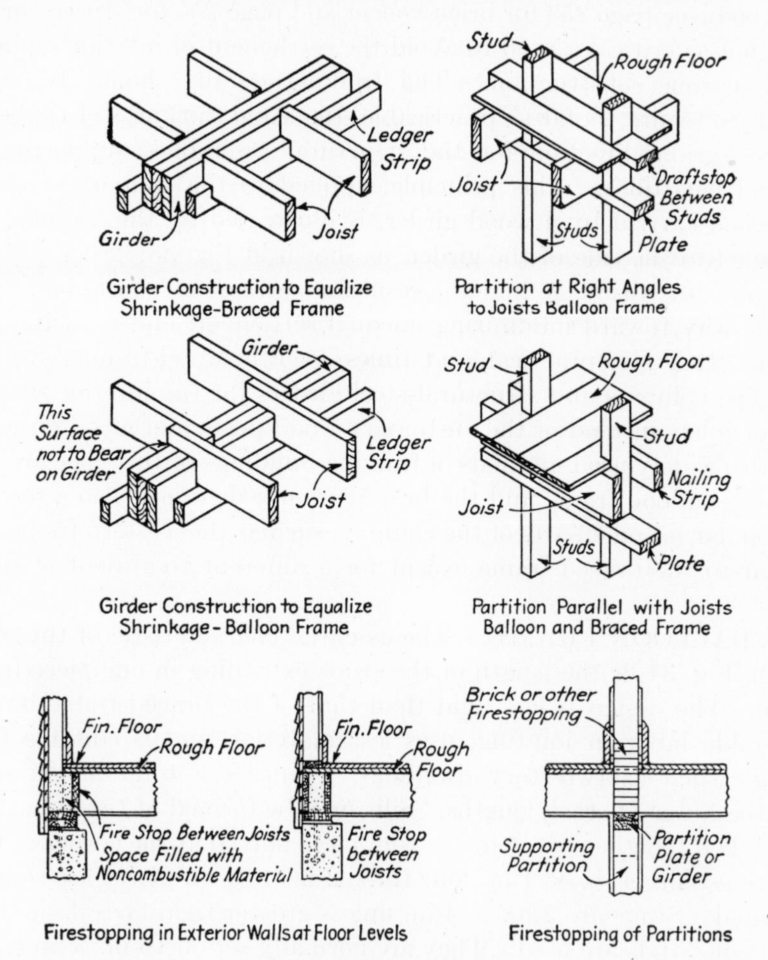

Fig. 33. Typical Details for Wood-Framed Construction. Courtesy, National Lumber Manufacturers' Association.

the joists. Building paper is placed between wood floors, as in the bearing-wall designs; ceiling construction is the same, as described on page 89.

Nonbearing partitions require no special provision for their support unless they are parallel to the floor joists. In this case a double joist is used beneath the partition. The construction is similar to that of the exterior walls, with 2-in. × 4-in. studs at 16-in. centers. In the typical designs illustrated, these studs should rest directly upon the cap of the supporting partition. Double studs are used at sides of openings with wood lintels or trusses across the heads. Bridging is cut in between the studs near mid-height for lateral support and for restriction of the spread of fire. Fire-stopping is important. Typical details are shown in the illustrations.

In buildings of this type, where exterior walls as well as interior framing are of wood (see page 253 for brick veneer and page 255 for stucco surfaces), there is not as critical a need to avoid the settlement of interior supports as in wall-bearing construction. The framing details should be studied, however, to secure, as far as practicable, the same thickness of timber used in a cross-grain direction for the structural assemblies supporting both walls and partitions. This principle, applied to the support of the floor joists, when carried by a wood girder, is illustrated by the use of a ledger strip nailed to the side of the girder, as shown in Fig. 33. Such provisions do not prevent shrinkage and the resulting settlement of the building but go a long way toward minimizing unequal settlement and reducing plaster cracking. It is also practicable at times, even in wood-framed structures, to use pipe columns and structural-steel girders for the interior support of first-floor joists instead of the customary wood posts and wood girders.

The two widely used methods of framing buildings of this type are identified as the balloon frame and the braced frame; there are also a few variations popular in some parts of the country, such as the western frame, which is similar to the braced frame except for a different treatment of sills and girts.

THE BALLOON FRAME. The essential characteristic of this system, shown in Fig. 34, is the length of the studs extending in one piece from sill to plate. The design is less rigid than that of the braced frame but saves considerable labor in jointing, uses less material, and is suitable for low buildings, such as two-story dwellings, requiring a total height of stud within the range of stock lengths. Sills may be formed of two 2-in. × 4-in. pieces spiked together or a 4-in. × 4-in. piece halved at the corners. Corner posts are usually 4 in. × 4 in., but three 2-in. × 4-in. pieces are sometimes substituted. Studs are 2 in. × 4 in. unless greater rigidity is desired, when 2-in. × 6 in. studs are used. They are normally set on 16-in. centers. This is a satisfactory spacing for interior lath and exterior sheathing; for typical designs it also conforms with the spacing for floor joists and enables their exterior ends to be spiked to the studs.

The outer ends of the first-floor joists rest on the sill and need no other support. For the upper floors a ⅞-in. × 6-in. board, called a ribbon, is let into the inner faces of the studs and corner posts a distance equal to its thickness and nailed in place to form a rest for the joists. If 2-in. × 6-in. studs are used, a 2-in. × 6-in. ribbon is appropriate. Across the tops of the studs and corner posts is placed the plate, which is a 4-in. × 4-in. piece or two 2-in. × 4-in. pieces spiked together. The plate carries the roof rafters or serves as a base for dormer or gable construction.

As the essential framing elements of this assembly are very light, the sheathing boards are often laid diagonally, except under stucco. These boards are ordinarily 7/8 in. × 6 in. or 8 in. and either tongued and grooved or ship-lapped, but the stronger fiber boards or plywood may be used.

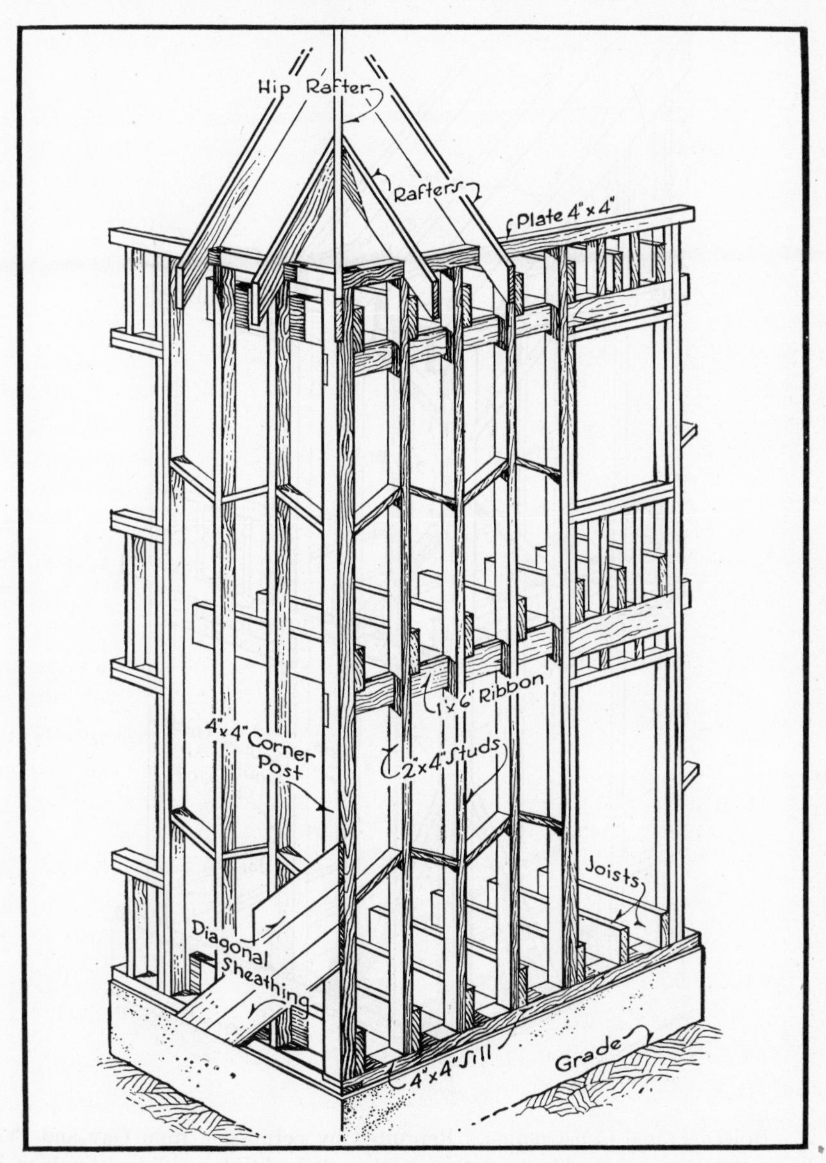

FIG. 34. Balloon-Frame Construction. Reprinted by permission from Gay and Parker's *Materials and Methods of Architectural Construction*, 2nd edition, published by John Wiley & Sons.

Substantial nailing to each stud is essential. Cross-bracing should also be placed between the studs as shown for the purposes of stiffening the frame and impeding the spread of fire in the space between sheathing and plaster, which is open except for insulation. It should be remembered that fire-stopping is very important in structures of this type. In exposed locations additional diagonal bracing, in a direction opposite to that of the sheathing,

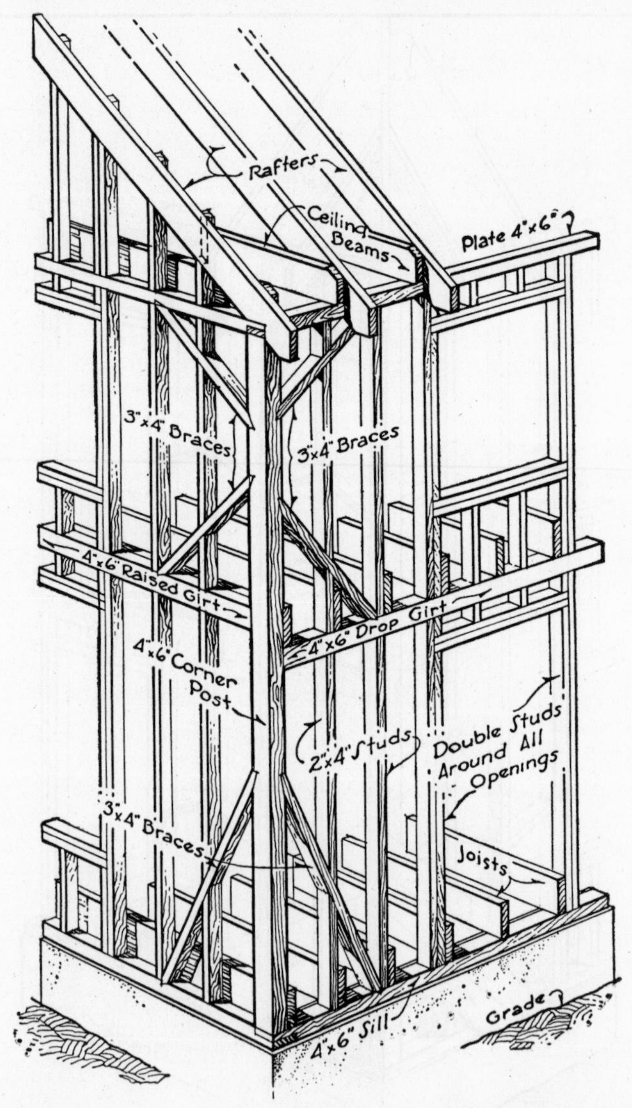

FIG. 35. Braced-Frame Construction. Reprinted by permission from Gay and Parker's *Materials and Methods of Architectural Construction*, 2nd edition, published by John Wiley & Sons.

should be used to provide wind resistance. Such bracing can be in the form of ⅞-in. × 6-in. boards let into the outer faces of the studs.

The interior framing is similar to that described for wall-bearing construction, except as noted in the introduction to this article. The illustrations show a typical design for hipped-roof construction and some of the more essential framing details.

THE BRACED FRAME. In this type of framing the exterior studs extend only through a one-story height, and comparatively heavy timbers called girts are used to strengthen the building frame and support the joists of floors above the first, as shown in Fig. 35. With the exception of the studding, all structural members are usually somewhat heavier than those used for the balloon frame, and the entire assembly is much stronger. The sill should be at least 4 × 6 in.; corner posts, extending from sill to plate, are of similar section. The size and spacing of studs for both exterior walls and partitions are the same as for the lighter construction; the girts are let into the corner posts, preferably with mortised and tenoned joints, and strengthened by knee braces. This design develops a much more rigid structure. The drop girt serves as a support for the exterior ends of the joists at floors above the first; the raised girt is placed with its upper surface flush with the floor joists. Both are normally 4- × 6-in. pieces. The diagonal braces are 3 × 4 in. or 4 × 4 in. The arrangement and details of the interior framing are practically the same as those for the balloon design.

Article 12. Prefabrication

INTRODUCTION. In the building industry "prefabrication connotes a degree of factory assembly beyond that which is customary in conventional practice. The usual processing of lumber in a wood-working mill, which results in producing boards, flooring, and standard lengths of dimension stock, is not prefabrication. Only when the work of fabricating, which would normally be done at the building site, is accomplished in a mill or factory, would the term be applicable.

During recent years, however, the amount of work done "off the job" has greatly increased. This applies to elements as diverse as welded-steel trusses and assembled plumbing installations. Such units are often called prefabricated but might be a part of a structure otherwise erected by conventional methods. Because of this modern trend, prefabrication is a relative rather than a specific designation implying a method of construction by which economy is gained through the standardized and highly mechanized shop manufacture of building elements, the assembly of which is carried to the highest practicable degree. For many reasons not pertinent to this discussion, the more complete types of prefabrication have been largely confined, up to the present time, to the single-family dwelling, military hospitals and barracks, and small service or industrial structures. In the future the same principles will be applied to multifamily housing.

As is evident from the foregoing comments, the customary shop fabrication of many standard building elements, such as metal window sash and frames, spandrel designs, and assembled floor units, merges into prefabrication. Neither is there any reason from the viewpoint of the designer to seek a clear line of demarkation. The precast concrete framing mentioned on page 48, is a type of prefabrication which is very close to many systems including precast wall, floor, and roof slabs. These assemblies have always been considered in this category.

Because of the difficulty of transporting large units, most of the newer types of prefabricated floor designs, many of which are still in an experimental stage, are shaped as panels. Long enough to span 12 to 18 ft between supports, they are only a few feet in width. In principle, they serve the same purpose as the lighter types of structural floors described in Chapter Four. The only essential difference is that the ideal prefabricated section should furnish an acceptable ceiling and floor finish, as well as the other standard requisites, without the necessity of additional work at the site.

Several of the wall designs shown in Chapter Seven, such as the steel panel illustrated on page 263, are types of shop-fabricated units similar in principle to those employed for prefabricated dwellings. Many of the newer designs in laminated wood used for both beams and trusses (see page 225) are characteristic of present-day trends which gain economy by shop manufacture. All the wall designs employing steel or plywood sheets, applied over a frame or made up into panels, merge into the more complete types of prefabrication. The only essential difference is that the ideal prefabricated wall unit, like the prefabricated floor unit, should supply all characteristics in one section, requiring neither surface finish or other treatment after delivery to the site.

The application of prefabrication to one-story structures needed by the armed forces, such as hospitals, barracks, and service buildings, was extensively developed during World War II. Although influenced to a certain extent by the temporary availability or scarcity of particular materials and the need for reducing the space required for shipment to an absolute minimum, these designs are of considerable significance. They represent the result of extensive research and observation under varying climatic conditions from the Far North to the Tropics. Further information about the designs used by the United States Engineer Corps will be found in "Prefabricated Barracks for the Army," by David F. Bauer, *Civil Engineering*, September, 1945.

It is not within the scope of this text to give a detailed description of prefabrication, but it seems desirable that the designer should have a general knowledge of the subject. For this reason a few typical examples of the more representative types are presented.

DESIGNS IN METAL. Steel sheets supported by structural-steel frames composed of standard sections have been used for many years as enclosing walls for various types of industry. Modern methods applying

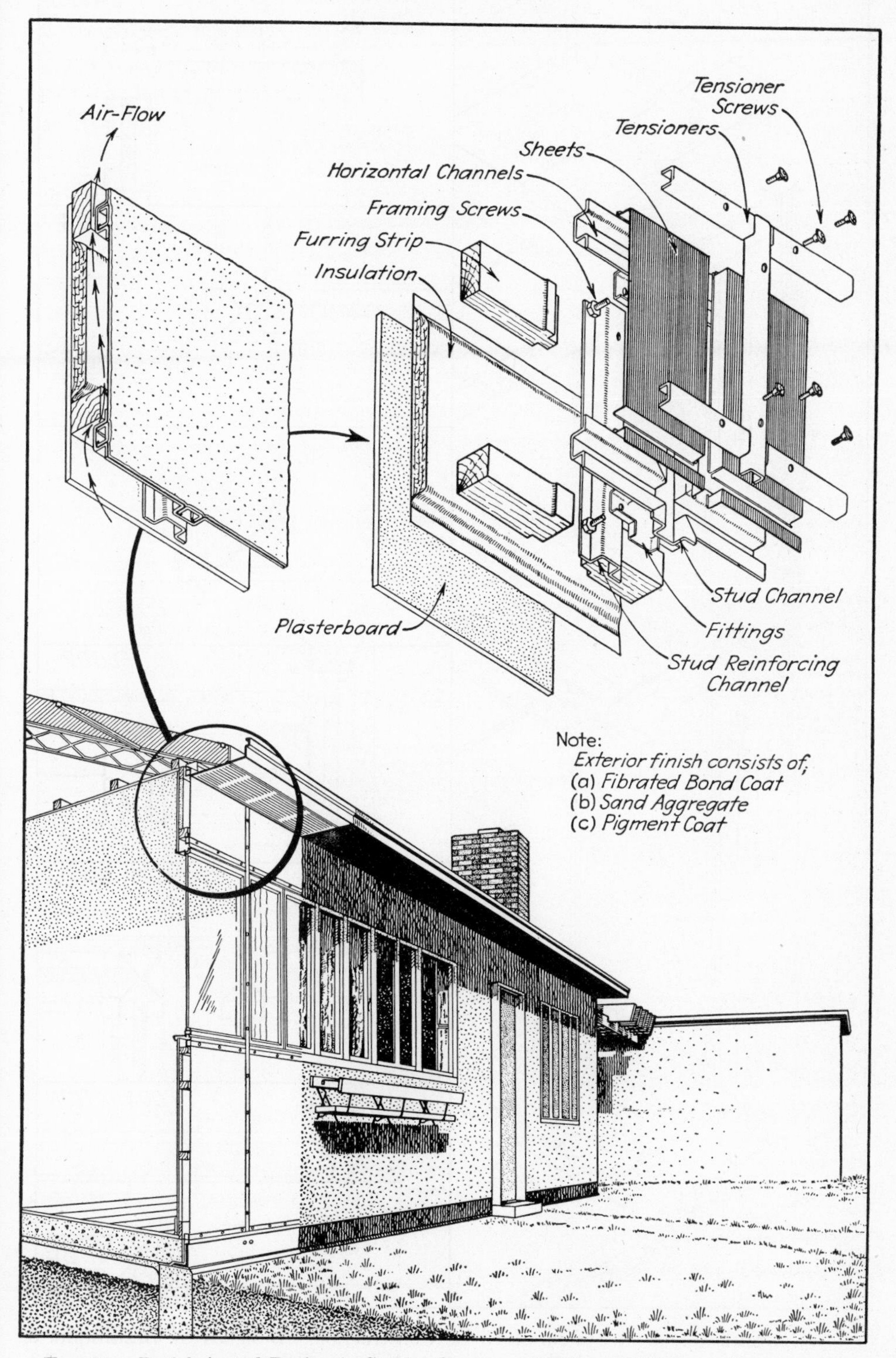

Fig. 36. Prefabricated Design in Steel. Courtesy, William H. Harmon Corporation.

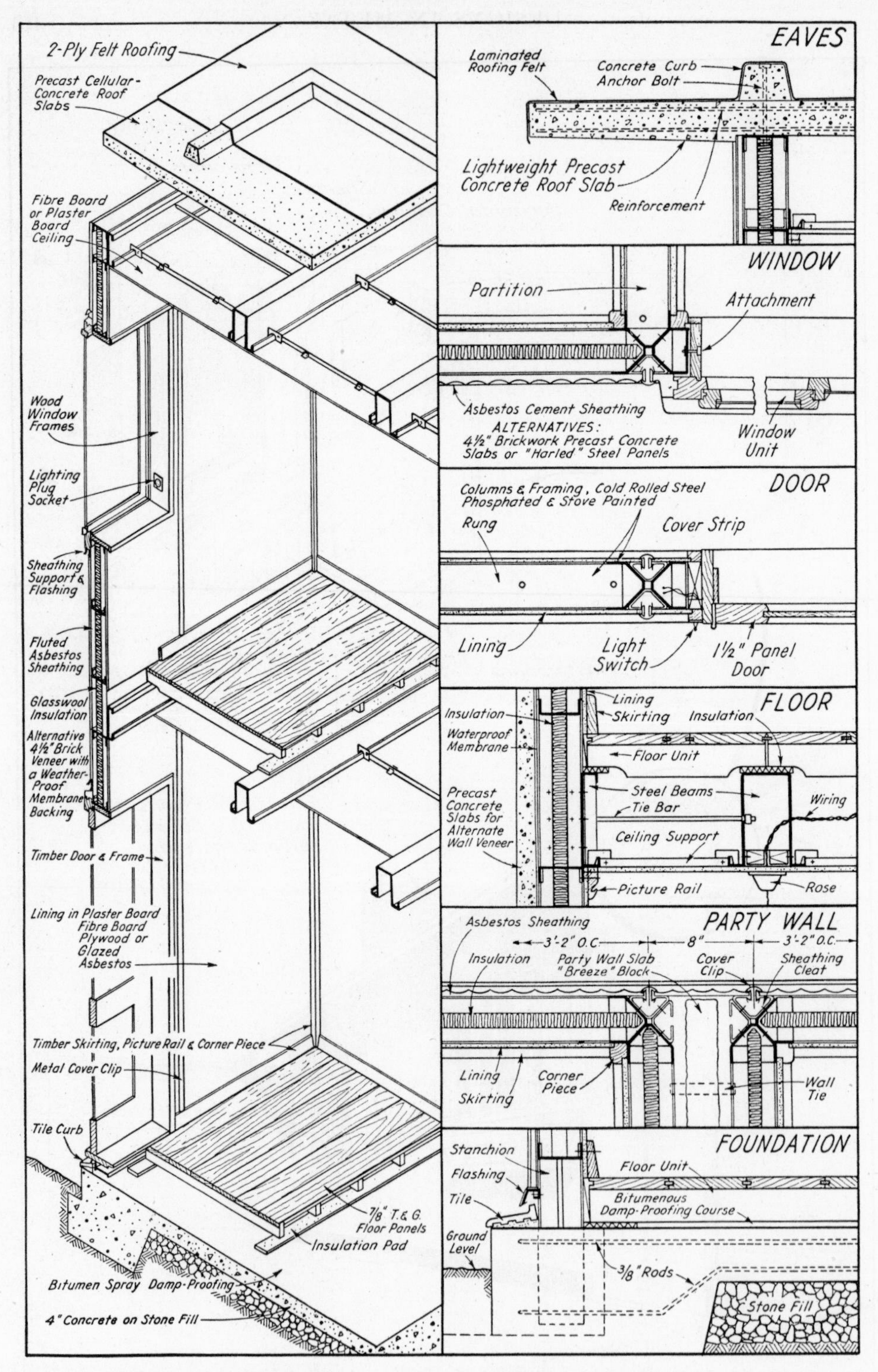

FIG. 37. Braithwaite Unit System of House Construction. Designed by Braithwaite & Company, Engineers, Ltd., London, England.

to semiprefabricated buildings assemble such frames upon the ground, after which steel sheets are bolted to them, permitting large sections to be raised as a single unit. In the typical, one-story industrial building prefabricated-steel trusses are hoisted into position over supporting columns.

After the structural roof has been completed by installation of purlins, ready-formed steel sheets are applied to furnish a continuous deck. Steel window sash and doors are then installed in openings left in the wall panels. All connections are made with bolts. The more fully prefabricated designs, some of which utilize aluminum instead of steel, involve much more complete shop manufacture. Entire wall, partition, floor, and roof panels are developed to the extent that little remains to be done at the site other than to assemble the component parts. Figure 36 shows a design in steel.

The Stran-Steel design, already mentioned in relation to light-weight building frames, has been very popular for many types of prefabricated and semiprefabricated structures and may be surfaced with any appropriate material. Assemblies employing sheet steel from 12 to 24 gage, bent to form angles or other structural shapes, have been widely used by the army. Placed on foundation posts, the walls and roof are formed as flat metal surfaces by drawing the sheets tightly with bolts to obtain weather-tight joints. Plywood is used for the floor finish; wall-board, for interior lining of walls and roof.

Although most British designs are not appropriate for conditions existing in this country, Fig. 37 represents a very interesting assembly known as the Braithwaite Unit System of House Construction, offered for two-story dwellings. The architect, Mr. F. R. S. Yorke, F.R.I.B.A. of London, states that similar details are appropriate for three-story steel-framed flats.

DESIGNS IN CONCRETE. Prefabrication in this field is represented by the precasting of concrete slabs, often of cellular or tubular type, intended for use as wall, partition, floor, or roof sections. Many systems have been patented during the past 40 years. Some designs have been dropped after the construction of one or two test houses; others have been applied more or less successfully over long periods of time.

Good results can be obtained from the viewpoint of occupancy as well as that of structure. This fact has been amply demonstrated by the thirty-odd houses built at Forest Hills, New York, over 30 years ago by the Atterbury Precast Sectional System. These buildings, which have been recently inspected, represent one of the few examples where such designs have proven satisfactory over a period of many years. The reasons why this type of construction has not been more widely accepted up to the present time would be of only historical interest.

From the viewpoint of the designer, there is good reason to believe that such a system has economic possibilities for either individual dwellings or larger structures where standardization and modular design are practicable.

There must be, however, a local demand of sufficient size to absorb the cost of a large, modern casting plant, and a suitable concrete aggregate must be comparatively cheap in order for the product to compete favorably with other types of prefabrication.

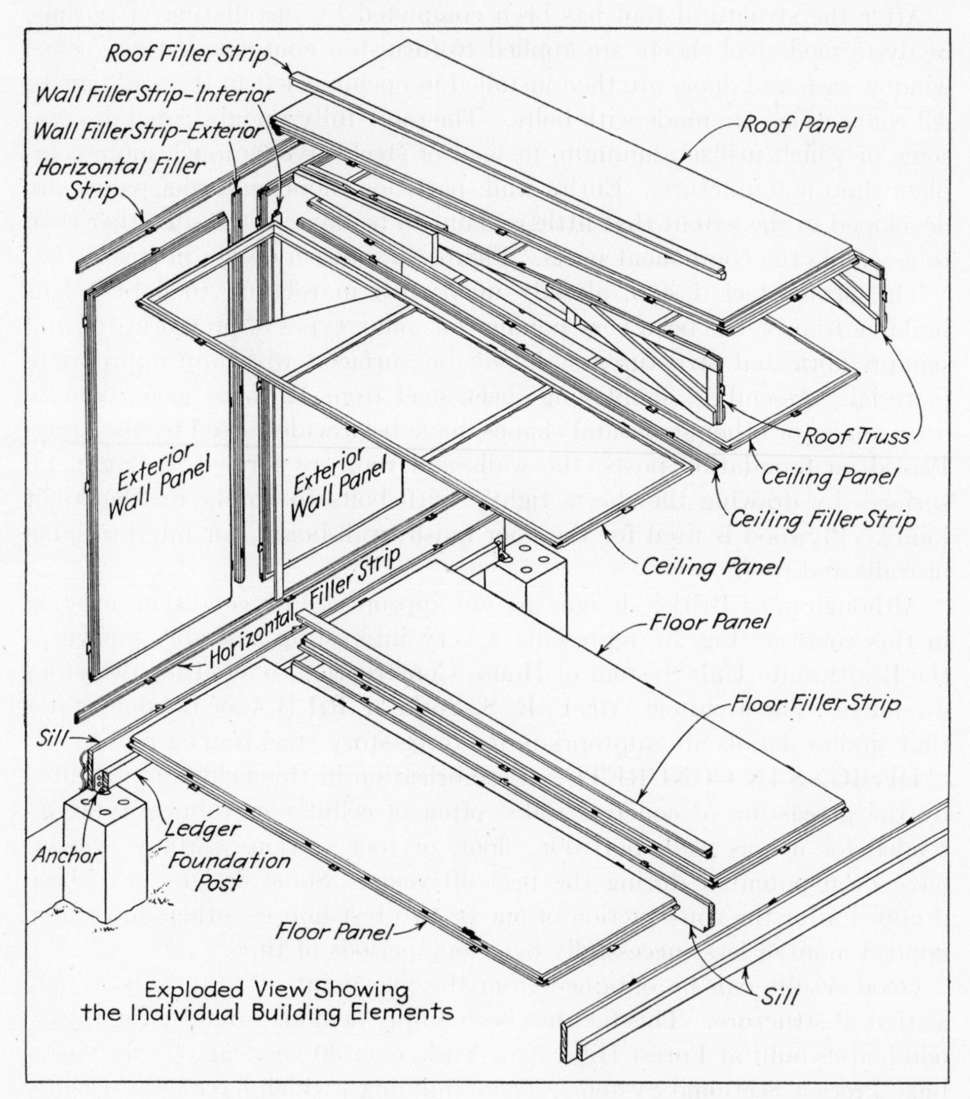

FIG. 38. Prefabricated Design in Wood.

A completely different system in concrete is identified as "tilt-up construction." The basic idea is not new, but only recently has it been developed to the extent of competing economically with the more usual construction methods. Reinforced-concrete wall panels, cast in a horizontal position and combined where required with both insulation and vapor seal, are tilted into position on concrete foundations. After panels are erected, corner columns of reinforced concrete are poured in place. This system with certain variations has been used for more than one thousand structures, but its application is at present limited to one-story buildings.

A design controlled by Vacuum Concrete, Inc., combines the precasting

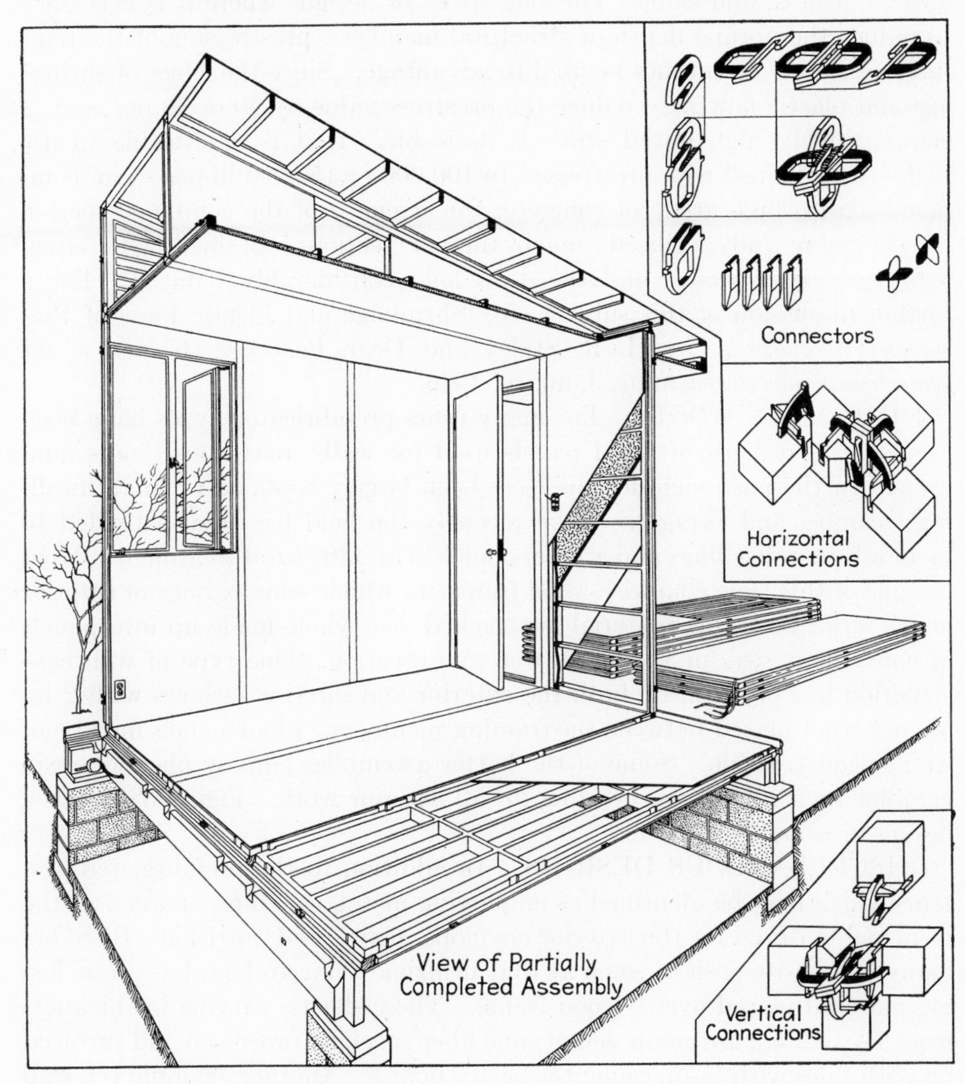

Courtesy, General Panel Corporation.

of thin reinforced-concrete panels with a vacuum treatment which removes excess water. This process permits speedier erection and results in greater ultimate strength in the concrete. Poured in a horizontal position, an insulating material of micaceous composition is cast monolithically with the concrete. Panels are erected by means of vacuum-lifting devices and locked into place to form the exterior wall assembly. Although still in the process of development, this system has excellent possibilities, particularly for one-story housing units.

Although prestressed reinforcement has been most widely used in the walls of reinforced-concrete tanks, it has an application for precast concrete girders, beams, and slabs. For long spans or designs where it is necessary to reduce the normal depth of structural members, prestressing of the reinforcement may sometimes be used to advantage. Since the effect of shrinkage and plastic flow may reduce the prestress value by 60 or 70 per cent, a comparatively high initial stress is desirable. If it is practicable to use high-strength steel wire prestressed to 100,000 or 150,000 lb per sq in, combined with a high grade of concrete, the strength of the combined section can be more fully utilized, much thinner sections obtained with equal load-carrying capacity, and the dead load considerably reduced. For a further discussion of this subject see "Shrinkage and Plastic Flow of Prestressed Concrete," by H. R. Staley and Dean Peabody, *Journal of the American Concrete Institute*, January, 1946.

DESIGNS IN WOOD. For many years prefabricated types have been available in designs of wood panels used for walls, partitions, floors, and roofs. In the past such designs have been largely confined to small dwellings, camps, and garages. More recently the field has been extended to include larger dwellings and greater choice in architectural treatment. Most designs of this type comprise wood frames to which some variety of exterior and interior surfacing material is attached, the whole made up into panels of convenient size for transportation and erection. One type of wall construction has plywood on both the exterior and interior surfaces with 2 in. of rock wool placed between the framing members. Floor panels may be of similar construction. Some of the better assemblies employ phenolic resin combined with hot-press bonding for all exterior work. Figure 38 shows a design in wood.

MISCELLANEOUS DESIGNS. In addition to the prefabricated systems which may be identified as employing metal, concrete, or wood as the principal material for the exterior envelope, floors, and partitions, there are many composite designs, such as that utilizing Cemesto board as an inclosing material placed over a wood frame. These sheets, varying in thickness from 1⅛ to 2 in., are composed of cane fiber specially processed and surfaced on both sides with ⅛-in. cement-asbestos board. Another example is a wall panel of convenient dimensions and a total thickness of 1½ in., comprising an insulating fiber board surfaced upon both sides with ¼-in. plywood.

Constant developments can be expected in the application of various plastics, metal, and glass assemblies. Progress should be followed by the designer through the technical press and reports from research or testing laboratories. The broad application of prefabrication offers a very hopeful prospect of eventually reducing housing cost.

Chapter Four

CHOOSING THE STRUCTURAL FLOOR SYSTEM

The choice of the floor system is a very important step in planning the structure of a building. There are the long- and short-span designs, types particularly suitable for heavy loads, such as those required in industry, and others which are appropriate only for light loads. They vary greatly in fire resistance and the facilities offered for embedment of conduit and application of ceiling or floor finishes. The choice should be based on the architectural and structural requirements of the building, supplemented by estimates of cost.

INTRODUCTION. The following articles describe the various structural floor systems which are the most popular in this country at the present time or appear to have potential value. In this text a "system" identifies the structural assembly spanning between supports furnished by the framing members or bearing walls. The descriptions indicate the particular application of each type to conditions which will be known by the designer at this stage of his work. Maximum spans and limiting dimensions given in the text conform with structural standards generally accepted but should be checked before final design because of the unfortunate variation in building-code requirements. A résumé of the considerations which should govern the choice of floor construction is presented in Article 8 of this chapter.

As different building trades are involved in erecting the various designs, labor rates, as well as prices of materials, affect the relative cost, and any valid comparison of cost must be based on local conditions. It is also true that the continued use in some localities of a particular type of floor construction may have developed an economy in its erection, reflected in contract prices, which cannot be foreseen without familiarity with local practice.

Article 1. Long-Span Designs for Structural-Steel Framing

The systems identified in this text as "long-span" designs are those which ordinarily require no beams except along the center lines of columns. As a group, they are particularly suited to light and medium, uniformly distributed superimposed loads from 40 to 100 lb per sq ft and to spans from 15 to 30 ft. They have a wide application for many classes of construction, such as residential, institutional, and office buildings; some systems, as noted in the text, are often economical for the more lightly loaded industrial buildings.

REINFORCED-CONCRETE RIBBED CONSTRUCTION: ONE-WAY SYSTEMS. Designs in this class generally comprise a thin, lightly reinforced-concrete slab 2 to 3 in. thick, supported by and cast monolithically with reinforced-concrete ribs or joists, as they are sometimes called, spaced from 12 to 30 in. apart, face to face, and separated by voids or by filler blocks. This slab, poured over the tile or other type of filler, is referred to as the "topping." The ribs, supplemented by the slab, form a series of T-beams constituting the supporting elements of such systems. The width of the ribs is normally 4, 5, or 6 in., as demanded by the structural requirements. The ribs should be straight and of a depth not over three times their width if of rectangular cross-section, or three times their average width if narrower at the bottom, as in the metal-pan system shown on the opposite page. The slab thickness should be at least one-twelfth of the clear distance between ribs.

Reinforced-concrete bridging, usually 4 in. wide and equal in depth to that of the ribs, is desirable on long spans except where the type of filler block used between the ribs gives adequate lateral support. Beneath non-bearing partitions, such as are usually built of clay tile, gypsum tile, or light-weight cement-aggregate tile, a rib of increased width may be used to carry the additional load. These systems are seldom economical for spans less than 10 or 12 ft, such as may occur across corridors, a solid reinforced-concrete slab being the usual choice even where a ribbed design is used for the longer spans upon both sides.

In an assembly of this kind, where filler blocks are used, rigid electrical conduit is generally placed either in the topping or in a light-weight fill, normally 2 or 3 in. deep, laid over the topping. A fill is often required unless the topping is of sufficient thickness to permit embedment. Occasionally, a block 1 in. less in depth is used along the conduit run to increase the thickness of the concrete sufficiently to accommodate small pipes. In the metal-pan system described in the following paragraph it is sometimes practicable to run conduit in the open spaces between ribs.

METAL-PAN SYSTEM. Over voids formed by steel forms,[1] Fig. 1, the minimum thickness of the slab, or topping, should be 2½ in.; 3 in. is a usual maximum. If the metal-pan system is specified, there is the option of using light-weight, corrugated-steel forms and leaving them permanently in place, or a somewhat heavier type designed for removal and a number of

[1] Wood or plywood forms are occasionally employed for the same purpose, but metal is generally more economical. Except for the material used to enclose the void between ribs and details in regard to the forming, all characteristics are identical.

reuses. The first method enables the contractor to attach metal lath, serving as a base for the plaster of the ceiling below, before the pouring of the concrete. If the removable type of pan is used, the lath must be attached to anchors left in the underside of the concrete ribs, necessitating a separate operation after the completion of the structural floor. Forms are very simply constructed. A single plank 6 to 10 in. wide is placed beneath

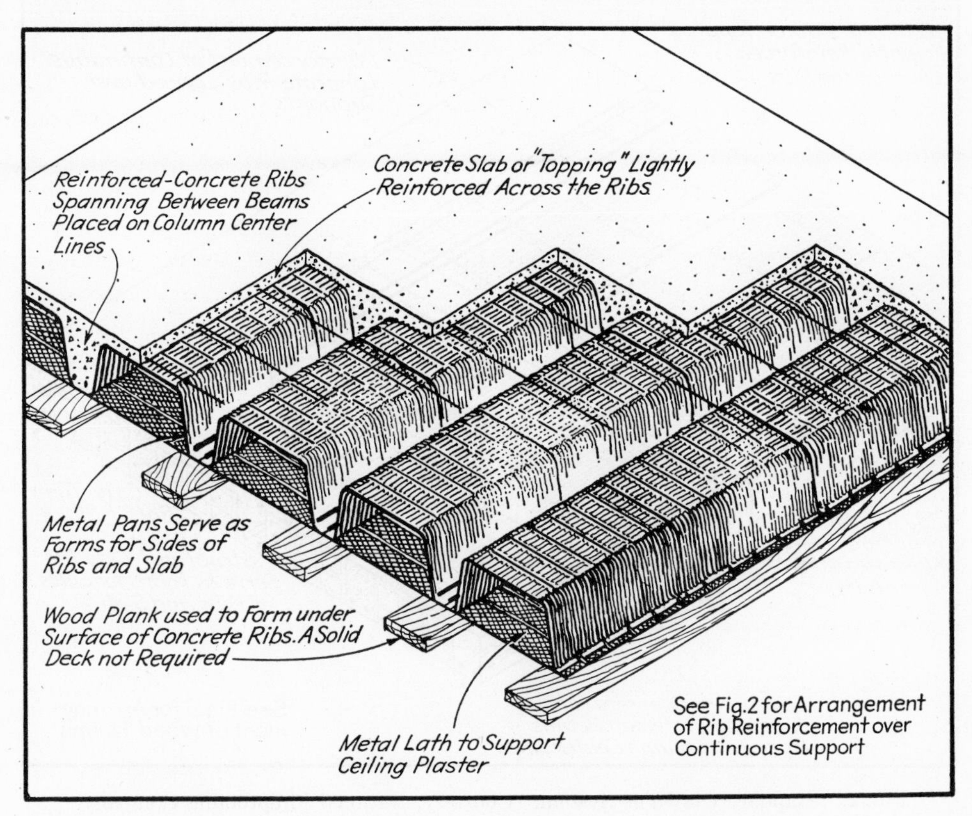

FIG. 1. Metal-Pan System. Courtesy, Truscon Steel Company.

each rib; the planks are supported by a system of stringers resting upon 4- × 4-in. uprights or adjustable shores. Where this system is used with structural-steel framing, the steel beams connecting the columns permit the suspension of a part of the form work, thereby eliminating some of the shores.

Metal pans are manufactured in standard widths of 20 and 30 in., a generally accepted maximum for this type of construction. Smaller widths are available for filling odd spaces.[2] Standard depths vary, by 2-in. increments, from 6 to 14 in. Metal pans are assembled by lapping the ends. Appropriate lengths are supplied by the manufacturers to suit any length

[2] For additional information refer to the Concrete Reinforcing Steel Institute.

of floor panel. The ends of each line of pans, where in contact with the concrete, are closed by metal caps. End units are furnished with tapered sides or with both sides and top tapered so as to enlarge the cross-section of the concrete rib, or of both rib and slab, adjacent to supports where the effect of shear or negative bending moment may be critical. The metal-pan

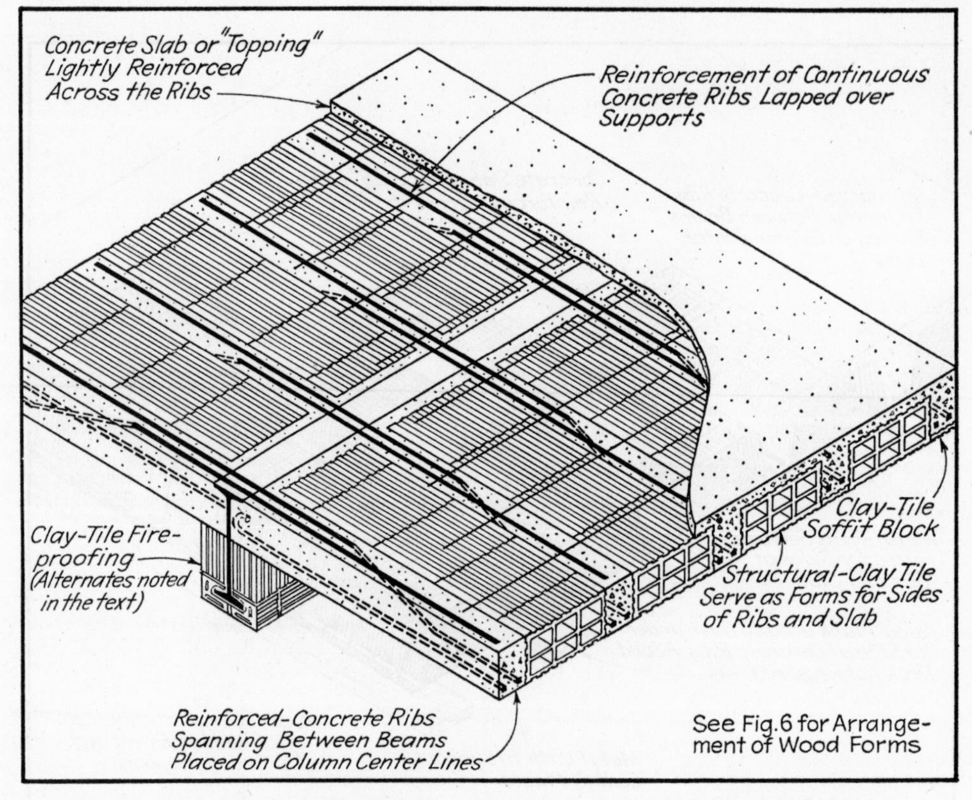

FIG. 2. Standard Clay-Tile System. Courtesy, National Fireproofing Company.

system is particularly economical for spans from 15 ft to 30 ft under uniformly distributed superimposed loads up to about 100 lb per sq ft.

STRUCTURAL-CLAY-TILE SYSTEMS. Over structural-clay-tile fillers, Fig. 2, the minimum thickness of the slab in standard construction is preferably 2 in.,[3] but a 1½-in. thickness is used. The form work is of the same general type as that employed for the metal-pan system except that, where the smaller sizes of tile are used, it is generally desirable to build a continuous surface such as is required for a solid concrete slab rather than an open system with forms only beneath the ribs. The lower faces of the tile provide an excellent surface for plastering, and no metal lath is needed except on the lower flanges of structural-steel beams and girders if they are fire-

[3] See opposite page for exception.

proofed with concrete. For the purpose of obtaining a uniform tile surface, soffit blocks of the same material are often provided as "facers" along the bottoms of the ribs, as shown in Fig. 2. This practice is recommended to obtain a better bond for the plaster applied beneath the ribs, aside from the possibility of discoloration if facers are omitted. Because of the necessity of using a rather wet concrete mix for the ribs, their undersurfaces are often very smooth, and trouble due to lack of adhesion between the concrete and the base coat of plaster may arise. The ends of each line of tile, where in contact with the concrete, are generally closed by sheets of metal or other appropriate means.

Structural-clay tile suitable for this type of construction are made 12 × 12 in. in plan with depths from 3 to 12 in. The 12- × 16-in. and 16- × 16-in. tile are made from 3 to 10 in. in depth. A 12- × 20-in. size is made in depths ranging from 4 to 10 in. Oblong tile, the 12- × 16-in. and 12- × 20-in. types, are assembled with the longer dimensions perpendicular to the concrete ribs. As a 5-in. rib would normally be used with a 16-in. tile, the center-to-center spacing is 21 in. A 6-in. width of rib, appropriate for a 20-in. tile, results in a 26-in. center-to-center spacing. A 2-in. minimum thickness of topping is placed over these larger sizes of tile, corresponding to the 1½-in. absolute minimum applying to the 12- × 12-in. units. For most designs the 16-in. width or in some cases the 20-in. width is more economical than the smaller size. These larger units have been particularly popular for schools, dormitories, and housing projects. Tiles of less width are used at the ends of the rows to increase the width of the ribs adjacent to supports. The more economical spans for loads corresponding to such classes of occupancy are 15 to 24 ft.

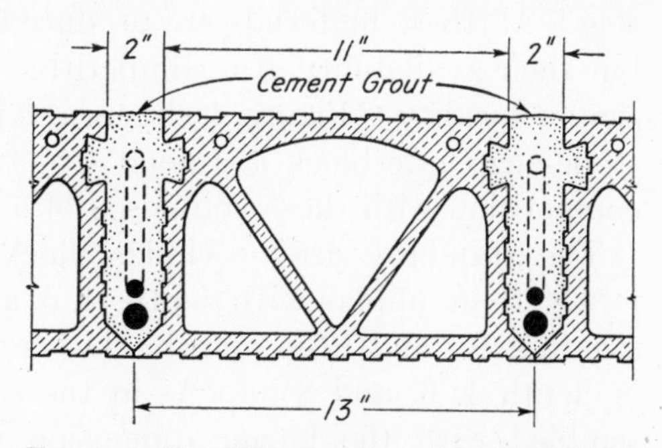

Fig. 3. Clay-Tile System, with Special Tile Forming Soffits of Concrete Ribs. Courtesy, National Fireproofing Company.

A variation of the standard clay-tile system is illustrated in Fig. 3. Where a fill, or a type of finish floor assembly capable of protecting the upper shells from injury due to concentrated loads, is placed over the tile, this system is used without any topping. Because of the cost of transportation and the fact that the special clay required for tile of this type is available only in eastern Pennsylvania, its use is limited to the Pittsburgh-Chicago area.

Another variation of the standard clay-tile system was developed by Mr. Elwyn E. Seelye, consulting engineer of New York City. Between each 16- × 16-in. tile is placed an 8- × 16-in. tile, 1 in. less in depth. The primary purpose of this arrangement is to develop the compressive value of the top shell of the tile. The thickness of topping over the deeper tile is generally reduced to 1 in. This design is identified as the Nassau system.

Gypsum-Tile System. Gypsum-tile filler blocks are used with reinforced-concrete ribs in an assembly similar to the clay-tile systems. A minimum topping thickness of 2 in. is desirable. The form work is the same as for the clay-tile design. Gypsum fillers are made in two standard sizes. One is 19 in. wide by 18 in. long; depths are 6, 8, 10 and 12 in. The other size is 12 in. wide by 30 in. long; depths are 3, 4 and 5 in. The 19- × 18-in. size is used with a 5-in. rib, and the 12- × 30-in. size with a 4-in. rib, giving a center-to-center spacing for ribs of 24 in. and 16 in., respectively. Tile with one solid end are furnished for use at the termination of each line for the purpose of preventing the entrance of concrete. If a continuous gypsum ceiling is desired, soffit blocks of the same material are supplied as facers for the concrete ribs. Such blocks are recommended, as for the clay-tile systems. As the rapid absorption of the gypsum block, when brought in contact with the wet concrete, causes the concrete to become unworkable, these tile are now surfaced with chip-board paper to reduce absorption.

Concrete-Block Systems. The essential features of these designs are similar to clay-tile construction, except that the fillers between the reinforced-concrete ribs are hollow block composed of portland cement combined with sand, gravel, crushed stone, cinders, slag, Haydite, Waylite, Super-Rock, or other light-weight aggregate. Haydite was described on page 39; Waylite and Super-Rock are made from expanded blast-furnace slag. All these materials are produced in many parts of the United States, but their availability at a competitive price should be checked for any particular locality. Figure 4 shows a typical design. Although the sand or stone-aggregate block is a good structural unit, its weight limits its use in competition with those composed of a lighter material.

The standard size of cinder block or tile, as they are often called, is 8 × 16 in. in plan with depths 4, 6, and 8 in. Some plants make the same size in a 10- and 12-in. depth. Others supply units 8 × 18 in. in plan and of depth 4, 6, and 8 in. As in the case of clay tile, these blocks are assembled with the longer dimension perpendicular to the concrete ribs. Soffit blocks of the same material are provided as "facers" along the bottoms of the ribs to obtain a uniform surface for plastering and should be used.

Haydite makes an excellent filler block, very strong for its weight. Sizes are not standardized but are usually 8 or 9 in. × 16 in. in plan and 4, 6, or 8 in. deep. An 8- × 9- × 16-in. unit weighs only 20 lb in comparison to a weight of about 28 lb for the 8- × 8- × 16-in. cinder block. In localities where Haydite or a similar material can be obtained at an advantageous price, it may also be used as an aggregate for the reinforced-concrete ribs and topping, thereby saving considerable dead load and obtaining a complete Haydite surface for the application of plaster.

A variation of the standard concrete-block system is illustrated in Fig. 5. The design provides a uniform surface for plastering without the use of

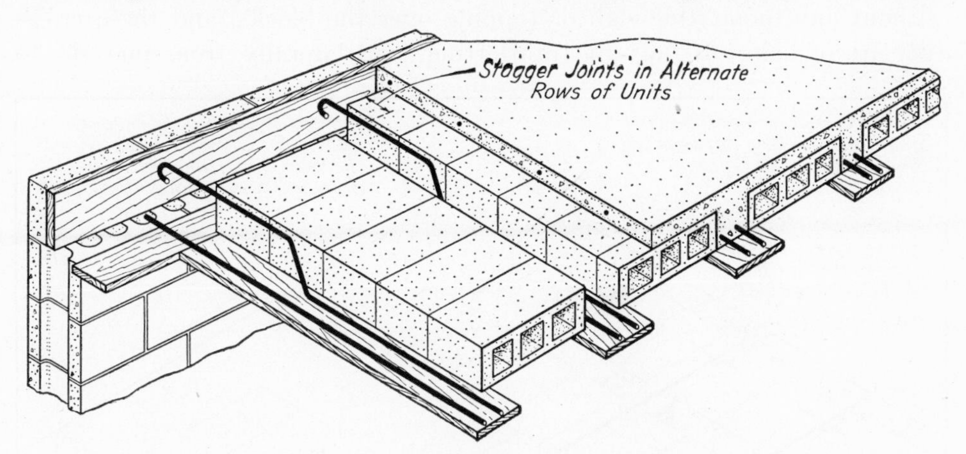

Fig. 4. Standard Concrete-Block System. Courtesy, Portland Cement Association.

soffits. Sizes are as shown. This system, only recently developed, appears to have excellent possibilities, especially for residential construction, but its availability should be checked. When it is desired to improve the sound absorption of the ceiling, blocks made from Waylite, known as "Soffitile," may be employed. The one size of Waylite block now manufactured has a

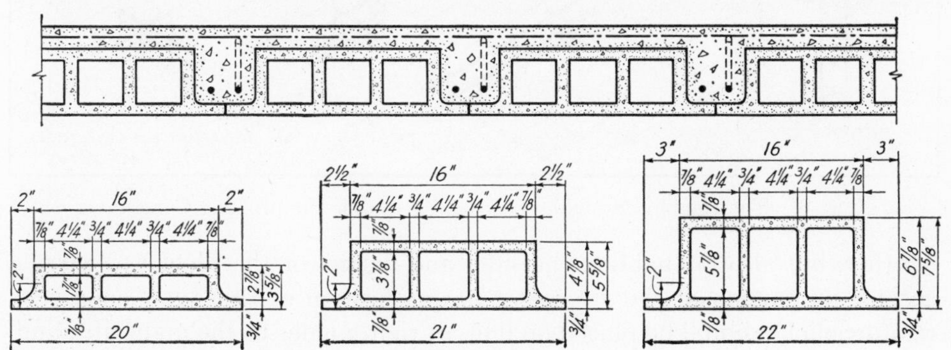

Fig. 5. Concrete-Block System, with Special Block Forming Soffits of Concrete Ribs. Courtesy, Portland Cement Association.

ceiling face 8 × 21 in. and a depth of 5⅝ in. It weighs about 24 lb and is assembled with 5-in. ribs.

The use of slag as an aggregate for precast filler blocks is represented by the Slagblok system, shown in Fig. 6. These blocks are manufactured in 4, 6, and 8-in. depths. When the two halves are joined, they form a unit 16 × 16 in. The vertical shells of the blocks bond well with the concrete of the ribs and present solid faces on all four sides. A unique feature of this system is the 4-in. rib, placed between the rows of blocks perpendicular to the main ribs. This feature is desirable for a number of reasons. The Slagblok design, unlike the other popular block systems, is often used without any monolithic slab or topping over the blocks, and these cross-ribs are of help not only in transferring load laterally from one rib to

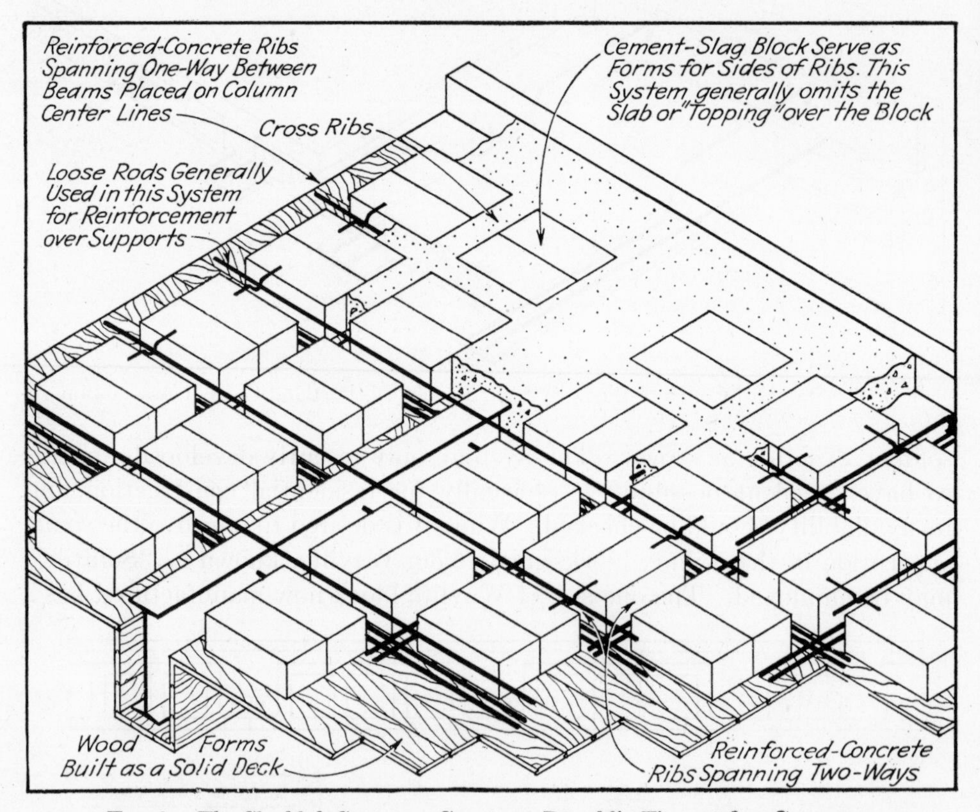

Fig. 6. The Slagblok System. Courtesy, Republic Fireproofing Company.

another, but also in enabling the sides and flanges of the blocks to carry a greater proportion of the stresses. In any system of this type some steel reinforcement should be placed on lines at right angles to the main ribs, and, if there were no slab over the blocks, this would be impossible. The design is excellent but at present is available only within a 300-mile radius of New York City, as all block are manufactured in northern New Jersey.

Fibercrete System. A novel method of obtaining sound-deadening qualities in connection with a structural floor design features the use of Fibercrete blocks as fillers between reinforced-concrete ribs. Fibercrete is made of mineralized wood fibers bound together under pressure with portland cement. It is similar to Porete (see page 124), but of less density. Uniformly porous throughout, it does not deteriorate when exposed to water and has good fire resistance. Manufactured 20 in. wide and in lengths of 80 in., the Fibercrete units can be laid in parallel rows to provide a joist width of 5 in. or can be cut in pieces 20 × 20 in. for use in a two-way system (see page 116). Various depths are available. One-half-inch soffit blocks of the same material are supplied for use beneath the concrete ribs.

Fibercrete filler units contribute no structural strength but provide an excellent base for the application of plaster and are helpful in reducing sound transmission through the floor. The dead load is also considerably less than for the block systems. This design is particularly appropriate for apartment houses. It has been used quite extensively in Washington, D. C., and appears to have excellent possibilities for wider adoption. Figure 7 shows a typical section.

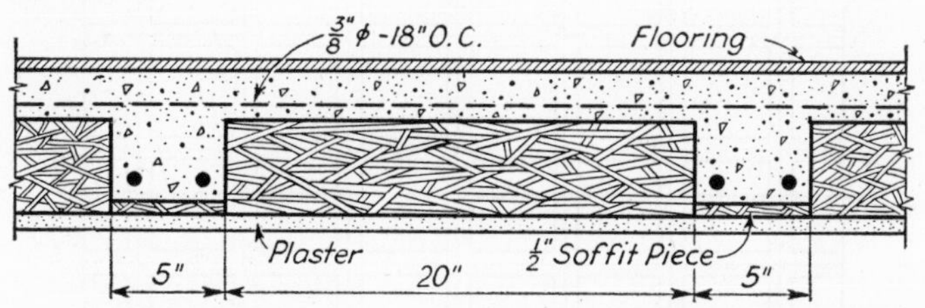

Fig. 7. The Fibercrete System. Courtesy, Porete Manufacturing Company.

REINFORCED-CONCRETE RIBBED CONSTRUCTION: TWO-WAY SYSTEMS. Where floor panels are square or approximately square, it may be economical to run the reinforced-concrete structural ribs in two directions, thereby forming, with the filler units, a type of flat plate which requires a supporting beam or bearing wall on each of the four sides of the panel. Such a construction is identified as a two-way design and is economical where the panel dimensions permit a fairly equal distribution of the total load in each direction. The particular application of such designs is for buildings which require a number of large square or approximately square panels, from 20 to 25 ft. between column center lines, and preferably with floor areas large enough to permit several continuous panels of about the same size. The two-way Slagblok system is shown in the lower portion of Fig. 6.

It is impossible to state definitely an exact ratio of length to breadth within which a two-way design is economical, as there is an appreciable variation among the different building codes in regard to the proportion of total load to be carried in each direction of oblong panels. In general, however, the designer should consider the possibility of using a two-way design for square panels or those in which the ratio of the long to the short side is not greater than one and one-third to one. If the ratio is greater, some economy may still be gained in the panel design itself, but the question should be carefully checked, as the advantage will probably be cancelled by the cost of the supporting members or additional labor in placing the steel in two directions.

The characteristics of the two-way designs are similar to those of the one-way with the important exception that the pan or filler block, surrounded on four sides by concrete, must present a solid surface against the adjoining rib or one which will at least prevent the entrance of any appreciable amount of concrete into the interior of the void or filler. With the metal-pan system, this requirement is met by supplying steel domes. These

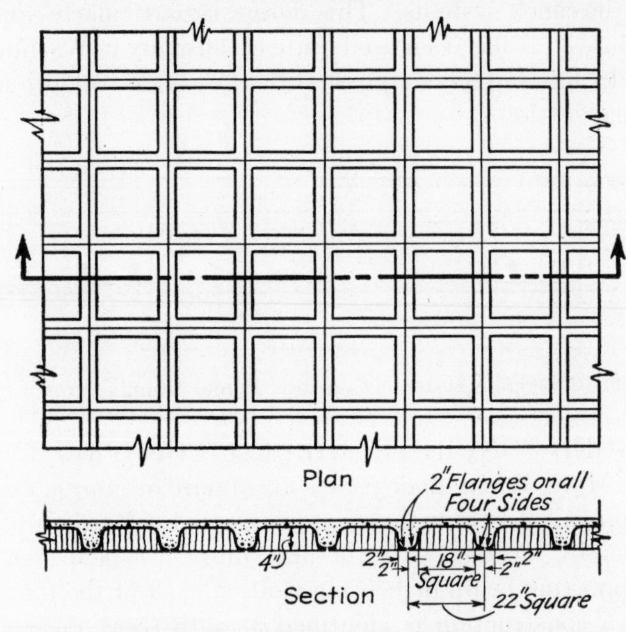

FIG. 8. The Grid System. Courtesy, Grid Flat-Slab Corporation.

are identified as the grid system and are furnished in two sizes: the 8-in. depth 19 × 19 in., and the 4-in. depth 18 × 18 in. The width of the rib, controlled by the flange width of the dome as shown in Fig. 8, is 5 in. for the deeper type and 4 in. for the shallower. The 8-in. domes have been used on a 36-ft × 38-ft panel, with a 6-in. depth of concrete topping over the domes, for a uniformly distributed superimposed load of 125 lb per sq ft. The 4-in. depth has been used on a 20-ft × 20-ft panel, with a 2-in. topping, for a similar load of 100 lb. All are of the removable type.

When structural-clay tile are used in a two-way design, closures are usually employed to eliminate the entrance of the concrete into the cells of the blocks. In the case of the 16- × 16-in. units, a size which is well adapted to two-way construction, a type of tile has been designed to minimize the entrance of concrete. For the gypsum system the manufacturers supply a block with four solid faces. As the Slagblok unit is composed of two open halves placed together, it presents solid faces on all four sides and is particularly suitable for two-way designs. As mentioned on page 115, the Fibercrete unit is merely cut into squares 20 × 20 in.

The width of the concrete ribs and the thickness of the concrete slab, placed monolithically with the ribs over the dome or filler, are the same as described for the one-way designs. There is obviously no need for special bridging. Except for the metal domes, form work is built in a continuous surface. It is not generally practicable to use an open system for two-way block construction. As the steel domes are equipped with flanges 2 or 2½ in. wide, which meet beneath the ribs, they permit an economical system of open form work.

COMPARISON OF THE CONCRETE-JOIST OR RIBBED DESIGNS. It is apparent that the lighter-weight metal-pan designs can be used under the same loading conditions on longer spans than the heavier clay-tile or concrete-block assemblies. On the other hand, these heavier assemblies furnish a more substantial section and eliminate the necessity of metal lath to carry the ceiling below. There is also a saving in the cost of plastering. The steel dome is appropriate for either light or heavy loads where panel dimensions are square or nearly square and has an application for industrial buildings with flat-slab floors to lighten the dead load of the central panels, as mentioned on page 73. The particular economy of this system occurs where it is permissible to accept the waffle-like appearance of the coffered ceiling without the addition of lath and plaster.

The cinder, slag, Haydite, and other light-weight aggregate block systems compete with clay tile on an economic rather than a structural basis. For example, in many parts of New England where cinders are available, a cinder-block design is probably the better choice. In the Chicago district clay-tile assemblies have competed favorably with even metal pans which, in most parts of the country, are usually cheaper than the block systems, even including the required lath and additional plaster. In the gypsum system the hollow tile do not add to the structural strength of the assembly to any such extent as the clay or concrete-block units, but they are lighter in weight, which is an advantage particularly evident in structures of many floors.

The Slagblok system has been effectively used for numerous types of occupancy from hotels and office buildings to warehouses and some industrial plants. Like others of this type, however, it is most suitable for light or medium loads and has a particularly valuable application for two-way work. Its use is limited geographically, as noted on page 114. The Fibercrete design has the advantage of light weight and provides an excellent surface for the application of plaster. It is also helpful in reducing sound transmission, but the filler unit has no structural value.

SMOOTH CEILINGS AND EQUIDEPTH SYSTEMS. These designs feature a concrete slab reinforced in two directions but without drop panels or flared capitals over the columns. To take the place of these elements, short lengths of structural steel I-beams or channels are employed as shown in Fig. 9. Except for a section over the columns about 5 ft square for panels 20 ft × 20 ft, floor slabs may be of solid concrete or of cellular design employing light-weight fillers, such as clay tile, or coffered by steel domes. If fillers or domes are used, a large proportion of the floor construction is of the concrete-joist or rib type, effecting a reduction in dead load.

With clay-tile fillers, tile soffit blocks may be placed beneath the reinforced-concrete ribs and under the solid portion of the slab over column

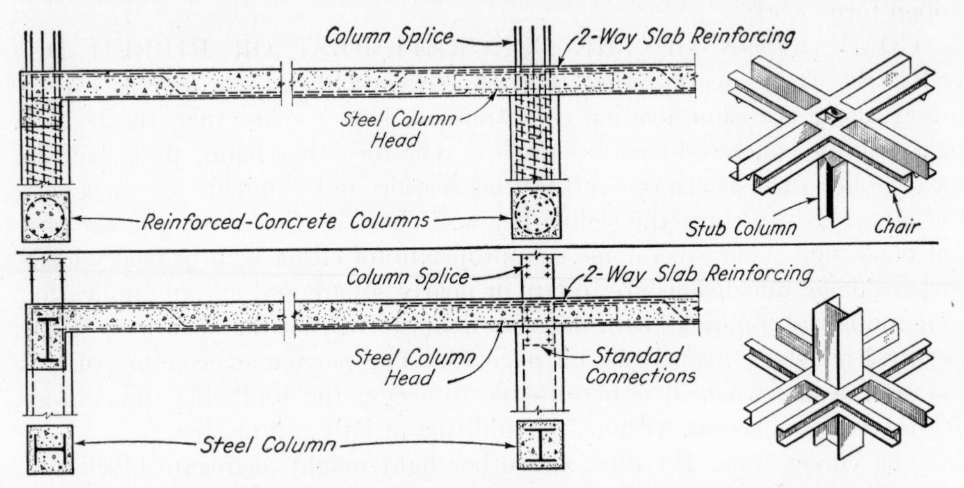

Fig. 9. The "Smooth-Ceilings" System. Courtesy, Smooth Ceilings System, Inc.

capitals to provide a uniform surface for plastering. This practice is recommended where plaster is to be applied unless the surface is roughened by the application of a suitable chemical compound or other effective means. Lack of adhesion to a smooth concrete surface may cause the plaster to fall even after a number of years. This necessity for obtaining a firm bond between plaster and concrete applies to all such surfaces and has no special significance for this design. These systems are appropriate for multifamily, institutional, and commercial buildings. They have been used successfully for a number of structures, including a large housing project in New York City.

PRECAST CONCRETE-JOIST CONSTRUCTION. The joists are cast of stone, cinder, Haydite, or other light-weight aggrega e concrete and manufactured in standard depths, varying by 2-in. increments, from 6 to 14 in. Special joists having a depth up to 22 in. and flanges up to 16 in. wide may be obtained from some manufacturers. These are suitable for comparatively heavy loads on spans up to 30 ft. Figure 10 shows typical sections of the Lith-I-Bar design, which is made with Haydite and two assemblies with structural-steel framing. Haydite, as noted on page 39, produces a very strong concrete weighing about one-third less than sandstone concrete of equal strength. It is used not only for precast units but

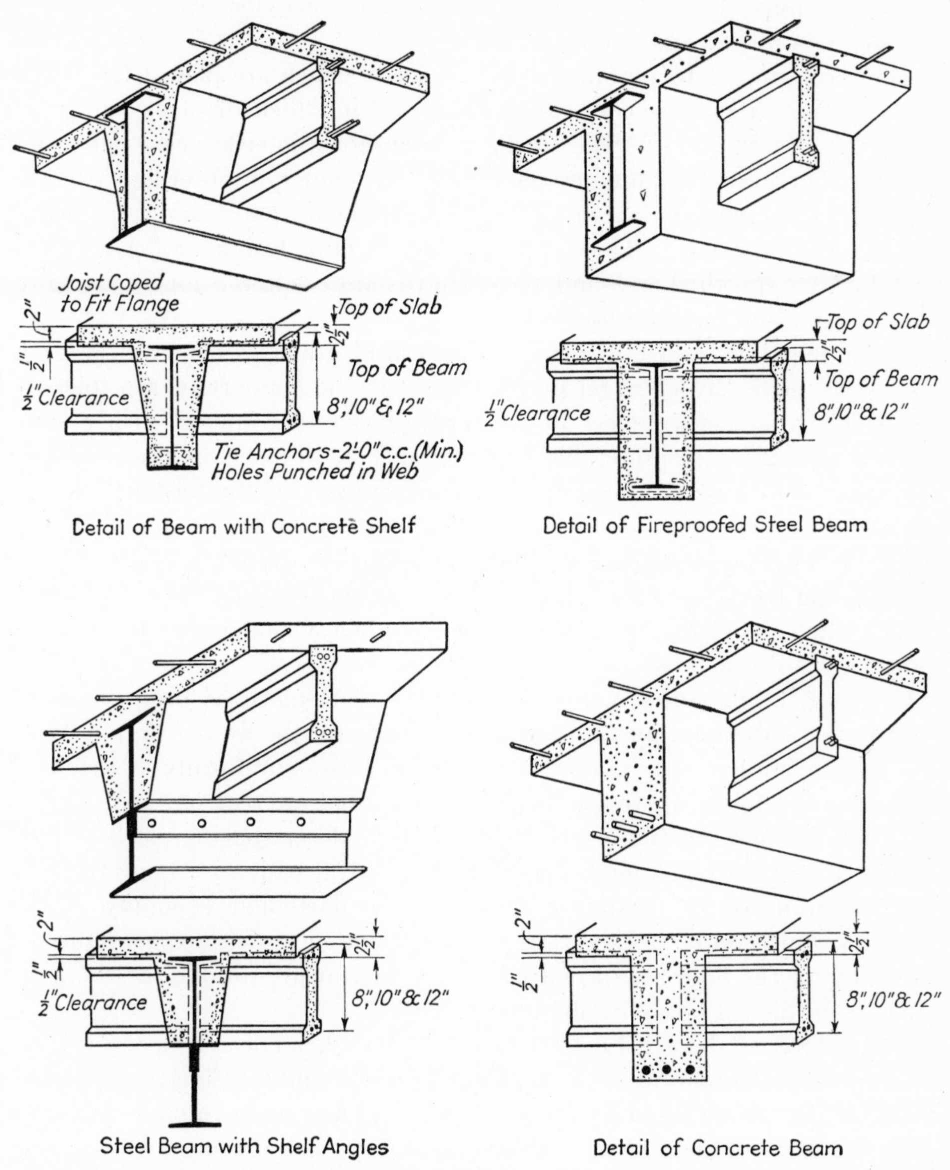

FIG. 10. Assembly Details for Precast Concrete Joists. Courtesy, Dextone Company.

also as an aggregate for structural work cast-in-place where saving in weight is essential and the material available at an advantageous price.

Precast concrete joists have their particular application to wall-bearing designs and to comparatively low buildings. They are seldom appropriate for structures more than a few stories in height, as the system does not furnish very much lateral support to the building frame. Although identified ordinarily with light loads and comparatively long spans, precast concrete joists may also be found satisfactory for the heavier loads required in commercial and storage buildings.

The structural slab, spanning between joists which are placed from 2 to 5 ft apart, is of precast concrete from 2 to 3 in. thick or of cast-in-place concrete of a minimum 2½-in. thickness, reinforced in either case with wire mesh. If precast, the units are usually of slag, cinder, or other light-weight aggregate concrete, which may also be chemically expanded. Concrete plank are appropriate. They are attached by clips to anchors cast in the joists. A 2¾-in. thickness and 10-ft lengths are used on a joist spacing of 5 ft for light and medium floor loads.

When the slab is cast in place, a structural grade of concrete is used. Forms are generally of wood or plywood. If the support of the joists is furnished by structural-steel or reinforced-concrete framing, rather than by bearing walls, it is preferable to cast the slabs in place, as the assembly is much more rigid and the slab provides T-flanges for the joists, thus permitting a wider spacing of the joists. With either design the possibility of cracks developing along lines parallel to the girders should be considered in determining the type of floor finish. Over an unexcavated area or above a hung ceiling, welded-wire fabric backed by heavy paper can be used to economize on form work.

Bridging, in the form of a concrete rib cast-in-place, is used on spans over 16 ft for the 8-in. joist and on longer spans for the deeper units. With a 2½-in. concrete slab poured over 14-in. joists, uniformly distributed superimposed loads up to 75 lb per sq ft can be carried on spans up to 30 ft with a joist spacing of 2 ft 9 in. With a closer spacing, such as 2 ft, heavier loads can be supported on the same span, which is about the economical limit for the standard design. The particular economy of the system occurs where it is permissible to leave the joists exposed on the underside of the floor. Especially well-finished joists suitable for this purpose are furnished by many manufacturers.

PRECAST CONCRETE-CORED DESIGNS. The Flexicore system comprises structural units 12 in. or more in width and of a length and depth required for the particular span and load. They are available in many localities and can be used with bearing walls or steel or reinforced-concrete framing. The round cores shown in the cross-section, Fig. 11, are obtained by expanding elastic tubes to form the inner void, about which stone, gravel, or light-weight aggregate concrete is poured in steel moulds. The standard units are 12 in. in width and 6 in. in total depth. With adequate steel reinforcement, prestressed in shop manufacture, they can be used on clear spans up to about 20 ft. Although a superimposed load of 50 lb per sq ft would be the approximate limit on such an extreme span, the system can be designed on shorter spans for superimposed loads of several hundred pounds per square foot.

These slabs have a particular application for residential occupancy but have been used successfully for more heavily loaded structures. They provide an extremely shallow unit having a dead load of only 30 to 40 lb per sq ft, depending upon the type of aggregate used in the concrete. Because of the slight variations in top surface characteristic of all such unit construction, it is recommended that a mortar topping about ½ in. thick be applied as a base for linoleum, asphalt tile, or similar surface finishes. No

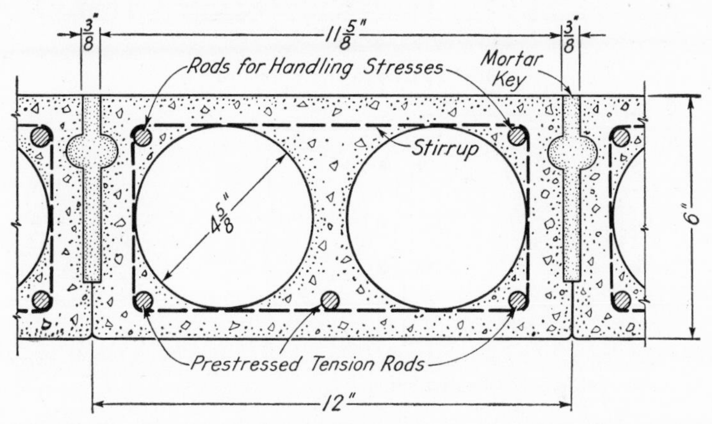

FIG. 11. Vertical Section of Typical Flexicore Unit. Courtesy, Flexicore Company.

floor forms are needed. Ceiling surfaces are reasonably smooth, and rigid conduit or flexible cable can be run within the structural thickness of the slab. Although this system is used in many parts of the country, its availability should be checked for any specific locality.

Two other systems, composed of precast concrete blocks of special design, fall into this same classification. In both cases a somewhat similar structural unit is produced, not as a single casting, but by assembling the block into "plank" or slabs before placement on the floor or roof. Blocks are held together by means of threaded steel rods or pipes, the former acting as reinforcement.

Cast of light-weight aggregate, the blocks are manufactured with smooth end faces to permit close contact on assembly, which may be done either in a shop or on the site. After grouting of longitudinal joints, a concrete topping may be poured over the surface, as is done in the typical block and ribbed assemblies, if required for additional strength. The depth of the completed slabs varies from 4 in. for a shallow block used without topping to about 10 in. where an 8-in. block is covered with 2 in. of concrete. The design shown in Fig. 12 is based on prestressing the steel reinforcement and may be used on spans up to about 24 ft. It has been employed quite extensively in Illinois. A somewhat similar design, for which the steel is not prestressed, was developed in the Middle West, but its use has been limited to the Milwaukee district.

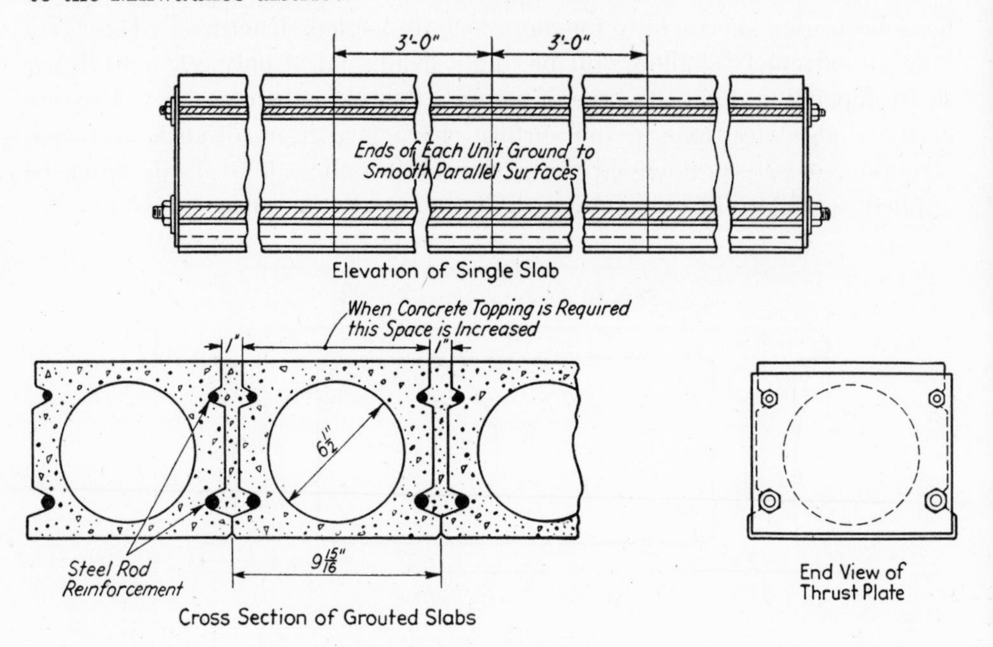

FIG. 12. Details of Prestcrete Block and Assembly. Courtesy, Illinois-Wisconsin Concrete Pipe Company.

PREFABRICATED CLAY-TILE SYSTEM. This design comprises longitudinal rows of clay tile, 12 in. wide and of either 4-in. or 6-in. depth, assembled by means of a round steel rod called a "bolt," as shown in Fig. 13. The contact faces of the tile are machine ground so that, when drawn together by means of the bolts, equipped at each end with heavy plate washers, they form a stiff, prestressed reinforced-tile slab. Lips projecting

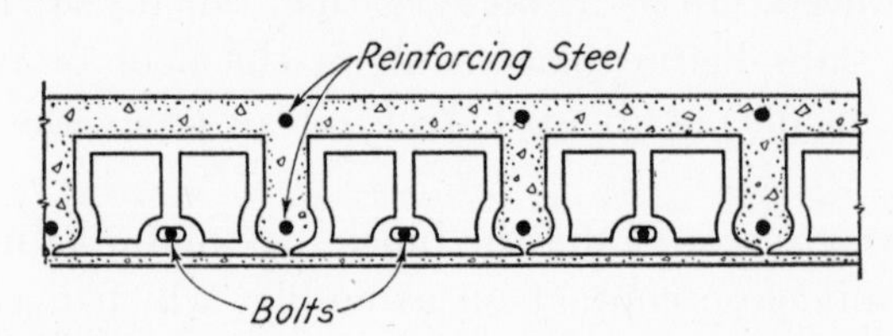

FIG. 13. The Kalex System. Courtesy, Whitacre Engineering Company.

from the lower edges of the tile serve to retain the concrete of the ribs, which is poured between each row of tile after the slabs are in place. This feature saves the cost of form work.

A substantial concrete topping, $1\frac{1}{2}$ in. to 2 in. thick, is applied over the entire surface if required to obtain the necessary structural depth. Where this topping is unnecessary, the surface of tile and ribs is brought to a uniform level by the application of a thin mortar coat. The 6-in. tile with a 2-in. topping is capable of supporting a uniformly distributed superimposed load of 100 lb per sq ft on clear spans up to about 16 ft. The weight of the 6-in. tile, assembled with 2 in. of concrete topping, is 50 lb per sq ft; without topping the weight is 25 lb per sq ft. For roof construction a 4-in. tile is appropriate for spans up to 12 ft. A 2-in. concrete topping is used if required for structural depth. This design weighs 44 lb per sq ft; without topping it weighs 19 lb. As the underside of the structural slabs presents a continuous tile surface, plaster is applied directly. Assemblies of this type have their particular application for low buildings and residential occupancy. Up to the present time their use has been limited to Illinois and Ohio.

OPEN-TRUSS STEEL-JOIST CONSTRUCTION. These units, shown in Fig. 14, have today practically replaced the solid pressed-steel sections which were commonly called "metal lumber." The design is well suited to buildings intended for comparatively light floor loads and those where a high degree of fire resistance is not demanded, but is more appropriate for low than for high buildings and seldom meets the requirements of industrial occupancy. It competes in the same field as the precast concrete joist. Unlike the concrete joist, however, it is not recommended for use with a reinforced-concrete frame. Joists are attached to supporting steel beams by anchor rods or, preferably, are welded to the top flange of the structural member. They are supplied in depths varying, by 2-in. increments, from 8 to 16 in. Steel bridging, in the form of rods or fabricated from ¾-in. channels, is placed at a maximum spacing of 7 ft.

The structural slab, spanning between the joists, which are spaced from 12 to 30 in.[4] apart, is usually of concrete 2 to 2½ in. thick, poured in place over ribbed-wire fabric of close mesh or welded-wire fabric backed by heavy paper. A 2½-in. concrete slab poured over 16-in. joists can support a uniformly distributed superimposed load of 75 lb per sq ft on spans up to 30 ft with a joist spacing of 21 in. This is about the economical maximum for this system. Spans are limited by the Steel Joist Institute to 24 times the depth of joist. This limit would permit the use of a 16-in. joist up to 32 ft between supports, but the spacing would be too close for economy except where loads were very light. For use beneath wood floors, the manufacturers attach a wood nailing strip to the upper chord of the joist, which permits direct nailing of the superimposed wood flooring. This type is suitable for residential work where the fire hazard can be accepted. For open-truss steel joists of special design suitable for spans up to about 60 ft, see page 213, Chapter Six.

[4] The Steel Joist Institute specification limits the spacing of joists to 24 in. for floors, 30 in. for roofs having a poured concrete slab, and 7 ft for roofs having a steel deck or wood surface.

A special application of the open-truss steel joist with structural-steel framing involves the use of Aerocrete. This is a processed material composed of portland cement, sand, and water, to which a small amount of an aerating compound composed principally of aluminum powder is added in mixing. Placed like concrete, it expands before hardening to approximately twice the original volume. It has been used with 12-in. open-truss steel joists,

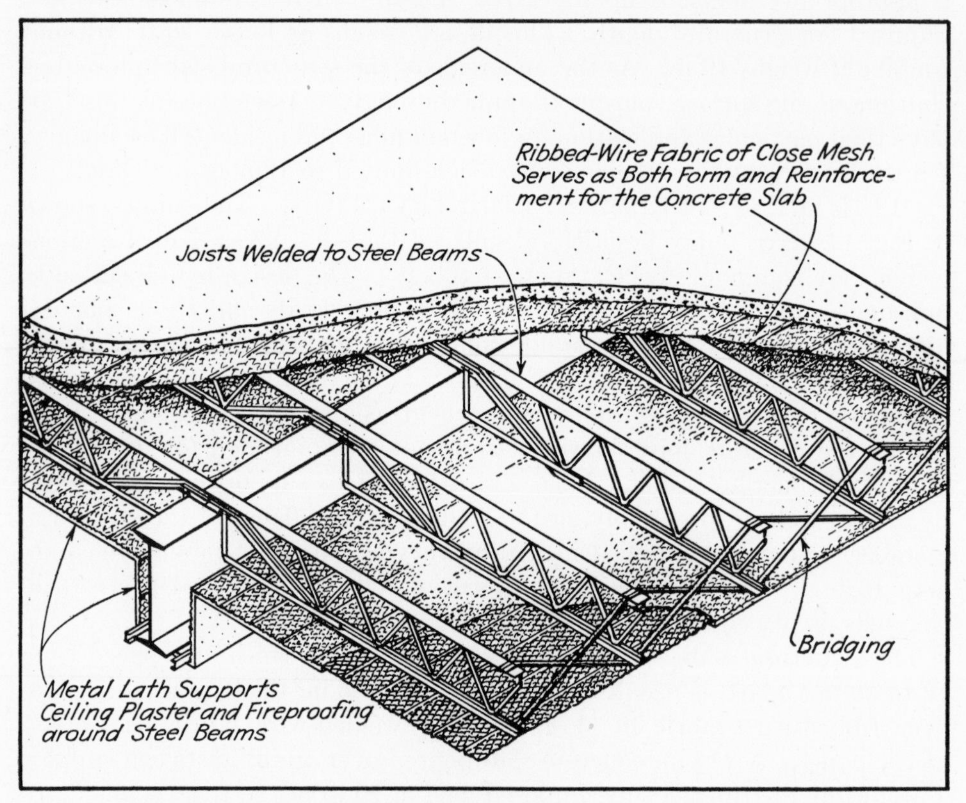

FIG. 14. Open-Truss Steel Joists. Courtesy, Truscon Steel Company.

spaced on 16-in. centers. The joists are enclosed in a flat slab of Aerocrete, which, after expansion, is 15½ in. deep and is surfaced with ½-in. portland-cement mortar placed monolithically. This design can support a superimposed load of 75 lb per sq ft on a 29-ft clear span.

A similar system is cast with Porete, which is a cement-aggregate mixture also expanded through the chemical action of aluminum powder. Both of these furnish excellent designs with structural-steel framing but in the past have usually been more expensive than other comparable types of long-span construction. In this connection it should be noted that any chemically expanded concrete poured-in-place should be thoroughly cured before the application of surface coverings such as linoleum. Not only thorough curing but roughening of the lower surface of the slab is essential if plaster is to be applied. Because of the difficulty of obtaining a permanent bond it is recommended that forms be carefully built to insure smooth surfaces and that ceilings be painted rather than plastered.

At least three other designs comprise open-truss steel joists separated by one or two specially formed clay tile. Narrow concrete ribs enclose the joists; a monolithic concrete topping is applied. Figure 15 shows a typical section. These systems have the common characteristic of using the joists as reinforcement for the tile-concrete assembly, thereby saving considerably on form support, but have been employed to only a very limited extent up

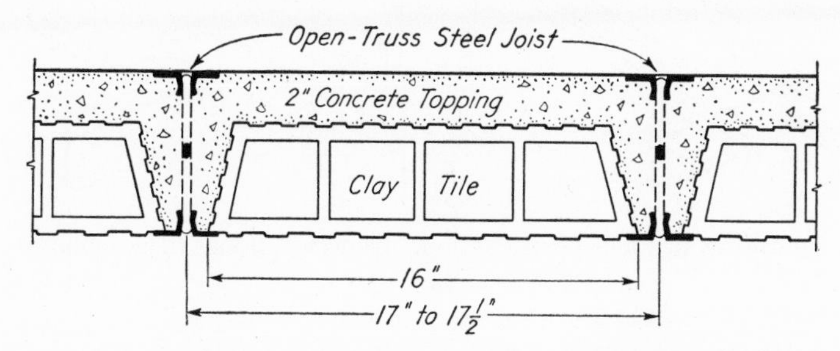

Fig. 15. The Tilecrete System. Courtesy, Tilecrete Floors, Inc.

to the present time. Open-truss steel joists may also serve as reinforcement for the ribs of the standard metal-pan system described on page 109.

The open-truss steel joist is useful as a support for practically any type of precast gypsum or cement-aggregate plank or slab, except channel shapes or other special designs. Sheets of Porex, 1¾ in. thick, composed of mineralized wood fiber bound together with portland cement, may be used for the lighter residential loads on spans up to about 2 ft between joists. A ½-in. mortar finish laid over the top serves as a base for linoleum, asphalt tile, or similar floor finish.

JUNIOR BEAMS. Light-weight, hot-rolled structural-steel I-beams, identified by the manufacturers as "Junior Beams," may be used in floor or roof construction at a spacing greater than that of the standard types of the open-truss steel joist. Depths vary, by 1-in. increments, from 6 in. to 12 in. The weight of the 6-in. beam is 4.4 lb per ft, and that of the 12 in., 11.8 lb; the lighter beam would normally be used on spans from 12 to 14 ft, and the 12-in. depth on spans up to about 24 ft. For typical residential construction the spacing of the beams varies between 2 ft 6 in. and 3 ft 10 in. on centers. Figure 16 shows two assemblies comprising a 2½-in. reinforced-concrete slab and alternate types of floor finish. This design has an occasional application for the floors of residential buildings and other types of occupancy where the superimposed loads are comparatively light.

It can be used with complete structural-steel framing or with wall-bearing construction having an interior framing of steel. Most connections in residential work are made by stirrup or angle hangars. Bolts are used where required, or sections may be welded.

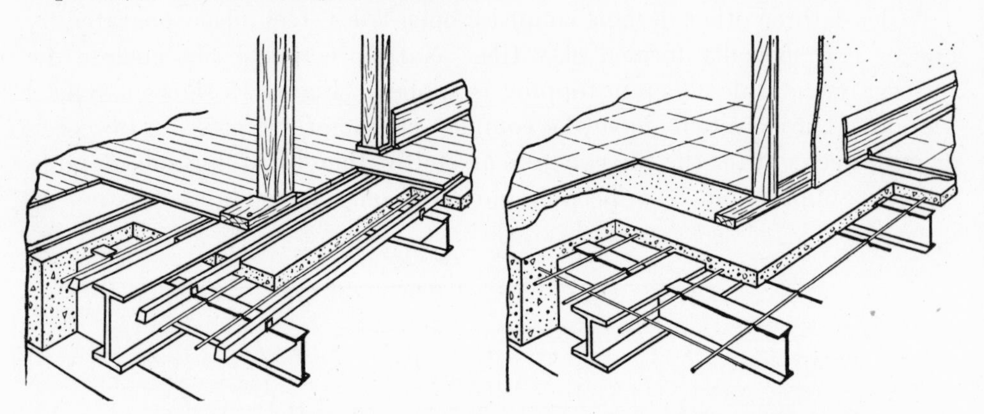

Fig. 16. Junior Beams in Floor Construction. Courtesy, Jones & Laughlin Steel Corporation.

STRAN-STEEL JOISTS. These joists are light-weight, cold-formed steel sections and may be used as floor joists for the lighter load requirements and moderate spans. Manufactured of 16- to 11-gage copper-bearing steel and in depths from 6 to 9 in., they are spaced from 12 to 32 in. on centers. The typical assembly comprises a 2-in. reinforced-concrete slab, supported by corrugated metal laid over the joists as shown in Fig. 17. With a spacing of 18 in., a 9-in. 13-gage joist, with a 2-in. concrete slab, can support a uniformly distributed superimposed load of approximately 60 lb per sq ft on an 18-ft span. Twenty feet is about the limit for light loads. These units have their particular application for low structures designed for residential occupancy. They are used appropriately with structural-steel framing or bearing walls. They also appear in the complete light-steel assemblies described on page 48.

STEEL-PLATE AND SHEET-STEEL CELLULAR FLOOR SYSTEMS. As a group, these are used most widely for roof construction and are consequently described in Chapter Five, but some types are applicable to floors. Although occasionally economical for spans up to 25 ft, they are particularly appropriate for short-span designs and are therefore discussed in Article 2 on page 133. They could be used with reinforced-concrete framing but are far more suitable for structural-steel assemblies.

The "Battledeck" system, composed of structural-steel I-beams carrying a steel plate welded to the top flanges, is seldom appropriate for the floors of buildings.

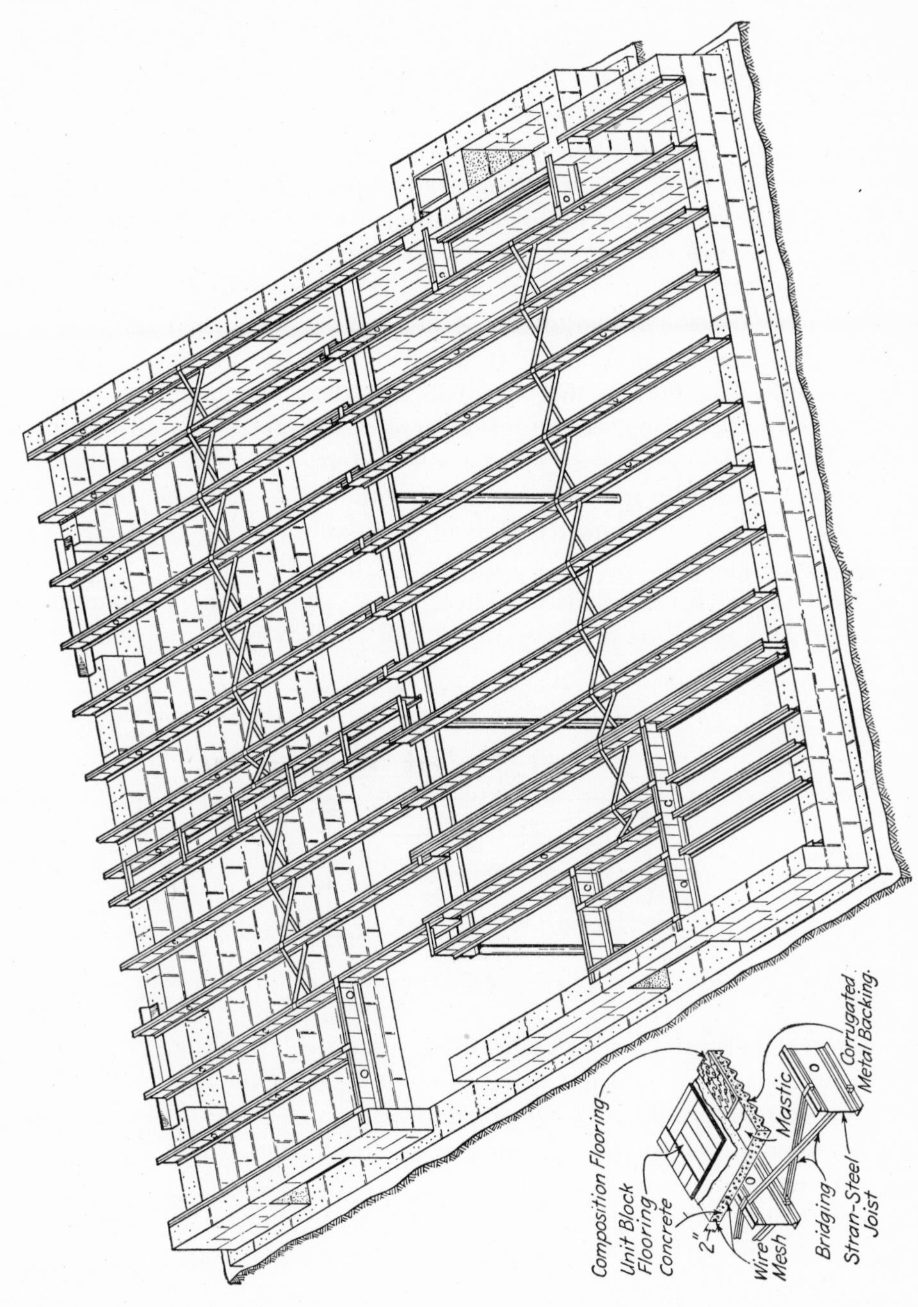

FIG. 17. Typical Design for Stran-Steel Joists. Courtesy, Great Lakes Steel Corporation.

Article 2. Short-Span Designs for Structural-Steel Framing

Although any of the previously described structural floor systems can be used for short as well as for long spans, their particular advantage is the fact that they can span from 15 to 30 or even, in some cases, to 35 ft, thereby eliminating beams except along column center lines. The short-span designs, on the other hand, require structural supports spaced from 6 to 10 ft apart, which are usually in the form of intermediate beams dividing each column bay into two, three, or four comparatively narrow panels as described on page 66. Within this group are several different systems adaptable to a wide variation of loading conditions. They have been used extensively for all types of occupancy from residential to industrial. If the designer has decided upon a short-span design, it is not difficult to choose an appropriate type of floor construction to meet his specific conditions, but the decision between a long- or short-span system, as noted on page 66, should be very carefully made, as it greatly influences the structural economy of the building. For most classes of occupancy, one of the long-span systems is generally preferable for buildings of moderate height.

STONE-CONCRETE SLABS. These slabs usually have a minimum thickness of 4 in. for floors and 3½ in. for roofs. They represent one of the

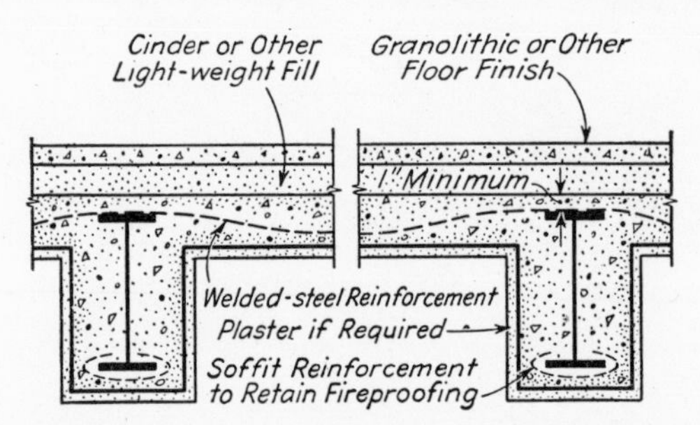

FIG. 18. Short-Span, Reinforced-Concrete Slabs Supported by Structural-Steel Framing.

well-known structural floor systems used with steel framing. Although cinder concrete is cheaper than stone concrete where cinders are produced locally, satisfactory cinders are not available in many parts of the country, and stone-concrete slabs may be an excellent selection where one of the other lighter-weight systems could not be used to advantage or a lighter-weight aggregate obtained economically. Figure 18 shows a typical design which would appear the same for stone or lighter-weight aggregate.

In short-span assemblies of this type, comprising structural-steel framing and concrete slabs, the beams may be connected to the girders so that the top surfaces of the two are at the same level, or the beams may be dropped sufficiently to avoid coping their upper flanges, as discussed on page 68. The first option, shown in Fig. 19, is usually preferable.

In this design the structural-concrete slab is often finished flush with the upper surface of the structural steel, but it is better practice to provide a minimum thickness of 1 in. of concrete over the upper flanges. This

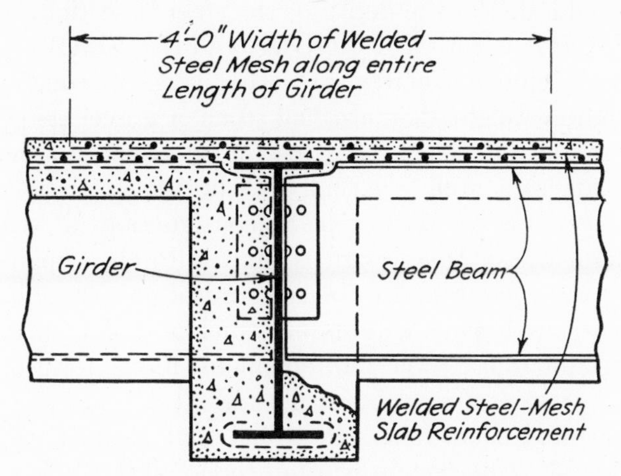

Fig. 19. Beam-and-Girder Connection with Special Reinforcement in Concrete Slab over Girder.

concrete serves as protection for the welded-wire reinforcement of the slabs where it passes over the beams and permits the introduction of a 4-ft width of the same steel mesh along the girders, placed with the heavier wires at right angles to the girder flanges. This additional reinforcement minimizes the probability of cracks developing parallel with the sides of the girders.

Stone-concrete slabs, or those composed of any aggregate which produces a suitable undersurface, have their particular economy where it is possible to avoid plastering ceilings. If ceilings must be plastered, surfaces should be sufficiently rough to give adequate bond, as mentioned on page 118.

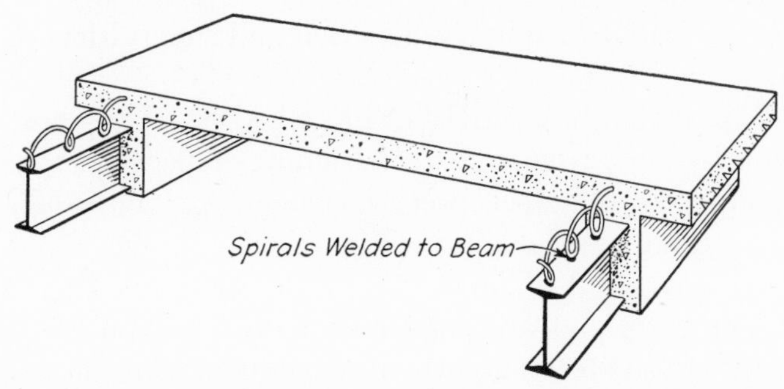

Fig. 20. The Alpha System. Courtesy, Porete Manufacturing Company.

An interesting variation of standard construction consists of a steel spiral electrically welded to the top flange of a structural-steel beam. This design, illustrated in Fig. 20, results in the slab assisting the steel as a compression flange. Although much more frequently used in highway bridges than in buildings, it has an application for long spans, over 40 or 45 ft, when supporting heavy loads. Under such conditions this design permits an economical reduction in the depth of the steel H-section.

LIGHT-WEIGHT CEMENT-AGGREGATE SLABS. For steel-framed structures, cinder concrete and other types of concrete employing aggregates of lighter weight than crushed stone or gravel are generally more economical than the heavier aggregates for short-span designs. The so-called "cinder-concrete arch," actually a short-span slab, (Fig. 18) has been for many years a standard type of construction in New York City. The more general use of this design is limited to clear spans of not over 8 ft, but 10-ft spans were found to be economical on a large housing operation in New York in 1946. A minimum thickness of 4 in. is required for floor and 3½ in. for roofs. The reinforcement, in the form of welded-wire mesh draped over the supporting structural-steel beams, is designed for the span and loading conditions. Provided that clean, hard, well-burned cinders are available, this system is often economical. It is heavily penalized in cost if a hung ceiling is required to conceal the beams.

Several types of light-weight aggregate concrete, such as Haydite, Waylite, and chemically expanded cement-aggregate mixtures like Aerocrete, Porete, and Gritcrete, are also used for both short-span floor and roof slabs. Haydite was described on page 39; Waylite, on page 112; Aerocrete and Porete, on page 124. Gritcrete is also a chemically expanded concrete containing a graded gravel aggregate. These materials may be used in the place of cinders for designs similar to Fig. 18, or, if flat ceilings are desired, the slab may be cast the full depth of the steel beams, plus the fireproofing requirement. Such a system is appropriate only for light loads and comparatively short beam spans but has been used for university residential buildings. Although structurally adequate, the chemically expanded concretes require particular care in specification and supervision, as mentioned on page 124.

PRECAST CEMENT-AGGREGATE SLABS. For short-span floor systems supported by structural-steel framing, especially where it is unnecessary to fireproof the steel, precast cement-aggregate slabs may often be used to advantage, although their particular application is for roofs. These slabs are composed of small-size stone aggregate, Haydite, or other light-weight aggregate and are reinforced with a galvanized, welded-steel mesh. The structural-steel supports are spaced to conform with the stock sizes of the slabs; for a large order, the slabs may be especially designed by the manufacturers.

A typical assembly employing Haydite, which produces a very satisfactory slab for this purpose, is shown in Fig. 21. This system has been used successfully for many types of occupancy from industrial buildings to schools. An 18- × 4¾-in. slab of channel design, having a web thickness of 2¼ in. and comparatively light reinforcement, is suitable for a superimposed load of 75 lb per sq ft on spans up to about 10 ft. Considerably

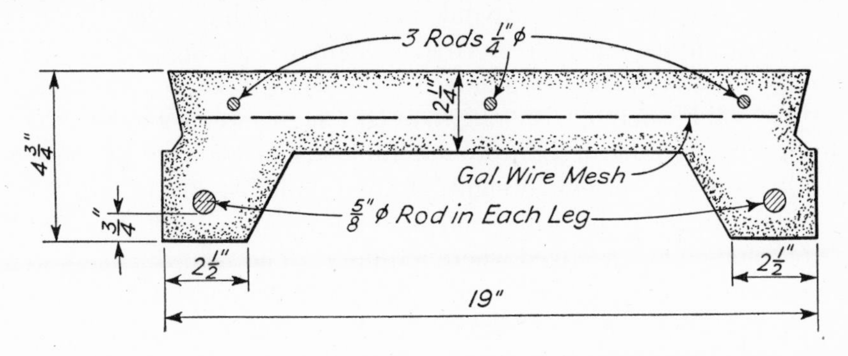

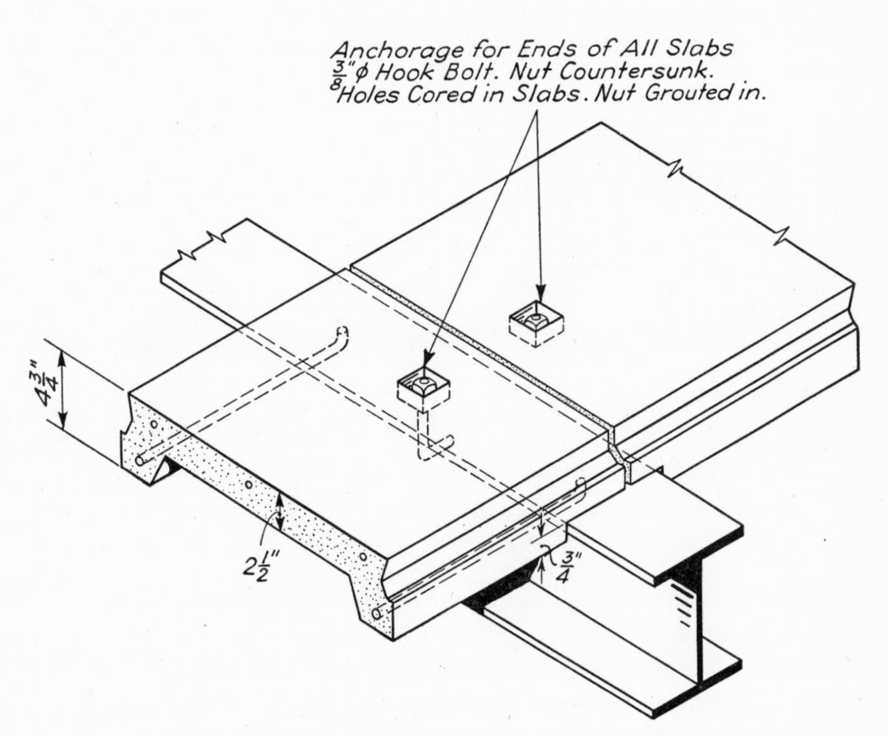

FIG. 21. Precast Haydite Slabs with Steel Framing. Courtesy, The Cooksville Company Ltd., Toronto, Canada.

heavier loads can be carried by increasing the steel. The weight of this section is 22 lb per sq ft. Slabs rest upon the steel or concrete beams, to which they may be bolted if required. Joints are grouted and trowelled level. Beneath linoleum or asphalt tile, a mortar surfacing is applied. Ceramic floor tile or quarry tile are laid in mortar directly upon the precast slabs. If wood floors are required, metal clips are inserted in the grout between the slabs at suitable intervals, usually 16 in. on centers, to which the sleepers are fastened.

Precast slabs of chemically expanded concrete, such as Porete, may also be used to advantage where a short-span, light-weight unit of this type is appropriate. Porete slabs are made in two styles. The channel section, composed of solid concrete with a light-weight aggregate, is 2¾ in. or 3½ in. deep and is appropriate for light or medium loads on spans up to about 8 ft. The plank, composed of light-weight, aerated, nailable concrete, is 2 in. or 2¾ in. thick, 16 to 24 in. wide, and manufactured in lengths up to 9 ft. Edges are tongued and grooved where required. The 2-in. thickness weighs 12 lb per sq ft and may be used over wood joists, steel beams, or open-truss steel joists. It is capable of supporting a uniformly distributed, superimposed load of 100 lb per sq ft on a span of 5 ft. The Cantilite plank, composed of light-weight, chemically expanded concrete, is another similar unit used more widely for roofs but also suitable for short-span floor construction.

FIELD-POURED GYPSUM SYSTEMS. Floor and roof slabs, carried by structural steel bulb-tees or light-weight mine-rails and reinforced with welded-steel mesh as shown in Fig. 22, may be cast-in-place of gypsum.

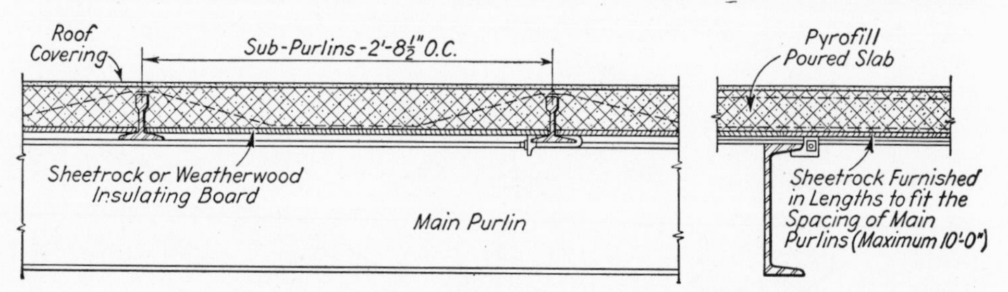

Fig. 22. Field-Poured Gypsum Short-Span Floor or Roof System. Courtesy, United States Gypsum Company.

The only admixture with the gypsum is wood shavings reduced to a fiber in a swing-hammer mill. The standard for the dry mixture is 12½ per cent by weight of fiber and 87½ per cent of gypsum. When wet to the proper consistency and dried, this mixture produces a material having an ultimate compressive strength of 500 lb per sq in and a weight of approximately 52 lb per cu ft. Mixtures having less fiber and producing a greater compressive strength are also used. For additional information on this subject see "Reinforced Gypsum Concrete," American Standards Association, *Standard* A59.1, 1945. Wood or plywood forms are hung from the steel beams, which can be effectively fireproofed with the same material or with precast gypsum units designed to fit a wide range of structural shapes.

An alternate design, suitable for superimposed loads from 40 to 60 lb per sq ft, comprises light-weight structural-steel beams or open-truss steel joists spaced not over 36 in. on centers, eliminating the necessity for the bulb-tees or mine-rails. The gypsum slab, from 2 to 3 in. thick, is reinforced with welded-steel mesh as required for the load and span. If linoleum or a composition floor covering is used over such construction, a special surface treatment is required.

PRECAST GYPSUM SLABS. These slabs have their particular application to roof construction, but there are a number of both solid and hollow units designed for spans up to about 10 ft. Gypsum plank are not generally used for floors, but, as the 2-in. thickness is capable of carrying 75 lb per sq ft on a 7-ft span, they can be employed for this purpose on short-span construction, provided that a suitable surface treatment is chosen which would meet architectural requirements and protect the surface from "punching."

BRICK AND STRUCTURAL-CLAY-TILE ARCHES. In the past ordinary well-burned common brick were used to form segmental arches spanning between steel I-beams for short-span designs carrying heavy loads. Many years ago this system was largely replaced by flat and segmental arches formed of clay tile. This material had the advantage of less weight, and special shapes were provided for fireproofing the lower flanges of the steel beams at the haunches of the arch. Segmental clay-tile arches are now obsolete, but the flat arch is still occasionally employed where conditions are favorable. Its particular application is for medium and comparatively heavy loads and spans not over about 6 ft. In most districts stone concrete or a light-weight-aggregate concrete is more economical for short-span designs. Only one large structure has been erected with this system in the New York metropolitan district for a number of years, and it has not been popular in the San Francisco metropolitan area since the earthquake of 1906.

REINFORCED-BRICK SLABS. Brick laid on edge with small rods embedded in the mortar joints have been used for slab construction on short-span designs. This system, however, although employed to a limited extent in England and in India and other parts of Asia, is usually uneconomical under conditions existing in the United States.

STEEL-PLATE AND SHEET-STEEL CELLULAR FLOOR SYSTEMS. These designs are more common for roof decks than for floors, but several types of ribbed or cellular construction are appropriate for use in combination with a concrete slab or fill. As a group, these types have their particular application for short-span structural-steel framing and supply a comparatively thin, light-weight floor section. If the type of occupancy permits the use of a steel ceiling on the soffit of the structural floor, they have an added economic advantage. Designs can be adapted to light or heavy loads.

A system providing space for the installation of electrical wiring within the thickness of the structural floor is illustrated in Fig. 23. Although usually more appropriate for short-span designs, this assembly may be economical on spans up to 25 ft. It has a broad application for many types of occupancy and has recently been used in a number of large structures, including office buildings, government buildings, and factories.

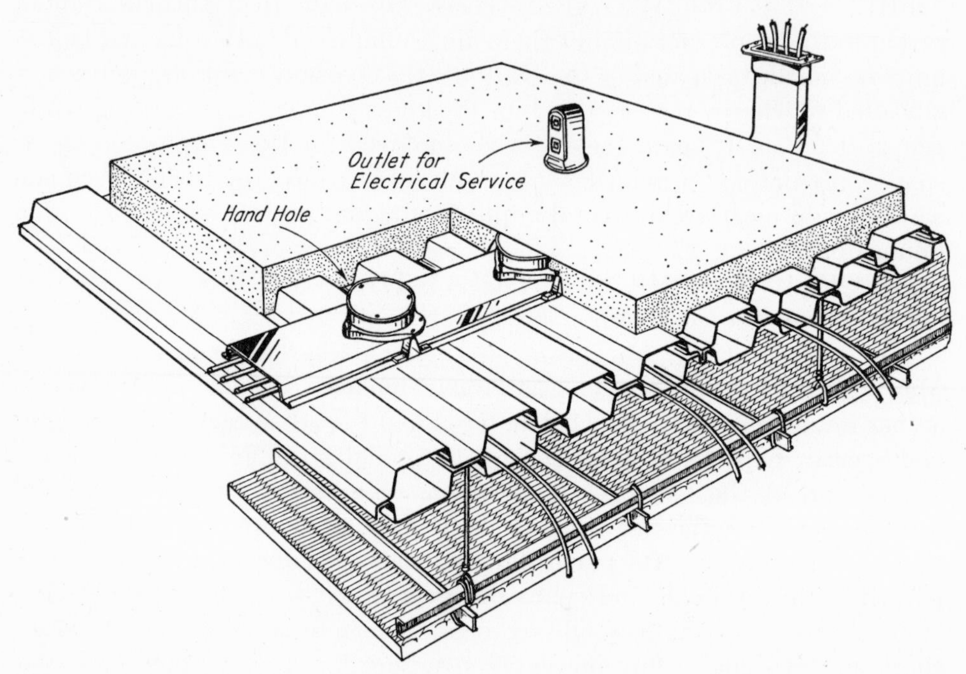

FIG. 23. Sheet-Steel Cellular Floor Construction. Courtesy, H. H. Robertson Company.

WOOD-PLANK FLOORS. For industrial buildings such as textile mills, where the weight of the machines, except looms, is comparatively light, heavy plank may occasionally be used to advantage for the structural floors spanning between steel beams if the fire risk can be accepted. Such a floor has the advantage of facilitating the bolting down of the machines in any desired location. An automatic sprinkler system is often installed beneath floors of this type.

Article 3. Long-Span Designs for Reinforced-Concrete Framing

The following systems, which were described in Article 1, are also appropriate for use with reinforced-concrete framing: metal-pan system, page 108; structural-clay-tile systems, page 110; gypsum-tile system, page 112; concrete-block systems, page 112; Fibercrete system, page 114; corresponding two-way systems, page 115; smooth ceilings and equidepth systems, page

117; precast concrete-cored designs, page 120; prefabricated clay-tile system, page 122.

PRECAST CONCRETE-JOIST CONSTRUCTION (page 118). When using this system with reinforced-concrete framing, the slabs spanning between joists should be cast-in-place rather than precast. The reasons for this preference, as applied to structural-steel framing, were given on page 120. When used with reinforced-concrete framing, there is the additional advantage that the slab supplies a flange for the concrete beam.

FLAT SLABS DESIGNED WITH SPECIFIED MOMENT COEFFICIENTS. As the choice of this design imposes specific limitations upon the location of supporting columns, it was discussed in Chapter Three, page 73. Normally employed with a complete reinforced-concrete assembly, it can be adapted to exterior bearing-wall construction with interior columns of reinforced concrete. It is not used with structural-steel framing. As previously noted, its particular application is for multistory factories, warehouses, and garages. Although often an excellent choice for the lighter industrial and garage loads, such as 125 lb per sq ft, it is particularly appropriate for heavier construction, where the superimposed load ranges from 200 to 300 lb per sq ft of floor area. The chief characteristic of the system is the flared column capital, which is not objectionable for types of occupancy such as mentioned above, but is inappropriate for buildings requiring many partitions along column center lines.

A variation from the standard system, involving a diagonal arrangement of columns, was discussed and illustrated on page 76. This has a limited application where the use of the floor space favors such a column location and is similar to the three-way system developed many years ago by Mr. David W. Morrow. Other variations, such as the circumferential, developed by Mr. Edward Smulski, apply almost exclusively to the disposition of the reinforcement.

FLAT-PLATE, RIGID-FRAME DESIGNS. As these designs are complete structural assemblies, rather than floor systems, they were discussed in Chapter Three, page 77. Although generally associated in buildings with the wide-span construction used for roofs, the rigid-frame analysis has a valuable application to structural floors of even moderate span. The floor construction is similar in appearance to that of the standard flat-slab design without the large column heads, which are objectionable for so many kinds of occupancy. Typical sections were shown on page 77 and 79. Systems of this type can be used only with a complete reinforced-concrete frame. They should be considered very favorably, as they often prove more economical than beam-and-slab assemblies. All these designs, comprising solid concrete slabs, provide facility for embedment of conduit or other pipes, and the smooth surfaces of floor and ceiling can be utilized to save expense on fill or finishes.

Article 4. Short-Span Designs for Reinforced-Concrete Framing

STONE-CONCRETE SLABS. This is the only short-span system described in Article 2 which is generally appropriate for use with reinforced-concrete framing. The typical assembly, commonly referred to as beam-and-girder, illustrated on page 66, may be appropriate for industrial occupancy, warehouses, or other heavily loaded structures where the conditions

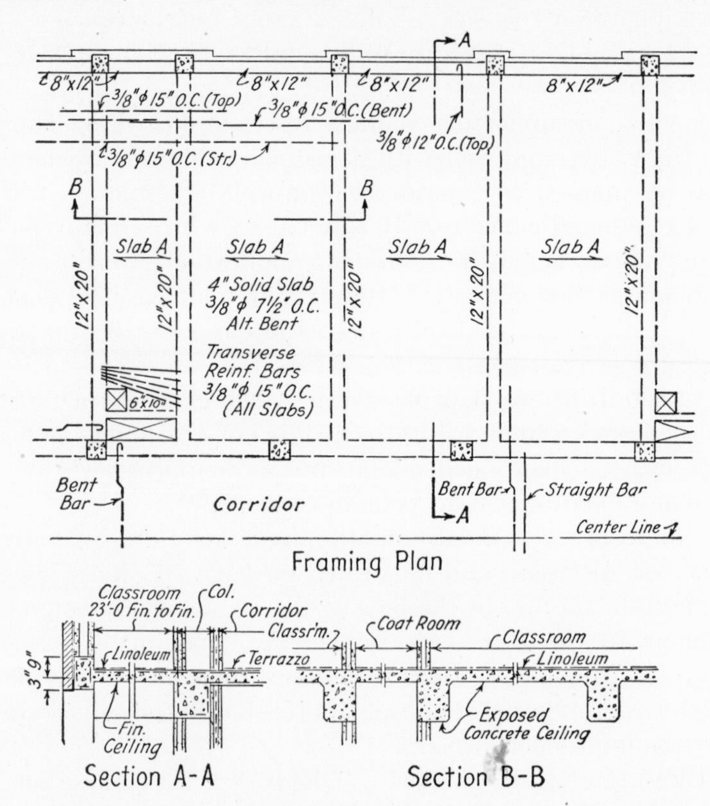

FIG. 24. Beam-and-Slab Construction in Reinforced Concrete.

mentioned on page 75 preclude the use of a flat slab designed with specified moment coefficients, or make a flat-plate, rigid-frame analysis too complicated. Such systems have also been used for post offices and other types of public buildings where the concrete-ribbed systems were incapable of carrying heavy concentrations or meeting economically other desired requirements. Furthermore, the simplicity of these designs may recommend them for many types of even small and moderate-sized buildings, particularly where ceilings can be left unplastered. Figure 24 shows a typical plan for an elementary school house. The cost of form work, however, is proportionately high for this system with concrete framing, particularly for low buildings where only a few uses can be obtained.

Slabs composed of cinder concrete, Haydite, or other light-weight aggregates, or the chemically expanded concretes, such as Aerocrete and Porete, are generally inappropriate for reinforced-concrete framing. One particular exception is the possibility mentioned in Chapter Three of using a light-weight aggregate such as Haydite, which is capable of producing a high-grade structural concrete, for the entire framing as well as for the floor system, which would be poured in place. Precast concrete slabs are not recommended for use with reinforced-concrete framing on short-span designs, except where all structural elements are prefabricated. Seldom would it be possible to design such systems to compete economically with the more appropriate assemblies. Field-poured gypsum systems could not be used successfully with any normal design supported by a reinforced-concrete frame. Some steel-plate and sheet-steel cellular floor systems can be adapted to reinforced-concrete framing but are far more appropriate for structural steel. The same is true of wood-plank floors.

Article 5. Floor Systems for Wood Framing

If wood framing is used with exterior bearing walls, with or without interior bearing walls, there are two common alternates: an ordinary wood-joist design or heavy-timber construction. For buildings fully framed in wood, ordinary wood joists are generally employed. The structural deck supported by the joists may be of 7/8-in. matched boards, plywood, or a similar material, as mentioned on page 89. Any of the lighter-weight precast units, such as gypsum plank or Porex slabs, could likewise be placed in the same manner as for wood-framed roofs.

Both the heavy-timber and wood-joist floor assemblies are so well standardized and closely related to the framing that their descriptions were included in Chapter Three. Adaptations of wood framing for wide-span designs are given in Chapter Six. Various prefabricated assemblies of wood were discussed in Chapter Three. Special requirements for cellarless buildings are given in Article 6.

Article 6. Floor Construction on or near the Ground

FIRST-STORY FLOOR. Floors laid on the ground or raised only sufficiently to obtain ventilation and access to utilities have acquired particular significance recently in relation to the cellarless designs popular for many types of small dwellings.

If the floor is self-supporting, any appropriate structural system previously described may be used. As the more substantial designs are generally too expensive for small structures, a wood-framed floor is the usual choice. Ventilation of the space beneath the floor is imperative. Wood is particularly vulnerable to the comparatively stagnant, moist air of sealed spaces.

Openings in the foundation walls, about 1 sq ft in area and placed just above grade on all four sides, are enough for small buildings. They should be covered by grilles. This provision protects the wood from rotting but wastes heat unless the floor is well insulated. If part of the cellar is fully excavated and contains the house-heating unit, no problem exists, as the heat from this section can be allowed to pass entirely beneath the floor and eliminate the danger of either water vapor or chilling of the surface.

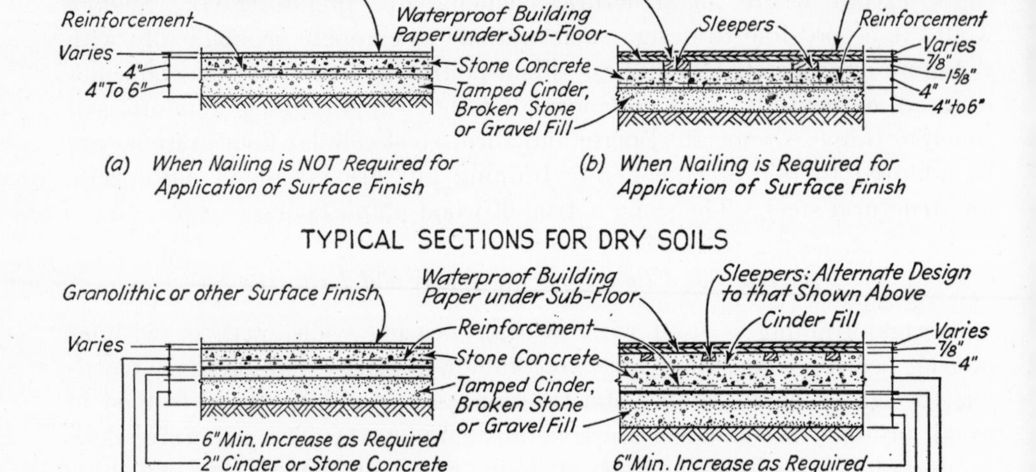

Fig. 25. Floor Construction on Soil.

If the floor is laid upon the ground, a concrete slab with a granolithic or other desired surface, as shown in sketches (*a*) and (*c*) of Fig. 25, is often appropriate. A bituminous compound, added to the concrete or incorporated in the finish, increases resilience. Matched wood flooring may be nailed to wood sleepers, as shown in sketches (*b*) and (*d*) of Fig. 25, or the finished wood floor may be bedded in mastic, applied directly to the concrete slab. As a primary necessity is the elimination of moisture, a porous fill, composed of cinders or gravel, is recommended even over "dry" soils. A dampproofing course, comprising a single layer of waterproof building paper, may be placed over the fill, beneath the stone-concrete slab. Any degree of moisture is harmful to both wood surfacings and linoleum. Bituminous materials such as asphalt tile are less vulnerable, but dampness is always very objectionable from the viewpoint of occupancy even if the building materials are not actually injured. Even for floors of cellarless buildings, laid at or slightly above the level of the surrounding ground, an actual waterproofing course or some of the provisions shown in sketches (*c*) and (*d*) may be desirable. These two designs, however, have their particular application to basement and cellar floors.

Any suitable material may be used as fill, and sleepers may be replaced by a 2-in. thickness of a light-weight concrete, composed of portland cement and a fine mineral aggregate, forming a base to which the underfloor is nailed. If wood sleepers are used, they should be treated with a preservative. A layer of hard-burned clay tile may occasionally be placed to advantage beneath wood floors to provide additional insulation but should be laid over a concrete slab to insure against unequal settlement.

The provisions for drainage and dampproofing are much simpler where floors are placed near natural grade than for basements or cellars, but surface and roof water should be effectively diverted from the building by shallow gutters or drains. The common practice in rural and suburban districts of raising the grade of the lawn about 6 in. adjacent to building walls is to assist in effecting the same purpose. With these provisions, a porous fill, 4 to 6 in. deep, beneath a concrete slab 3 or 4 in. thick should be adequate for floors where the surface of the slab is a foot or more above the adjacent grade unless the structure is located at the bottom of a natural drainage area. In this case the floor should be raised to a safe height by grading.

Insulation is discussed on page 173. The same principles apply to floors laid on or near the ground. For floors laid on the ground there is, however, the additional requirement of insulating around the outer edges between the concrete floor and adjacent walls. Such insulation also serves the purpose of providing for volumetric change that may occur in the slab and eliminates the need for any other type of joint between floor and walls. Tests have indicated the advantages of the design illustrated in Fig. 26, both in conserving heat and obtaining a more uniform temperature gradient within the building.

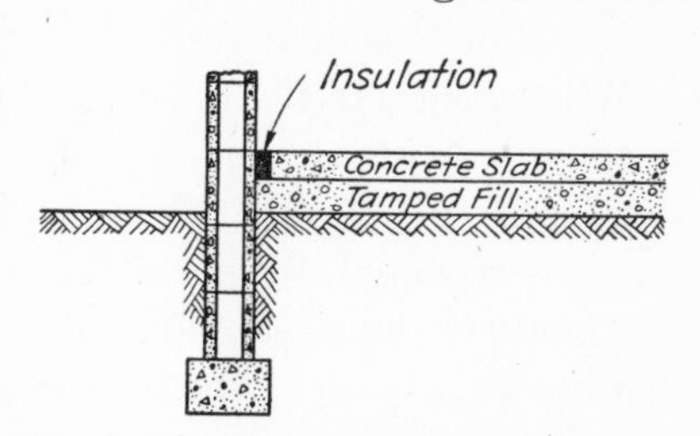

FIG. 26. Edge Insulation of Concrete Floors Laid on Soil.

The possibility of heating ground-floor rooms by means of pipe coils embedded in the concrete, forming the floor slab, should not be overlooked. Although such systems are most efficient where the surface of the concrete is left exposed, good results may be obtained with coverings of linoleum or similar materials. Several systems, usually employing hot water as a heating medium, are at present available. Radiant designs of this type, applicable to either floor or ceiling installation, may be higher in first cost than the more conventional systems but are economical in operation and, if properly designed, produce excellent results. They are being rapidly developed by several of our foremost national manufacturers and constitute one of the more important developments in modern heating.

BASEMENT AND CELLAR FLOORS. When placed over soil which is known to remain comparatively dry at all seasons, 4 to 6 in. of porous fill, cinders, gravel, or crushed stone, as for floors slightly above the natural grade, should be adequate as a base for concrete slabs, provided that land-tile drains, laid in a porous material, are installed around the building at

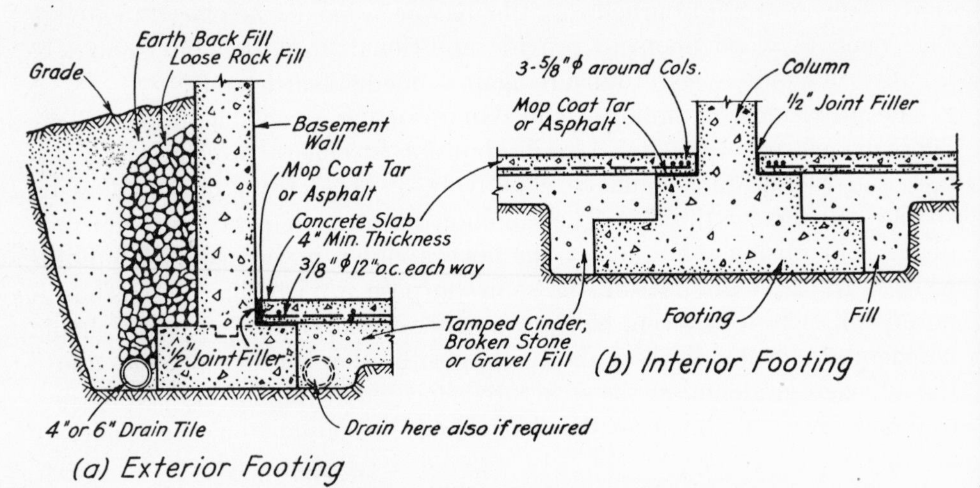

FIG. 27. Arrangement of Drain Tile for Shallow Basements.

the footing level, as shown in Fig. 27. Such a design is often appropriate for shallow basements.

When concrete floors are laid over soil which is actually wet or likely to become wet at certain seasons of the year, the thickness of fill should be increased to possibly 12 in. and supplemented, where considerable water may be expected, by parallel lines of land tile laid in the fill 3 or 4 ft apart. All land-tile lines should be connected with tight-jointed clay sewer pipe leading to a sewer, storm-water drain, dry well, or preferably, if grades permit, to the surface. A minimum pitch of ¼ in. to 1 ft should be used.

If grades are unfavorable and where cellars are deep, it is often necessary to install either a sump pit and automatic electric pump or a complete system of waterproofing. Under these conditions the floor construction should approximate the details shown in sketches (*c*) and (*d*) of Fig. 25, and the waterproofing will be carried up the exterior walls well above the potential water level, as shown for the membrane method in sketch (*a*) of Fig. 28. An excellent description of the other systems of waterproofing commonly used is given in the Report of the Joint Committee on Standard Specifications for Concrete and Reinforced Concrete, 1940.

Where there is any probability of an actual hydrostatic head occurring at the level of the bottom of the floor slab, provision must be made either to relieve or to resist the resulting pressure, and an appropriate type of waterproofing installed. To relieve pressure, ground water may be drained into a central sump, from which it is raised by an electric pump. This system of drainage has been successfully used in some of the deeper basements of New York City. Sketch (*a*) Fig. 28, shows an arrangement of membrane waterproofing for such a condition where the outside face of the wall is accessible below grade. If the outside is not accessible, the same type of waterproofing may be placed on the inner surface and retained by a masonry

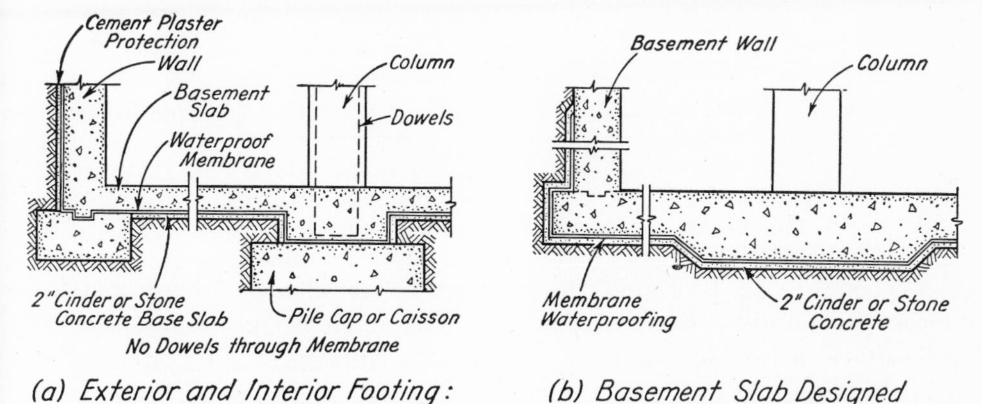

FIG. 28. Arrangement of Waterproof Membrane for Deep Basements.

or concrete seal. If conditions do not demand membrane waterproofing, less expensive treatments may be applied to either the exterior or the interior surfaces.

The alternate possibility is to design the foundation to resist the hydrostatic pressure. For such a purpose the basement floor may be constructed as an inverted flat slab or other heavily loaded structural assembly. Such a section is shown in sketch (*b*), Fig. 28. The pressure is resisted by the weight of the building carried down through the columns. The design shown on page 372 in Chapter Nine on foundations is an adaptation of this same principle.

Concrete floors laid within a building need not be cut into blocks by through-jointing, as is very desirable for unreinforced sidewalks and the pavement of yards. Joints should be made, however, at re-entrant angles and along lines where slabs meet walls, columns, or other vertical surfaces unless continuity is a prime requisite. As an added precaution against cracks, in dry locations, and for large floor areas, "dummy joints" may be formed along column center lines; these are shown in Fig. 29.

Although it is customary to lay concrete floors upon well-compacted fill without reinforcement, the addition of small steel rods, such as ⅜-in. rounds, at 10 or 12-in. centers in each direction is recommended to insure against cracks resulting from initial shrinkage of the concrete or uneven settlement of the supporting fill. These rods are placed at the height shown in the illustration.

Concrete floors to be covered by flagstones, slate, brick, or quarry tile are roughly screeded to a true surface but need not be trowelled, as these materials are laid in a setting bed of mortar or occasionally, particularly if brick is used, in a bituminous mastic. For linoleum or a material similarly applied, the surface should be very smooth in order to avoid uneven wear.

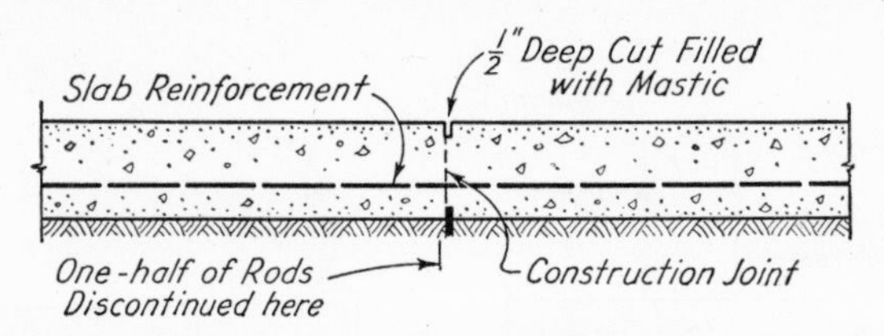

FIG. 29. Dummy Joint in Concrete Floor Slab Laid on Soil.

If a concrete finish is desired, the floor can be trowelled to a hard, metallic surface, integrally colored or painted. The reference given on page 27 will serve as a specification guide and may be supplemented by information available from the Portland Cement Association.

Article 7. Sound Insulation

The use of acoustical surfaces and the methods of their installation do not directly affect the choice of structural elements. Neither does the actual design of auditoriums and other buildings or rooms where hearing is essential fall within the scope of this text. The general acoustical requirements demanded by the particular type of occupancy should, however, be borne in mind, so that the sound transmission of any proposed assembly, such as a floor or partition, may be included with the other characteristics in making a selection. This point is particularly important today, as some of the lighter-weight designs may warrant investigation. It is also essential that the structural work be planned with the acoustical requirements in mind. In some cases the architectural plan may be influenced by a desire to remove certain rooms as far as practicable from the source of disturbance. Rooms where quiet is particularly essential may be located on a court rather than on a street. Isolation, from the viewpoint of plan, of a room designed for a use which can be expected to cause considerable noise, such as a game room, will naturally reduce the cost of sound insulation.

The following paragraphs broadly identify the ways in which unwelcome sounds may enter a building or a particular room within a building.

a. Airborne noises may pass through open windows or any other opening in the building envelope. This fact implies the desirability, where exterior sound levels are high or the use of the structure demands an exceptionally quiet interior, of supplying mechanical rather than natural ventilation, eliminating cracks around doors or windows, and carefully locating fresh-air inlets.

To reduce sound transmission through floors and partitions, which is particularly important for multifamily dwellings, all openings around pipes and telephone or light receptacles should be tightly caulked, and receptacles should not be placed back to back on opposite sides of a partition. Although

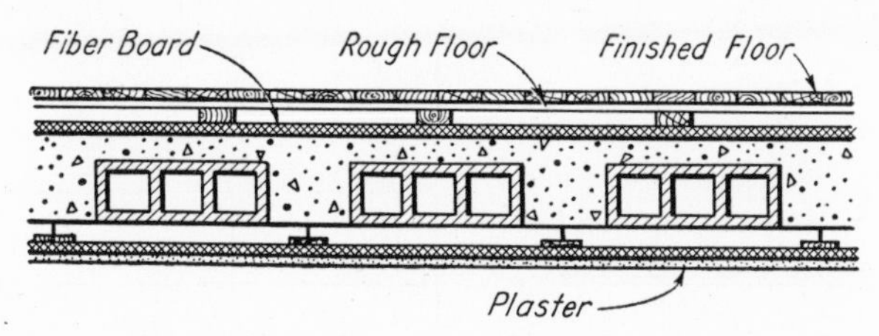

Fig. 30. Design for a "Floating" Floor. Redrawn from "Sound Insulation of Wall and Floor Construction," by V. L. Chrisler, *Report BMS* 17, 1939, National Bureau of Standards, United States Department of Commerce.

it is not customary to require highly developed designs in soundproof door construction, except for special types of occupancy, the entire door assembly should be checked from an acoustical viewpoint when placed in walls or partitions through which the passage of sound would be objectionable. A door should have a rating at least equal to the construction in which it is placed and be well fitted.

b. Airborne noises may pass through building assemblies such as exterior walls, floors, and partitions. This is due to the fact that the impact of successive sound waves, striking a surface such as a sheet of glass actually causes it to vibrate as a diaphragm. A part of the original energy of the sound waves is then transmitted to the air upon the other side. In the case of a floor, wall, or partition, vibrations are caused in the component materials which likewise transmit a portion of the energy to the other side of the assembly, where the vibration of the surface produces sound.

A "floating" floor, such as is shown in Fig. 30, is quite effective in lowering the transmission of airborne noises but much less satisfactory when subjected to impact. A combination of floating floor with a suspended ceiling, provided that the ceiling has a flexible support, has been shown by the Bureau of Standards tests to be a decided improvement. For broadcasting rooms a type of floated construction, involving springs and other special devices, has been used. Sound-insulating values of various assemblies are presented in the table on page 144 as sound-transmission losses. The transmission loss is given in decibels for an average of five or more

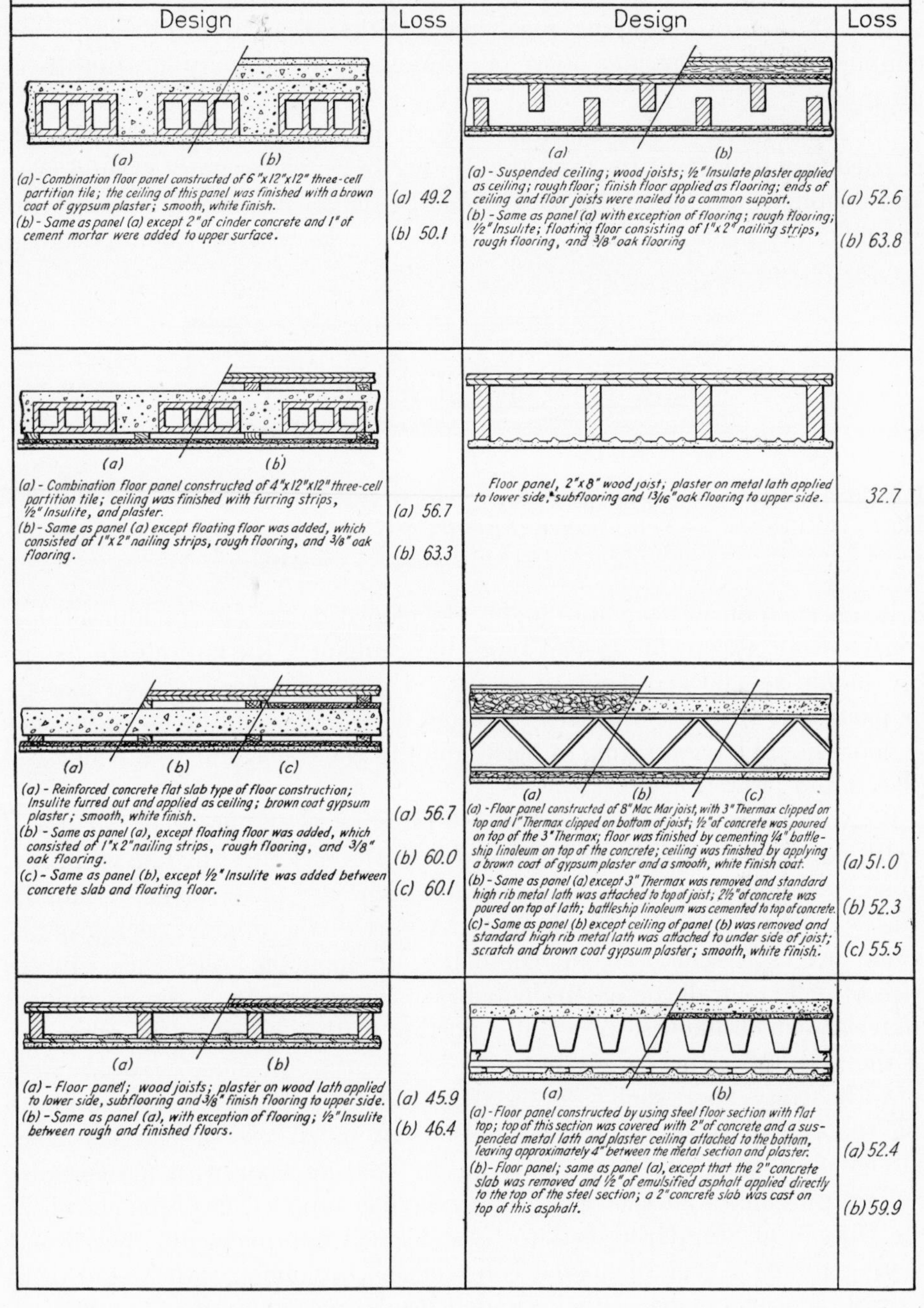

SOUND TRANSMISSION LOSS FOR VARIOUS FLOOR ASSEMBLIES IN DECIBELS FOR FIVE FREQUENCIES FROM 256 TO 1,024

Design	Loss	Design	Loss
(a) - Combination floor panel constructed of 6"x12"x12" three-cell partition tile; the ceiling of this panel was finished with a brown coat of gypsum plaster; smooth, white finish. (b) - Same as panel (a) except 2" of cinder concrete and 1" of cement mortar were added to upper surface.	(a) 49.2 (b) 50.1	(a) - Suspended ceiling; wood joists; ½" Insulate plaster applied as ceiling; rough floor; finish floor applied as flooring; ends of ceiling and floor joists were nailed to a common support. (b) - Same as panel (a) with exception of flooring; rough flooring; ½" Insulite; floating floor consisting of 1"x2" nailing strips, rough flooring, and 3/8" oak flooring	(a) 52.6 (b) 63.8
(a) - Combination floor panel constructed of 4"x12"x12" three-cell partition tile; ceiling was finished with furring strips, ½" Insulite, and plaster. (b) - Same as panel (a) except floating floor was added, which consisted of 1"x2" nailing strips, rough flooring, and 3/8" oak flooring.	(a) 56.7 (b) 63.3	Floor panel, 2"x8" wood joist; plaster on metal lath applied to lower side, subflooring and 13/16" oak flooring to upper side.	32.7
(a) - Reinforced concrete flat slab type of floor construction; Insulite furred out and applied as ceiling; brown coat gypsum plaster; smooth, white finish. (b) - Same as panel (a), except floating floor was added, which consisted of 1"x2" nailing strips, rough flooring, and 3/8" oak flooring. (c) - Same as panel (b), except ½" Insulite was added between concrete slab and floating floor.	(a) 56.7 (b) 60.0 (c) 60.1	(a) - Floor panel constructed of 8" Mac Mar joist, with 3" Thermax clipped on top and 1" Thermax clipped on bottom of joist; ½" of concrete was poured on top of the 3" Thermax; floor was finished by cementing ¼" battleship linoleum on top of the concrete; ceiling was finished by applying a brown coat of gypsum plaster and a smooth, white finish coat. (b) - Same as panel (a) except 3" Thermax was removed and standard high rib metal lath was attached to top of joist; 2½" of concrete was poured on top of lath; battleship linoleum was cemented to top of concrete. (c) - Same as panel (b) except ceiling of panel (b) was removed and standard high rib metal lath was attached to under side of joist; scratch and brown coat gypsum plaster; smooth, white finish.	(a) 51.0 (b) 52.3 (c) 55.5
(a) - Floor panel; wood joists; plaster on wood lath applied to lower side, subflooring and 3/8" finish flooring to upper side. (b) - Same as panel (a), with exception of flooring; ½" Insulite between rough and finished floors.	(a) 45.9 (b) 46.4	(a) - Floor panel constructed by using steel floor section with flat top; top of this section was covered with 2" of concrete and a suspended metal lath and plaster ceiling attached to the bottom, leaving approximately 4" between the metal section and plaster. (b) - Floor panel; same as panel (a), except that the 2" concrete slab was removed and ½" of emulsified asphalt applied directly to the top of the steel section; a 2" concrete slab was cast on top of this asphalt.	(a) 52.4 (b) 59.9

Reprinted from "Sound Insulation of Wall and Floor Construction," by V. L. Chrisler, *Report BMS* 17, 1939, and Supplement 1940, National Bureau of Standards, United States Department of Commerce.

frequencies. A decibel is the unit of sound intensity. For example, the intensity level of average conversation is often approximated as 45 decibels. Additional information will be found in the references from which these tables were abstracted.

c. Noise results from vibrations transmitted to the building frame. Such vibrations may be caused by street or railroad traffic or by pumps, blowers, and other machines located within the building and may necessitate the insulation of structural elements, such as building foundations, from the source of vibration. If a provision of this nature is necessary, it should be studied in the initial stage of design, as noted on page 56. There are two general means of insulating the structure from the source of such disturbance: an actual structural separation, or the introduction of nonhomogeneous materials chosen to impede the passage of vibrations.

Machines located within a building should be placed on resilient mountings or foundation beds designed to absorb vibrations of the particular frequency generated by the apparatus. The sound isolation of such installations is facilitated by placing them under, rather than over, rooms where their noise would be objectionable. Soft and yielding floor coverings are most helpful in reducing impact noises such as normally occur in residential and institutional buildings.

The elimination of objectionable sounds originating within a building requires not only a study of operating machines but also a careful review of all the mechanical installations. It is impossible to present any list which would be complete for a specific structure, but the designer should give particular attention to such matters as the grading of steam pipes, the sound deadening of soil lines, and the planning of ventilating systems to obtain comparatively low air velocities at the grilles. Sound-absorbent duct linings are also helpful but should be fire resistive and approved by the underwriters from the viewpoint of fire risk.

An excellent treatment of the entire subject of sound control from a very practical viewpoint is presented in *Acoustics of Buildings*, Third Edition, by F. R. Watson, John Wiley & Sons, 1941. Recommendations based upon British practice are given in *Principles of Modern Building*, Vol. 1, by R. Fitzmaurice, published by His Majesty's Stationery Office, 1939. Additional information may be obtained from the Acoustical Materials Association.

Article 8. Considerations Affecting the Choice of the Structural Floor System

As the various assemblies for self-supporting floors have been developed to meet specific architectural, structural, and fire-resistive requirements, the designer should bear in mind the particular characteristics of each system so that they may be compared with the demands for the building under design. Before proceeding to select the floor system it is therefore desirable to identify the matters which should be considered in making such a comparison.

Material Used for Framing. The designer has already decided between structural steel or reinforced concrete, with the possibility of wood framing for low buildings. This decision will be one of several guides in selecting the floor system, as it has been seen that some systems not only are particularly suited to steel or concrete but cannot be used except with one or the other. For example, buildings framed in structural steel cannot have the flat-slab or rigid-frame designs described on page 73, but any other system mentioned in this text can be used, from the heaviest short-span construction to a combustible wood-joist assembly. If the building is framed in reinforced concrete, any one of the systems noted as appropriate on pages 134 to 136 can be chosen.

The selection for wall-bearing buildings follows the type of interior framing as just described, with the exception that, if interior bearing walls are used, the flat-slab design with specified moment coefficients will be impossible. For such structures, however, the entire interior framing, particularly above the first floor, is often of wood or unprotected steel, and wood joists are a frequent choice. Such a design is illustrated on page 88. For wood-framed structures, wood joists, supported by wood framing, or unprotected steel girders and pipe columns, as shown on page 97, are the normal choice.

Size, Shape, and Continuity of Floor Panels. The distance which a floor system is required to span between adjacent supports may influence the choice, as the dead load of the heavier designs becomes excessive for the longer spans. The ratio of length to width of panel usually determines the advantage of a one-way as compared to a two-way system (see page 115). This same ratio of length to width and the requirement for continuity between at least three consecutive panels may preclude the use of the standard flat-slab design, as noted on page 75.

Need for Structural Stability. Such a requirement would be important for certain types of industrial occupancy where manufacturing processes cause vibration and would exclude consideration of the lighter systems, such as the open-truss steel joist. Where the effect of lateral forces due to wind or earthquakes is a factor in the design, preference is given to systems which have sufficient strength to act as stiffening elements of the building assembly.

Required Degree of Fire Resistance. As there is a wide range in the relative fire resistance of the structural floor systems, the designer should choose one that meets the demands of the local code or good practice for the location and type of occupancy. The selection should also be consistent, from the viewpoint of fire resistance, with the rest of the construction in order to obtain a favorable insurance rate on both building and contents. It should be remembered, however, that even a 4-hour rating may be obtained for comparatively vulnerable steel-plate designs by the use of a Vermiculite plaster carried by metal lath.

Light or Heavy Floor Loads. As almost every type of floor construction has been developed to meet economically the structural requirements of some specific load bracket, as noted in the preceding articles, the designer has another definite guide in his selection because he knows the type of occupancy and consequently the necessary live load. He has also developed a preliminary specification to the extent that the character and corresponding weight of the floor finish and ceiling treatment are known. Consequently, by adding these three weights, the superimposed load is obtained. This is the load to be used in even the preliminary choice of system. Furthermore, consideration should be given to the possibility of heavy concentrated loads or moving loads, to resist which certain systems are obviously more suitable than others.

Desirability of Flat Ceilings. This consideration involves the choice between a long- or a short-span system and was discussed in Chapter Three on page 66, as it affects the design of the floor framing.

Ceiling Finish. The character of the undersurfaces of the various floor systems should be considered in relation to the ceiling finish. Structural-clay tile, gypsum, Slagblok, and Haydite, such as illustrated in Figs. 2 and 6, provide an excellent base for two-coat plaster, whereas the metal-pan and steel-joist systems, Figs. 1 and 14, with lath beneath, require the equivalent of three coats. Stone-concrete slabs require only two coats of plaster, but the surface may be too smooth to furnish adequate bond. Where sprayed-paint applications are practicable, they can be economically finished with two coats of paint. Ceilings of long-span design can obviously be plastered more cheaply than similar short-span surfaces because of the labor of finishing around beams. If duct space is needed beneath the floor, a hung ceiling may be necessary. This requirement would favor a short-span design.

Floor Finish. At this point the designer should think of the electrical conduit or other pipes that may have to be concealed within the thickness of the floor. Aside from the possibility of using a hung ceiling, which is not an economical solution except for air ducts and larger pipes, there are two alternatives: choice of a system that provides space within the structural slab, or use of a fill between the slab and the finish floor. Any type of solid concrete slab cast-in-place is ideal for the accommodation of such utilities when used with a reinforced-concrete frame but generally requires a fill when used with steel, unless the slab is raised sufficiently to permit passing the conduit over the upper surfaces of the steel beams. Conduit and small pipes can often be run within the structural thickness of reinforced-concrete ribbed construction, but this may require increasing the thickness of the topping. They are easily accommodated within the typical open-truss steel-joist system and with precast concrete joists, unless the plastered ceiling is omitted. Several other designs, as noted in the text, are suitable for the accommodation of conduit. A study of the proposed section, in relation to the floor framing, will indicate when a fill is required. This consideration may influence the choice of system.

The suitability of the upper surface of the structural floor to receive the specified finish, or wearing surface, should also be evaluated in making comparisons. The entire design should be studied in order to select, not necessarily the most economical structural system, but the most economical assembly, comprising ceiling finish, structural floor, and floor finish, that will meet the architectural and engineering requirements.

WEIGHT OF FLOOR SYSTEM. A minor matter in buildings of only a few stories, but important in higher structures, is the dead load of the system itself. This consideration seldom governs the choice, except in borderline cases, but it should be remembered. The weights per square foot for the various floor designs can be computed from the weights of materials given in the table on page 14 or obtained from the manufacturer sponsoring the system. It is a simple matter to approximate the difference for two competing systems and to check the effect upon the supporting members. Such a computation should be carried out for one typical tier of interior columns down to and including the footing.

THICKNESS OF FLOOR SYSTEM. This matter is also of small importance for low buildings, but the designer should recognize the fact that every inch added to the floor thickness, from the face of ceiling to the surface of the finish, is an additional inch added to the height of every vertical element in the entire building. Where the required ceiling height must be computed to the lower faces of beams or girders, this matter may actually affect the choice of the floor system. It favors the flat-slab designs with their variations, and, where the principal beams can be placed over partitions, as is usual, the long-span systems are preferable to the short-span systems.

HEAT AND SOUND INSULATION. The choice of appropriate materials and methods for insulation against either heat loss or heat gain is not a structural matter but should be considered in connection with the structural elements. Although seldom of importance in relation to floor design, except beneath unheated spaces such as an attic or over an open veranda, the heat-insulating value of two competing designs or the facilities for installing insulating materials may have to be considered. The subject is discussed in relation to roofs and exterior walls on pages 173 and 269.

The acoustical requirements for diminishing sound transmission through a floor may influence the choice of structural design or demand a particular type of assembly, such as is illustrated on page 143. Even when the only requirement is the application of sound-absorbing ceiling surfaces, proper provision for their installation may affect the selection of the structural floor.

Comparative Estimates of Cost. A careful analysis of the various possible systems that may be employed for the structural floor design will usually result in reducing the practicable alternates to two or at most three types. The final step is to make sketches of the proposed assemblies to illustrate a typical floor panel, including the supporting members of the structural frame, which should be designed with reasonable accuracy. Accompanied by the necessary general information concerning building dimensions and plot conditions, the sketches should enable any competent builder familiar with the local situation to make a fairly accurate estimate of cost for each system. This estimate will permit the designer to make a final decision.

Chapter Five

CHOOSING THE STRUCTURAL ROOF SYSTEM

Many light-weight systems are available for both flat and pitched roofs. These systems vary considerably in length of span, weight, and adaptability to the application of surfacing materials. Other qualities, such as heat-insulating value or appearance of the undersurface, are often important. A suitable choice requires a thorough analysis of the entire roof assembly on an architectural, structural, and economic basis. Wide-span designs in steel, reinforced concrete, and wood are discussed in Chapter Six.

INTRODUCTION. The following articles describe the various types of structural roof systems, or roof decks, as they are often called, which are the most popular in this country at the present time or appear to have potential value. In this text a "system" identifies the structural assembly spanning between the framing members, such as beams, rafters, or principal purlins. The descriptions and the illustrations of each design indicate both their particular application and the type of framing required to furnish support. Maximum spans and limiting dimensions conform with standards generally accepted for the various systems but should be checked before final design because of the unfortunate variation in building-code requirements. A résumé of the considerations which should govern the choice of roof construction is presented in Article 10 of this chapter.

When selecting the floor system, the designer is primarily concerned with the material used as structural framing, the character and amount of the superimposed load, the span, the degree of fire resistance, and the general fitness of the design to meet economically the requirements of the entire building. In the case of "flat" roofs (the term identifies horizontal surfaces, or those only slightly sloped in one or more directions for the purpose of drainage) we have practically the same considerations except in regard to live load. This is seldom over 40 lb per sq ft unless the roof is intended for occupancy.

Pitched and curved roofs, except for wide-span designs such as those comprising rigid frames or bents, arches or domes of reinforced concrete, and certain applications of precast concrete members, are always framed in steel or wood. The same general considerations apply as in the case of flat roofs, but there is the additional and very important requirement of providing a deck to which the elements comprising the finished surface, such as shingles or slate, can be attached. For systems which furnish a finished roof surface, as well as a structural deck, such as the large cement-aggregate tile and sheets of corrugated metal, the reflection versus absorption of radiant heat may be a factor, as well as the coefficient of heat transmission. If surfaces are designed with a considerable pitch, structural reasons may favor types having the greater resistance to wind. In districts subject to earthquakes, those having the stronger connections between deck and framing elements are preferred.

As roofs form one of the enclosing surfaces of a building, the heat transmission is important where interior temperatures appreciably different from exterior temperatures are to be maintained for extended periods. A low transmission coefficient will obviously reduce the cost for additional insulation. The appearance of the undersurface, which varies considerably for different designs, or the probable cost of applying a desired finish is also important for some types of occupancy. The general subject of flashing is discussed on page 278, as it does not influence the choice of the structural roof system and should be carefully planned in relation to wall construction, but many of the details shown in this chapter illustrate good practice. In comparing the advantages of competing designs, the cost of maintenance should be included.

Article 1. General Considerations Applying to Pitched Roofs

The minimum desirable incline for wood, asbestos, or asphalt shingles, slate, and the ordinary types of roofing tile, such as the Spanish Imperial and Mission, is 6 in. vertical to 1 ft horizontal. If the slope is less, special provision is required to make the roof watertight, such as laying the slate in bitumen.[1]

"Built-up" roofing, comprising usually either three or four layers of roofing felt, cemented together with coal-tar pitch or asphalt, and surfaced with slag or gravel, is used principally for flat roofs but may be laid on any slope up to 4 in. to 1 ft if "nailability" is provided. This is ordinarily accomplished by employing a type of roof deck which has good nail penetration and retention, but the roofing may be nailed into a suitable insulation if the insulation is cemented with bitumen to the roof deck. If the slope is less than 2 in. to 1 ft, nailing is not required. This is the usual condition for flat-roof designs. Roofs sloped more than 4 in. to 1 ft may be surfaced with a wide-salvage type of roll-roofing or with a built-up roofing laid in either hot bitumen or cold plastic cement, but without slag or

[1] An absolute minimum recommended for standard wood shingles is 4 in. vertical to 1 ft horizontal. Slate may be laid to a pitch somewhat less than 6 in. vertical to 1 ft horizontal, if the "head-lap" is increased from 3 in. to 4 in.

gravel. In both cases nailing is required. Roll-roofing has a mineralized surface available in a number of colors. It has been used for roofing concrete arches such as the field house at Swarthmore College, Pennsylvania.

Thin sheet metals like copper and aluminum can be used on a slope of ¼ in. per ft or greater, provided that the proper type of seam is specified, but are more appropriate for steeper surfaces. Sheets of corrugated metal and corrugated cement-asbestos board, serving both as a structural roof deck and surface finish, should generally have a minimum slope of 4 in. to 1 ft. Interlocking steel-plate designs, when occasionally used in the same manner without a membrane covering, are difficult to make tight on slopes less than 3 in. to 1 ft.

Article 2. Pitched-Roof Systems for Steel Framing

Except for the wide-span designs described in Chapter Six, steel assemblies ordinarily comprise structural-steel rafters with or without a system of purlins and, if necessary, subpurlins, supporting some type of precast slab, composition, glass, or sheet-metal unit which forms the structural deck of the roof. Wood plank are occasionally used. The more popular precast designs are described in the following paragraphs. Cast-in-place systems are occasionally employed on roofs of moderate pitch but are seldom the best choice.

PRECAST CEMENT-AGGREGATE SLABS AND CHANNEL SECTIONS. Several types of light-weight units, precast of portland cement and aggregates, such as Haydite, blast-furnace slag, and slag products, are widely employed for structural roof decks over steel framing. A flat slab of 2½-in. thickness is used on spans up to about 5 ft, but the more popular designs, suitable for longer spans, are of channel shape. Standard units are manufactured by many firms, with a wide geographical distribution, for a purlin spacing of 8 to 12 ft, and heavier units for longer spans, up to approximately 20 ft between supports, are furnished by some manufacturers. All are thoroughly reinforced.

These designs are appropriate for roofs surfaced with slate, clay tile, and other ornamental materials, as well as those protected by built-up or roll-roofing. The weight per square foot of the slab or channel section varies from about 12 to 30 lb. Excellent nailing and nail retention are provided when required by casting a special material 1¼ in. thick monolithically with the top surface. Some designs furnish a layer of insulating or acoustical material cast integrally with the concrete on the underside. Such finishes are available in a number of shades. Vermiculite plaster, a highly fire-resistant product derived from micaceous minerals, may be placed on the upper surface for heat insulation, as shown in Fig. 1, or on the bottom for acoustical improvement. Figure 2 shows a typical application to pitched-roof construction. The precast cored design, described on page 120, is also appropriate for pitched surfaces and saw-tooth construction, as shown in Fig. 3. This design would be economical where the same type of unit was used for the flat areas of the roof deck.

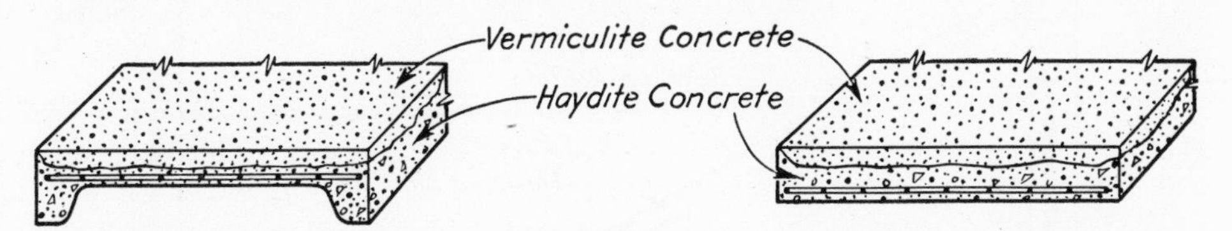

FIG. 1. Light-Weight Aggregate Slabs with Monolithic Insulation. Courtesy, Truscon Steel Company.

A type of roofing slab which requires no surface protection is identified as "red rib-tile," the upper surface being red. Such slabs are popular for industrial buildings. The undersurface is the gray color of the cement-Haydite mixture. A standard size is 24 in. wide, 52 in. long, and 1⅛ in. thick. The tiles cover an area of 8 sq ft, resting directly upon steel purlins,

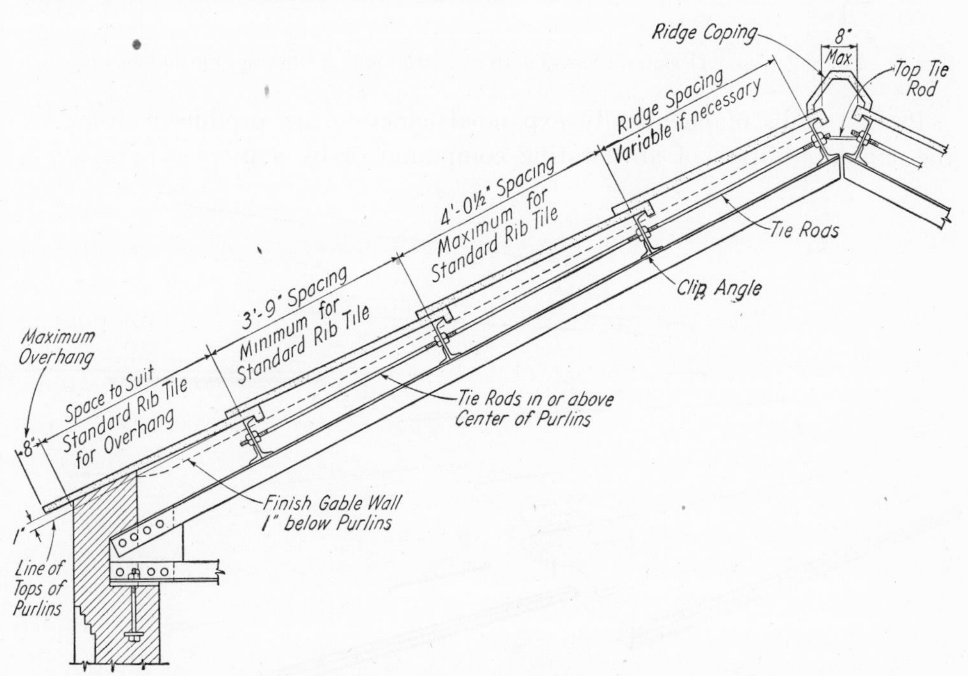

FIG. 2. Roof Deck of Rib-Tile. Courtesy, Truscon Steel Company.

over which they are hooked. Special sizes are available. Weight is 16 lb per sq ft. Tile may be shaped as shown in Fig. 4, which also illustrates the inclusion of glass panels. These are of wire glass embedded in the concrete during manufacture. Each slab is provided with its own condensation gutter. As they are of an interlocking type and of the same dimensions as the standard units, any amount of daylighting may be obtained without special framing.

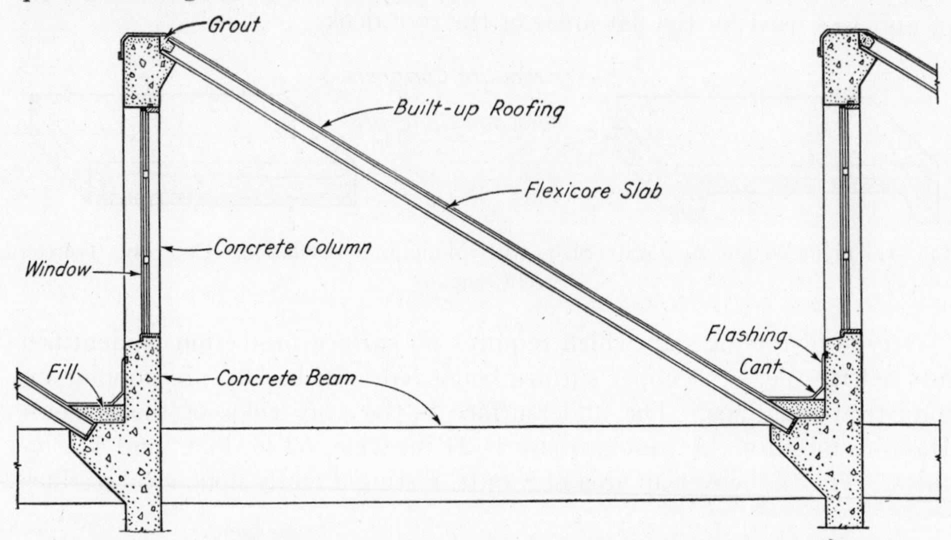

Fig. 3. Precast, Cored Design on Saw-Tooth Construction. Courtesy, Flexicore Company.

Precast slabs of chemically expanded concrete are produced either by the simple addition of an aerating compound or by a process in which a

Fig. 4. Interlocking Roof Tile with Glass Insert Panels. Courtesy, Federal American Cement Tile Company.

"foam" ingredient is beaten up with portland cement and an appropriate mineral aggregate. They are available in the same plain-slab units and channel sections as just described for Haydite or other light-weight aggregate designs. For example, one manufacturer supplies plain slabs which are 24 in. wide and from 2 to 3½ in. thick. They are of suitable length for spans up to 5 or 6 ft between purlins or other supports. Channel sections are of the same width and are 3½ in. deep for spans up to an extreme limit of 10 ft. All are thoroughly reinforced. They compete with the Haydite or other designs, employing merely a light-weight aggregate without aerating compound or special process. The availability of all such products manufactured by proprietary methods should be checked by the designer before their use is considered.

PRECAST GYPSUM TILE AND PLANK. Solid units 3 × 12 × 30 in. in size, supported by subpurlins of special inverted T-section to provide adequate bearing for the slabs, or tiles, as they are often called, are also appropriate for pitched-roof decks. These units have the same general application as the cement-aggregate slabs but are not widely used at the present time. The gypsum tile are reinforced top and bottom with welded-wire mesh. A typical design, employing bulb-tee subpurlins, can support a superimposed load of 35 lb per sq ft of roof surface on a rafter spacing up to nearly 8 ft. Slate of moderate thickness or clay tile are retained by nailing into the gypsum. Solid gypsum units, 3 in. thick, weigh 17 lb per sq ft.

Hollow gypsum units 3 and 4 in. thick and of the same horizontal dimensions are also available. They have a slightly greater insulating value than the solid tile and are considerably lighter in weight but are appropriate only for comparatively flat roofs, as they do not provide nailing facilities. Gypsum plank can be used on pitched roofs, but their chief application is for the comparatively flat surfaces and extensive roof areas of industrial plants, for which they are very popular. They are described in Article 3.

CEMESTO BOARD. This material, previously mentioned on page 106 in connection with prefabrication, can be used on pitched roofs but is particularly appropriate for flat roofs in designs such as is shown on page 166.

CAST-IN-PLACE SYSTEMS. In the past, extremely dry mixtures of cinder concrete, reinforced with steel rods or welded-wire mesh, were used even on comparatively steep slopes. Nailing was obtained by embedment of wood strips, or a 2-in. layer of nailing concrete was spread over the surface. This was a slow operation, and since the improvement of precast units, furnishing adequate nail penetration and nail retention, there is seldom economy in using any cast-in-place design on other than comparatively flat roofs except in the case of concrete arches, which are discussed in Chapter Six.

CLAY-TILE SLABS. A clay-tile unit, identified as a "book-tile" because of its interlocking design, has for many years been used for structural roof decks having a close subpurlin spacing. The tile are 3 in. thick,

12 in. wide, and from 11 to 24 in. long. The standard 18-in. and 24-in. lengths require subpurlin spacings of 19 in. and 25 in. respectively. Although generally more expensive than the precast gypsum or cement-aggregate slabs, and not extensively employed at present, they form an excellent roof of considerable structural strength. Their particular application is for types of industry where water drip due to condensation, or the spalling of the undersurface of the roof, might be particularly troublesome.

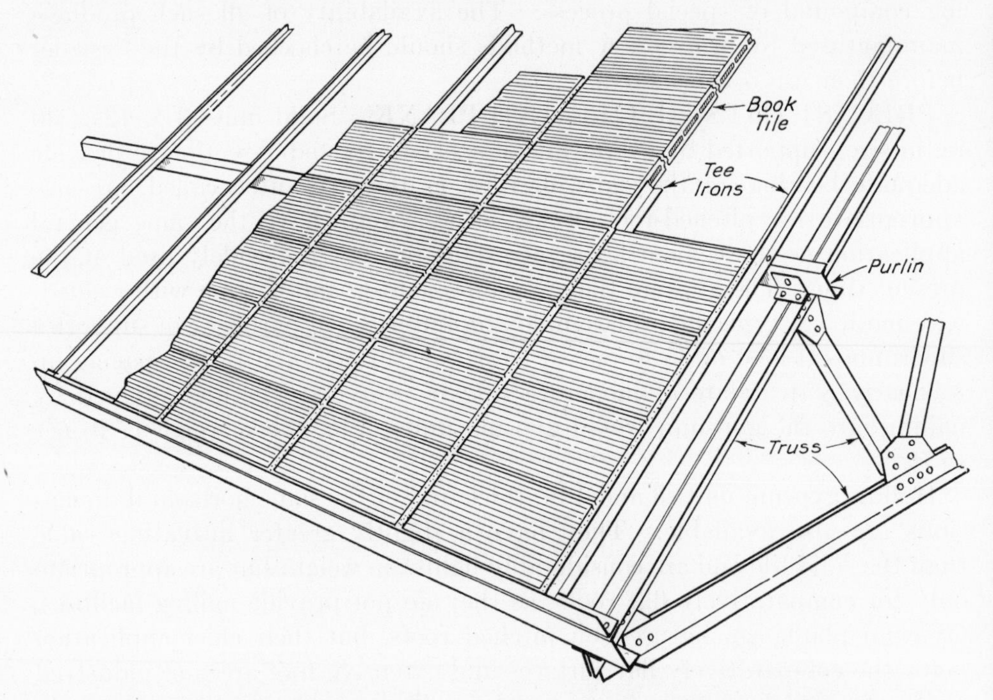

Fig. 5. Roof Deck of Clay Tile. Courtesy, National Fireproofing Company.

Figure 5 shows a typical design. An appropriate type of felt roofing would be used for surface waterproofing.

CORRUGATED CEMENT-ASBESTOS BOARD. This material, usually composed of about 85 per cent portland cement to 15 per cent by weight of asbestos fiber, is fire resistant and has low heat transmission and good surface reflection. It can be used without other covering for roofs having a minimum slope of 2 in. vertical to 12 in. horizontal, but a steeper pitch is preferable. The average thickness is $\frac{3}{8}$ in.; sheets are usually 3 ft 6 in. wide and from 3 to 10 ft long. Weight is about 4 lb per sq ft. Maximum purlin spacing for standard types is 4 ft 6 in. Sheets are lapped one corrugation at sides and 6 in. at ends. When used over steel framing, they are attached to purlins by means of clips and bolts. Units of the same material are furnished for ridges, eaves, and other special requirements. This type of roof deck has its particular application to industrial buildings but may also be appropriate for other kinds of occupancy. It has been used for gymnasiums, auditoriums, and even small dwellings.

CORRUGATED WIRE GLASS. For work where day-lighting is essential, sheets of corrugated glass reinforced with wire are furnished in widths of about 2 ft 4 in. and of length to span between purlins spaced up to 5 ft on

Fig. 6. Roof Deck of Corrugated Glass Panels. Courtesy, H. H. Robertson Company.

centers. Two types of glass are available: the white and the actinic, which has an amber color. The actinic glass diminishes the effect of the radiant heat from direct sunlight. Corrugated glass should not be used on slopes less than 4 in. vertical to 12 in. horizontal. At least this pitch is essential to permit the condensation gutters to function. When properly installed, the surfaces are practically self-cleansing.

Unlike the corrugated cement-asbestos units, which are often used in conjunction with corrugated glass panels, sheets are not lapped at the sides but are assembled ½ in. apart. A metal cover cap protects the joint. On the cheaper types of work this is of galvanized steel, but copper, aluminum, Monel metal, and stainless steel are used where the additional expense is warranted. The same metals are employed for ridge caps and other special

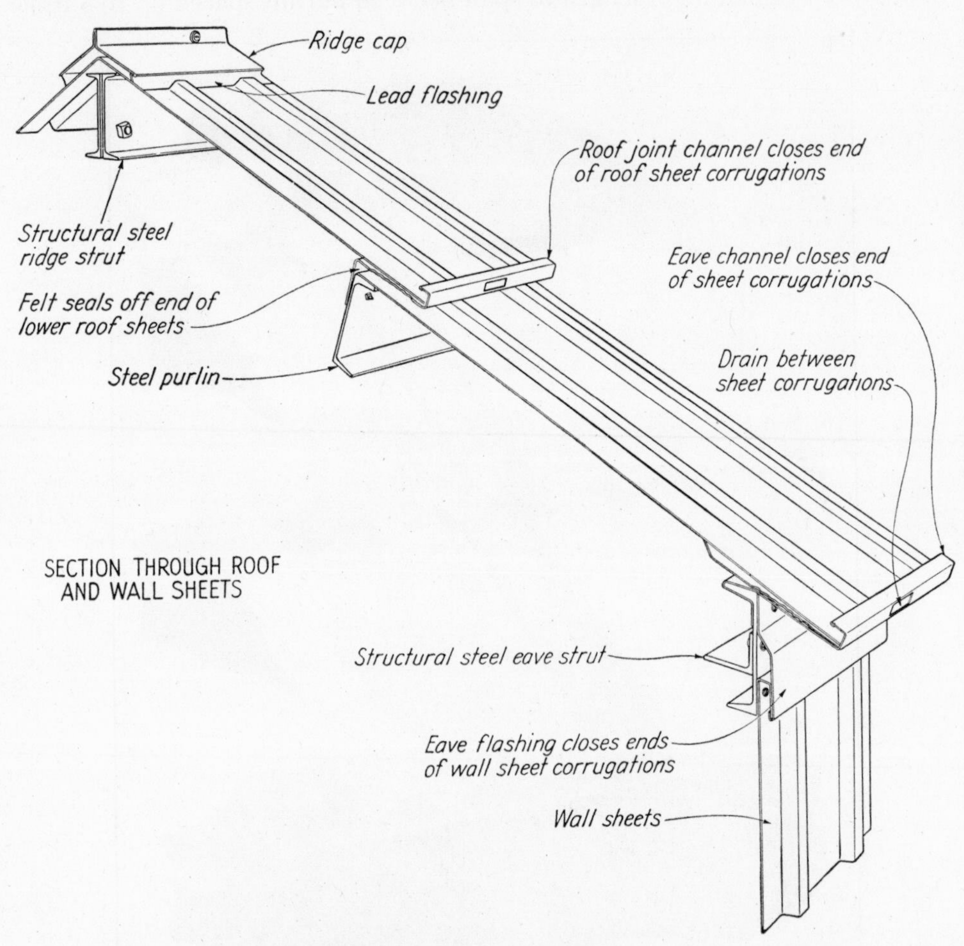

Fig. 7. Corrugated Metal Roof Deck. Courtesy, Blaw-Knox Company.

requirements. End laps of 3 in. are made over purlins, to which the sheets are clipped and bolted. This type of roof deck has a general application where day-lighting is essential and is widely used for large skylights or saw-tooth construction so often demanded in industrial buildings. It is also appropriate for museums and art galleries. Figure 6 shows a typical design.

CORRUGATED METAL AND STEEL ROOF DECKS. Many types of corrugated metal sheets are used to form roof decks over steel purlins or steel or wood rafters. These materials have their particular application to the pitched roofs of one-story industrial buildings and are popular for the cheaper types of work. Details are shown in Fig. 7. Corrugated, galvanized steel or iron is available in standard-sized sheets. Zinc alloys furnish a more durable surface which does not require painting. Cold-rolled hard copper can also be used, but a copper-clad corrugated steel sheet with a layer of asbestos felt cemented with asphalt between the two metals is more generally applicable. The asbestos felt is helpful as insulation. Another popular design is of similar construction but surfaced with a

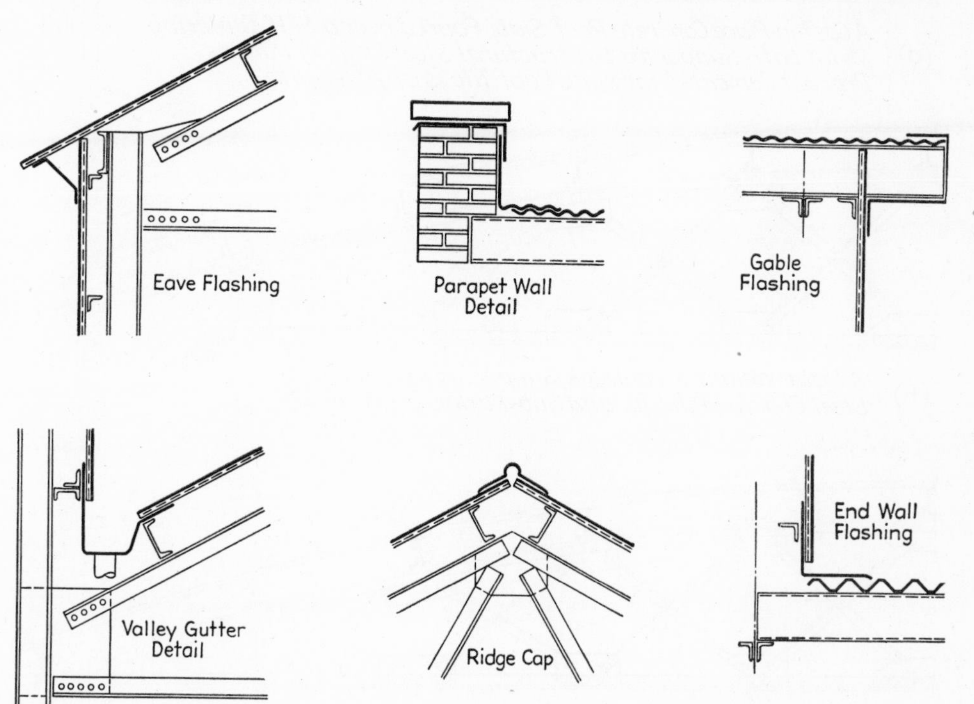

Fig. 8. Typical Details for Protected Metal Roofing. Courtesy, H. H. Robertson Company.

bituminous and felt, factory-applied sealing coat, which may be left in its natural black or maroon color or painted. Details are shown in Fig. 8.

The plain corrugated metal designs require a purlin spacing varying from 2 ft 6 in. for the 16-oz copper to about 5 ft for the steel and zinc alloys. Side connections between sheets, which vary in width from about 2 to 3 ft, are generally made by lapping the corrugations, but some copper designs employ a joint cover like a ridge cap. End connections are made by a 4-in. to 6-in. lap. Sheets may usually be obtained of any desired length up to 10 ft. The built-up designs, comprising corrugated steel, insulation, and surface protection, have very obvious advantages over the bare steel sheets from the viewpoint of permanence and heat transmission. Purlin spacing for various gage thicknesses of a typical type varies from 10 ft for an 18-gage steel to 7 ft for a 24-gage steel.

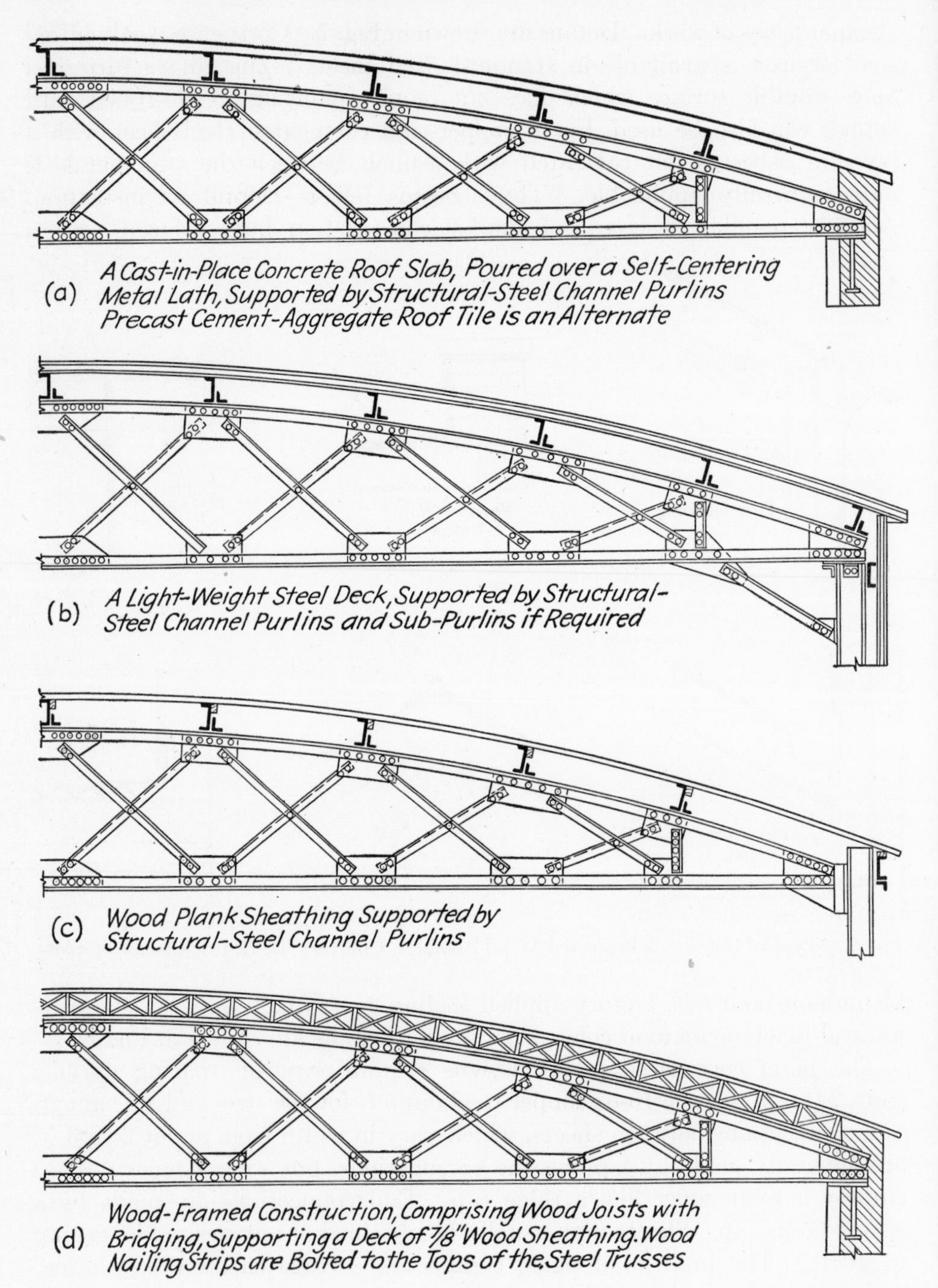

FIG. 9. Four Types of Roof Decks over Steel Trusses. Courtesy, George L. Mesker & Company.

Some of the more modern steel deck designs, such as that illustrated on page 169, are appropriate for the pitched roofs of industrial buildings or other structures where the architectural appearance can be accepted, but as their chief application is for flat roofs, they are described on page 167. The thin sheet metals, such as copper and aluminum, except the corrugated designs described above, are used for surface finishes and not for structural roof decks.

WOOD PLANK. A 2-in. nominal thickness is sometimes used for pitched-roof decks over steel framing with a purlin spacing up to 6 or 8 ft, but one of the systems described above is usually a better choice except when the support is furnished by wood trusses, arches, or rigid frames of wood.

Figure 9 shows four types of roof decks appropriate for use over steel bowstring trusses. The cast-in-place concrete slab (*a*) is probably the least desirable but can be used on slight slopes. A surface protection, such as built-up or roll roofing, would be required in all cases. Insulation is often necessary, particularly beneath a steel deck, as shown in sketch (*b*).

Article 3. Pitched-Roof Systems for Wood Framing

Wood is generally used for roof framing above walls similarly built and for wall-bearing construction having an interior framing of wood. It is also used occasionally for semi-fire-resistant buildings. In this case the floor immediately below the roof is of noncombustible construction and considered a firestop. Slate, tile, or other noncombustible material being used as a surface finish provides considerable protection from an exterior fire.

The structural design of such roofs is well standardized and may be found in many reference books. The roof deck, supported by wood rafters, can be solid boarding, plywood, various composition boards such as laminated Sheetrock, or shingle lath. Shingle lath is customarily used under wood shingles, as it provides better ventilation than a solid surface. Solid boarding, however, may be used under wood shingles for the purpose of obtaining a warmer roof and is common practice beneath other conventional roof-surfacing materials when supported by wood framing. Boards are usually matched, either tongue-and-groove or shiplap. A ⅞-in. thickness is standard.

A layer of roofing felt and sometimes insulation is placed beneath the tile, slate, or asbestos shingles which are retained by nailing into the wood deck. Where Sheetrock is used, it must be covered by built-up waterproofing or a type of roll-roofing. Some styles of tile and some sheet-metal designs require wood battens. Corrugated sheets of steel, asbestos-protected steel, copper, zinc, corrugated asbestos board, or corrugated glass can also be used over wood rafters. The various proprietary designs formed of sheet steel, as described on page 167, are a possibility but are much more appropriate for steel framing.

Article 4. General Considerations Applying to Flat Roofs

Roofs intended for recreational or other uses require live loads equal to corresponding types of occupancy. If the addition of future stories is probable, the roof is designed as a structural floor, provision being made for the extension of columns. Even aside from such special requirements, it is often desirable, as mentioned in Chapter Three, to use the same structural system for the roofs of multistory buildings as for the floors. This is usually a good choice unless the roof design involves large skylights, saw-tooth construction, or other structural assemblies which cannot be built economically by the same methods. The broadest application for the light-weight types of roof construction described in the following paragraphs is in the one-story, steel-framed industrial building and other large roof areas.

When the design of the structural roof is similar to that of the floors, the roof deck, except for wood-framed assemblies, should usually be laid without slope. If it is desired to pitch the finished surface, which should be done at least around points of drainage, a light-weight fill is used. This should be kept to the minimum thickness required for grade except where a greater depth is warranted for the purpose of insulation. Built-up waterproofing with a slag or gravel finish is then laid over the entire assembly, which would normally include insulation and vapor seal as described on page 173. As usually applied, roofing gravel weighs 400 and slag 300 lb per square (100 sq ft). Gravel is appropriate for pitches up to about 2 in. to 1 ft; slag for steeper pitches, as the angularity of the particles lessens the probability of its rolling. If the roof is intended for occupancy, the slag or gravel is omitted, and the desired surface finish laid over the waterproofing.

When the design of the structural roof comprises a light-weight system, the framing is sloped to provide drainage, and no fill is required.

Article 5. Flat-Roof Systems for Steel Framing

If the same design used for the floors is retained for the roof, any system described in Articles 1 and 2 of Chapter Four may be appropriate. Where it is desired to employ a light-weight system, one of the following can be chosen.

PRECAST GYPSUM TILE AND PLANK. Any type of precast gypsum tile described in Article 2 as suitable for pitched roofs can be used on flat roofs, but nailing facilities are not necessary. The most popular gypsum unit for flat roofs is the plank. Standard sizes are 2 × 15 in. × 10 ft and 2 × 15 in. × 8 ft. Steel-bound and reinforced with welded, galvanized steel mesh, they are of tongue-and-groove design and readily clipped to the supporting purlins spaced from 30 in. to about 6 ft, as required by the superimposed load. They weigh 12 lb per sq ft. Plank are surfaced with a built-up waterproofing, and insulation can be placed between the

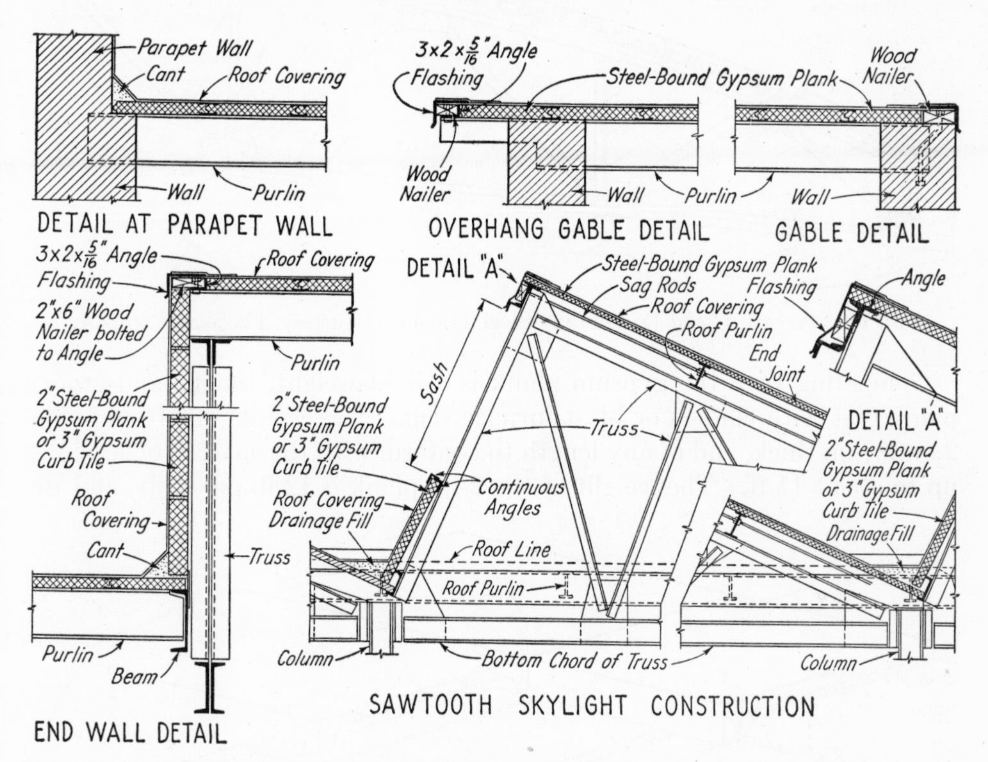

FIG. 10. Typical Details for Gypsum Plank Roof Decks. Courtesy, United States Gypsum Company.

two if desired. Figure 10 shows a typical assembly for a flat roof and for saw-tooth construction. Their light weight and ease of erection make them very popular for industrial use, but they should not be placed in locations where they will be subjected to moisture or high humidity.

PRECAST CEMENT-AGGREGATE UNITS. Any type of precast cement-aggregate unit described in Article 2 as suitable for pitched roofs can be used on flat roofs. Figure 11 shows Flexicore slabs placed over steel trusses, and Fig. 12 a channel design composed of light-weight aggregate. As in the case of the gypsum products, a built-up waterproofing is required over the roof deck, and units adapted to nailing would not be chosen. This fact opens the field for stone-aggregate slabs, which are manufactured for spans up to about 10 ft between supports. They are composed of a high-grade concrete, reinforced with welded-wire mesh. As such slabs are considerably heavier than gypsum plank, Porete, or Haydite and similar light-weight aggregate slabs or channel sections, they are chosen only where special conditions or price favors their use.

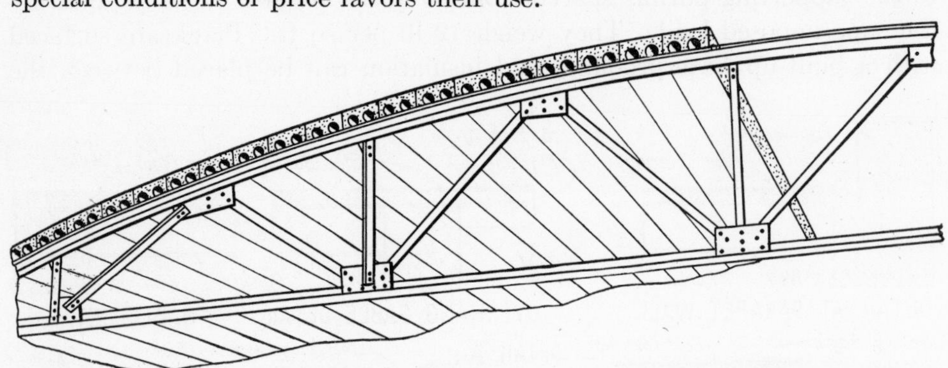

FIG. 11. Precast, Cored Design over Steel Trusses. Courtesy, Flexicore Company.

Competing with the gypsum plank is a light-weight, tongue-and-groove plank cast with cinders or blast-furnace slag. These units are 16 in. wide, 2 or 2¾ in. thick, and of any length to conform with the spacing of supports up to about 11 ft. The weight of the 2-in. plank is 12 lb per sq ft, and the

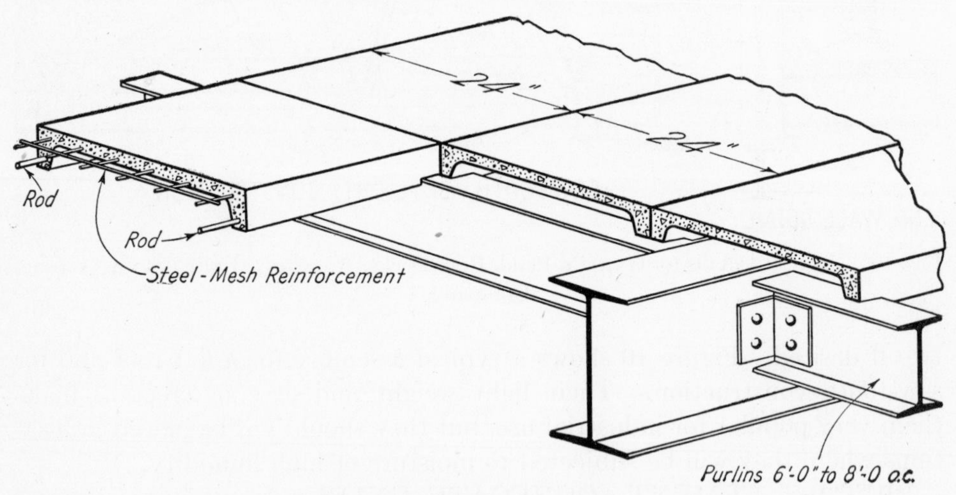

FIG. 12. Roof Deck of Light-Weight Aggregate Channel-Slabs. Courtesy, Dextone Company.

top surface may be prepared for nailing. This depth is used on purlin spans up to 7 ft for superimposed loads of about 50 lb per sq ft.

Material identified by the manufacturers as Porex combines a mineralized wood fiber with portland cement to produce a uniformly porous and fire-resistant slab which has good heat insulation and sound absorption. These slabs are about 7 ft long, 1 ft 20 in. wide, and 1¾ in. thick. They may be supported by U-shaped subpurlins 22 in. on centers, spanning between the beams or principal purlins of a steel-framed roof as shown in Fig. 13. The total weight of this assembly, composed of the Porex slab, ¼-in. cement-mortar finish, and subpurlins, is 9 lb per sq ft. The maximum span between rafters or principal purlins is 8 ft. Built-up roofing is laid directly over the cement-mortar finish. The Porete products have been shipped to many sections of the country, but as all are manufactured in New Jersey, the designer should check their availability before planning to use them.

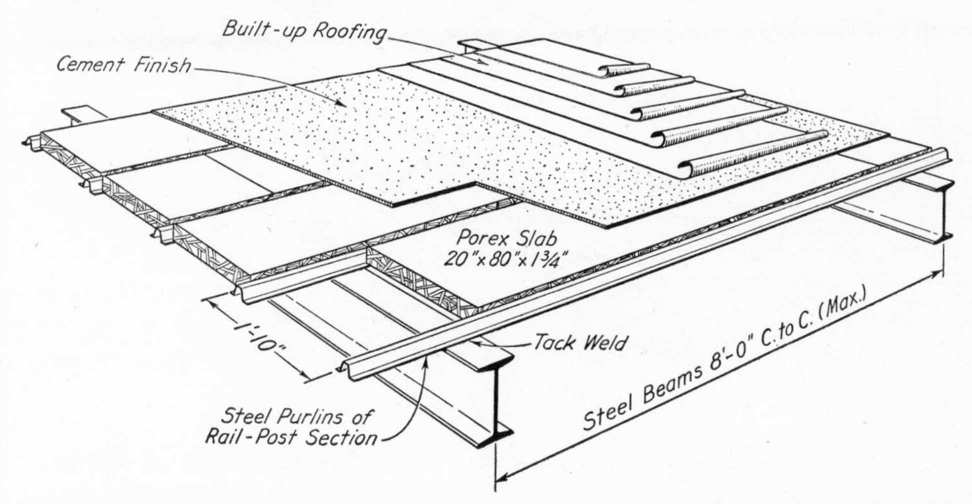

Fig. 13. Roof Deck of Precast Porex Slabs. Courtesy, Porete Manufacturing Company.

CEMESTO BOARD. The standard width is 4 ft. Lengths vary from 4 to 12 ft. The 1⁹⁄₁₆-in. and 2-in. thicknesses are appropriate for roof decks. Corresponding weights are 4.8 and 5.3 lb per sq ft. The Cemesto section, composed of Celotex cane fiber surfaced on both sides with ⅛-in. cement-asbestos board, provides considerable insulating value combined with an attractive, light gray undersurface. A 4-ft purlin spacing is used. Support may be furnished by rolled-steel sections or open-truss steel joists. Figure 14 shows the open-truss design with wood nailers. Figure 15 shows an application over either steel or wood.

CORRUGATED CEMENT-ASBESTOS BOARD. The application of this material to pitched roofs, for which it serves as both a roof deck and surface finish, was described on page 156. It is also employed as a deck on flat roofs. In this case it is covered by a built-up waterproofing. One or more layers of rigid insulation, laid over the corrugated board, provides a smooth surface, and additional insulation is often obtained by filling the corrugations with granulated cork and asphalt as shown in Fig. 16.

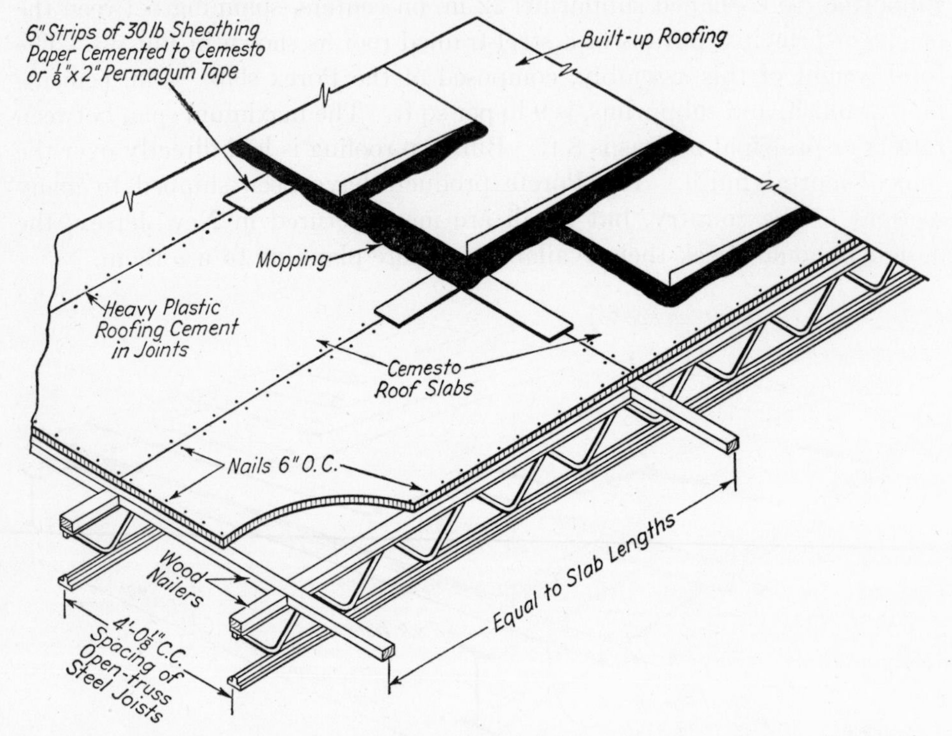

FIG. 14. Cemesto Slabs over Open-Truss Steel Joists. Courtesy, Celotex Corporation.

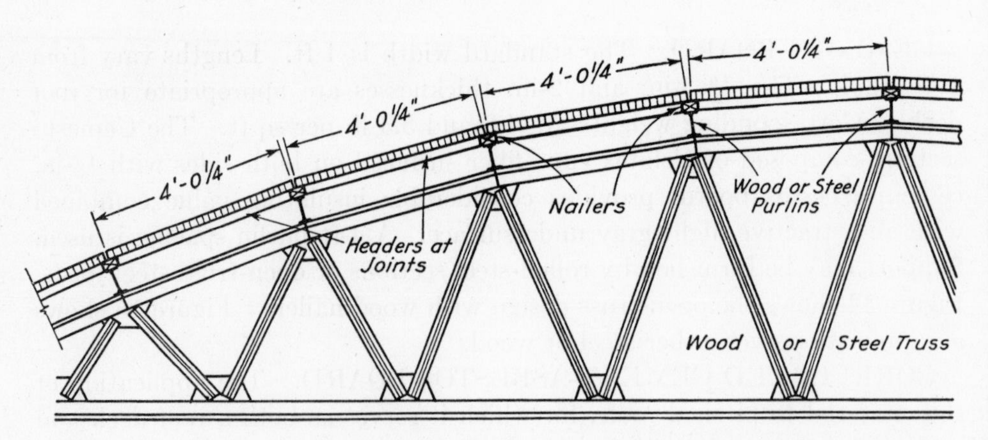

FIG. 15. Cemesto Slabs over Bow-String Trusses. Courtesy, Celotex Corporation.

STEEL ROOF DECKS. For comparatively flat roofs, particularly for one-story structures with steel framing, roof decks composed of inter-

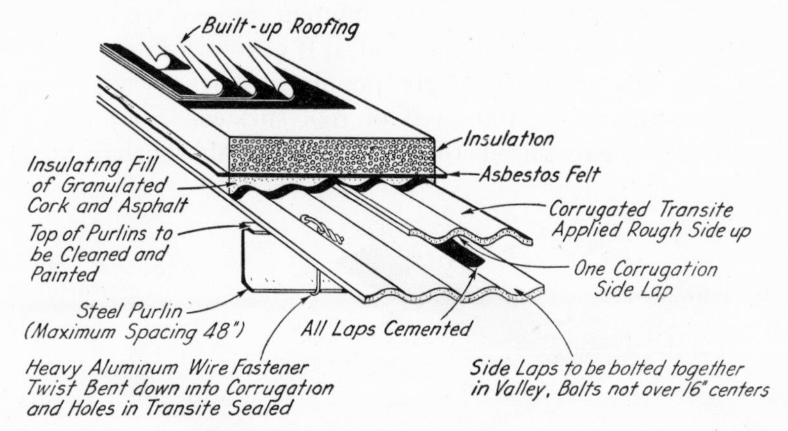

FIG. 16. Corrugated Cement-Asbestos Boards on Flat-Roof Construction. Courtesy, Johns-Manville.

locking plates have a broad application. Although most popular for industrial work, they are often appropriate for other kinds of occupancy, such as public buildings. Economical in first cost and speedily erected, some types may be combined with any required degree of insulation or acoustical treatment. They are surfaced with a built-up waterproofing as shown in Fig. 17.

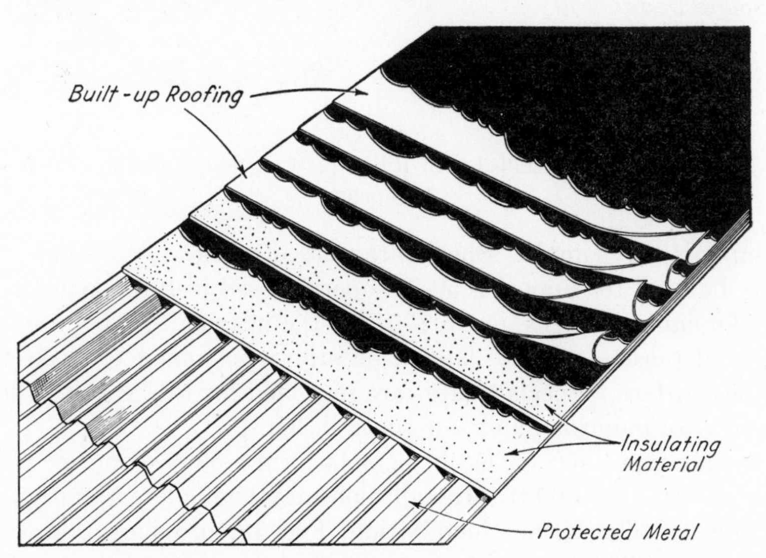

FIG. 17. Corrugated Protected Metal on Flat-Roof Construction. Courtesy, H. H. Robertson Company.

The units comprising a steel deck vary considerably in the different designs. Widths are usually 12 to 16 in., and the depth of ribs is from $1\frac{1}{2}$

to 2 in. for the shallower or lighter types and from 3 to 5½ in. for those intended for longer spans. Manufactured of copper-bearing steel or iron, in thicknesses from 22 to 16 gage, the different styles vary in weight from approximately 200 to over 600 lb per 100 sq ft of roof surface. The 18- and 20-gage thicknesses are particularly popular. They weigh respectively about 320 and 240 lb per 100 sq ft of roof surface. Shop-painted with baked-on enamel or galvanized, they present a durable surface finish.

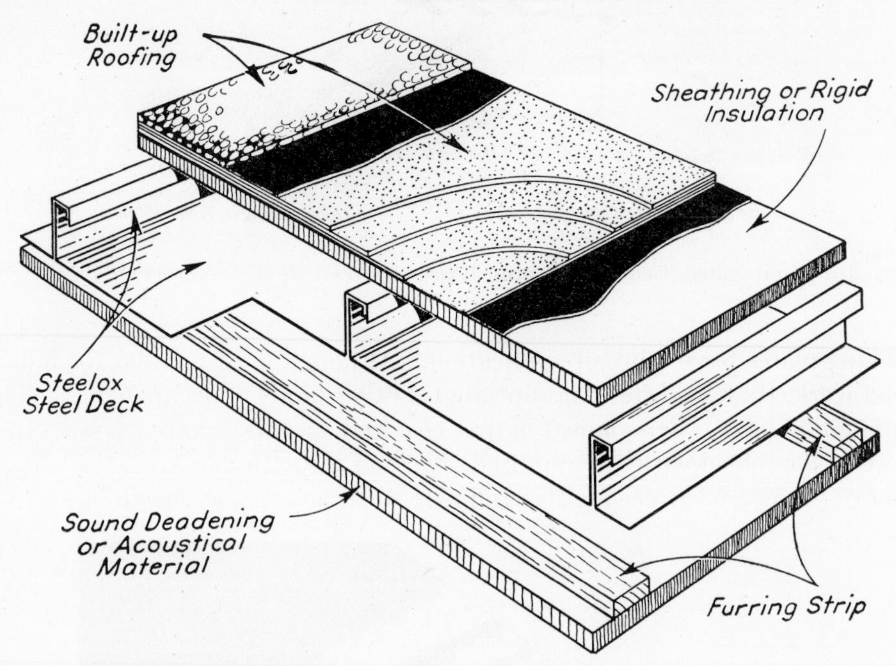

Fig. 18. Steel Roof Deck Installed with Ribs Up. Courtesy, The American Rolling Mill Company.

Assembly is very simple. Sheets are welded to the steel beams or purlins and may be used to support a 50-lb superimposed load on spans from 4 to 5 ft for the lighter designs, up to 25 ft for the heavier. Plates usually span over several purlins and are lapped or otherwise joined to make a tight, continuous surface. Special plates are provided for ridges and valleys, the construction of monitors, and saw-tooth designs.

The lighter types may be easily bent to form a curved surface where the radius is not less than 60 ft. Installation may be made with either ribs up or ribs down. The former installation, Fig. 18, provides a smooth steel ceiling on the soffit but requires some type of sheathing on top, which may be steel or iron sheets, wood, or preferably a rigid insulation laid over the tops of the ribs to serve as a base for the built-up waterproofing. Such an arrangement has the advantage of providing space between the ribs for additional insulation. If the units are assembled with ribs down, Fig. 19, a smooth top surface is available upon which rigid insulation is usually placed beneath the waterproofing. If the appearance or sound reflection

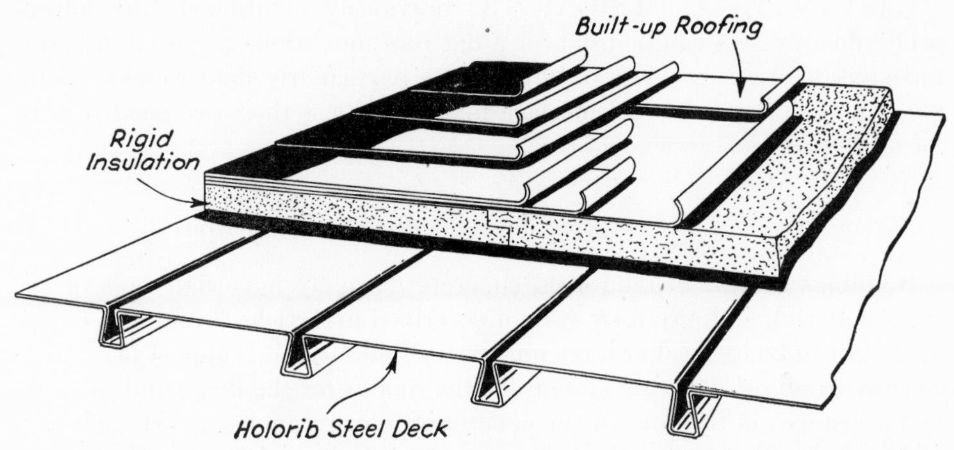

FIG. 19. Steel Roof Deck Installed with Ribs Down. Courtesy, Detroit Steel Products Company.

of the ribbed ceiling is objectionable, various combinations of acoustical materials or additional insulation may be applied to the lower surface.

A very interesting assembly designed particularly for industrial buildings is shown in Fig. 20. The advantages are low heat transmission, excel-

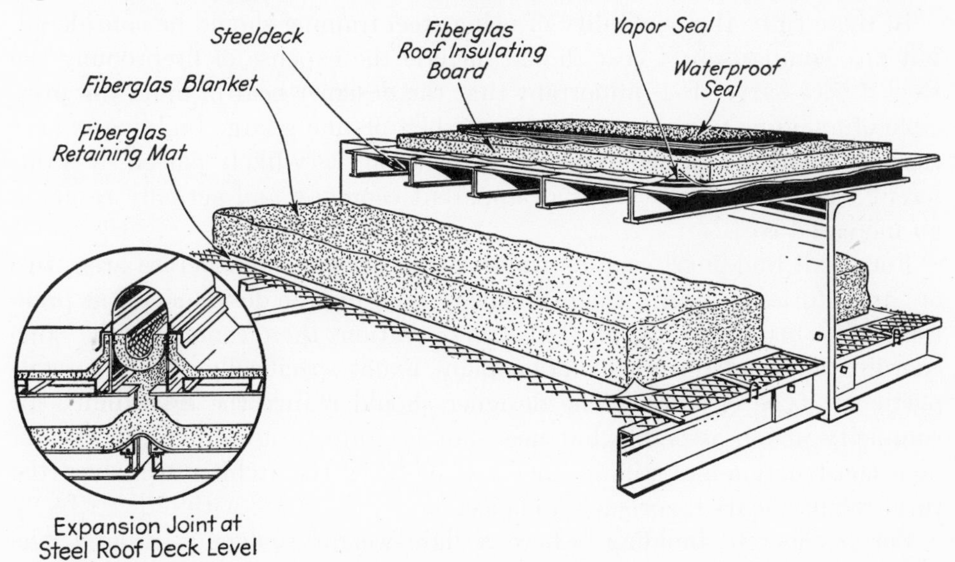

FIG. 20. Steel Deck Assembly with Fiberglas Insulation. Courtesy, Truscon Steel Company.

lent sound absorption, a surface which greatly assists in shadowless lighting, and one that is both fire and shatter resistant. With slight modifications to meet special conditions, this assembly has been used successfully in a number of manufacturing plants.

CAST-IN-PLACE DESIGNS. As previously mentioned, any appropriate floor system can be used for a flat roof, but where a special design is introduced for the purpose of obtaining a particularly light-weight assembly, it is best to avoid cast-in-place material unless there are good reasons for such a choice.

Article 6. Flat-Roof Systems for Concrete Framing

Buildings framed in reinforced concrete normally have flat roofs of the same material, and any floor system described in Articles 3 and 4 of Chapter Four can be used. For large multistory buildings, it is almost invariably cheaper to retain the same system for the roof as for the floors and to avoid minor changes in the sizes of the concrete framing members, such as beams and girders. This is customary for even heavily loaded factories and warehouses, as noted on page 72. A change to some light-weight type of structural-steel framing, combined with precast cement-aggregate or gypsum units, is seldom desirable, unless there are obvious reasons for the choice. Exceptions previously noted would be for designs requiring large skylights, saw-tooth construction, or assemblies involving a type of work difficult to execute with concrete cast-in-place.

In these cases the possibility of using steel framing should be considered, but any comparison of cost should include the expense of fireproofing the steel if necessary. It is important that the designer bear in mind the principle of avoiding unnecessary changes when planning large buildings where the introduction of a new type of construction, very likely placed by a different trade, may well cancel an apparent economy and actually result in an increased cost.

For small buildings, such as wall-bearing designs of moderate area, two or three stories in height, the principle of unifying the design as far as practicable has little significance. On such operations there cannot be the same coordination, and the construction plant is not specifically chosen for one particular type of work. The designer should realize the desirability for simplicity in job assembly but need not hesitate to use different types of floor construction and still another roof design if the architectural or structural requirements favor such a choice.

For a concrete building, where a light-weight system is desired, the longer-span precast units described as appropriate for steel framing can be used over reinforced-concrete framing but are more economical with steel. When precast units are supported by reinforced-concrete beams, they do not furnish the compression flange formed by a slab cast monolithically with the beam. The beam must consequently be designed in a less economical rectangular shape or a T-section obtained by expensive form work.

This condition generally applies to beam or girder assemblies. An exception is the use of precast concrete units for roof decks when supported by rigid frames or arch rings, such as are described in Chapter Six.

Article 7. Flat Roofs Framed of Wood

A wood-joist construction, similar to that employed for the floors, is generally used to support the roof deck of flat-roofed buildings framed in wood. The structural surface is sloped to provide drainage. Except in mill construction, the problem of fire resistance is usually secondary to that of insulation, but where a 2-hour rating is required, it can be obtained by a hung ceiling carrying a type and thickness of plaster approved by the National Board of Fire Underwriters. The following materials and systems are appropriate for the roof deck.

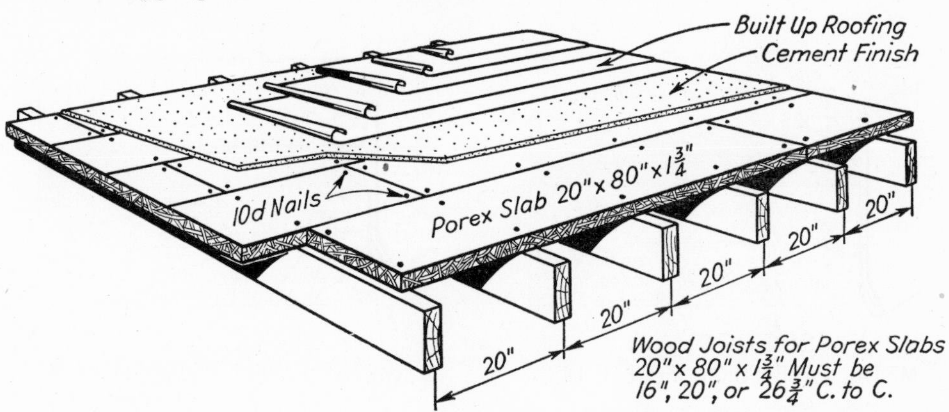

FIG. 21. Precast, Porex Slabs over Wood Joists. Courtesy, Porete Manufacturing Company.

WOOD BOARDING, PLYWOOD, AND COMPOSITION BOARD. As in the case of pitched roofs, tongue-and-groove or ship-lap solid boarding is often used. It is either ⅞ in. thick or of a nominal 2-in. thickness with a wider joist spacing. Plywood is satisfactory structurally but has not the heat-insulating value of composition boards such as laminated Sheetrock, which has a gypsum core enclosed in tough paper.

PRECAST GYPSUM UNITS. As in the case of steel framing, the gypsum plank described on page 163 are appropriate for use over wood joists or purlins. The plank are nailed to the supporting members. Anchor straps or clips are used where necessary. Built-up waterproofing is applied over the surface.

PRECAST CEMENT-AGGREGATE UNITS. Any type described on pages 152 to 154 can be used over wood framing, but the channel sections and thicker slabs are inappropriate. The thinner and lighter-weight units, such as the Porex slab, are suitable for the comparatively close spacing of wood joists and furnish a high degree of heat insulation and sound absorption. The 1¾-in. thickness is used on a joist spacing of 1 ft 8 in., and the

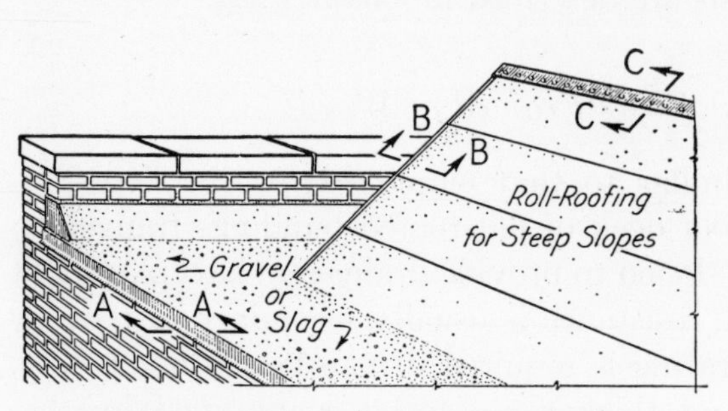

DIAGRAMMATIC SKETCH SHOWING
SECTION LINES

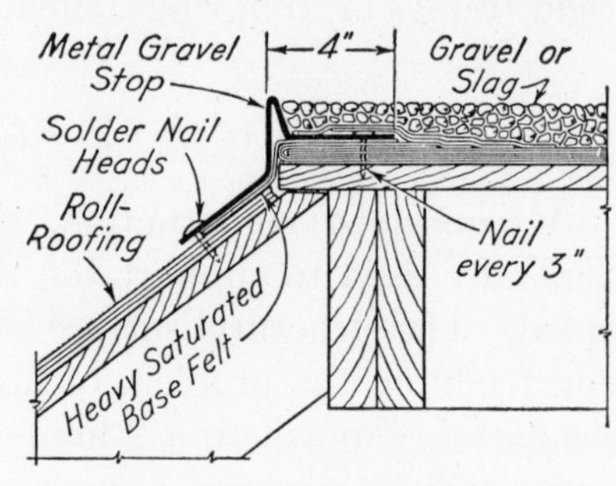

DETAIL FOR FLAT & STEEP
ROOF CONNECTION

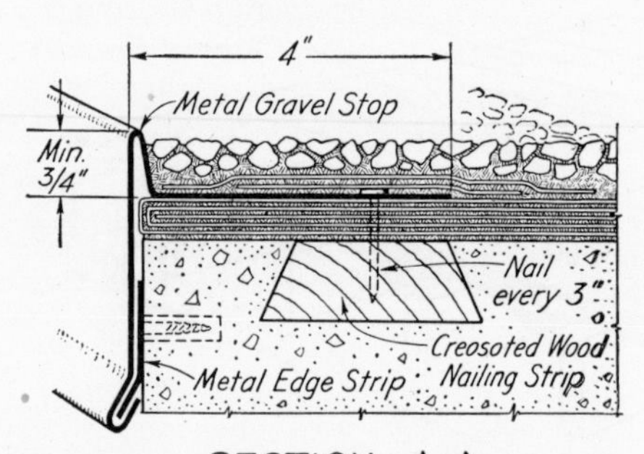

SECTION A-A
METAL EAVE FOR CONCRETE DECK

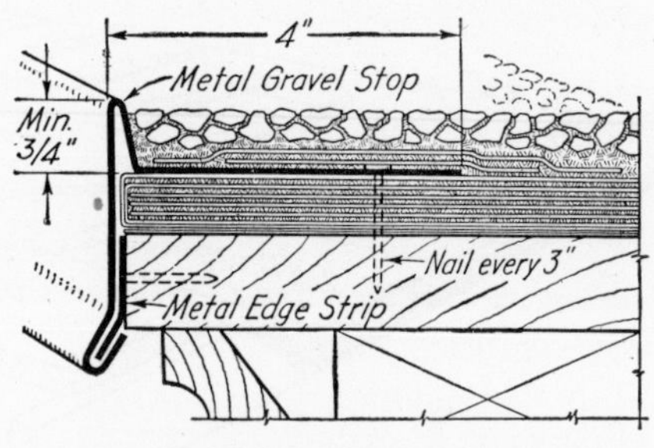

SECTION A-A
METAL EAVE FOR WOOD DECK

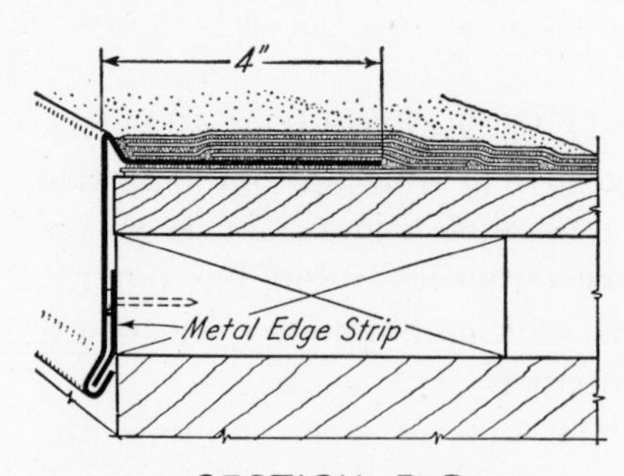

SECTION B-B
GABLE EDGE FOR STEEP ROOFS

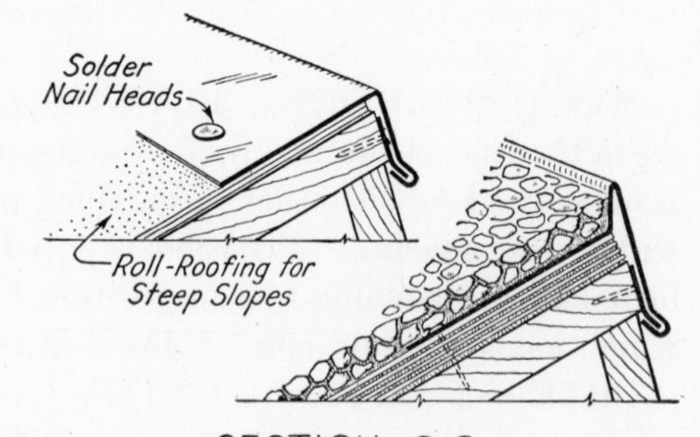

SECTION C-C
METAL RIDGE FOR SAWTOOTH SKYLIGHT

Fig. 22. Eave and Edge Details for Built-up Roofing. Courtesy, The Barrett Division of the Allied Chemical and Dye Corporation.

3-in. thickness on a spacing of 3 ft 4 in. In both cases ¼ in. of cement mortar is applied to the top surface, which serves as a base for the built-up waterproofing, as shown in Fig. 21. From the viewpoint of structural economy, designs of this type are seldom desirable. Their particular application is for conditions where the added heat insulation or acoustical improvement is worth the additional expense.

CAST-IN-PLACE SYSTEMS. The gypsum design described on page 132 is sometimes used over wood joists on a spacing of about 2 ft 6 in. Special anchor straps connect the gypsum slab to the wood supports. A variation is the use of ½-in. Sheetrock with 2 in. of poured gypsum over the top. If the gypsum is unreinforced, the design may be used on a 16-in. center-to-center joist spacing. With reinforcement, the spacing may be increased to 36 in. Light-weight cement-aggregate mixtures are also cast-in-place both over wood joists and between them. In the former case a paper-backed galvanized welded-wire mesh is used between joists having a maximum spacing of 2 ft 8 in. In the latter design a form is attached to the soffits of the joists, and the material poured between them is finished flush with their upper surfaces. In both cases ¼ in. of cement mortar serves as a base for the built-up waterproofing. Although such a system may be useful to meet special conditions, designs of this type, employing wood joists as a support for poured materials, cannot be recommended as good construction.

Because of the very extensive use of built-up roofing, Fig. 22 is introduced to illustrate appropriate methods of finishing the eaves and edges of roofs for the more typical conditions. These sections of the roof assembly, as well as the flashing, discussed on page 278, should receive consideration by the designer.

Article 8. Heat Transmission and Insulation

The relative resistance of various structural roof decks to the passage of heat is sometimes an important factor. In order that the designer may be able to identify the extent to which this consideration should influence his decision, a résumé of the subject is given in this article, together with a brief discussion of the principal types of insulating materials. The tables on pages 178 to 183 provide a basis for estimating the reduction in heating load to be obtained by the use of the more usual types of insulation. An authoritative and complete treatment of this entire subject is given in the *Guide*, yearly publication of the American Society of Heating and Ventilating Engineers.

HEAT LOSSES AND HEAT GAIN. It is important that the heat loss in cold weather and the heat gain in warm weather be kept to the lowest practicable minimum for all buildings where interior temperatures appreciably higher or lower than exterior temperatures are maintained over extended periods. These losses or gains occur as follows:

a. By the infiltration of air through cracks because of faulty construction or the normal leakage along contact faces of sash and doors. If the exterior and interior temperatures are different, there is a heat loss or gain. This is minimized by careful fitting of all elements comprising the building envelope. Particular care is necessary between masonry foundations and wood superstructures, along the eaves of sloping roofs, and around openings where wood, rolled-steel, or hollow metal frames are caulked against adjoining walls.

b. By transmission through the various surfaces comprising the building envelope. If the envelope is of solid, homogeneous material, such as a concrete roof slab, heat passes through the section by conduction. If there is an air space below the slab, such as may exist above a hung ceiling, heat crosses the air space by radiation, conduction, and convection. Passing through the plaster of the ceiling by conduction, it will leave the outer surface by radiation, conduction, and convection.

In designing the heating plant, the requirement for ventilation, that is, one or more air changes per hour for the occupied spaces within the building, must also be considered. If this air volume were not supplied by infiltration, additional natural or mechanical ventilation would be required to make up the difference. The warming of this additional air is part of the heating load.

The conductivity of homogeneous materials varies with their density and the amount of moisture which they contain. In general, it is higher for the more dense materials, but for some of fibrous composition there are optimum densities for lowest conductivity. As conductivity decreases with the mean temperature at which the transmission coefficient is determined, the designer should, for extreme temperatures, make certain that the transmission coefficients applying to the contemplated assembly are appropriate for his condition of exposure.

The amount of heat transferred from a surface by radiation depends upon the emissivity of the surface and the temperature difference between the boundaries of the air space contained within the building assembly. Conduction and convection are affected by the width and shape of the air space, air movement within the space, and the roughness of the boundary surfaces. A large proportion of the total heat transfer across air spaces, such as exist in furred walls or between the joists of roof construction, may be by radiation. This fact indicates the value of metallic surfaces such as aluminum foil and specially coated sheets of steel, which have low emissivity and capacity to reflect infra-red rays. The transfer of radiant heat is independent of the width of such a space, but to limit the total conductance, spaces of this type should be at least ¾ in. wide. In referring to heat-reflective materials it is undesirable to use the term "brightness," which has no specific significance. The important characteristics are emissivity and reflectivity, properties which identify the necessary functions.

TRANSMISSION COEFFICIENTS. Most of the units and building assemblies described in the preceding articles as appropriate for structural roof decks offer appreciable resistance to the transfer of heat by conduction. This factor is ordinarily recorded as a coefficient representing the number of British thermal units transmitted per hour per square foot of surface for each degree difference in temperature between the inside and outside air. Coefficients applying to the more conventional assemblies are given in the *Guide* of the American Society of Heating and Ventilating Engineers. The tables on pages 178 to 183 are abstracted from this excellent authority. For the newer types of roof construction, not likely to be recorded in the *Guide*, the manufacturers or sponsors of the materials or assemblies can, in most cases, furnish reliable data of a similar nature applying to their specific products.

As the transmission coefficients of the various designs are quite different, they should be considered in making a choice. In most climates and for most types of occupancy, applied insulation is desirable; but, if the unit used for the roof deck furnishes considerable resistance to the passage of heat, less insulation is necessary. The reflection versus absorption of radiant energy from the sun may also be a factor as it affects the heat gain in warm weather.

TYPES OF INSULATING MATERIALS. Broadly classified, these materials fall into two groups. The first comprises those having a low density and comparatively low conductivity. These materials offer resistance to the passage of heat by conduction. The second group, which has a more limited but still valuable application, comprises metallic surfaces used as boundaries of air spaces within the construction of walls, ceilings, or roofs. These materials act as reflectors of the radiant heat waves. The first group is divided into three classes identified as rigid insulation, flexible types, and insulating fills. The second group has no subdivisions, but various metals are used to accomplish the purpose.

RIGID INSULATION. This is generally in the shape of boards ½ to 1 in. thick. One variety is composed of wood, cane, and other vegetable fibers pressed into sheets sufficiently rigid to be nailed upon joists or studding. Pressed cork is also used in the form of sheets up to several inches in thickness. Such types have their particular application for low-temperature installations. Many of these insulating boards may be used under built-up waterproofing or as a base for plaster on ceilings or exterior walls, and some are attractively finished on one face for use as exposed interior surfaces. Others are coated with bitumen or enclosed in a waterproof paper to guard against the passage of water vapor. Insulation boards of this type are also furnished with one face surfaced with aluminum foil in order to combine the functions of low heat conduction with the reflection of radiant heat.

This same group includes units such as blocks and short boards or slabs formed of inorganic materials. One of the newer and better varieties in this category is Foamglas, supplied in blocks 12 × 18 in., varying in thickness from 2 to 6 in. Mineral wool is also available in blocks 12 × 36 in., varying in thickness from 1 to 4 in. These two materials compete with slabs of comparable size made of pressed granulated cork. They have their particular application for roof insulation. They are laid in coal-tar pitch or asphalt between the roof deck and the built-up waterproofing.

Flexible Insulation. This term applies to types of insulation that are not sufficiently rigid to be used beneath built-up waterproofing but have their application as fillers between wood studs in exterior wall construction and between the joists of flat roofs and rafters of pitched roofs. Although very widely used in connection with wood-framed structures, they are also appropriate for application between furring strips on the

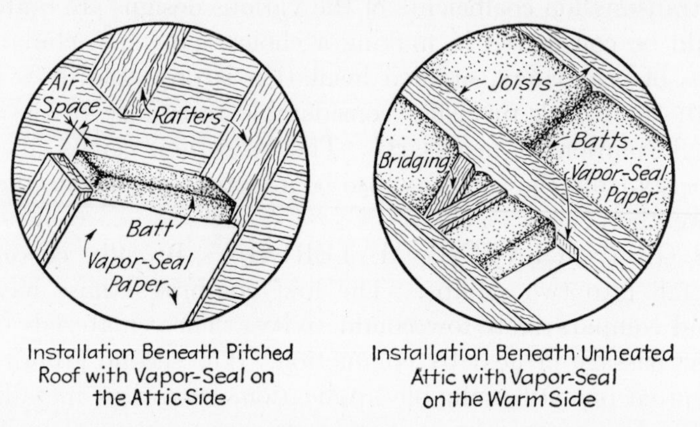

Fig. 23. Application of Flexible Insulation. Courtesy, Johns-Manville.

inside of masonry walls and between floor or roof joists in steel-framed assemblies, if provision is made for their attachment. Figure 23 shows typical uses.

One type is composed of various organic materials, such as wood fiber and cotton, treated in a manner to render them very light and fire resistant. Another variety is derived from inorganic materials and identified as mineral, rock, or glass wool. Mineral wool is in the form of fine, interlaced mineral fibers. Composed principally of silicates of calcium and aluminum, it looks like loose wool or cotton. Rock wool is made from natural rock or a combination of limestone and shale. Slag wool is derived from iron, copper, or lead blast-furnace slag. Glass wool is made from silica sand, soda ash, and limestone.

Units composed of these materials are furnished in the form of batts, blankets, or quilts, as may be desired to suit the spaces in which the insulation is to be placed. The usual thickness is 2 or 4 in., and the insulating material is often surfaced on one side with a waterproofed-paper covering, which acts to a certain extent as a vapor seal but is generally inferior to the provision noted on page 185. When installing either the rigid or flexible type of insulation, particular attention should be given to avoid any cracks or openings between the sheets, batts, or blankets through which heat transfer can occur.

INSULATING FILLS. Many insulating materials are furnished in a granulated form, often the size of small pellets. Several of the newer varieties, particularly those derived from expanded mica and diatomaceous earth, are appropriate for locations where it would be difficult to install the flexible types. They are also used for high-temperature insulation. Mineral and glass wools are furnished in loose form for hand packing where required.

A micaceous aggregate mixed with portland cement to form an insulating fill has an application over concrete roof decks. Pumice has been used for

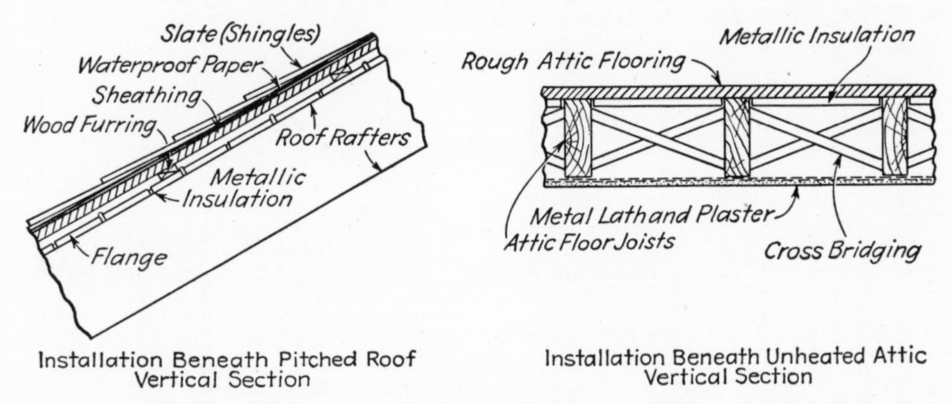

FIG. 24. Application of Reflective Insulation. Courtesy, American Flange and Manufacturing Company.

the same purpose. Precast concrete slabs containing a Vermiculite composition provide a degree of insulation beyond that furnished by most other light-weight aggregates. Although best known as a fireproofing material, Vermiculite plaster has a high heat-insulating value and may be used for this purpose where a plaster application is appropriate. The word "Vermiculite" identifies a group of minerals that are derived from certain varieties of mica.

REFLECTIVE INSULATION. Several types of metals are used for this purpose. They are generally in the form of foil mounted on paper or very thin all-metal sheets. The better types maintain their effectiveness under service conditions. If installed as continuous surfaces, they also provide an excellent vapor seal (see page 184). Aluminum foil mounted upon a strong paper backing is a popular design. Thin sheets of steel, finished to a dull luster, are also effective. These materials are installed as one of the boundaries of an air space, which should be at least ¾ in. across. Figure 24 shows typical uses.

COEFFICIENTS OF TRANSMISSION (*U*) OF FRAME CONSTRUCTION CEILINGS AND FLOORS

(From *Heating Ventilating and Air-Conditioning Guide*, 1946)

Coefficients are expressed in Btu per hour per square foot per degree Fahrenheit difference in temperature between the air on the two sides and are based on still air (no wind) conditions on both sides.

Type of Ceiling	Insulation between, or on Top of, Joists (No Flooring Above)												With Flooring * (On Top of Ceiling Joists)		Number
	None	Insulating Board on Top of Joists		Blanket or Bat Insulation † between Joists ‡			Vermiculite Insulation between Joists ‡			Mineral-wool Insulation between Joists ‡			Single Wood Floor §	Double Wood Floor ‖	
		½ in.	1 in.	1 in.	2 in.	3 in.	2 in.	3 in.	4 in.	2 in.	3 in.	4 in.			
	A	B	C	D	E	F	G	H	I	J	K	L	M	N	
No ceiling		0.37	0.24										0.45	0.34	1
Metal lath and plaster ¶	0.69	0.26	0.19	0.19	0.12	0.093	0.18	0.14	0.11	0.12	0.093	0.077	0.30	0.25	2
Gypsum board (⅜ in.) plain or decorated	0.67	0.26	0.18	0.19	0.12	0.092	0.18	0.13	0.10	0.12	0.092	0.077	0.30	0.24	3
Wood lath and plaster	0.62	0.25	0.18	0.19	0.12	0.091	0.17	0.13	0.10	0.12	0.091	0.076	0.28	0.24	4
Gypsum lath (⅜ in.) plastered **	0.61	0.25	0.18	0.19	0.12	0.091	0.17	0.13	0.10	0.12	0.091	0.076	0.28	0.24	5
Plywood (⅜ in.) plain or decorated	0.59	0.24	0.18	0.19	0.12	0.091	0.17	0.13	0.10	0.12	0.091	0.076	0.28	0.23	6
Insulating board (½ in.) plain or decorated	0.36	0.19	0.15	0.16	0.10	0.082	0.14	0.12	0.097	0.10	0.082	0.069	0.22 ††	0. 19 ††	7
Insulating board lath (½ in.) plastered **	0.35	0.19	0.15	0.15	0.10	0.081	0.14	0.11	0.096	0.10	0.081	0.068	0.21	0.18	8
Insulating board lath (1 in.) plastered **	0.23	0.15	0.12	0.12	0.089	0.072	0.12	0.097	0.084	0.089	0.072	0.061	0.16	0.14	9

* For coefficients for constructions in Columns M and N (except No. 1) with insulation between joists, refer to table on page 271. *Example*: The coefficient for No. 3-N of this table is 0.24. With 2 in. blanket insulation between joists, the coefficient will be 0.093. (See table on page 271.) (Column D of table on page 271 applicable only for 3⅝ in. joists.)

† Based on insulation in contact with ceiling and consequently no air space between.

‡ Coefficients corrected for framing on basis of 15 per cent area, 2 in. × 4 in. (nominal) framing 16 in. on centers.

§ 25/32 in. yellow pine or fir.

‖ 25/32 in. pine or fir subflooring plus 13/16 in. hardwood finish flooring.

¶ Plaster assumed ¾ in. thick.

** Plaster assumed ½ in. thick.

†† For 25/32 in. insulating board sheathing applied to the under side of the joists, the coefficient for *single* wood floor (Column M) is 0.18 and for *double* wood floor (Column N) is 0.16. For coefficients with insulation between joists, see table on page 271.

COEFFICIENTS OF TRANSMISSION (*U*) OF CONCRETE CONSTRUCTION FLOORS AND CEILINGS

(From *Heating Ventilating and Air-Conditioning Guide,* 1946)

Coefficients are expressed in Btu per hour per square foot per degree Fahrenheit difference in temperature between the air on the two sides, and are based on still air (no wind) conditions on both sides.

Type of Ceiling	Thickness of Concrete,* Inches	Type of Flooring					Number
		No Flooring (Concrete Bare)	Tile † or Terrazzo Flooring on Concrete	1/4 In. Battleship ‡ Linoleum Directly on Concrete	Parquet § Flooring in Mastic on Concrete	Double Wood Floor on Sleepers ‖	
		A	B	C	D	E	
No ceiling	3	0.68	0.65	0.45	0.45	0.25	1
	6	0.59	0.56	0.41	0.41	0.23	2
	10	0.50	0.48	0.36	0.36	0.22	3
1/2 in. plaster applied to underside of concrete	3	0.62	0.59	0.43	0.43	0.24	4
	6	0.54	0.52	0.39	0.39	0.22	5
	10	0.46	0.44	0.34	0.34	0.21	6
Metal lath and plaster ¶—suspended or furred	3	0.38	0.37	0.30	0.30	0.19	7
	6	0.35	0.34	0.28	0.28	0.18	8
	10	0.32	0.31	0.26	0.26	0.17	9
Gypsum board (3/8 in.) and plaster **—suspended or furred	3	0.36	0.35	0.28	0.28	0.19	10
	6	0.33	0.32	0.27	0.27	0.18	11
	10	0.30	0.29	0.24	0.24	0.17	12
Insulating board lath (1/2 in.) and plaster **—suspended or furred	3	0.25	0.24	0.21	0.21	0.15	13
	6	0.23	0.23	0.20	0.20	0.15	14
	10	0.22	0.21	0.19	0.19	0.14	15

* For other thicknesses of concrete, interpolate.
† Thickness of tile assumed to be 1 in.
‡ Conductance of linoleum 1/4 in. thick is 1.36. Values in Column C may be used with sufficient accuracy for concrete floors covered with carpet.
§ Thickness of wood assumed to be 13/16 in.; thickness of mastic, 1/8 in. ($k = 4.5$).
‖ Based on 25/32 in. yellow pine or fir subflooring and 13/16 in. hardwood finish flooring with an air space between subfloor and concrete.
¶ Thickness of plaster assumed to be 3/4 in.
** Thickness of plaster assumed to be 1/2 in.

COEFFICIENTS OF TRANSMISSION (*U*) OF CONCRETE FLOORS ON GROUND WITH VARIOUS TYPES OF FINISH FLOORING

(From the Guide of the American Society of Heating and Ventilating Engineers)

$U = 0.10$ Btu per hour per square foot per degree Fahrenheit temperature difference between the ground and the air over the floor. Until more complete data are available, it is recommended that a coefficient of 0.10 be used for all types of concrete floors on the ground, with or without insulation. For basement wall below grade, use the same average coefficient (0.10). For further data see *ASHVE Research Report* 1213, "Heat Loss Through Basement Walls and Floors," by F. C. Houghten, S. I. Taimuty, Carl Gutberlet, and C. J. Brown (*ASHVE Transactions*, Vol. 48, 1942, p. 369).

COEFFICIENTS OF TRANSMISSION (U) OF PITCHED ROOFS

(From *Heating Ventilating and Air-Conditioning Guide*, 1946)

Coefficients are expressed in Btu per hour per square foot per degree Fahrenheit difference in temperature between the air on the two sides and are based on an outside wind velocity of 15 mph.

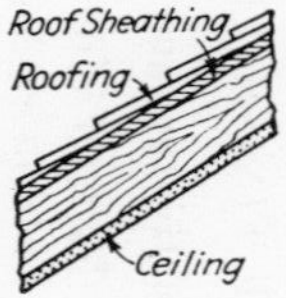

Type of Ceiling (Applied Directly to Roof Rafters)	Wood Shingles (On 1 × 4 Wood Strips † Spaced 2 In. Apart)				Asphalt Shingles or Roll Roofing (On Solid Wood Sheathing) †				Slate or Tile * (On Solid Wood Sheathing) †				Number
	Insulation between Rafters				Insulation between Rafters				Insulation between Rafters				
	None	Blanket or Bat (Thickness Below)			None	Blanket or Bat (Thickness Below)			None	Blanket or Bat (Thickness Below)			
		1 in.	2 in.	3 in.		1 in.	2 in.	3 in.		1 in.	2 in.	3 in.	
	A	B	C ‡	D ‡	E	F	G ‡	H ‡	I	J	K ‡	L ‡	
No ceiling applied to rafters	0.48 §	0.15	0.10	0.081	0.52 §	0.15	0.11	0.084	0.55 §	0.16	0.11	0.085	1
Metal lath and plaster ‖	0.31	0.14	0.10	0.081	0.33	0.15	0.10	0.083	0.34	0.15	0.10	0.083	2
Gypsum board (3/8 in.) decorated	0.30	0.14	0.10	0.080	0.32	0.15	0.10	0.082	0.33	0.15	0.10	0.083	3
Wood lath and plaster	0.29	0.14	0.10	0.080	0.31	0.14	0.10	0.081	0.32	0.15	0.10	0.082	4
Gypsum lath (3/8 in.) plastered ¶	0.29	0.14	0.10	0.079	0.31	0.14	0.10	0.081	0.32	0.15	0.10	0.082	5
Plywood (3/8 in.) plain or decorated	0.29	0.14	0.099	0.079	0.30	0.14	0.10	0.081	0.31	0.15	0.10	0.081	6
Insulating board (1/2 in.) plain or decorated	0.22	0.12	0.090	0.072	0.23	0.12	0.091	0.074	0.24	0.13	0.092	0.074	7
Insulating board lath (1/2 in.) plastered ¶	0.22	0.12	0.088	0.072	0.22	0.12	0.090	0.073	0.23	0.12	0.091	0.074	8
Insulating board lath (1 in.) plastered ¶	0.16	0.10	0.078	0.064	0.17	0.10	0.079	0.065	0.17	0.10	0.080	0.066	9

* Figures in Columns I, J, K, and L may be used with sufficient accuracy for rigid asbestos shingles on wood sheathing. Layer of slater's felt neglected.

† Sheathing and wood strips assumed 25/32 in. thick.

‡ Coefficients corrected for framing on basis of 15 per cent area, 2 in. × 4 in. (nominal), 16 in. on centers.

§ No air space included in 1-A, 1-E or 1-I; all other coefficients based on one air space.

‖ Plaster assumed 3/4 in. thick.

¶ Plaster assumed 1/2 in. thick.

COMBINED COEFFICIENTS OF TRANSMISSION (*U*) OF PITCHED ROOFS * AND HORIZONTAL CEILINGS—BASED ON CEILING AREA †

(From *Heating Ventilating and Air-Conditioning Guide*, 1946)

Coefficients are expressed in Btu per hour per square foot of ceiling area per degree Fahrenheit difference in temperature between the air on the two sides, and are based on an outside wind velocity of 15 mph.

Ceiling Coefficient ¶ (From the table on page 178)	Type of Roofing and Roof Sheathing						Number
	Wood Shingles on Wood Strips ‡			Asphalt Shingles § or Roll Roofing on Wood Sheathing ‖			
	No Roof Insulation (Rafters Exposed) ($U_r = 0.48$)	½ In. Insulating Board on Under Side of Rafters ($U_r = 0.22$)	1 In. Insulating Board on Under Side of Rafters ($U_r = 0.16$)	No Roof Insulation (Rafters Exposed) ($U_r = 0.53$)	½ In. Insulating Board on Under Side of Rafters ($U_r = 0.23$)	1 In. Insulating Board on Under Side of Rafters ($U_r = 0.17$)	
	A	B	C	D	E	F	
0.10	0.085	0.073	0.066	0.087	0.074	0.067	19
0.11	0.092	0.078	0.07	0.094	0.079	0.071	20
0.12	0.099	0.082	0.074	0.10	0.083	0.075	21
0.13	0.11	0.087	0.078	0.11	0.088	0.079	22
0.14	0.11	0.091	0.081	0.11	0.093	0.083	23
0.15	0.12	0.096	0.084	0.12	0.097	0.086	24
0.16	0.13	0.10	0.087	0.13	0.10	0.089	25
0.17	0.13	0.10	0.090	0.13	0.10	0.092	26
0.18	0.14	0.11	0.093	0.14	0.11	0.095	27
0.19	0.14	0.11	0.095	0.15	0.11	0.098	28
0.20	0.15	0.11	0.098	0.15	0.12	0.10	29
0.21	0.15	0.12	0.10	0.16	0.12	0.10	30
0.22	0.16	0.12	0.10	0.17	0.12	0.11	31
0.23	0.16	0.12	0.10	0.17	0.12	0.11	32
0.24	0.17	0.13	0.11	0.18	0.12	0.11	33
0.25	0.17	0.13	0.11	0.18	0.13	0.11	34
0.26	0.18	0.13	0.11	0.19	0.13	0.11	35
0.27	0.18	0.13	0.11	0.19	0.13	0.12	36
0.28	0.19	0.14	0.12	0.19	0.14	0.12	37
0.29	0.19	0.14	0.12	0.20	0.14	0.12	38
0.30	0.20	0.14	0.12	0.20	0.14	0.12	39
0.34	0.21	0.15	0.12	0.22	0.15	0.13	40
0.35	0.22	0.15	0.13	0.22	0.15	0.13	41
0.36	0.22	0.15	0.13	0.23	0.15	0.13	42
0.37	0.23	0.15	0.13	0.23	0.16	0.13	43
0.45	0.25	0.17	0.13	0.26	0.17	0.14	44
0.59	0.29	0.18	0.14	0.30	0.19	0.15	45
0.61	0.29	0.18	0.15	0.31	0.19	0.15	46
0.62	0.30	0.19	0.15	0.31	0.19	0.15	47
0.67	0.31	0.19	0.15	0.33	0.20	0.16	48
0.69	0.31	0.19	0.15	0.33	0.20	0.16	49

* Calculations based on ⅓ pitch roof ($n = 1.2$), using the following formula:

$$U = \frac{U_r \times U_{ce}}{U_r + \dfrac{U_{ce}}{n}}$$

where U = combined coefficient to be used with ceiling area.
U_r = coefficient of transmission of the roof.
U_{ce} = coefficient of transmission of the ceiling.
n = the ratio of the area of the roof to the area of the ceiling.

† Use ceiling area (not roof area) with these coefficients.
‡ Based on 1 x 4 in. strips spaced 2 in. apart.
§ Coefficients in Columns D, E, and F may be used with sufficient accuracy for tile, slate, and rigid asbestos shingles on wood sheathing.
‖ Sheathing assumed 25/32 in. thick.
¶ Values of U_{ce} to be used in this column may be selected from the table on page 178.

COEFFICIENTS OF TRANSMISSION (*U*) OF FLAT ROOFS COVERED WITH BUILT-UP ROOFING; NO CEILING—UNDERSIDE OF ROOF EXPOSED

(From *Heating Ventilating and Air-Conditioning Guide*, 1946)

(See the Following Table for Flat Roofs with Ceilings)

These coefficients are expressed in Btu per hour per square foot per degree Fahrenheit difference in temperature between the air on the two sides, and are based on an outside wind velocity of 15 mph.

Type of Roof Deck	Thickness of Roof Deck, Inches	No Insulation	Insulation on Top of Deck (Covered with Built-Up Roofing)							Number
			Insulating Board (Thickness Below)				Corkboard (Thickness Below)			
			½ in.	1 in.	1½ in.	2 in.	1 in.	1½ in.	2 in.	
		A	B	C	D	E	F	G	H	
Flat metal roof deck *		1.06	0.39	0.24	0.18	0.14	0.23	0.17	0.13	1
Precast cement tile	1⅝ in.	0.84	0.37	0.24	0.17	0.14	0.22	0.16	0.13	2
Concrete	2 in.	0.82	0.36	0.24	0.17	0.14	0.22	0.16	0.13	3
	4 in.	0.72	0.34	0.23	0.17	0.13	0.21	0.16	0.12	4
	6 in.	0.65	0.33	0.22	0.16	0.13	0.21	0.15	0.12	5
Gypsum fiber concrete † on ½ in. gypsum board	2½ in.	0.38	0.24	0.18	0.14	0.12	0.17	0.13	0.11	6
	3½ in.	0.31	0.21	0.16	0.13	0.11	0.15	0.12	0.10	7
Wood ‡	1 in.	0.49	0.28	0.20	0.15	0.12	0.19	0.14	0.12	8
	1½ in.	0.37	0.24	0.17	0.14	0.11	0.17	0.13	0.11	9
	2 in.	0.32	0.22	0.16	0.13	0.11	0.16	0.12	0.10	10
	3 in.	0.23	0.17	0.14	0.11	0.096	0.13	0.11	0.091	11

* Coefficient of transmission of bare corrugated iron (no roofing) is 1.50 Btu per hour per square foot of projected area per degree Fahrenheit difference in temperature, based on an outside wind velocity of 15 mph.

† 87½ per cent gypsum, 12½ per cent wood fiber. Thickness indicated includes ½ in. gypsum board.

‡ Nominal thicknesses specified—actual thicknesses used in calculations.

COEFFICIENTS OF TRANSMISSION (*U*) OF FLAT ROOFS COVERED WITH BUILT-UP ROOFING; WITH LATH AND PLASTER CEILINGS *

(From *Heating Ventilating and Air-Conditioning Guide*, 1946)

(See the Preceding Table for Flat Roofs with No Ceilings)

These coefficients are expressed in Btu per hour per square foot per degree Fahrenheit difference in temperature between the air on the two sides, and are based on an outside wind velocity of 15 mph.

Type of Roof Deck	Thickness of Roof Deck, Inches	No Insulation	Insulation on Top of Deck (Covered with Built-Up Roofing) — Insulating Board (Thickness Below)				Corkboard (Thickness Below)			Number
			½ in.	1 in.	1½ in.	2 in.	1 in.	1½ in.	2 in.	
		A	B	C	D	E	F	G	H	
Flat metal roof deck 		0.46	0.27	0.19	0.15	0.12	0.18	0.14	0.11	12
Precast cement tile 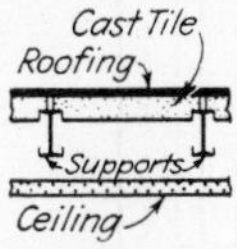	1⅝ in.	0.43	0.26	0.19	0.15	0.12	0.18	0.14	0.11	13
Concrete 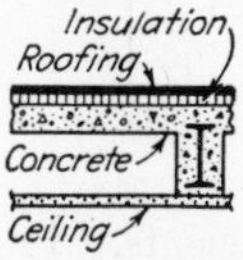	2 in.	0.42	0.26	0.19	0.14	0.12	0.18	0.14	0.11	14
	4 in.	0.40	0.25	0.18	0.14	0.12	0.17	0.13	0.11	15
	6 in.	0.37	0.24	0.18	0.14	0.11	0.17	0.13	0.11	16
Gypsum fiber Concrete † on ½ in. gypsum board 	2½ in.	0.27	0.19	0.15	0.12	0.10	0.14	0.12	0.097	17
	3½ in.	0.23	0.17	0.14	0.11	0.097	0.13	0.11	0.091	18
Wood ‡ 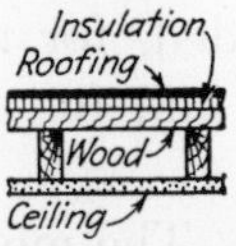	1 in.	0.31	0.21	0.16	0.13	0.11	0.15	0.12	0.10	19
	1½ in.	0.26	0.19	0.15	0.12	0.10	0.14	0.11	0.095	20
	2 in.	0.24	0.17	0.14	0.11	0.097	0.13	0.11	0.092	21
	3 in.	0.18	0.14	0.12	0.10	0.087	0.11	0.095	0.082	22

* Calculations based on metal lath and plaster ceilings, but coefficients may be used with sufficient accuracy for gypsum lath or wood lath and plaster ceilings. It is assumed that there is an air space between the underside of the roof deck and the upper side of the ceiling.

† 87½ per cent gypsum, 12½ per cent wood fiber. Thickness indicated includes ½ in. gypsum board.

‡ Nominal thicknesses specified—actual thicknesses used in calculations.

Article 9. Condensation and Vapor Seal

Two possibilities for condensation occur under normal conditions of occupancy: (*a*) Moisture may form on the interior surfaces of roofs, ceilings, or walls. This is referred to as surface condensation. (*b*) Moisture, in the form of water vapor, contained in the comparatively warm and humid interior atmosphere, may penetrate the inclosing surfaces and condense within the roof or wall assembly. This is identified as interstitial condensation.

SURFACE CONDENSATION. Surface condensation may be eliminated by either reducing the relative humidity of the interior or maintain-

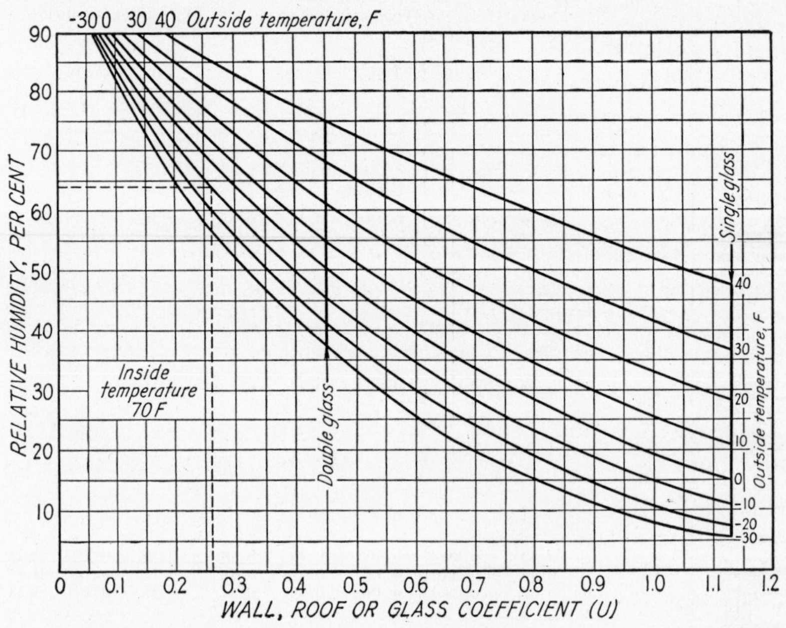

FIG. 25. Permissible Relative Humidities for Various Transmission Coefficients. From *Heating Ventilating Air Conditioning Guide*, 1946, Chapter 6.

ing the interior surfaces of the enclosing elements at or above the dew-point temperature. When high humidities are desired or are caused by the conditions of occupancy, the second alternative is the only solution, and insulation is often necessary. Figure 25 shows the relative humidities that may exist without danger of condensation for various exterior temperatures and transmission coefficients. The dotted line indicates the permissible relative humidity (64 per cent), if surface condensation is to be avoided, for an exterior wall or roof having a transmission coefficient of 0.26 and for an exterior temperature of $-10°$ F.

INTERSTITIAL CONDENSATION AND VAPOR SEAL. The more general use of weather stripping and the insulation of roofs, attic floors, and walls have resulted during the last decade in making the building envelope more resistant to the passage of air. This has been of obvious benefit in diminishing heat losses, but, combined with the tendency to provide a somewhat higher humidity in the atmosphere of the interior, has presented a problem in relation to buildings erected in the colder climates. This is particularly true of residential construction.

The difficulty arises in the fact that at temperatures normally maintained during the heating season, such as 70° F, combined with even a moderately moist atmosphere, such as 30 per cent relative humidity, there may be a higher vapor pressure within the building than outside. As water vapor passes very easily through most building materials, it enters the surfaces of plastered walls, ceilings, or other elements of the structural envelope. On its way through the roof or wall construction a colder zone is reached, the temperature of the moisture-laden air is lowered to the dew point, and condensation occurs. This happens particularly in well-constructed, insulated buildings equipped with heating systems which provide relatively high humidities and has caused the deterioration of insulation, swelling of wood, and the discoloration of interior surfaces.

It is apparent that lowering the relative humidity of the interior atmosphere will lessen the probability of interstitial as well as surface condensation, but moderately high humidities are often desired and, even where not provided by the heating system, may be caused by conditions of occupancy. Planning the structural envelope to permit free passage of water vapor through the walls and roof to the exterior air would also prevent condensation, but this is impracticable for most buildings because of the need to minimize heat losses. The most effective means of guarding against condensation within either roofs or walls, except where ventilation is practicable, is to introduce a barrier formed of a material offering a high resistance to the passage of water vapor.

As the purpose of a vapor seal is to prevent the warm, moist air of the interior from entering the roof or wall assembly, it should be placed near the interior surface. It is imperative that it be installed on the warmer side of the insulation. If roofs are framed in open-joist construction, wood or steel, the seal may be in the form of a glossy-surfaced asphalt-impregnated and surface-coated sheathing paper, weighing at least 50 lb per 500 sq ft. Such paper can be applied directly to the bottoms of the joists or rafters, above the plaster or other finish. Sheets should be well lapped with mastic used at all joints. The same type of seal may be used above a hung ceiling. If this provision can be combined with ventilation between the joists or rafters, so much the better. Somewhat less effective are various brush or spray applications of a vapor-resistant finish applied to the interior surface of the ceiling or wall. Types of both rigid and flexible insulation are also available with vapor-resistant coverings on their inner surfaces, as previously mentioned.

For the typical flat-roof designs of fire-resistant buildings the condition is particularly critical, as the built-up waterproofing quite effectually prevents the natural escape of water vapor with the result that, if no precaution is taken, considerable moisture forms within the roof assembly. In designs of this type, a hung ceiling with vapor seal, and ventilation between ceiling and supporting slab, would be excellent but is often impracticable. The common alternative is to introduce a vapor seal on top of the concrete roof deck beneath the insulation. This seal is generally formed with two plies of impregnated roofing felt, laid in hot asphalt or coal-tar pitch. Moisture cut-offs, to isolate any local failure, are placed in a manner to divide the roof into areas not exceeding 2500 sq ft and around all parapets, penthouses, or other intersecting elements.

Although this design is generally accepted as good practice, considerable difficulty has occurred because of the fact that some water vapor may pass through the seal or movement of the surfacing materials rupture the waterproofing. Particularly when promenade tile has been used as a wearing surface, sufficient deterioration has frequently occurred to require complete resurfacing of the roof. This condition has become so critical that promenade tile have actually been removed from the roofs of many buildings. In some cases the built-up waterproofing has then been covered with ordinary slag or gravel; occasionally a colored aggregate, such as ground slate, has been applied to give a more attractive surface finish.

The subject is still under investigation. At the present time experience favors the use of an insulating material which will not deteriorate with moisture, particular care in placing the vapor barrier, and every possible provision to permit the expansion and contraction of the tile or other surfacing material, including its "setting bed," without danger of buckling or rupture of the built-up waterproofing. Tile joints should also be very carefully pointed and never "grouted," although grouting is, unfortunately, still common practice.

Ventilation between roof joists or in the open spaces occupied by the trusses supporting the roof deck is actually the best means of preventing condensation and should be used wherever the design permits. It is particularly recommended in sealed-off spaces beneath steel roof decks. Attic ventilation is also effective in eliminating condensation on the underside of roof surfaces but may be prohibitive from the viewpoint of heat losses. If attics are unheated, a vapor seal should be placed on the underside of the attic-floor insulation.

Additional information on this subject applying to wall construction is given on page 269. Interesting references are *Condensation in Walls and Attics*, by L. V. Teesdale, Forest Products Laboratory, Forest Service, United States Department of Agriculture, 1937; *Condensation Problems in Modern Buildings*, by the same author, published by the same service,

1941; Mineral Wool: Loose, Granulated, or Felted Form, in "Low-Temperature Installations," *Commercial Standard* CS105–43, National Bureau of Standards.

Article 10. Considerations Affecting the Choice of the Structural Roof System

As the various roof assemblies have been developed to meet specific architectural or structural requirements and, to a lesser degree, the fire-resistive standards, the designer should bear in mind the particular characteristics of each type in order that they may be compared with the requirements of the building under design. Before proceeding to select the roof system, with its supporting frame, it is therefore desirable to identify the matters which should be considered in making such a comparison.

MATERIAL USED FOR FRAMING. For flat roofs of multistory buildings there is the possibility, as previously described, of using the same structural system as for the floors. If this is impracticable because of special features of the roof construction, it is logical to use at least the same material, steel, concrete, or wood, as employed for the main structure, unless it is obviously inappropriate. The flat roofs of single-story buildings and all pitched roofs are normally framed in steel or wood, except for the wide-span designs in concrete, such as the arch, rigid frame, and dome. The appropriateness of each type of roof deck for each type of framing has been described in the preceding articles.

SPACING OF SUPPORTS IN RELATION TO THE TYPE OF ROOF DECK. The limiting spans for which the different designs are suitable have been given. They should be borne in mind so that the roof framing will be designed to fit economically with the type selected. The longer-span systems will obviously reduce the number of purlins or beams. For flat roofs, where saw-tooth construction is required, a system should be chosen that is adaptable to this purpose, as it is desirable to use the same material throughout. In districts subject to particularly high winds or the danger of earthquakes, the strength of connections between the various parts of the roof assembly should receive particular attention.

REQUIRED DEGREE OF FIRE RESISTANCE. The cost of providing the necessary fire-resistance rating may vary considerably with the different systems. Where this expense is a factor, it should be considered in the choice.

WEIGHT OF ROOF CONSTRUCTION. In the previous descriptions, the weights of the different types of roof deck have been given. These relative weights may favor one system at the expense of another, as reflected in the steel tonnage or cost of other supporting materials.

APPEARANCE OF CEILING. For certain types of occupancy appearance influences choice. Some assemblies are more attractive than others; some offer superior facilities for applying ceiling finishes, whereas others require a hung ceiling.

Heat Insulation and Reflection. As there is considerable difference in the heat transmission of the various roof assemblies, this variation may be an important consideration. The light-weight, porous materials are generally superior in this regard to those that are more dense, such as stone concrete. The gypsum products and some of the specially processed light-weight cement-aggregate units have considerable insulating value. The unprotected sheet metals, on the other hand, are particularly undesirable. For this reason certain designs combine an insulating material with the sheets forming the roof deck, as described on page 159. These compete with corrugated cement-asbestos board for the types of occupancy mentioned in the text. In comparing these with other possible designs, the relative heat loss should be roughly checked.

The steel deck has a structural advantage for many types of buildings but, like other sheet-metal designs, requires considerable insulation for most classes of occupancy. The cost of this insulation should be included in making comparative estimates, and the facilities offered for installing the insulation and vapor seal should be considered. The ability of a roof surface to reflect rather than to absorb the radiant heat from the sun is a factor in the consideration of a system which serves both as the structural deck and surface finish.

Possibility of Condensation. Although the application of the principles outlined in Article 9 will minimize the probability of water vapor condensing within the roof assembly or on interior roof surfaces, the designer should beware of choosing gypsum products or other materials particularly susceptible to moisture wherever the remotest danger exists. This consideration is particularly important for certain industrial occupancies where the manufacturing process causes a high humidity. It also applies to insulating materials, which should be of a type that will not deteriorate in the presence of moisture or show any appreciable degree of absorption.

Acoustical Properties. There is a wide variation in the sound-absorption value of the various roof systems. Where this is a factor, the designer should choose a type of material which meets the requirements of occupancy or make certain that the system chosen provides ample opportunity for applying acoustical materials to the undersurface. Several manufacturers have given this subject particular attention. Precast units may be obtained with sound-absorptive surfaces, and special provision is made in some steel-deck assemblies.

Type of Roof Finish. Because of the extensive use of built-up waterproofing for flat roofs, this factor has little significance except for pitched surfaces. Practically every type of plank, slab, and channel design of gypsum or cement-aggregate composition is available with a nailing surface suitable for the application of slate, tile, and similar materials. Neither is there any difficulty in attaching the wood battens often used with the thin sheet metals, such as copper or aluminum, but some designs offer better facilities than others.

DURABILITY AND MAINTENANCE. These factors apply rather to roof-surfacing materials than to the structural deck. They have particular significance for those systems which combine the two features, such as the red-tile, corrugated cement-asbestos board, and corrugated glass. As the maintenance cost of extensive roof areas may be quite high, it should be estimated for competing designs.

ARRANGEMENT OF FLASHING. Although not directly influencing the choice of the structural roof system, the type of flashing should be chosen and the details studied in order that the entire assembly may work out satisfactorily. This subject is discussed on page 278.

COMPARATIVE ESTIMATES OF COST. A careful analysis of the various possible systems that may be employed for the structural roof deck will usually result in reducing the practicable alternates to at most two or three types. Comparative estimates should then be made, as for floor construction.

Chapter Six

WIDE-SPAN DESIGNS

During recent years many new types of rigid frames and arches have been developed in concrete, steel, and wood. The same materials are used in domical structures. The design of trusses, particularly suitable for commercial and industrial buildings, has been largely standardized. Except for the more traditional styles of architecture, these various means of obtaining comparatively wide spans have replaced the masonry arch and dome. Many have an important place in modern design from an esthetic as well as a utilitarian viewpoint. The photographs reproduced in this chapter have consequently been chosen to illustrate characteristic forms.

INTRODUCTION. Where the architectural plan of a building requires a wide, unobstructed floor area beyond the economic limits of standard steel beams or typical reinforced-concrete or solid-timber girders, these designs have their application. Even for comparatively short spans it may be desirable to employ some of the wide-span structural systems. This is illustrated by the applications of the rigid-frame analysis mentioned on page 78. It should be understood, however, that the economical spans given for the various types of beams, trusses, rigid frames, and arches are for average conditions. They do not necessarily limit the appropriate use of these structural forms.

From the viewpoint of the material, wide-span designs may be divided into the following groups:

a. Reinforced concrete designed as a rigid frame, shell arch, or shell dome. In building construction these have largely replaced the older types of concrete arches and domical forms. Reinforced-concrete trusses have also been built but are seldom an economical choice.

b. Steel used in the form of plate girders, trusses, rigid frames, and arches. Structural steel is also appropriate for the framing of domes.

c. Timber used in solid or laminated designs for trusses, rigid frames, and arch ribs, supplemented by framed arches. Arch ribs are occasionally employed for dome construction. Laminated beams and girders of rectangular section are also available, supplemented by plate girders composed of laminated sections, combined with webs of plywood.

d. Solid masonry in the form of arches, still used for the traditional styles. Solid masonry domes, however, have been practically replaced by either steel framing surfaced with stone or shell designs in reinforced concrete.

The illustrations in the text and the accompanying descriptions indicate as far as practicable the particular application of these vastly different types. The designer should base his choice upon the architectural form which he desires from a utilitarian and esthetic viewpoint, combined with the practical requirements of structural adequacy, fire resistance, and economy. Architecturally, both the interior and exterior appearance are often important factors, and even the clear height above the floor may be a determining feature. The difference in these characteristics is very apparent if we compare the steel truss and the steel arch, pages 207 and 220, and the reinforced-concrete rigid frame and the shell structures, pages 192 and 197. In buildings such as auditoriums and armories, where the areas roofed by these designs constitute a large part of the entire structure, the exterior form of the roof is an important part of the architectural composition. The selection of type should, therefore, be one of the first steps.

Structural adequacy does not usually determine the choice, as it can be obtained, within reasonable span limitations, by proper attention to the design. In districts subject to seismic disturbance, preference is given to assemblies having sufficient resistance to lateral forces to offer maximum protection. When soil conditions present the possibility of appreciable settlement, the more rigid forms should be used with caution and the design reviewed (see Chapter Nine). The relative fire resistance of exposed structural steel, wood, and reinforced concrete, although important for certain types of occupancy, does not ordinarily determine the selection of a wide-span assembly. Where the clearance above a floor is 20 ft or more, building codes and common practice seldom impose any restriction except when the contents of a building present a particular hazard. On the other hand, reinforced concrete with proper fireproofing over the reinforcement is preferable where the fire risk is an important factor.

Second only to these considerations is the need for a thorough study of all acceptable designs from the viewpoint of relative economy. This applies not only to the cost per square foot of the structural roof but to that of the appropriate wall assembly and all dependent work. The cost of the secondary framing members such as purlins, the facilities for applying an appropriate type of roof deck, the acoustical treatment, the insulation, the waterproofing, and the surface finish should be carefully checked. In some cases it may even be desirable to make preliminary sketches, accompanied by a very brief specification, for two or more architecturally acceptable designs. If these alternates require, as they often do, different wall, floor, or foundation treatment, each design should be sufficiently developed to enable an accurate computation of quantities. With this information available, comparative estimates can be obtained from a contractor. The probable cost for maintenance and the insurance rate on both building and contents should also be considered for each competing design.

Article 1. Concrete Rigid Frames, Arches, and Domes

RIGID FRAMES. The more common types have the appearance of a rather flat arch. The difference in rise of the crown and in sectional dimensions, in comparison with masonry arches, is a direct result of the structural analysis, as the use of considerable reinforcement permits high tensile

FIG. 1. Concrete Rigid Frames over a Gymnasium. Courtesy, Portland Cement Association.

stresses and full continuity between the spanning member and the supporting columns or legs. Figure 1 shows a design appropriate for a gymnasium. As in most arches, the lower ends of the legs are usually connected with a tie or restrained from outward movement by buttresses. The reinforced-concrete bents shown in Figs. 2 and 3 are also a type of rigid frame more commonly used in steel than in concrete.

Although particularly appropriate for the roofs of one-story buildings or one-story portions of multistory structures, the same forms are applicable to a wide variety of designs. They have been used throughout the United States in auditoriums, gymnasiums, hangars, armories, markets, and factories. The structural deck may be formed of poured concrete or precast concrete slabs, with or without purlins, as may be desired from the viewpoint of interior appearance or comparative cost. In some instances, such as a group of thirteen armories built for the Illinois National Guard, wood sheathing has been used for the roof deck. Economical spans are generally

Fig. 2. Concrete Bents in Hangar Construction. Courtesy, Portland Cement Association.

between 60 and 100 ft. Although there are many rigid frames having spans well over this limit, the dead load of the concrete usually makes one of such size more costly than a lighter-weight system. This fact is the reason for using hollow sections, as later described.

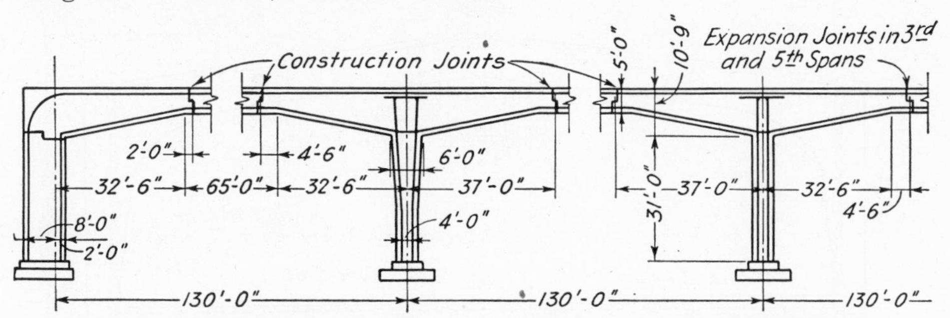

Fig. 3. Partial Transverse Section of Design Illustrated in Fig. 2. Each Bent Comprises Seven 130-ft Continuous Frames. Courtesy, Portland Cement Association.

When comparing the rigid frame in concrete with designs meeting the same structural requirements in steel or wood, the choice may be influenced, if not controlled, by the type of occupancy. If either wood or steel must be protected from fire or deleterious gases, the additional cost is an

FIG. 4. Concrete Rigid Frames in an Industrial Building. Design and Construction by the Austin Company.

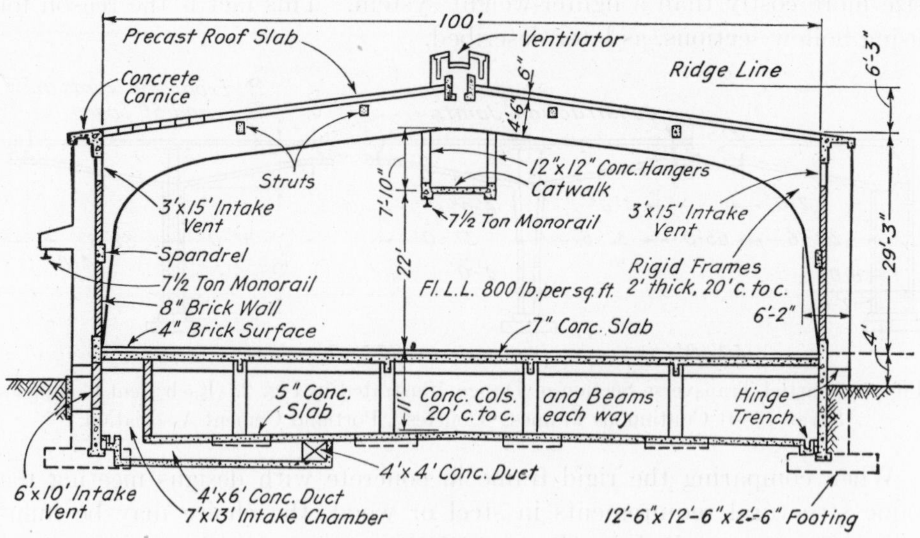

FIG. 5. Transverse Section of Design Illustrated in Fig. 4. Courtesy, *Engineering News-Record.*

important item. These considerations favored the choice of the design shown in Fig. 4 for a manufacturing plant.[1] The span is 100 ft. Frames were placed 20 ft apart. Hinges were provided in each leg near the floor level. Struts were used between the frames, but no purlins were required,

Fig. 6. Concrete Rigid Frames of Hollow Section. Courtesy, Portland Cement Association.

as precast Flexicore slabs (see page 121), designed with a camber to eliminate dead-load deflection, formed the roof deck, which was surfaced with built-up waterproofing. The catwalk and other details are shown in Fig. 5.

A variation of the typical rigid frame features hollow sections for both girders and columns. Box girders of hollow design have probably been more widely used on highway bridges than in building construction. An example is the bridge over an arm of Puget Sound, which has a span of approximately 190 ft. The frames shown in Fig. 6 have clear spans of

[1] For a detailed description of this design see "Rigid-Frame Concrete Industrial Plant," by A. F. Plant and S. J. Deitrick, *Engineering News-Record*, August 26, 1943.

77 ft.[2] They are spaced 18 ft apart. Girder depth varies from 5 ft at mid-span to 4 ft at the ends; they are 4 ft 7 in. wide. Girder webs vary in thickness from 12½ in. at the ends to 6 in. at mid-span. They are braced by the top and bottom slabs, which are of a uniform 6-in. depth, and by five diaphragms spaced 13 ft on centers. Details are shown in Fig. 7. Columns are of the same width as the girders and rest upon continuous footings.

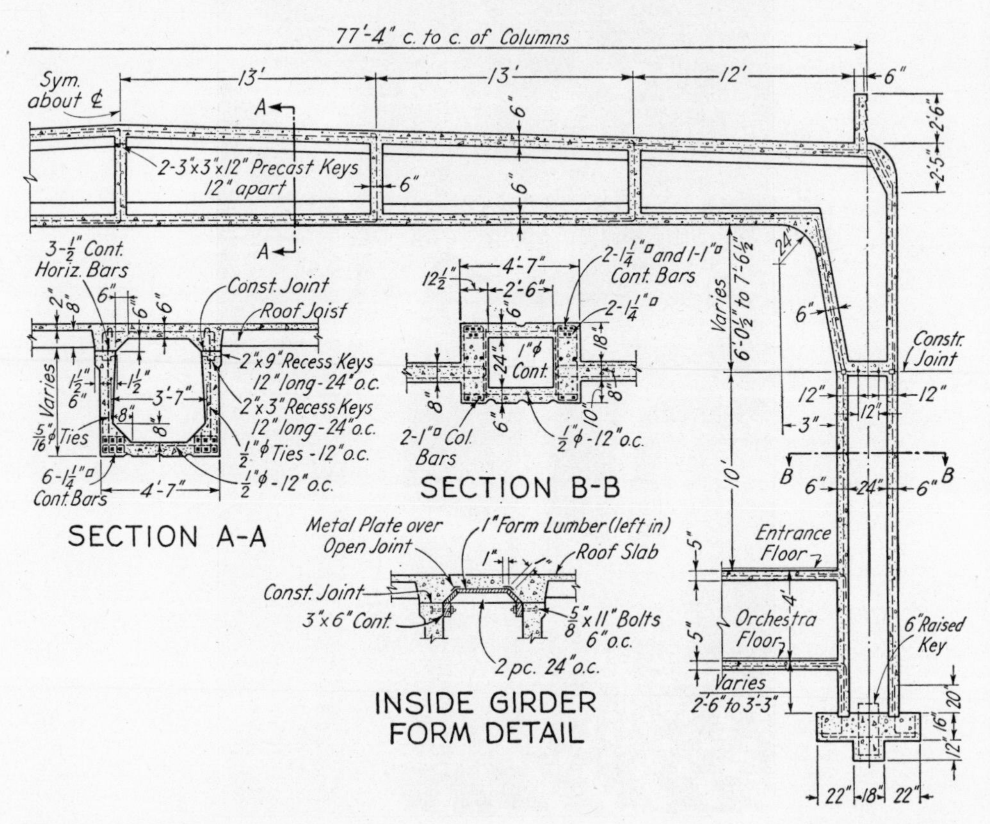

FIG. 7. Partial Transverse Section of Design Illustrated in Fig. 6. Courtesy, Portland Cement Association.

They are made 12½ in. thick at the sides, corresponding to the thickness of the girder webs at the section where they join. The inner and outer faces of the columns are each 6 in. thick. Precast concrete joists, exposed on the underside, serve as purlins carrying the roof deck. Since the erection of this structure in 1937, hollow leg and girder sections have been employed for a number of rigid frames, including the 140-ft spans of the National Guard Hangar at Des Moines, Iowa.

[2] For a detailed description of this design see *Architectural Concrete*, Vol. 3, No. 3, published by the Portland Cement Association.

SHELL ARCHES AND DOMES. Before about 1930 these designs were more common in Europe and South America than in this country. During recent years they have become popular for occupancies as diverse as factories, hangars, auditoriums, markets, and sewage-disposal plants. Spans up to approximately 300 ft have been constructed, and much longer ones are contemplated. Basically a single unit comprising a thin, reinforced-concrete curved plate, the shell arch or dome may be supported and stiffened by structural-steel or reinforced-concrete framing or masonry walls. Shells may be single span, multiple span, or various combinations

FIG. 8. Barrel-Shell Roof Construction for a Naval Seaplane Hangar. Courtesy, Roberts and Schaefer.

of each. From the viewpoint of economy singly curved shells are preferable, but other types of curves can be built. The dome shown on page 204 (New York City Planetarium) is often called a "doubly curved" shell.

The reinforced-concrete columns and other elements of the framing supporting shell roofs of the multiple barrel and butterfly types usually provide sufficient flexibility to obviate the need for hinges. A substantial curvature of the roof shell may be used to obtain stiffness against buckling. Increased stiffness is especially required as the span of the shell increases and where it is necessary to support special loads. A strong curvature, however, results in the shell section being comparatively steep for some height above the springing line. This is sometimes objectionable for architectural reasons and may require double forms, thereby increasing the cost. When a comparatively flat roof is designed with a long radius of curvature, the necessary stiffness is obtained either by thickening the shell section or by adding ribs. The choice depends primarily upon architectural preference and comparative cost.

Figure 8 shows a barrel shell which is only 3½ in. thick between ribs, and Fig. 9 a typical cross-section. For designs of this type, scaffolds supporting the forms represent a large proportion of the erection cost. Structures of little length are, therefore, comparatively more expensive than longer structures, which permit a greater reuse of forms. This is par-

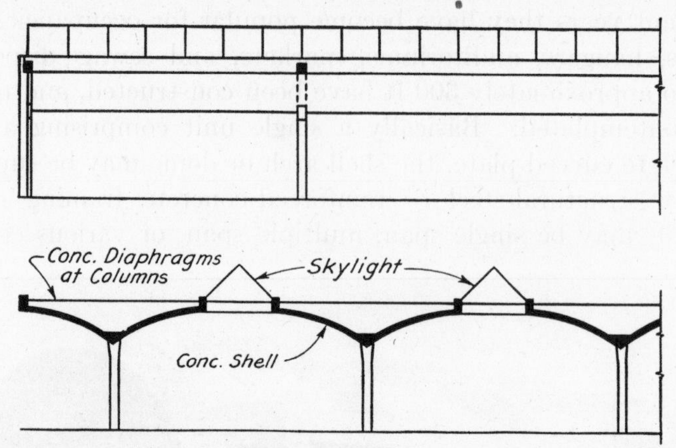

FIG. 9. Typical Transverse Section of Barrel Shells. Courtesy, Roberts and Schaefer.

ticularly true if high roofs are required. It is impossible to be specific in regard to the minimum and maximum rise which is structurally desirable for shell roofs. The illustrations show well-considered designs identifying

FIG. 10. Butterfly-Shell Roof Construction for an Industrial Plant. Courtesy, Roberts and Schaefer.

typical solutions. Each project should be studied in relation to the factors mentioned in this article. It is true, however, that the maximum slope of either arch or dome should not exceed 45° if double forms are to be avoided, unless the concrete is deposited by pneumatic means, as was done on the Hayden Planetarium.

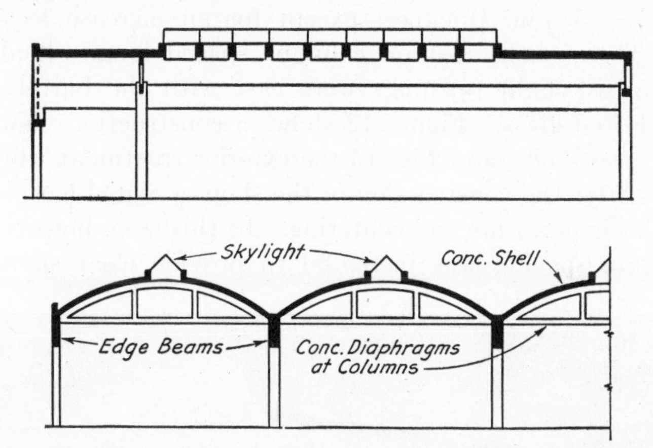

Fig. 11. Typical Transverse Section of Butterfly Shells. Courtesy, Roberts and Schaefer.

The butterfly design, a variation derived from the multiple barrel shell, is particularly suitable for garages. Figure 10 shows an interior view, and Fig. 11 a typical cross-section. For both designs the minimum economical span is about 30 ft, and the maximum about 60 ft. The construction meets any normal requirement for fire resistance and is superior to many other

Fig. 12. Barrel Shells under Construction at Wright Field. Courtesy, Roberts and Schaefer.

concrete types because of the even distribution of small reinforcing bars throughout the shell. It is far more flexible than would be supposed and can be adapted to saw-tooth designs.

The single-story engineering shop erected at Wright Field illustrates the application of the shell roof to industry. This building is 360 ft wide and 420 ft long. It is roofed by a series of nine concrete barrel shells, each of 40-ft span and 3½-in. thickness except for an increase to 5 in. at the haunches. These shells rest on columns spaced longitudinally 56 ft on centers. Curb-skylight openings were cast with the barrels and glazed with sand-blasted glass. Figure 12 shows a construction view identifying the shape of the shells, and Fig. 13 the exterior treatment which expresses their form. After the construction of the shop, a Signal Corps hangar was built with the same forms and centering. In this case, however, the longitudinal column spacing was increased to provide clear spans of 120 ft,

FIG. 13. Exterior of Design Illustrated in Fig. 12. Courtesy, Roberts and Schaefer.

and the barrels were supported by the deepened edge members, spanning this distance. Figure 14 shows a comparison of the two types. In the lower design, where shells are used as "cross barrels," a longitudinal column spacing up to 200 ft may be economical.

Reinforced-concrete arch rings, combined with shell construction, are illustrated by several large hangars, armories, auditoriums, and industrial plants built during recent years. Figure 15 shows the navy hangar at San Diego, California.[3] The designer should note the advantage of placing the main concrete arches so that the shells comprising the structural slab are supported from the intrados. This eliminates any projection of structural members below the undersurface of the roof and facilitates the movement of forms and falsework as the structure is poured section by section. Arches are of two-hinged type with a tie below the floor level. Hinges are of Mesnager design, consisting of reinforcing bars arranged in a fan-like system and permitting the rotation of the arch at the hinge while at the same time transferring the load to the footing.

[3] "Wide-Span Hangars for the U. S. Navy," by Anton Tedesko, *Civil Engineering*, December, 1941.

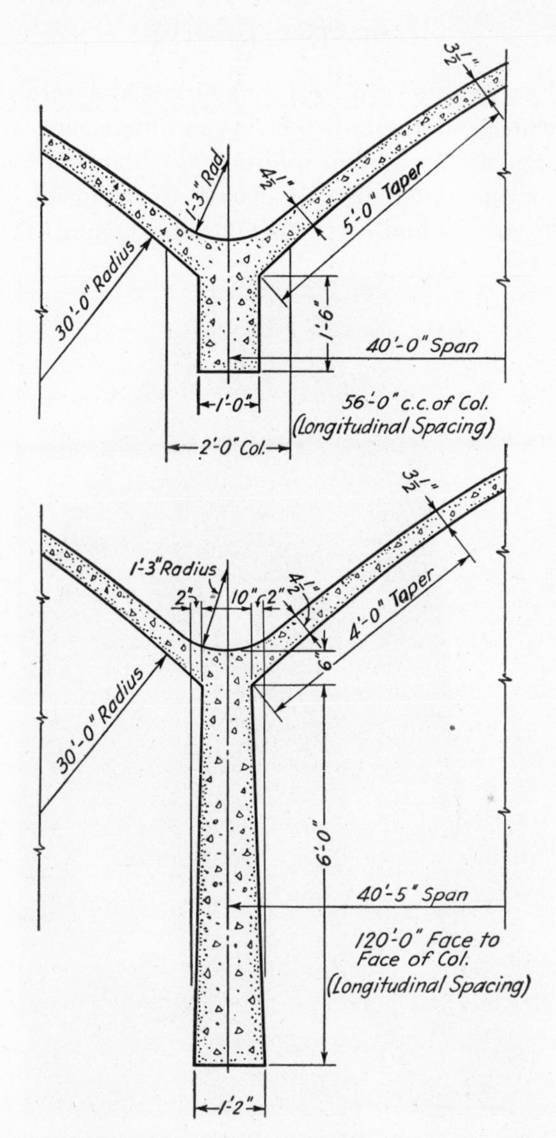

Fig. 14. Form of Edge Members for Barrel Shells. Courtesy, Roberts and Schaefer.

Fig. 15. Naval Hangar at San Diego, Calif. Official Photograph of the U. S. Navy.

The roof shell carries its own load and serves as lateral bracing for the arches. The thickness at the crown is 3½ in., increasing at the haunches. Auxiliary stiffening ribs, located at mid-points between arches, are 10 × 20 in.; double ribs of the same size are placed at expansion joints which lie between alternate arches and serve to take up unequal settlement as well

Fig. 16. Concrete Shells of the Hershey Ice Arena, Hershey, Pa. Courtesy, Roberts and Schaefer.

as volumetric changes. Figure 16 shows an interior of the Hershey, Pennsylvania, Ice Arena. Although this is not one of the newer buildings, this view illustrates the remarkable lightness of shell design. The span is 222 ft. Columns are spaced at 39 ft, and the overhanging cantilever at each end is approximately 19 ft.

Although not a shell roof, Fig. 17, of similar appearance, shows an interesting example of designing the enclosed area to meet the functional demands of the structure. This is an asphalt-mixing plant, and the elliptical shape is particularly suitable as an enclosure for the tanks and machinery. The four arch ribs are spaced 22 ft on centers. The clear span is 90 ft, and the height to the intrados approximately 85 ft. Concrete barrel arches 8 in. thick were poured between the ribs. The rib sections vary in depth from 6 ft 6 in. at the springing line to 5 ft at the crown. They are 2 ft 4 in. wide at the extrados, and 3 ft wide at the intrados. As the change in thickness occurs along the inner face of the barrels, a shelf is provided for their

FIG. 17. Construction View of Asphalt-Mixing Plant for New York City. Courtesy, Portland Cement Association.

support. Structural-steel shapes serve as reinforcement and were also used as a support for the forms, which may be seen in the upper right-hand portion of the illustration. This idea is a comparatively new development which eliminates all falsework within the structure and has an application to many types of concrete buildings as well as to wide-span assemblies.

The Planetarium and Market Hall, shown in Figs. 18 and 19, illustrate the two different treatments for domes. The Planetarium is a doubly curved shell, and the Market Hall is formed by the intersection of numerous cylindrical shells of single curvature having ribs at the lines of intersection. The diameter of the Planetarium is 81 ft; the shell thickness 3 in. down to 9 ft above the springing line. The span of Market Hall is 197 ft; the shell

FIG. 18. Construction View of Hayden Planetarium, New York City. *Gen Contr.*: White. Construction Company. Courtesy, Roberts and Schaefer.

FIG. 19. Market Hall, Basle, Switzerland.

thickness 3¼ in. The lower portion of the Hayden Planetarium is steel-framed, octagonal in plan.

The most economical method of waterproofing concrete curved surfaces is to apply a built-up or other bituminous type of roofing. The resurfacing of the concrete arch roof of the model-testing basin, at Carderock, Maryland, done under supervision of the Bureau of Yards and Docks, United States Navy Department, in 1945, consisted of built-up waterproofing

FIG. 20. Hayden Planetarium at Night. *Arch.:* Trowbridge and Livingston. Courtesy, Roberts and Schaefer.

retained in place by noncorrodible nails driven into treated wood strips attached to the concrete by means of expansion bolts. Three layers of ½-in. insulation board were laid in asphalt between the concrete roof deck and waterproofing. On portions of the roof having a slope of 6 in. or more to 1 ft, a three-ply membrane was placed with ⅛-in. of plastic cement between each layer. Where the roof slope was less, a four-ply membrane was laid in asphalt "mopped on." The reason for using plastic cement on the steeper slopes was to obtain a cleaner surface for the application of aluminum paint.

The exposure of the concrete shell, with no treatment other than a cement paint or liquid waterproofing compound, is not recommended. This procedure may be successful in the warmer climates but can hardly be expected to render the entire concrete deck watertight in localities subject to freezing temperatures. For monumental buildings, particularly domes, a sheet-copper or clay-tile roof has been used. The Hayden Planetarium was lined with 1½ in. of rock cork and surfaced with 1½ in. of nailing concrete, to which a copper surface was applied. Figure 20 shows the front elevation.

Article 2. Steel Girders, Trusses, Rigid Frames, Arches, and Domes

PLATE GIRDERS. These girders have been used in building construction over a period of many years for supporting floors or flat roofs where length of spans or load requirements were too great for rolled-steel sections when placed at an economical spacing. Figure 21 shows a typical design.

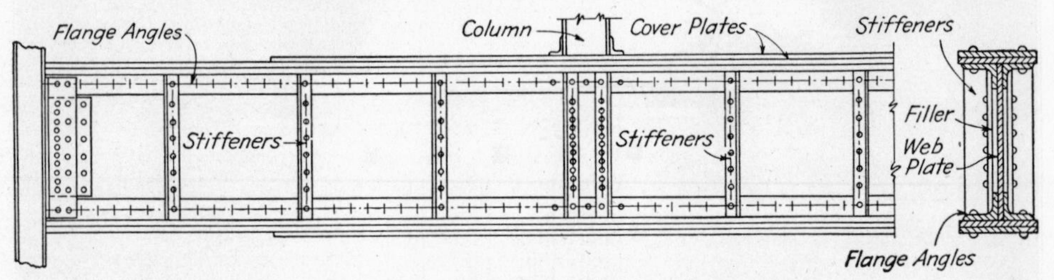

Fig. 21. Plate Girder.

As mentioned on page 60, standard wide-flanged steel girders 36 in. deep are available, and where loads are not excessive they may be appropriate for spans up to about 65 ft. Beyond this limit, which varies with the amount and character of the loading, or even for shorter spans, plate girders may be used for the support of floors where the omission of columns makes it necessary to carry concentrated loads across several bays.

This condition occurs when a ballroom or similar unobstructed area is required beneath superimposed stories. Such construction is always somewhat more expensive because of the difficulty of concealing deep structural members in addition to the weight of steel and cost of fabrication. Wherever practicable, the designer should place such large open spaces directly beneath a roof. In this connection it should be noted that, where conditions permit a choice among standard wide-flange steel girders, plate girders, and parallel chord trusses, the first two are generally more economical, even if somewhat heavier, than the truss design. An exception occurs where the trusses support sufficient load to warrant their being made full story height and concealed in the partitions.

TRUSSES. The steel truss is most widely used in buildings as a support for roofs. Figure 22 shows the more common designs. An appropriate choice depends upon many factors. Important considerations are the amount and type of loading, the length of span, the conditions imposed by occupancy, architectural preference, and the roof construction. Even secondary matters, such as the necessary provision for ventilation, lighting, and insulation, may influence the choice. It is consequently impracticable to make general recommendations which would have definite significance for any particular project. From a structural viewpoint, however, the following comments may be of some help.

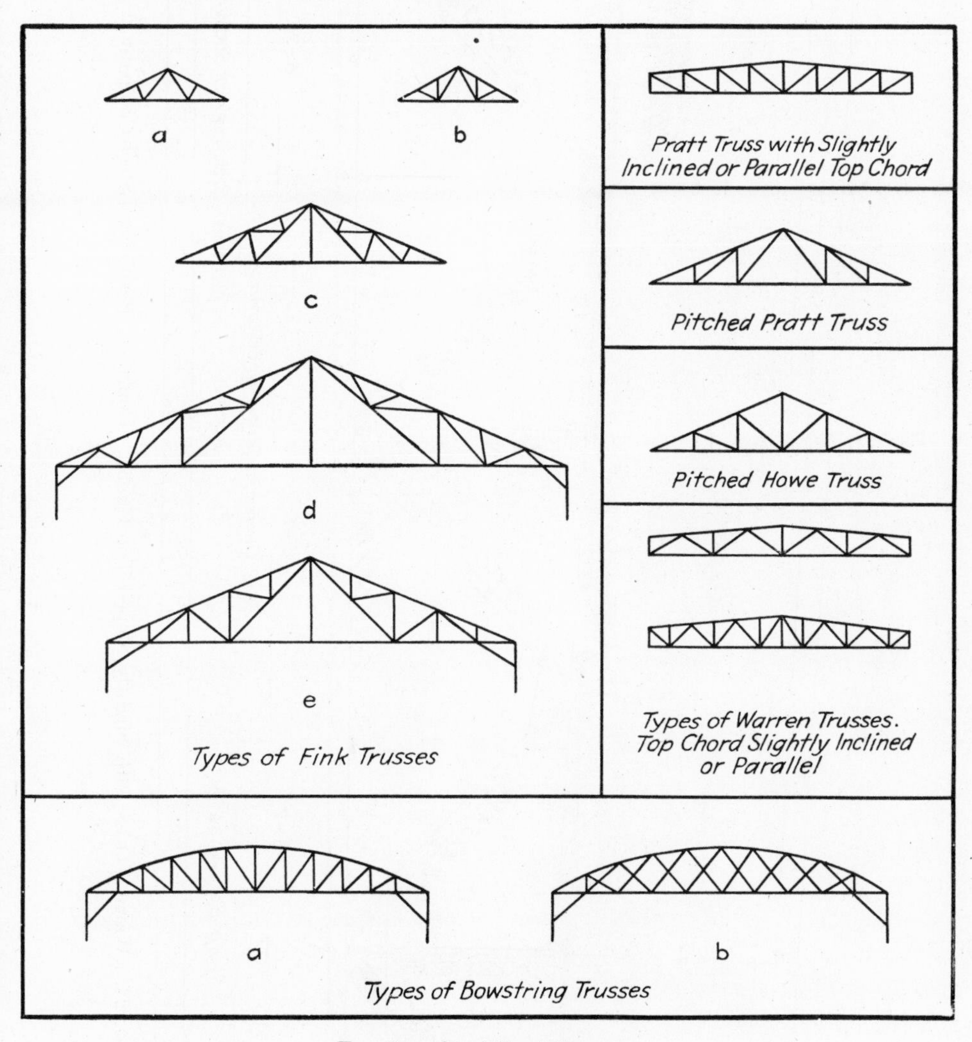

FIG. 22. Steel Roof Trusses.

For flat roofs having a slope from ¾ to 1¼ in. per ft, the Warren truss with slightly sloped top chord is widely used and is often an appropriate choice for spans from 30 to 200 ft, although most economical for spans up to 125 ft. This pitch is suitable for built-up waterproofing, which would ordinarily be laid over the roof deck as a surfacing material. Figure 23 shows a typical design. Figures 24 and 25 illustrate the application of the

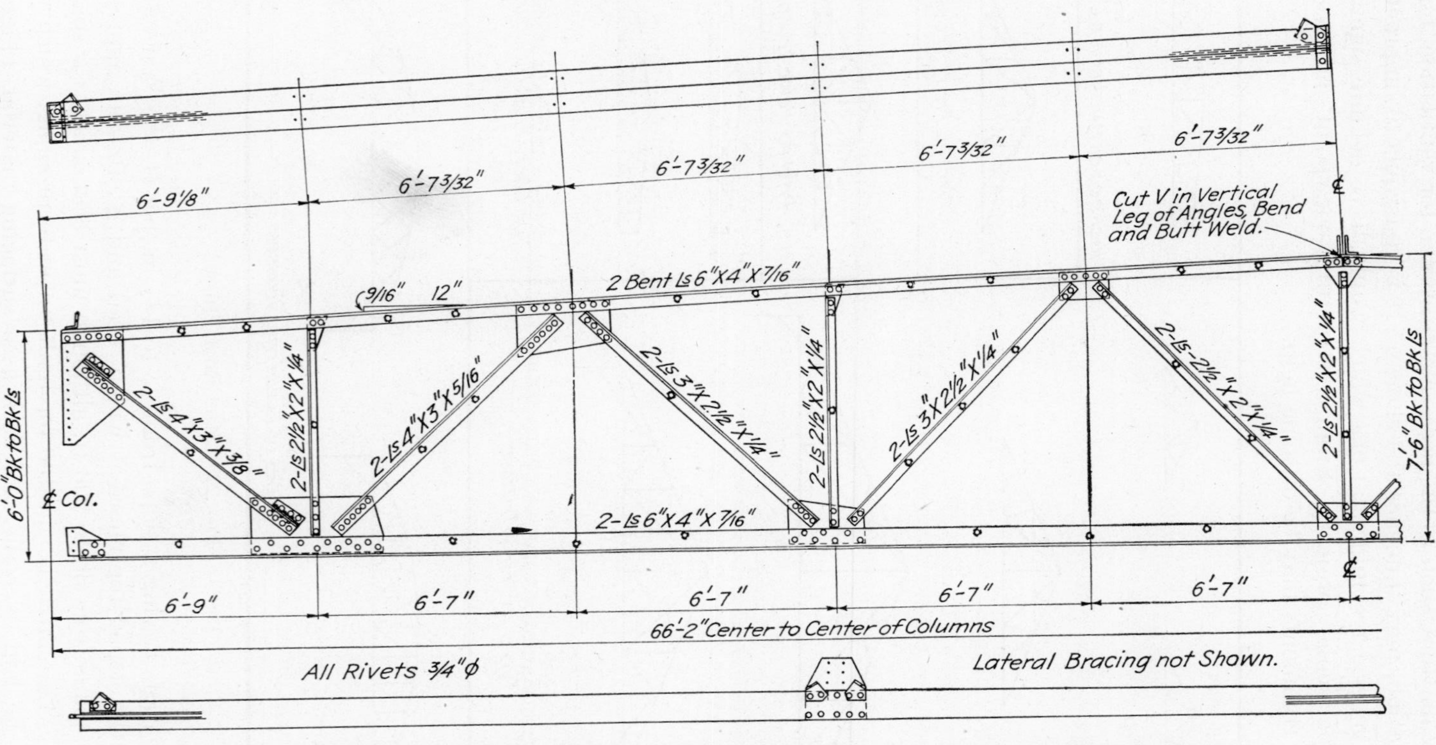

FIG. 23. Warren Truss with Slightly Sloped Top Chord. Courtesy, Bethlehem Steel Company.

Warren truss to industrial and monumental buildings, respectively. The Pratt truss, with slightly inclined top chord, may be considered an alternate for the same spans. Where either type is acceptable, the Warren is often preferred. Trusses having absolutely parallel chords are not as extensively used for spans over 50 ft, as many designers desire a slight pitch for drainage, and the top chord usually serves as a direct support for the roof construction. The Howe truss, with either parallel or slightly inclined top chord, is not usually as appropriate as the Warren or Pratt.

Fig. 24. Warren Trusses in Factory Construction. Courtesy, American Institute of Steel Construction.

For pitched roofs the Fink truss has a broad application to all types of occupancy. It is very widely used for steel-framed mill buildings as support for steel purlins carrying corrugated roofing and is equally suitable for residential or monumental structures. In such cases the roof deck would be selected as discussed in Chapter Five and surfaced with slate, tile, or other appropriate material. In its simplest form the Fink truss can occasionally be used advantageously on spans as short as 20 ft and is often economical for spans up to 125 ft. A popular slope is 5 in. in 1 ft. Figure 26 shows a typical design. Both the Pratt and the Howe trusses, with steeply inclined top chords, are also used for pitched roofs but are usually more costly than the Fink. Of the two, the Howe design is generally more expensive than the Pratt. Where a curved upper chord is acceptable, the bowstring truss may prove quite economical for moderate spans and has an application up to about 125 ft. Various designs are shown in Fig. 27. The crescent truss is far less common but has been employed occasionally.

In regard to the approximate depth of roof trusses supporting only roof loads on a 100-ft span, it may be said that both the Warren and Pratt trusses, with slightly inclined top chords, would have a depth of about 11 ft at the center and 6 ft at the ends. With parallel chords both would have a depth of about one-twelfth the span. For heavy loads, in addition to the weight of the roof construction, the depth of the parallel-chord design might be about one-tenth of the span. The Fink truss would have a depth

FIG. 25. Warren Trusses in the Municipal Auditorium, Topeka, Kansas. Courtesy, American Institute of Steel Construction.

of about 21 ft for a span of 100 ft, and the bowstring truss would be about 10 ft deep when supporting only roof loads.

The spacing of roof trusses depends primarily upon the requirements of the roof construction, the length of span, the cost of foundations, and the loads which they may be required to support in addition to that of the roof. In one-story mill-building construction, the length of the typical bay, which determines the spacing, usually varies between 20 and 28 ft. Expensive foundations obviously favor the upper limit. In planning many types of manufacturing buildings, the designer should give serious thought to the elimination of columns wherever practicable. A column once installed is a fixture, removable only by expensive alterations. A clear floor space may be eventually more economical, notwithstanding a higher first cost.

When using trusses, it should be remembered that they are supported, theoretically, in a manner to cause the reactions at the supports to be vertical for vertical loads. To obtain this condition horizontal movement due to any cause must be unrestrained. Provision for expansion or contraction due to temperature changes is important for long, exposed steel trusses

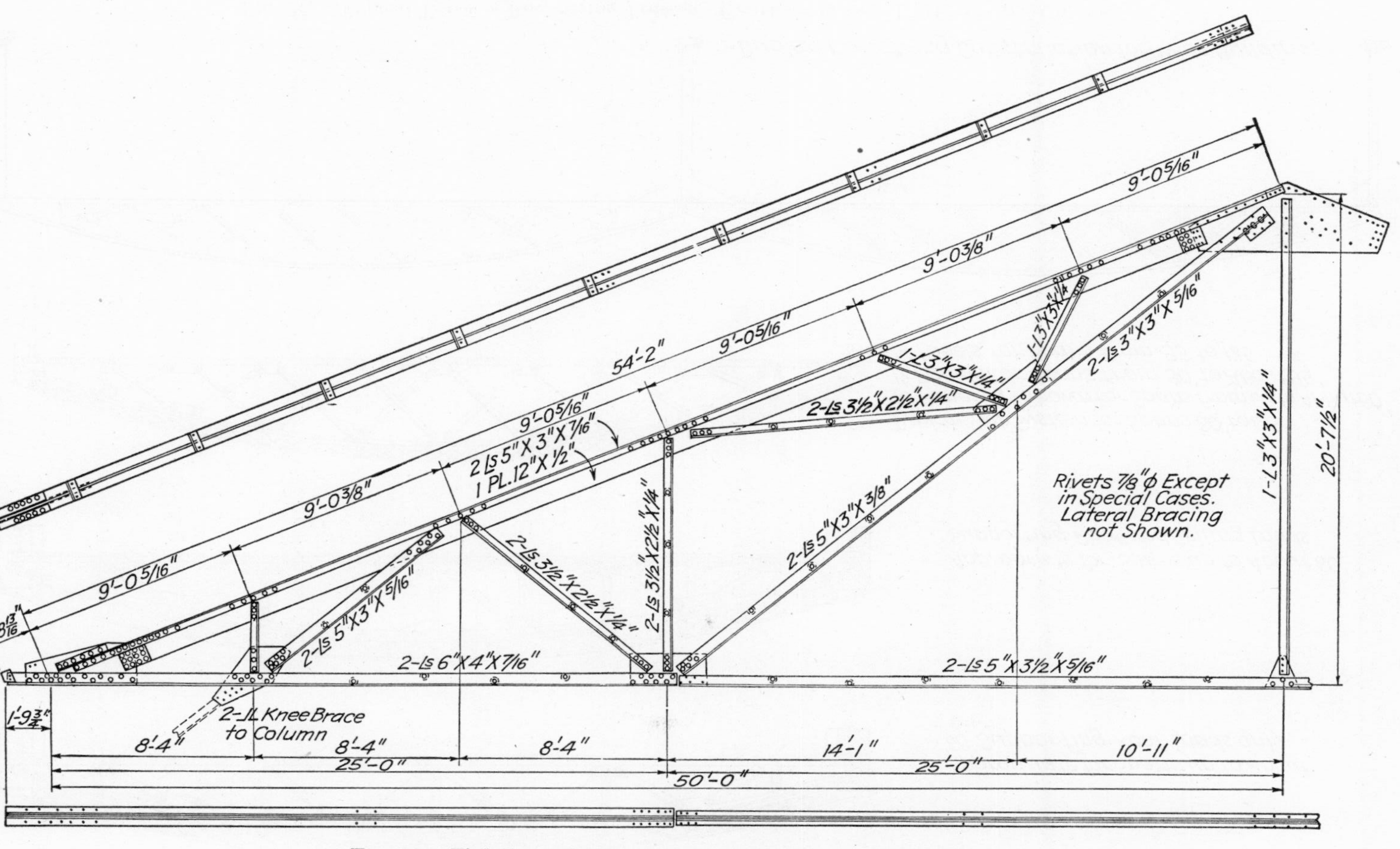

Fig. 26. Fink Roof Truss. Courtesy, American Bridge Company.

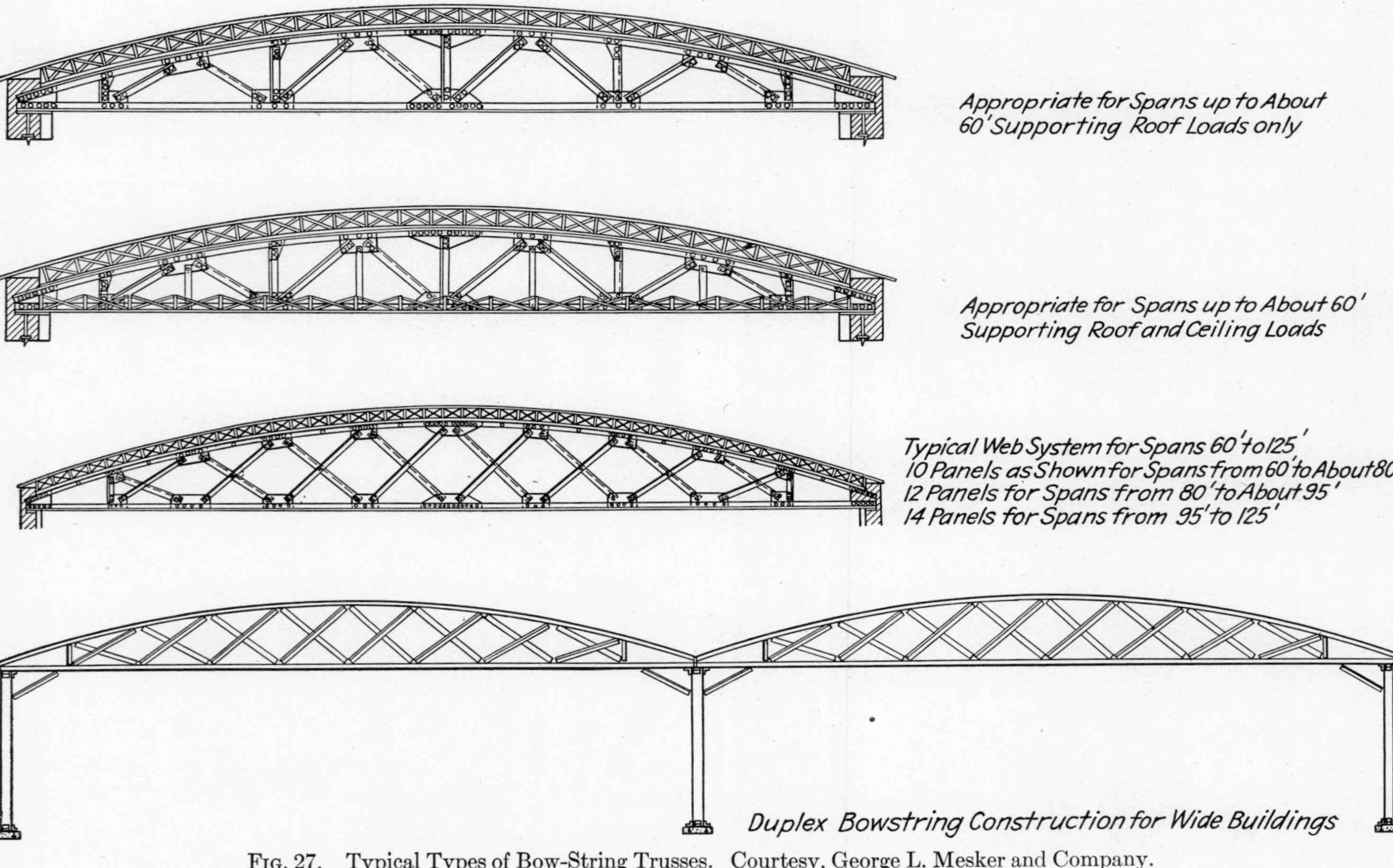

FIG. 27. Typical Types of Bow-String Trusses. Courtesy, George L. Mesker and Company.

resting on masonry or concrete abutments, such as those used for many railway bridges. As conditions in buildings are much less severe, trusses

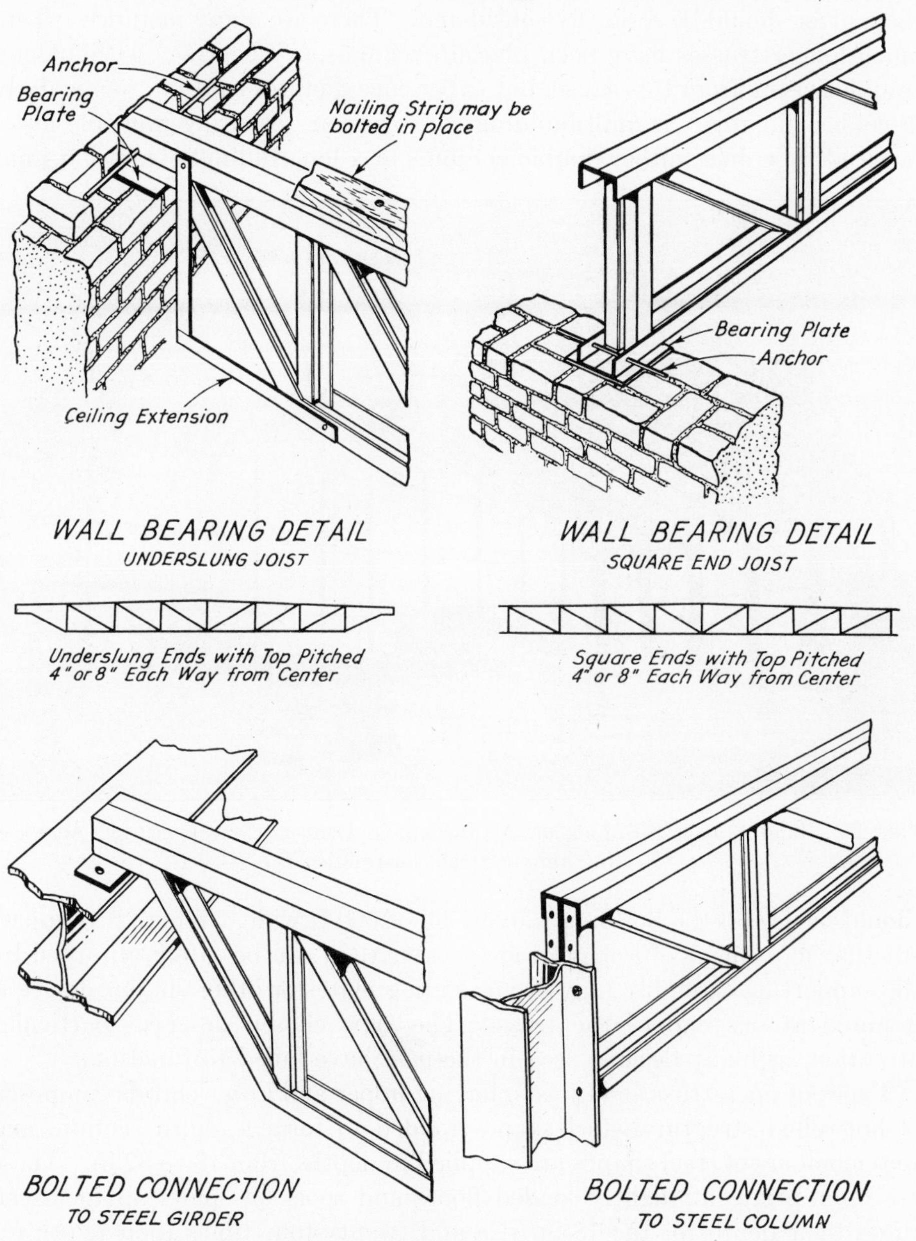

FIG. 28. Open-Truss Steel Joists for Wide-Span Designs. Courtesy, Ceco Steel Products Corporation.

spanning up to 125 ft, when framing into steel columns or resting on top of them, are connected to the columns with brackets or knee braces without any provision for end movement.

Where support is furnished by masonry walls or piers, no special provision is normally required unless spans exceed 50 ft. Beyond this length the matter should be seriously considered. There are many instances where much longer trusses have been placed over masonry bearings without any trouble arising from this cause, but experience dictates caution, particularly in colder climates. In mill-building construction, featuring multiple aisles serviced by cranes, either double columns or a longitudinal expansion joint

Fig. 29. Rigid Frames Spanning an Auditorium in Denver, Col. Courtesy, American Institute of Steel Construction.

should be used if the building is over 500 or 600 ft wide. Where it is apparent that movement of a magnitude greater than can be safely absorbed by the supporting assembly may occur, sliding plates or other similar device is required at one end of the truss. The type chosen deserves particular attention, as many designs used in the past have failed to function.

Types of open-truss steel joists, having upper and lower chords composed of hot-rolled structural-steel shapes welded to form a chord section, and web members of steel shapes are supplied in depths from 18 to 32 in. These are appropriate for lightly loaded floors and roofs on spans up to fifteen times their depth for the 18-in. size and twenty-four times their depth for the 32-in. size. Typical designs and details of end support are shown in Fig. 28. These trusses are manufactured with either square or underslung ends; top chords may be either pitched or flat. If pitched, the slope may be toward one end or in each direction from the center. Bridging is essential and is normally placed at approximately 10 ft on centers. These sections have been used quite extensively for the support of roofs over gymnasiums, assembly halls, and auditoriums in school buildings designed by the Architectural Department of the State of Virginia. They may be surfaced in the same manner as any other truss.

RIGID FRAMES AND ARCHES. Rigid-frame designs in structural steel have been widely used during recent years for spans from about 60 up to 200 ft. Although the more common form, shown in Fig. 29, may be comparatively low, a considerable clear height can be obtained by extending the length of the legs, as is illustrated in Fig. 30. These designs are

Fig. 30. Rigid Frames of Exceptional Height in Factory Construction. Courtesy, American Institute of Steel Construction.

appropriate for university field houses, hangars, gymnasiums, armories, and amphitheaters, as well as industrial plants. Figure 31 shows a rigid frame over a drafting room, and Fig. 32 an adaptation to saw-tooth construction. Sometimes referred to as arches, they are actually rigid frames, as high tensile stresses are developed.

A patented application sponsored by the American Bridge Company is known as beam-arch construction, although this type is also a rigid frame. The name is derived from the fact that the ends of the beams comprising the principal elements of the assembly are split longitudinally through the webs, and the inner flanges bent to predetermined curves providing the necessary increase in depth at points of maximum moment. Plates of a thickness conforming to the webs are then fitted into the resulting V-shaped openings. As these are securely welded or otherwise spliced to the beam webs, they function as an integral part of the expanded beam section.

Field erection is facilitated by shop fabrication in the largest sections that can be transported. Single-span rigid frames are usually designed

Fig. 31. Rigid Frames over a Drafting Room. Design and Construction by the Austin Company.

Fig. 32. Rigid Frames in Saw-Tooth Construction. Courtesy, American Institute of Steel Construction.

and erected as two-hinged assemblies. If it is desired to assume a three-hinged condition for dead loads, this may be maintained until the steel work is completely erected by using at the peak of the arch a temporary third pin-joint which is later replaced by riveting or welding. Particularly

FIG. 33. Beam-Arch Construction Spanning a National Guard Armory. Courtesy, American Bridge Company.

appropriate for buildings designed for public assembly, the typical form provides an open floor space with unobstructed vision and ample head room. It is structurally applicable to a wide range of roof slopes and to spans up to 200 ft. Figures 33, 34, and 35 show designs appropriate for different types of occupancy.

The diagrams in Fig. 36 illustrate various frames composed of short-length steel beams bolted, riveted, or welded together to form the ribs of

FIG. 34. Beam-Arch Construction Spanning an Industrial Building. Courtesy, American Bridge Company.

arches or rigid frames. Spans up to 300 ft have been built by this system, certain details of which are patented by the sponsors. With the exception of type (*d*), in which the horizontal component of the thrust is resisted by the equivalent of buttresses, a tie is provided beneath the floor construction.

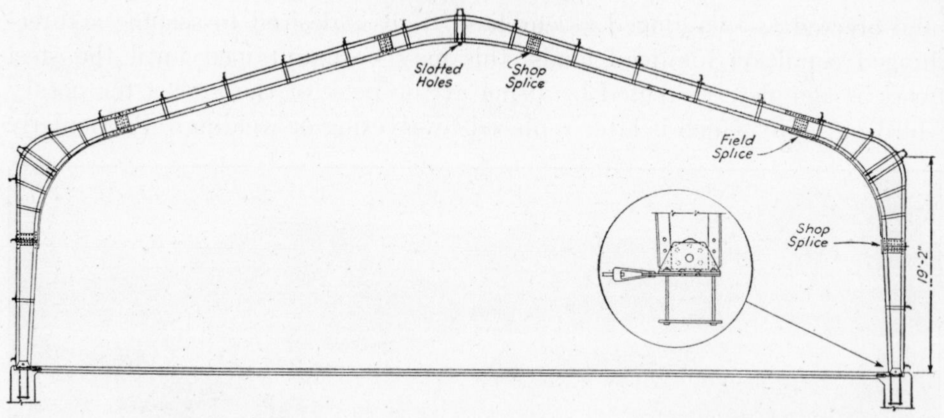

FIG. 35. Typical Rigid-Frame Design for a Hangar. Courtesy, American Institute of Steel Construction.

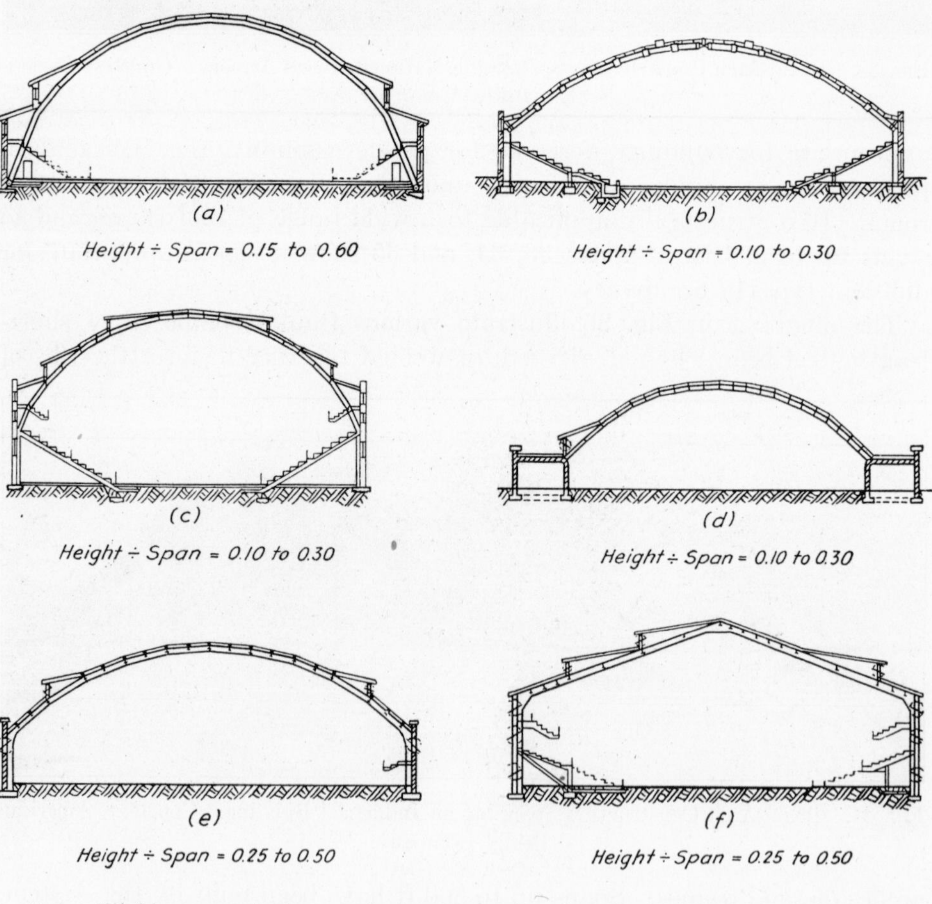

FIG. 36. Types of Steel Arches and Rigid Frames. Courtesy, Arch-Roof Construction Company.

These designs are usually of two- or three-hinged type. Although the three-hinged type permits a much simpler structural analysis, a hinge at

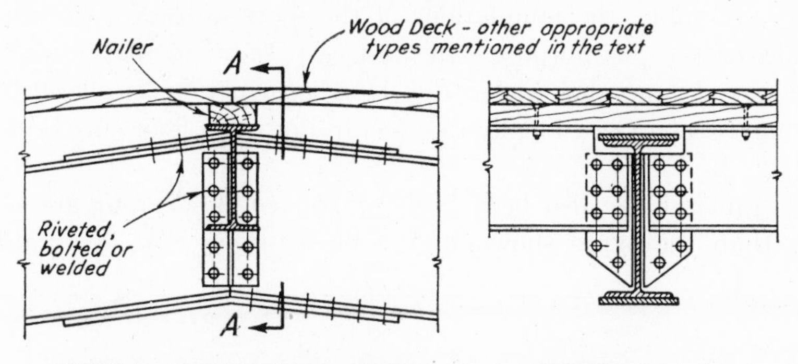

Fig. 37. Detail of Steel-Arch Crown Connection. Courtesy, Arch-Roof Construction Company.

the crown may require considerable additional expense, both in construction and maintenance, in order to provide for expansion of the roof deck without causing leakage through the waterproofing. Figure 37 shows a

Fig. 38. Steel Arches over a Gymnasium. Courtesy, Arch-Roof Construction Company.

rigid crown connection, and Fig. 38 an interior illustrating a popular application of such designs. Provision is made at the supports for expansion or contraction.

All rigid frames require some provision at the base of the legs or columns to resist the horizontal component of the inclined reaction. If soil conditions are favorable, the foundations of the more moderate spans may be designed to serve this purpose. In most cases a tie, in the form of a steel eye-bar or rod concealed within the floor construction, is placed between the column bases. Occasionally the steel framing of a floor may be designed as a tie.

Rigid frames have also been built of trussed design but are now less popular than the types shown in the illustrations. Welded rigid-frame

FIG. 39. Trussed Arches in Steel. Courtesy, American Institute of Steel Construction.

bents are occasionally economical. They were used in the Chicago water-filter plant built in 1944.

Large single-span steel arches may be built of trussed design, as shown in Fig. 39. Their particular application is for hangars and structures where spans up to 300 ft combined with considerable height are desired. Spans of 235 ft and heights over 180 ft above the floor were built during World War II by the Bureau of Yards and Docks for naval aircraft hangars. These are enormous structures 1058 ft long. Of somewhat lighter construction are the demountable hangars employing steel arches spanning 130 ft. A number of other designs, consisting of bolted arch ribs of pressed steel

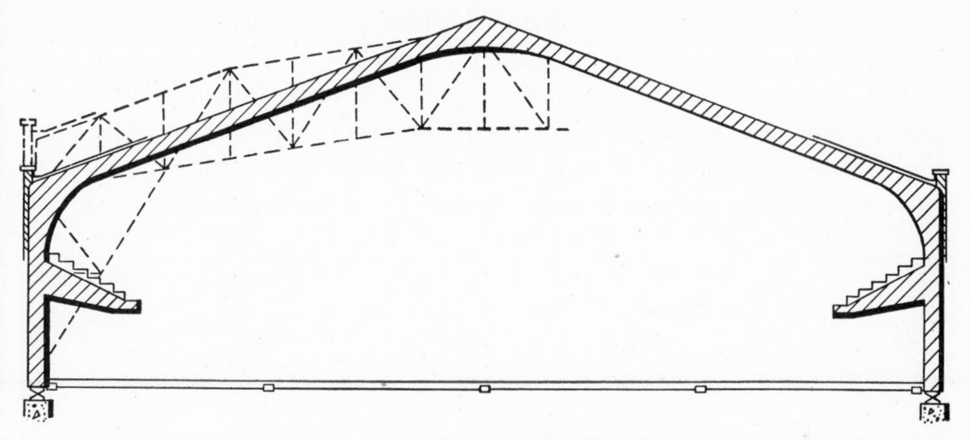

FIG. 40. Comparison of the Beam-Arch Design with Arch-Truss Construction. Courtesy, American Bridge Company.

FIG. 41. Steel Lamella Design Expressed in a Decorative Ceiling Treatment. Courtesy, Roof Structures, Inc.

and purlins of 20-gage steel channels, which provide as much as 190 ft clear span at the floor level, have been developed.

Steel arches are usually of two- or three-hinged design. The three-hinged arch has the advantage of being statically determinate, the reactions at the abutments being derived from the three basic equations of static equilibrium of forces in a plane. For the shorter spans and in

Fig. 42. Structural Steel Framing for Dome of Cyclotron, University of California. Courtesy, American Institute of Steel Construction.

constructions where the rise is comparatively low, the hinge at the crown is often omitted, resulting in a two-hinged design. Unless spans are over 200 ft, the beam-arch type of rigid frame is generally a better choice, as indicated by the two superimposed designs shown in Fig. 40.

The steel Lamella arch is appropriate for gymnasiums, auditoriums, and restaurants but has been less widely used than its counterpart in wood. Fabricated from short lengths of straight beams, bolted, welded, or riveted, it is somewhat more expensive in steel than in wood. Figure 41 illustrates a very attractive application. Appropriate spans vary from 30 to about 100 ft. The horizontal thrust of the arches may be resisted by a steel tie at wall height or by buttresses. Roof decks may be of steel, wood plank, precast concrete units, or other suitable material.

Fig. 43. The Jefferson Memorial, Washington, D. C. *Arch.:* Office of John Russell Pope, Daniel P. Higgins, and Otto R. Eggers, Associates; *Engr.:* Elwyn E. Seelye and Company.

DOMES. Steel is the usual structural support for domes surfaced with either stone or lighter-weight materials. Figure 42 shows a design consisting of trussed segments. Figures 43 and 44 illustrate the exterior and the dome construction of the Jefferson Memorial in Washington, D. C.

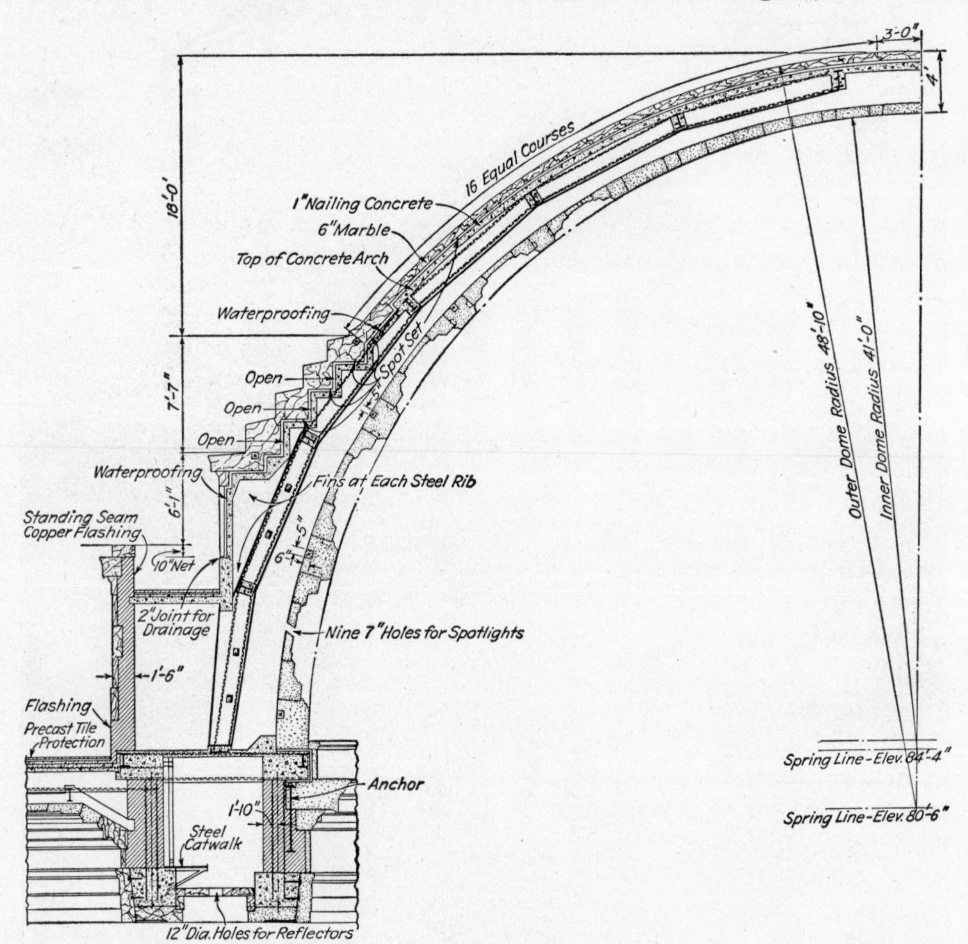

FIG. 44. Section Showing Structural-Steel Framing for Dome of Jefferson Memorial. *Arch.:* Office of John Russell Pope, Daniel P. Higgins, and Otto R. Eggers, Associates; *Engr.:* Elwyn E. Seelye and Company.

Article 3. Wood Girders, Trusses, Rigid Frames, Arches, and Domes

GIRDERS. Glued, laminated beams and girders are manufactured in straight rectangular sections or to special designs prepared by the architect. They may be employed for spans up to 60 ft or a little more but are particularly appropriate up to 50 ft. For example, when supporting a total uniformly distributed load of 50 lb per sq ft, a span of 40 ft, with a spacing of 14 ft on centers, would require a section about 25 in. deep by 9½ in.

wide. On a span of 60 ft with a spacing of 12 ft on centers, the same loading would require a section about 32 in. deep and 11½ in. wide. These figures are based on stresses generally accepted for such designs. As the deflection is rather high, beams are cambered. Among the largest of this type are those used for a gymnasium in Seattle. The span is 67 ft. Beams are 14 in. wide and 40 in. deep, built of 2-in. × 4-in. and 2-in. × 10-in. seasoned wood. Douglas fir forms the outer edges of the beams, and Sitka spruce the inner portions.

Laminated beams are manufactured with machine-planed and sanded surfaces, which may be finished to show the natural wood grain. Standard widths vary from 3⁵⁄₁₆ to 11 in., with depths as required. When estimated merely as structural units, they are generally more expensive than steel but are often economical when used as a finished product and exposed as part of the architectural treatment. For spans up to 30 ft, solid timbers are usually cheaper than laminated sections except for extremely heavy loads. Beyond that limit, wood trusses compete favorably in cost, but laminated sections may be useful when vertical clearance is limited.

TRUSSES. Although timber-latticed trusses have been used since about 1910 on 20-ft spans, particularly in New York City and Chicago, it was not until about 1925, under the impetus given by the National Committee on Wood Utilization, that the research work of the Forest Products Laboratory evolved a sound basis for timber design. Since that time the development of metallic connectors for timber joints and great improvement in the quality of synthetic glues have made possible our modern types. Better glues and improved manufacturing processes have also resulted in the production of plywoods of greater structural strength, which have their place as gusset plates for trusses and for webs of deep girders, as well as in surface-stressed panels and frames. Pressure impregnation of wood has recently been greatly improved. Some processes help to preserve the wood as well as to make it less vulnerable to fire. Among materials used are creosote petroleum, zinc chloride, Wollman salts, and pentachlorophenol solutions.

All these developments have resulted in placing timber among the structural materials for wide-span work wherever the location and type of occupancy do not demand a less inflammable material or the structural or architectural requirements favor either concrete or steel. In this connection it should be remembered that wood trusses are generally rated by municipal building codes in the slow-burning classification. When placed with a clear height of at least 20 ft above the floor, they are not usually fireproofed. Wood trusses may be supported by steel, concrete, or wood columns or by masonry piers or walls. Solid timbers are still widely used except for curved members, such as the two chords of a crescent truss and the upper chord of a bowstring truss, which would be laminated even if the lower chord were of solid section. Steel rods are also used for tensile members. Figure 45 shows the more common designs.

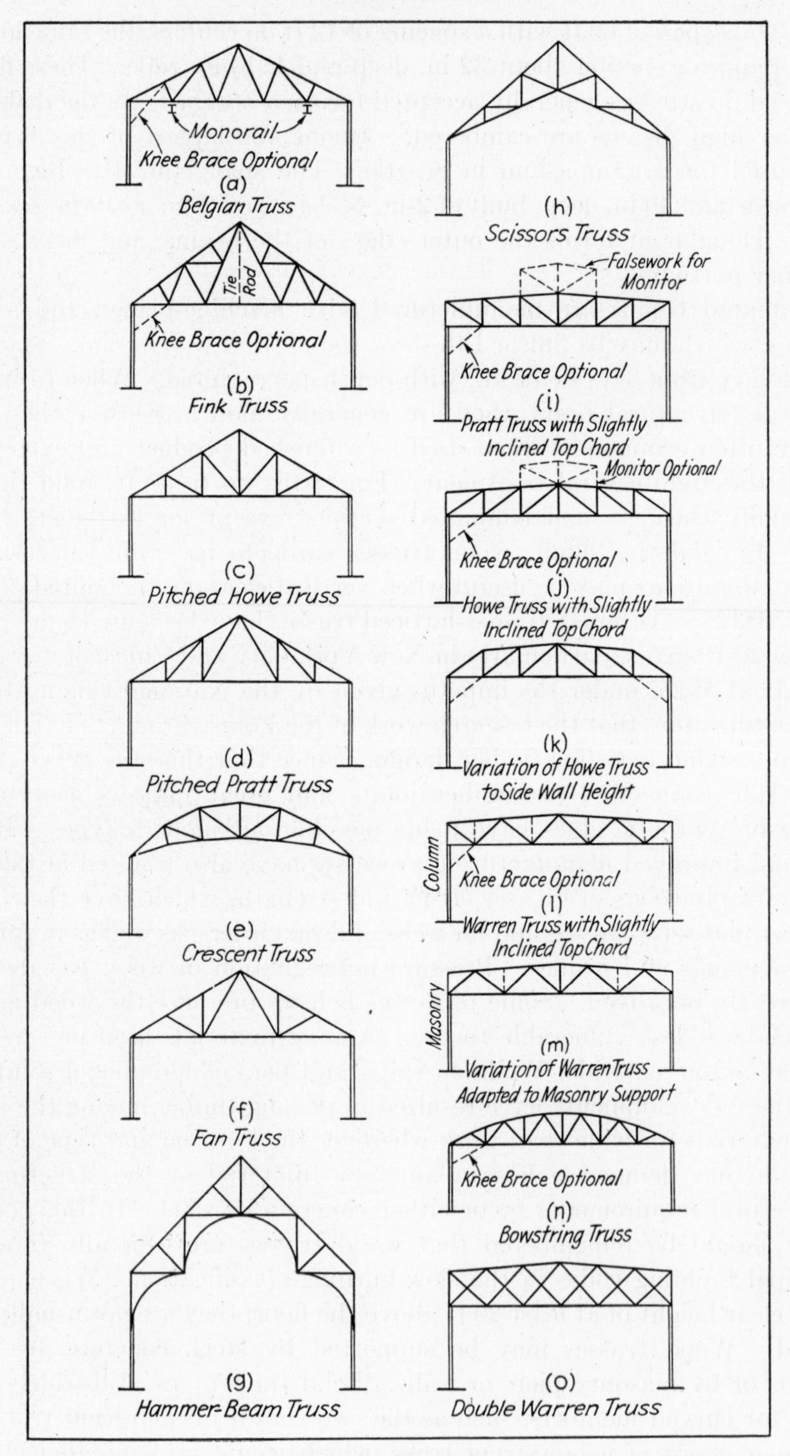

FIG. 45. Popular Types of Timber Trusses and Typical

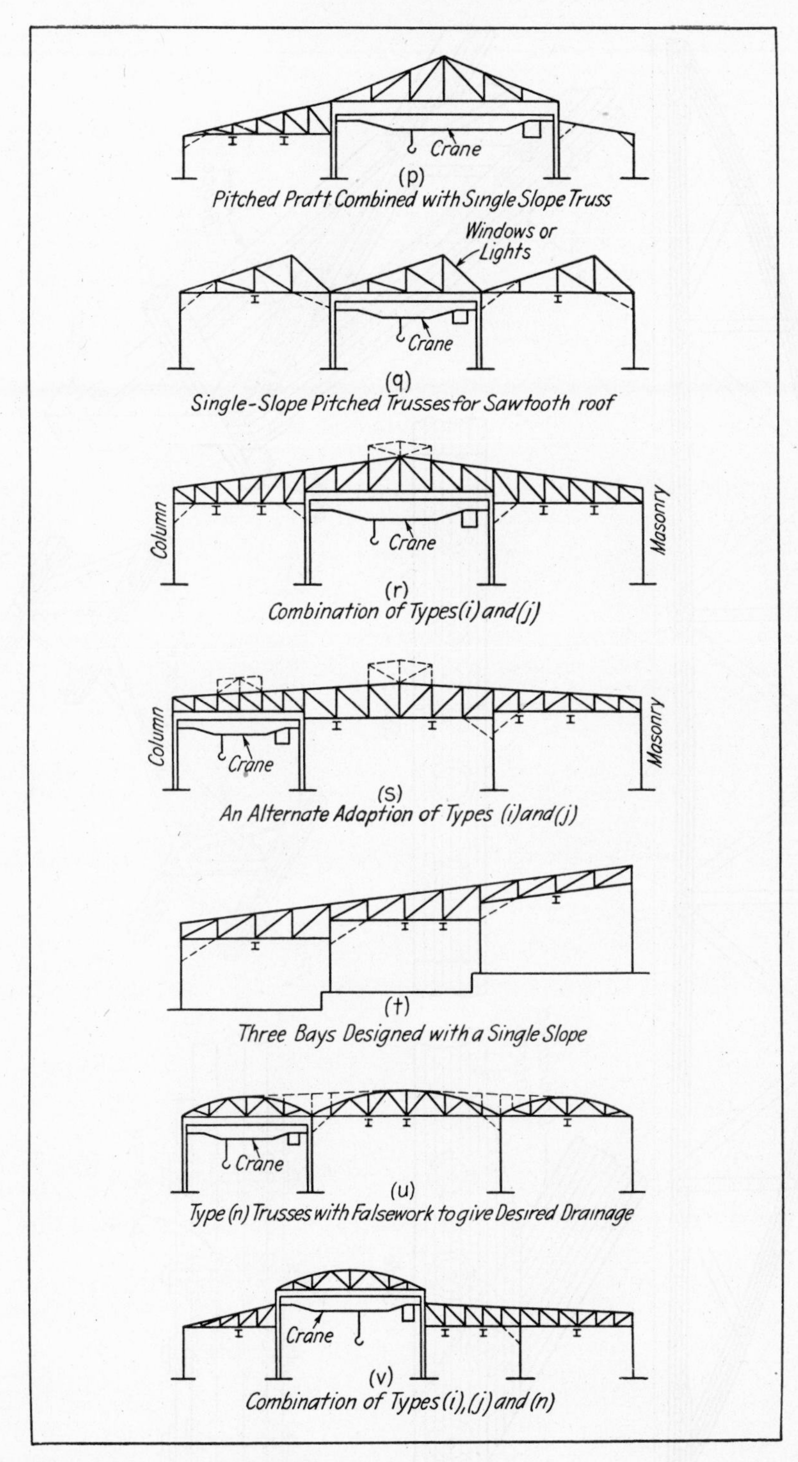

Combinations. Courtesy, Timber Engineering Company.

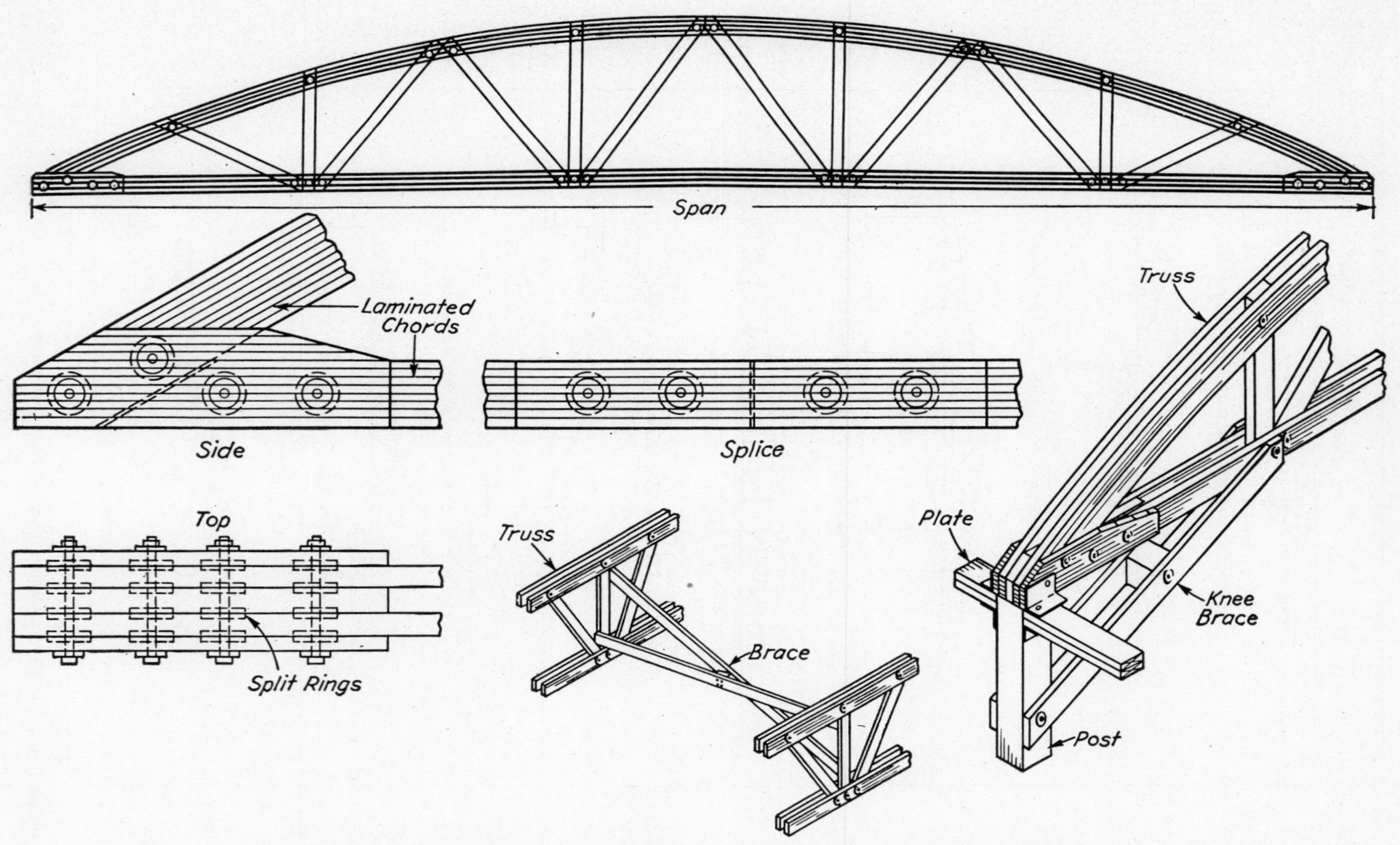

FIG. 46. Laminated Bow-String Truss. Courtesy, Timber Engineering Company.

The bowstring type is generally the most economical choice for spans from 40 to 150 ft where the form and interior appearance are acceptable. It is particularly suitable for spans between 80 and 120 ft. Its application is for the roofs of garages, hangars, stores, and industrial buildings. Figure 46 shows a typical design where laminated sections are used for both upper and lower chords. Figure 47 shows bowstring trusses being placed. When supporting a uniform roof-joist load of 40 lb per sq ft of horizontal projection (combined live and dead load), trusses of this type may be appropriately

FIG. 47. Installation of Bow-String Trusses. Courtesy, Timber Engineering Company.

spaced at 20-ft centers. For spans up to 60 ft it is sometimes economical to use a closer spacing, apply the roof sheathing directly to the top chord, and eliminate joists or purlins. If trusses are spaced over 22 ft apart, purlin trusses are used to carry the rafters and roof sheathing. If the span is 100 ft, the overall height of the truss will be about 13 ft. Under the same conditions the height for a 40-ft span will be about 7 ft. During World War II bowstring trusses were frequently used on spans from 150 to 200 ft, with a probable maximum of 232 ft, but in many cases the choice was dictated by the need to conserve structural steel. Timber bents, composed of 100-ft bowstring trusses, knee-braced to trussed wood columns 25 ft high, were also built during that period.[4]

In this connection the designer should realize that the cost of roof construction naturally increases as the spans are increased. This does not

[4] "Timber Rigid Frames and Trussed Columns," by C. G. Jennings and M. N. Salgo, *Engineering News-Record,* July 15, 1943.

mean, however, that there is no advantage in extending span lengths. Quite the opposite is the case, and one of the more important characteristics of modern design is the use of longer spans for both floors and roofs, as the advantages obtained often outweigh the increased cost. The additional expense should, however, be carefully considered. It is illustrated by the fact that timber bowstring trusses, suitable for a span of 75 ft, normally cost about 25 per cent more than for a span of 50 ft. Similarly, for a clear span of 100 ft, the cost of the trusses would be about 50 per cent

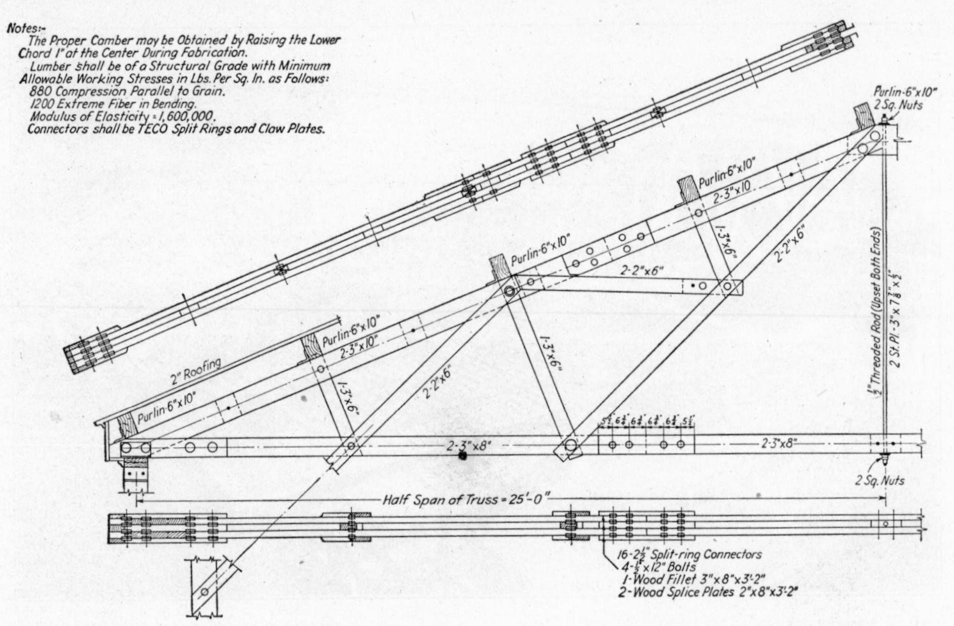

FIG. 48. Wood Fink Roof Truss. Courtesy, Timber Engineering Company.

more than for a 50-ft span. These figures are on a square-foot basis of roof surface and apply to wooden-roof construction.

Supplementing the bowstring designs, a number of other types have been standardized to meet special conditions encountered in roofing buildings. Examples are shown in Figs. 48 and 49. The Fink truss in wood can be used on spans up to about 90 ft but is seldom an economical choice beyond 60 ft. Because of the fact that the compression members near the center are comparatively short, Fink trusses are particularly appropriate for pitches greater than 25°. When other types are used upon such steep slopes, the length of compression members becomes excessive.

The pitched Pratt and Belgian trusses are appropriate for spans up to about 90 ft but more economical under 60 ft. They are preferable to the Fink when the roof slope is appreciably less than 25° and have replaced the Howe type in the Teco connector system of timber construction, as both have the shorter members in compression, whereas the opposite condi-

Notes:-
This Truss is Designed to be Used with Loads at Top Chord Panel Points Only. Purlins 6"x 12" are Satisfactory.
The Proper Camber may be Obtained by Raising the Lower Chord 3" at the Center During Fabrication.
Lumber shall be of a Structural Grade with Minimum Allowable Working Stresses in Lbs. Per Sq. In. as Follows:
880 Compression Parallel to Grain.
1200 Extreme Fiber in Bending.
Modulus of Elasticity = 1,600,000.
Connectors shall be TECO Split Rings and Claw Plates.

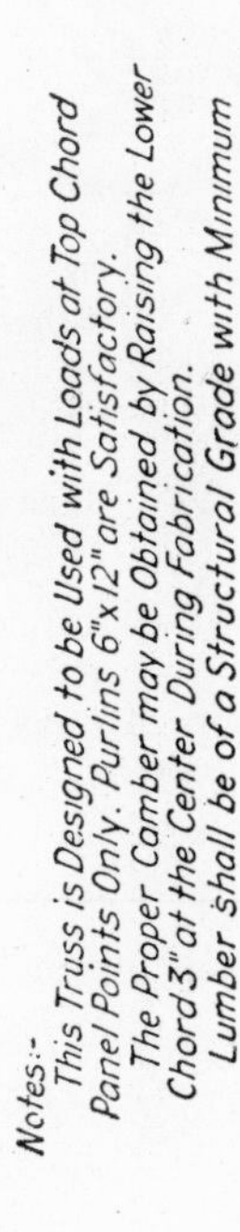

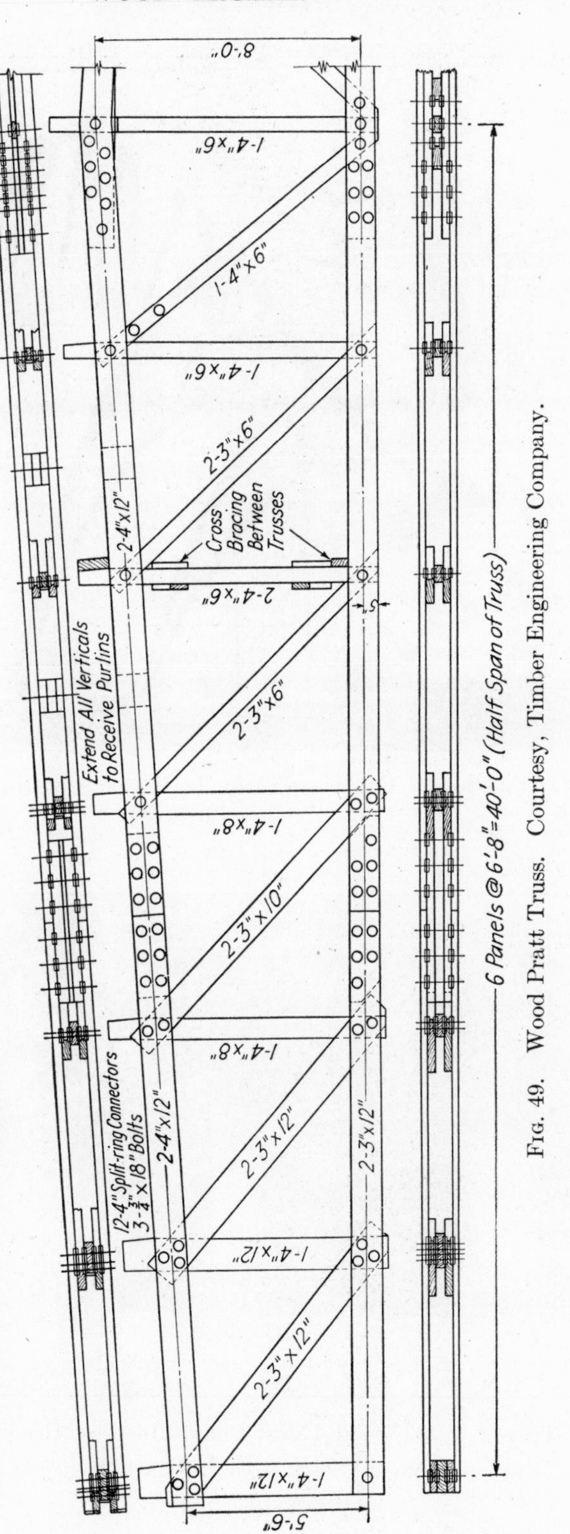

Fig. 49. Wood Pratt Truss. Courtesy, Timber Engineering Company.

FIG. 50. Installation of Crescent Trusses in Hangar Construction. Courtesy, Timber Structures, Inc.

FIG. 51. Trusses with Curved Lower Chords Increase Headroom over a Gymnasium. Courtesy, Roof Structures, Inc.

tion exists in the Howe. The scissors truss is seldom economical for a span over 60 ft. The Pratt, with slightly inclined or parallel top chord, is often economical for spans up to 120 ft and during World War II was used for 150-ft spans over an aircraft-assembly plant. These trusses were 18 ft deep and supported on laminated timber columns 54 ft high.

FIG. 52. Ornamental Trusses over a Chapel. Courtesy, Roof Structures, Inc.

All these types can be designed to carry a normal roof load of 40 to 60 lb per sq ft or of heavier section to support ceilings, monorails, or other concentrated loads. Lateral bracing of trusses must be considered in the final design. The roof deck of solid boards, boarding supported by wood purlins, or any of the appropriate materials described in Chapter Five helps to brace the upper chords. Additional bracing is introduced between the trusses as required by the stress analysis.

Closely related to the bowstring is the crescent type of truss, Fig. 50, employing glued laminated chords. Although particularly suitable for spans under 80 ft, it has been used in hangar construction up to about 160 ft. In some cases the upper chords were composed of three laminations of 2-in. × 10-in. plank and eleven laminations of 2-in. × 6-in. plank. This arrangement provided a 2-in. ledge on each side, upon which rafters

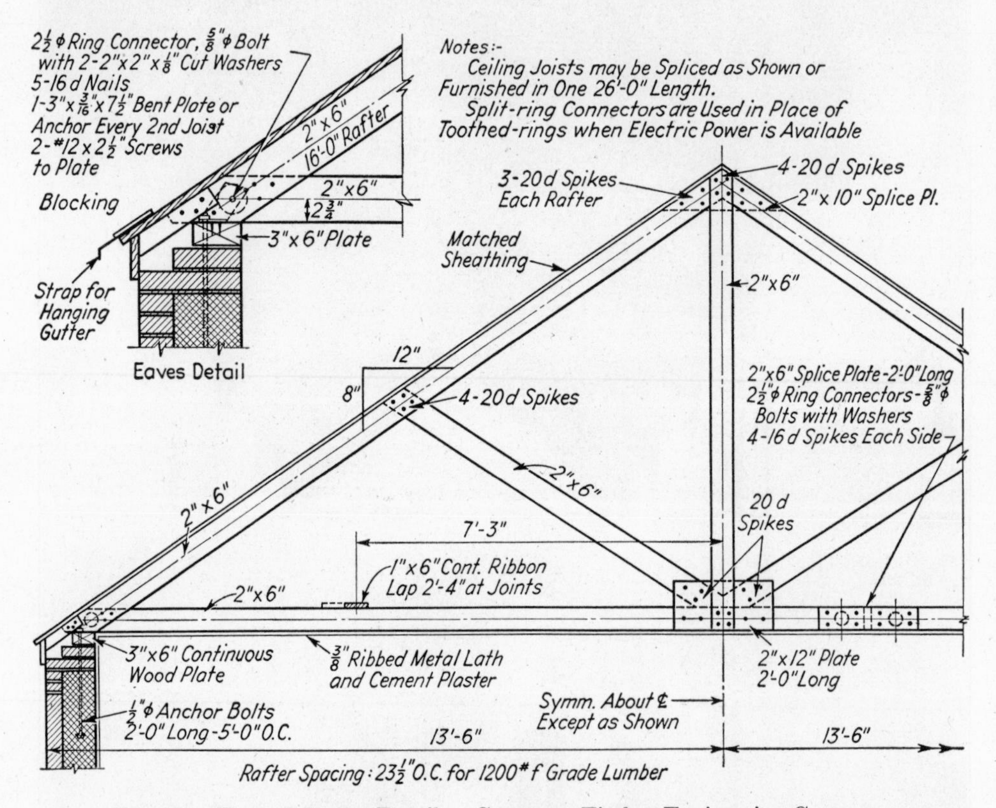

Fig. 53. Trussed-Rafter Details. Courtesy, Timber Engineering Company.

were supported, eliminating the need for the ledger strips shown in the illustration. The crescent, instead of the bowstring, design was chosen for these structures because it permitted the side walls of the hangars to be reduced in height. An interesting example of a curved lower chord is shown in Fig. 51.

The ornamental designs, such as the scissors and hammerbeam trusses, have their application for churches and types of occupancy where the very considerably increased cost is warranted by their appearance. Types such as are illustrated in Fig. 52 are built to the architect's drawings and specification.

Light-weight trusses, known as trussed rafters, Fig. 53, have their application for roof spans from 30 to 40 ft where it is desired to eliminate the

FIG. 54. Laminated Wood Sections of Rigid-Frame Type. Courtesy, Unit Structures, Inc.

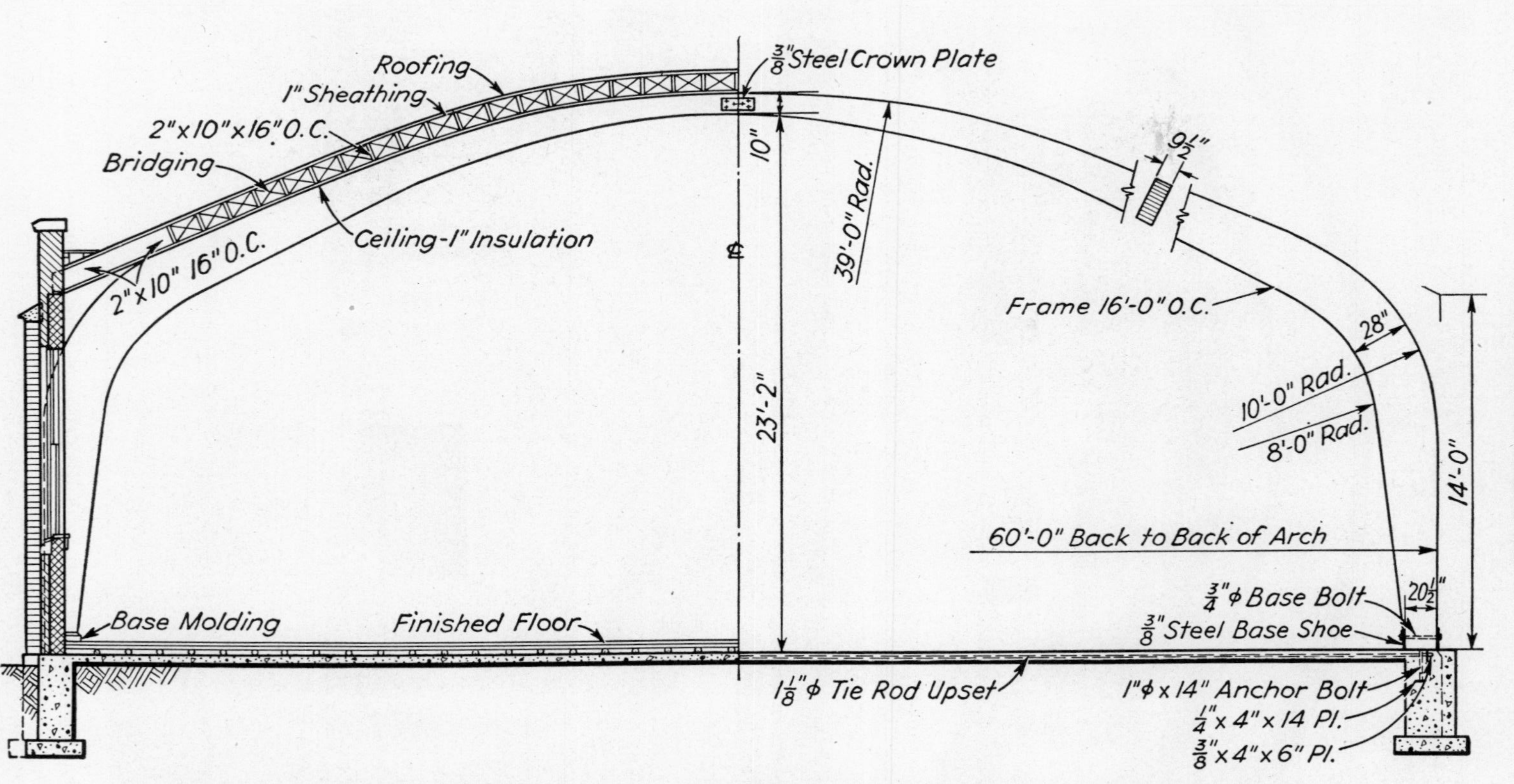

FIG. 55. Typical Design for a Laminated Section of Rigid-Frame Type. Courtesy, Unit Structures, Inc.

need for bearing partitions or other interior support. Trusses are placed up to 2 ft on centers and surfaced with 7/8-in. boards or other suitable material. They have been used for stores, barns, and many housing projects.

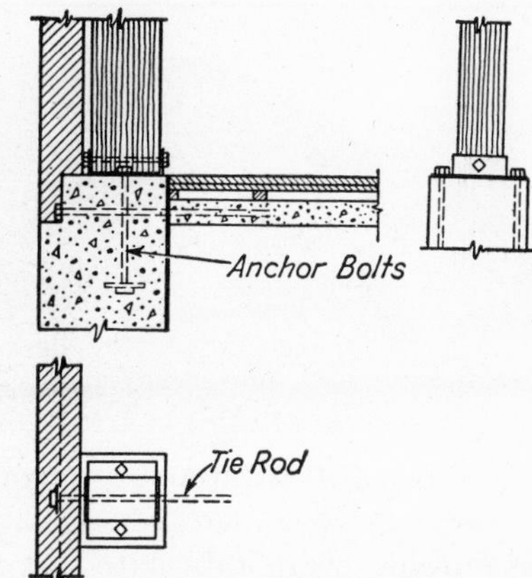

FIG. 56. Anchorage Detail at Base of Frames. Courtesy, Unit Structures, Inc.

RIGID FRAMES AND ARCHES. The rigid-frame types of laminated wood sections shown in Fig. 54 are particularly appropriate for spans from 30 to 100 ft. These two interior views illustrate the different designs that may be obtained. Similar sections have been used on spans up to about 175 ft. Frames may be spaced from 6 to 10 ft on centers, in which case the roof deck is usually of 2-in. plank spanning from rib to rib. If this spacing is too close, a heavier unit may be used with wood purlins, and the frames placed up to about 20 ft on centers. The various styles within this broad classification have their application for hangars, armories, gymnasiums, dance pavilions, and garages. Figure 55 shows a typical assembly including the steel rod serving as a tie to resist outward thrust, and Fig. 56 a detail of the anchorage.

Wood arches may be of framed or ribbed design. The usual forms are shown in Fig. 57. Framed designs are used for long spans with high rise.

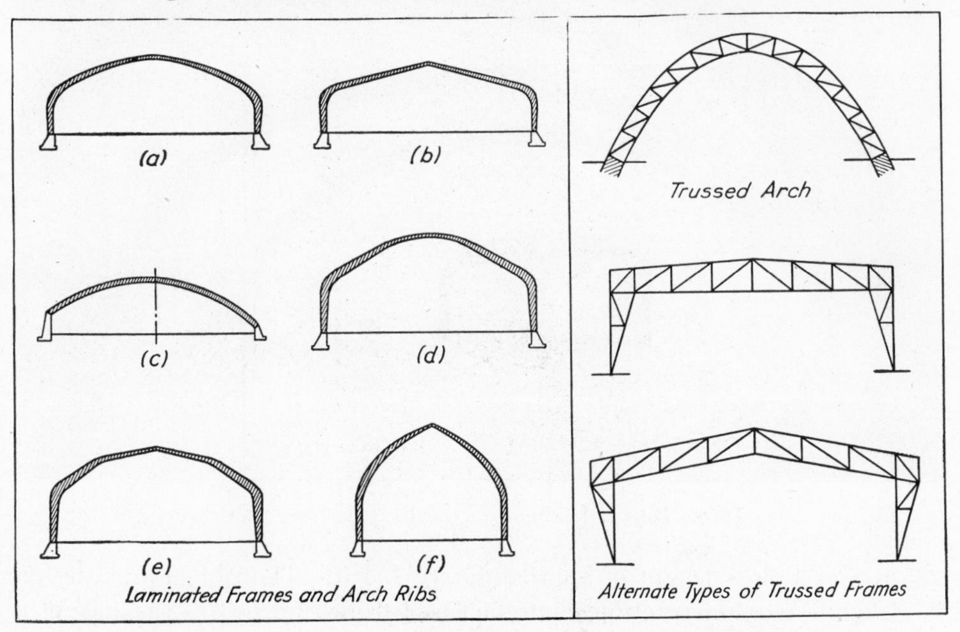

FIG. 57. Types of Wood Frames and Arches. Courtesy, Unit Structures, Inc.

They are normally three-hinged. Figure 58 shows the construction of two hangars built for the United States Navy and having 160-ft spans. These

FIG. 58. Wood Arches of Trussed Design. Official U. S. Navy Photograph.

assemblies were fabricated of short-length lumber jointed with bolts and metallic connectors. The wooden blimp hangars built for the navy during World War II were of this same type with a clear span of approximately

FIG. 59. Wood Arch Ribs of Laminated Design. Courtesy, Unit Structures, Inc.

235 ft and a clear height of approximately 153 ft. The ribbed arch design is of laminated construction, manufactured from thin boards, usually of a nominal 1-in. × 8-in. section. These boards are bent to the required curve

and glued together. Splices are staggered to prevent weakening of the arch. Generally three-hinged, the typical cross-section is rectangular but has been built in the form of an I-beam. I-beam sections were used on an industrial plant where the arches had a span of 120 ft and a rise of 72 ft. Ribs were 6 in. thick, and flanges 14 in. wide.[5]

Figure 59 shows a timber arch particularly appropriate for an auditorium. It is supported by buttresses, which may be at practically floor level or carried up 12 or 14 ft to wall height. In the latter case they may be designed as cantilevers, a tie being used at the base. Where buttresses are low, the detail shown in Fig. 60 is often appropriate. An inclined footing slab is another method which has been used to resist outward thrust for arches of moderate span where the allowable soil pressure is sufficient to permit a footing slab of reasonable area. The design may be of either two- or three-hinged type. Appropriate spans are from about 40 to 150 ft.

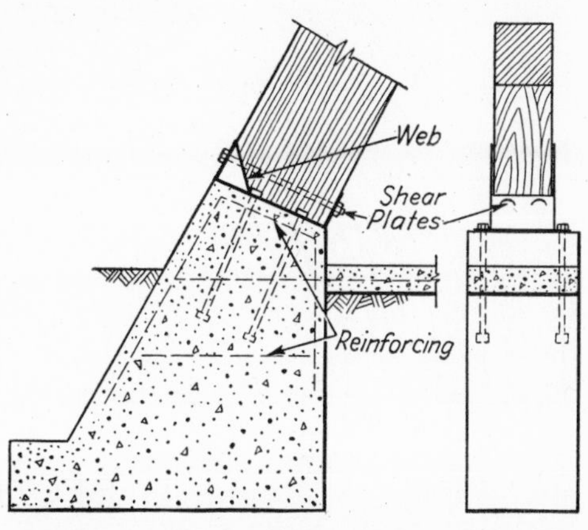

FIG. 60. Anchorage Detail at Base of Arches. Courtesy, Unit Structures, Inc.

Wood arches can be bent or shaped to almost any required form. This fact permits the designer to select a type particularly suited to his purpose. There is no maximum ratio of rise to span. A few years ago a laboratory was built with laminated wood arches having a rise of 66 ft on a span of only 54 ft. There is, however, a minimum rise, which is one-eighth of the span. In most cases the desired rise will be considerably higher, thus reducing the horizontal reaction and favoring a more economical design for the support. This type of arch has been used extensively for field houses, gymnasiums, airplane hangars, and county-highway garages, as well as drill halls built for the navy.

A particular application of the laminated arch is for band shells. The rings may be designed as concentric circles, Fig. 61, or as required to meet the most exacting acoustical requirements.

Arch-rib designs, such as those shown in Fig. 62, are appropriate for hangars on spans comparable with that indicated in the illustration. Somewhat heavier sections may be obtained for longer spans. As in the case of the heavier laminated arch rings, these sections are erected in two units, each half continuous from foundations to roof ridge. The usual spacing

[5] For a complete description of this design see "Pioneer Design in Laminated Wood I-Beams," by S. B. Barnes, *Engineering News-Record*, February 22, 1945.

for the lighter types is 2 ft on centers, and the roof deck of ⅞-in. boards is nailed directly to the ribs.

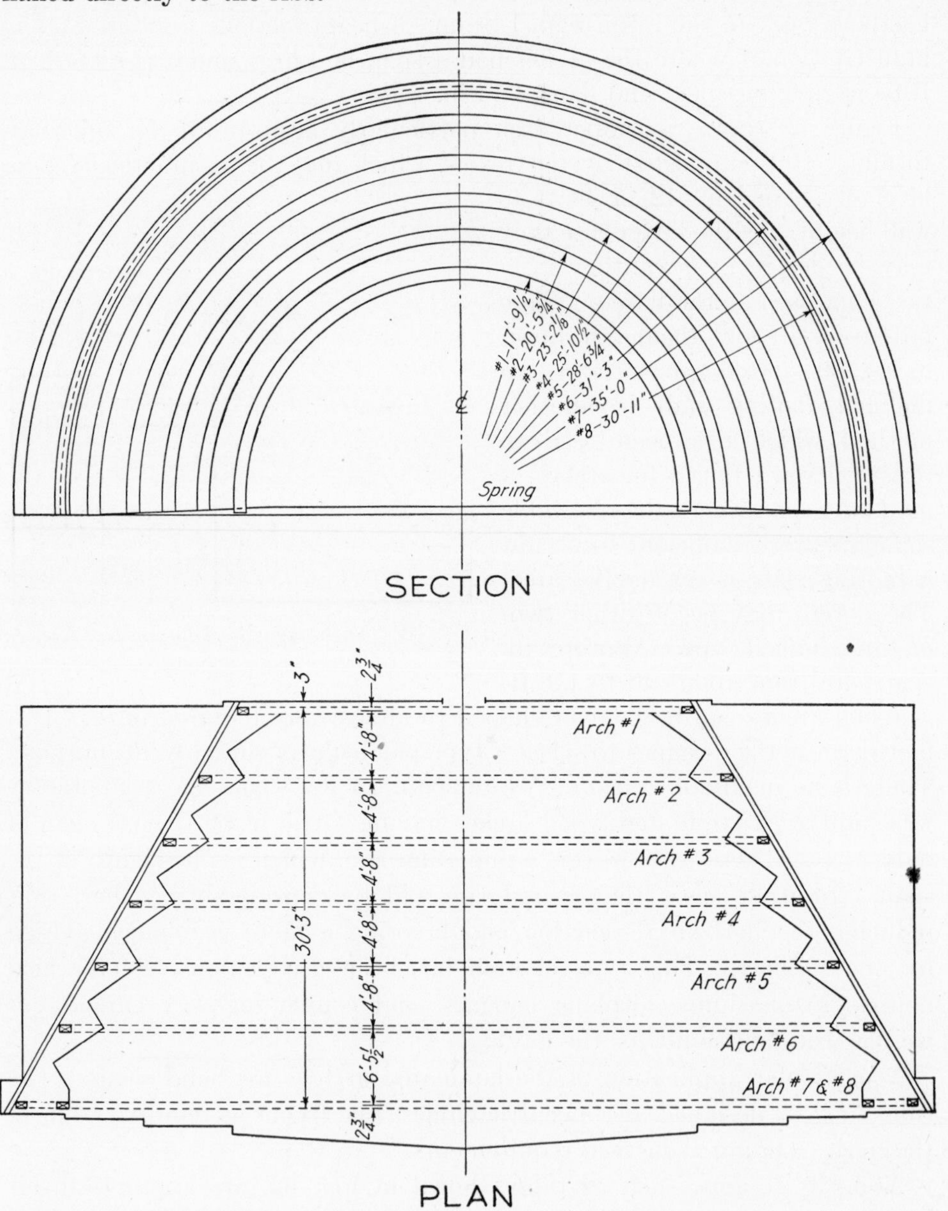

Fig. 61. Band Shell of Laminated Wood Arches. Courtesy, Unit Structures, Inc.

The styles identified as "tied rafters" and "segment rafters" are lightweight variations of arch design suitable for spanning openings at wall height. The segment rafter, however, may be carried to the floor. In this case a floor joist is utilized as a tie. Figure 63 shows a design that is usu-

FIG. 62. Light-Weight Arch Ribs on Small Hangar Construction. Courtesy, Rilco Company.

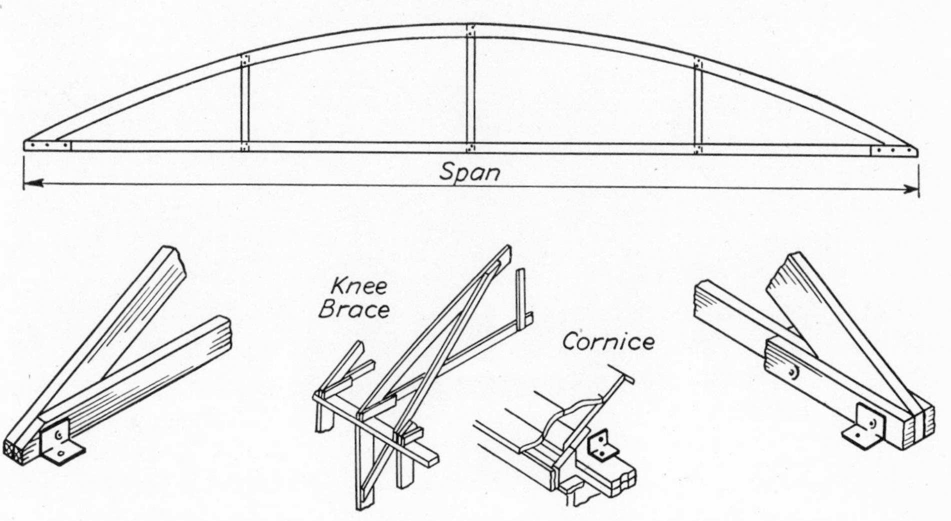

FIG. 63. Design Details of Tied Rafters. Courtesy, Rilco Company.

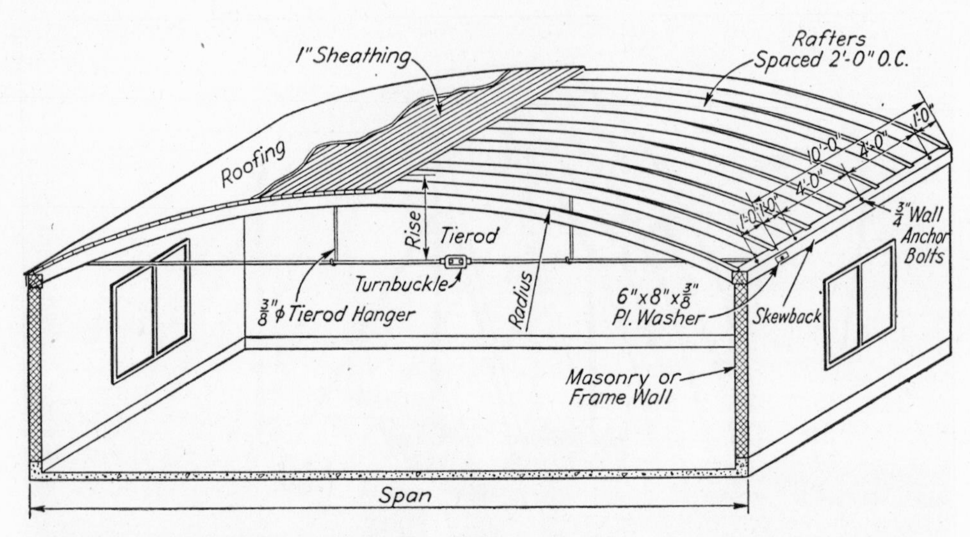

Fig. 64. Typical Roof Assembly Using Segment Rafters. Courtesy, Rilco Company.

Fig. 65. The Wood Lamella Design. Courtesy, Roof Structures, Inc.

ally placed on 2-ft centers for spans up to 50 ft, but a heavier type can be used on a 10-ft spacing up to a 100-ft span. It is appropriate for markets, dance pavilions, and garages. The segment rafter, Fig. 64, is used for warehouses and barns. Typical spacing is shown in the illustration, which applies to spans from 30 to 50 ft.

The Lamella design in steel was described on page 222. Figure 65 shows the same design in wood, where buttresses are provided to resist the arch thrust, thereby eliminating the need for a tie at wall height. Lamella

Fig. 66. Laminated-Wood Arch Ribs Used in Dome Construction. Courtesy, Unit Structures, Inc.

arches have been widely used for many types of buildings varying from garages to auditoriums. The arrangement of short units placed in a diamond pattern is characteristic. Although one of the older designs, they are still popular for many types of occupancy.

DOMES. Figure 66 shows an application of laminated arch ribs to dome construction. Small domes of this type present no particular difficulty to the structural designer. If the foundations cannot be constructed to resist the thrust, buttresses or tie-rods are used.

Article 4. Masonry Arches and Domes

For the traditional architectural styles masonry is still used to a limited extent in arch and vault construction where spans are comparatively short, but very seldom as the structural support for wide spans or domes. Even for masonry exteriors, the support is normally furnished by structural-steel framing combined with a reinforced-concrete slab, as illustrated on page 224. If interior masonry vaulting is desired, it is usually designed to be merely self-supporting, and the entire remaining live and dead loads are carried by structural steel or reinforced concrete.

Fig. 67. The Guastavino System Applied to a Vaulted Ceiling. Courtesy, Guastavino Company.

Unique in the field of masonry arch and domical construction, the Guastavino system has often been used for the structural support of such assemblies but appears to have its particular application as an interior self-supporting shell furnishing an appropriate ceiling finish for monumental buildings. Whether used as a structural system or merely as a lining, the section is built up with several layers of clay tile laid in portland-cement mortar. The tile vary in size from 6 × 12 in. to 6 × 24 in. and are 1 in. thick. Steel reinforcing rods of 3/8-in. diameter are laid in the joints when required. Soffits may be plastered or finished with ceramic or acoustic tile.

The typical timbrel arch construction, consisting of three courses of tile, is only about 4 in. thick at the crown and weighs 40 lb per sq ft. The dome of the Buhl Planetarium in Pittsburgh, Pennsylvania, a span of 71 ft 6 in., has a uniform thickness of 6 1/2 in., representing the entire structural section and comprising three layers of 1-in. solid clay tile with one layer of 2-in. hollow tile. A continuous steel band is used at the springing line to resist tension. The dome is surfaced with copper. Figure 67 shows the more general application of this system to the vaulted ceiling of a chapel.

Chapter Seven

CHOOSING THE WALL ASSEMBLY

There are many types of wall and partition construction, differing widely in architectural appearance, structural characteristics, heat or sound transmission, and fire resistance. Their relative advantages for a specific project may be compared by a functional analysis, implementing the results of research and field experience which identify the means of accomplishing the desired objectives.

INTRODUCTION. The selection of the most suitable type of wall construction follows the same general principles that apply to the floors and roof. That is, the system or assembly should satisfy the architectural and structural demands of the building at the least possible cost, but the specific requirements by which the designer will compare the advantages of one type with another are quite different. These requirements are described in Article 2 as applying to an exterior wall. The same problem applying to interior walls and partitions is discussed in Article 3.

When using the better-known materials, arranged in conventional assemblies, the designer may have reasonable confidence in the recommendations of standard authorities. When employing the newer materials or more modern assemblies, a careful functional analysis is necessary, supplemented by a study of performance, if such a record is available, or by accelerated tests where there is no background of experience under a similar exposure.

Article 1. Definitions

As the names applied to some types of walls are not standardized, the following definitions are given as they appear in "A Glossary of Housing Terms," *Building Materials and Structures Report BMS* 91, National Bureau of Standards, 1942.

BEARING WALL is a wall which supports any vertical load in addition to its own weight.

COMMON WALL is a wall owned by one party but jointly used by two parties, one or both of whom is entitled to such use under the provision of a lease.

CURTAIN WALL is a nonbearing wall between columns or piers which is not supported by girders or beams.

ENCLOSURE WALL is an exterior nonbearing wall in skeleton construction anchored to columns, piers, or floors, but not necessarily built between columns or piers.

EXTERIOR WALL is any outside wall or vertical enclosure of a building other than a party or common wall.

FIRE-DIVISION WALL is a wall which subdivides a building to restrict the spread of fire, but is not necessarily continuous through all stories nor extended through the roof.

FIRE WALL is a wall which subdivides a building to restrict the spread of fire. It starts at the foundation and extends continuously through all stories to and above the roof.

FOUNDATION WALL is any bearing wall or pier below the first-floor construction.

NONBEARING WALL is a wall which supports no vertical load other than its own weight.

PANEL WALL is a nonbearing wall in skeleton construction built between columns or piers and wholly supported at each story.

PARAPET WALL is that part of an exterior, party, or fire wall extending above the roof line.

PARTITION is a wall that subdivides spaces within any story of a building. If designed to restrict the spread of fire, it is called a FIRE PARTITION.

PARTY WALL is a wall used jointly by two parties under easement agreement and erected at or upon a line separating two parcels of land that may be held under different ownership.

RETAINING WALL. (1) Any wall subjected to lateral pressure other than wind pressure. (2) A wall built to support a bank of earth.

SPANDREL OR SPANDRIL is the panel between the top of a window or door at one story and sill of a window or door at the story above.

The preceding definitions should be supplemented by reference to "A Glossary of Housing Terms," which contains a particularly useful glossary of terms applying to housing projects. The definitions given in the Building Code recommended by the National Board of Fire Underwriters will also be found helpful; but, as considerable variation exists in the terminology of building ordinances, the designer should acquaint himself with the vocabulary used by his local authority.

Article 2. Functional Analysis of an Exterior Wall

Notwithstanding the great variations possible in exterior wall design, from the primitive adobe of the Southwest to the complex assemblies including exterior facing, masonry backing, furring, and plaster, typical of our larger cities, there are certain basic principles which always apply. These are derived from the function of an exterior wall and may be made specific by a simple, diagrammatic representation of a wall section. Such an analysis is particularly significant today, when so many new forms of construction differing widely from traditional designs are available.

Let us consider an exterior wall above grade represented by the section shown in Fig. 1. A conventional type is chosen for the purpose of illustration, but the analysis is equally true for a wall of unhewn logs and for the more modern prefabricated sections. The following characteristics are always essential.

1. The exterior surface should be reasonably resistant to atmospheric conditions and have an acceptable appearance; in combination with the other elements of the assembly, it must be rain- and windproof.

2. The body, backing, or frame of the wall, in combination with the other elements of the assembly, must be structurally adequate to support its own weight, resist all applied forces, often transmitting them to the other elements of the structural frame, and provide the necessary fire resistance.

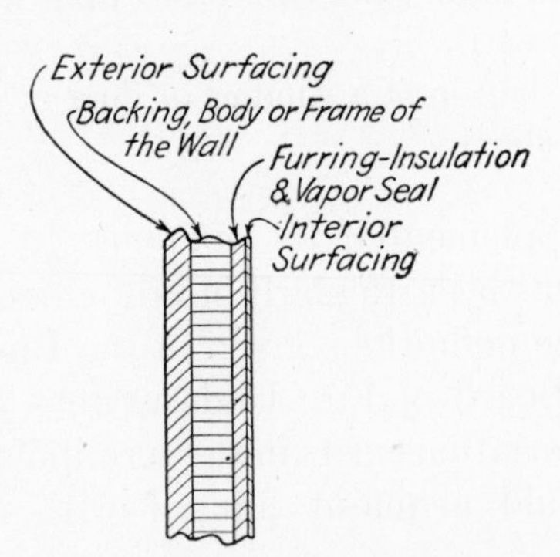

FIG. 1. Diagrammatic Section of an Exterior Wall.

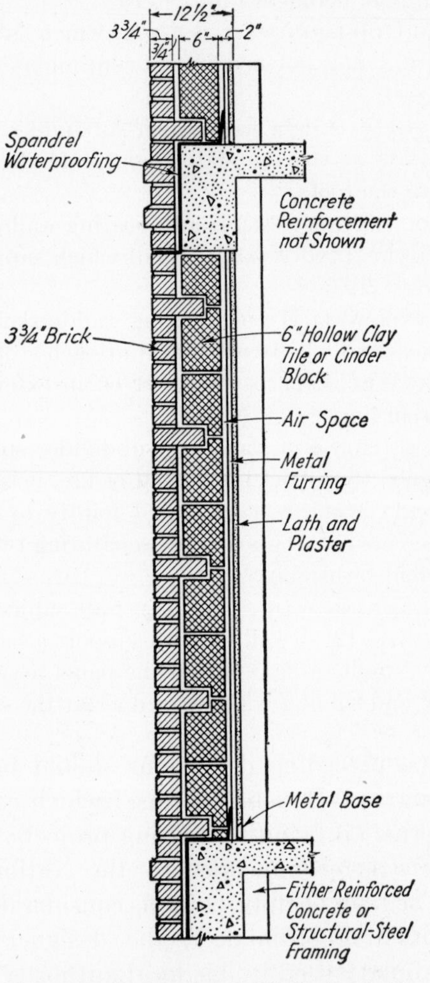

FIG. 2. Conventional Wall Assembly from Designs Used by the New York City Housing Authority.

3. Insulation from cold or heat and adequate provision against condensation of water vapor, either on the inner surface or inside the wall, appropriate for the locality and type of occupancy should be furnished. It may also be desirable to compare the sound transmission of competing designs.

4. The interior surfaces should meet the utilitarian demands of occupancy including, where necessary, light reflection and suitable sound absorption. They should also have an acceptable appearance.

5. The wall assembly which satisfies these requirements at the lowest first cost and expense for maintenance will generally be the best choice.

In a conventional design, such as that shown in Fig. 2, these demands are met by the use of different materials, but for some types of occupancy a far simpler section may perform the same functions. An example is the 8-in. reinforced-concrete panel wall often used for industrial buildings. Good concrete is reasonably resistant to atmospheric conditions. If cast in well-constructed forms, the exterior surface may be entirely satisfactory without any finish. If well designed and well built, it is durable and rain- and windproof. An 8-in. thickness should meet all structural and fire-resistance requirements. For many industrial buildings no special insulation is necessary. The interior concrete surface is often acceptable for industrial occupancy and may be painted if desired.

The better wall designs offered by the prefabricators satisfy the same requirements as the old conventional types: a durable, rain- and windproof exterior surface of acceptable appearance, adequate structural strength and fire resistance, low heat transmission and provision against condensation of water vapor, a satisfactory interior finish or a suitable surface for the application of a desired finish.

Article 3. Interior Walls and Partitions

Interior walls and partitions serve primarily to divide the enclosed space into rooms as demanded by the architectural design. In structures of only a few stories, interior walls may act also as supports for the floors and roof, in which case they are identified as bearing walls. Partitions, which are in effect interior walls extending through only one story, may also be designed for bearing but usually carry no load other than their own weight.

The general requirements for interior masonry walls and masonry partitions are similar to those for exterior walls, with the obvious exceptions derived from the fact that they do not form a part of the building envelope. Fire resistance is always desirable and becomes very important if the wall or partition is necessary to retard the spread of fire. The designer should note the definitions on page 247 which differentiate fire walls, fire-division walls, and fire partitions. The fire resistance, as it is recommended in the Underwriters' Code or demanded by the local building ordinance, should be checked, and a design chosen which provides the required fire rating.

Except for fire walls and some fire-division walls, the lighter types of masonry construction are more appropriate than solid brick or concrete. Clay tile, concrete-masonry units, and gypsum tile are widely used. All gypsum units are laid in gypsum mortar. The choice can often be determined by price alone, bearing in mind the cost of erection, the work of

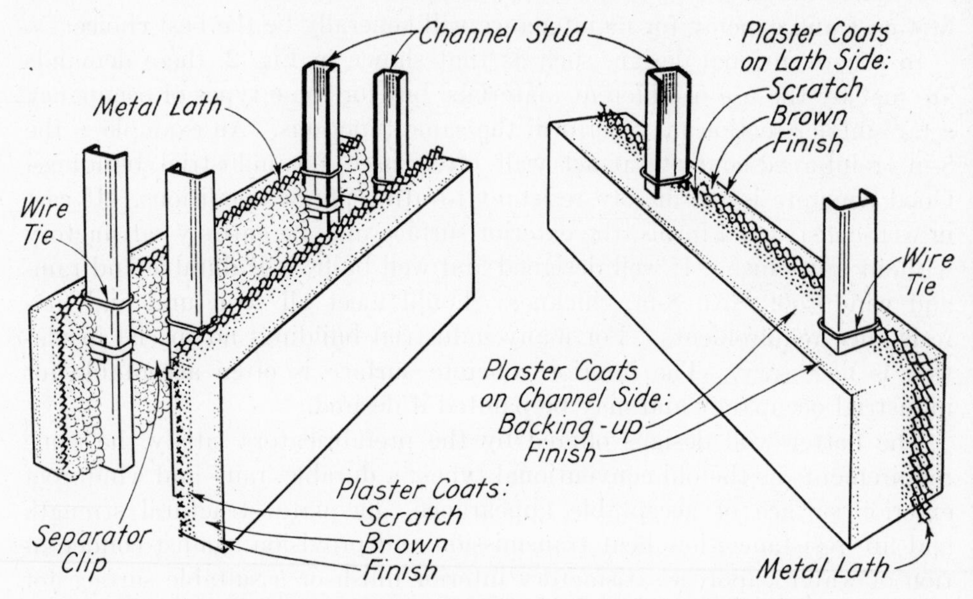

FIG. 3. Hollow and Solid Channel-Stud Partitions. Courtesy, Metal Lath Manufacturing Association.

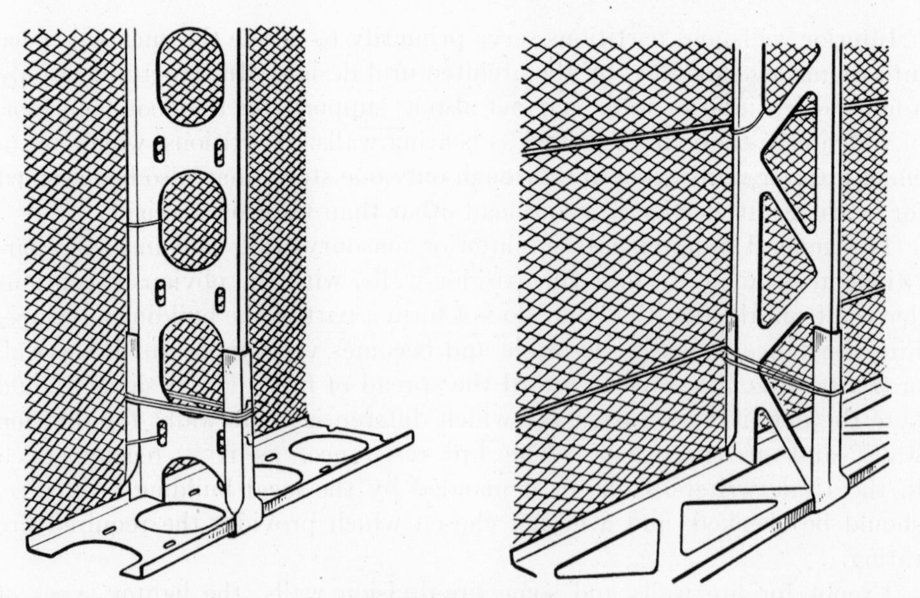

FIG. 4. Hollow Partitions with Prefabricated-Steel Studs. Courtesy, Metal Lath Manufacturing Association.

allied trades, and the weight as affecting structural framing. Figures 3 and 4 show the construction of steel-stud partitions, and Fig. 5 a comparison of weights for the more popular partition types. In some cases the saving in thickness gained by using a 2-in. solid plaster partition has been an important factor.

Although the heat transmission through interior walls and partitions can usually be neglected, sound transmission should be considered for many

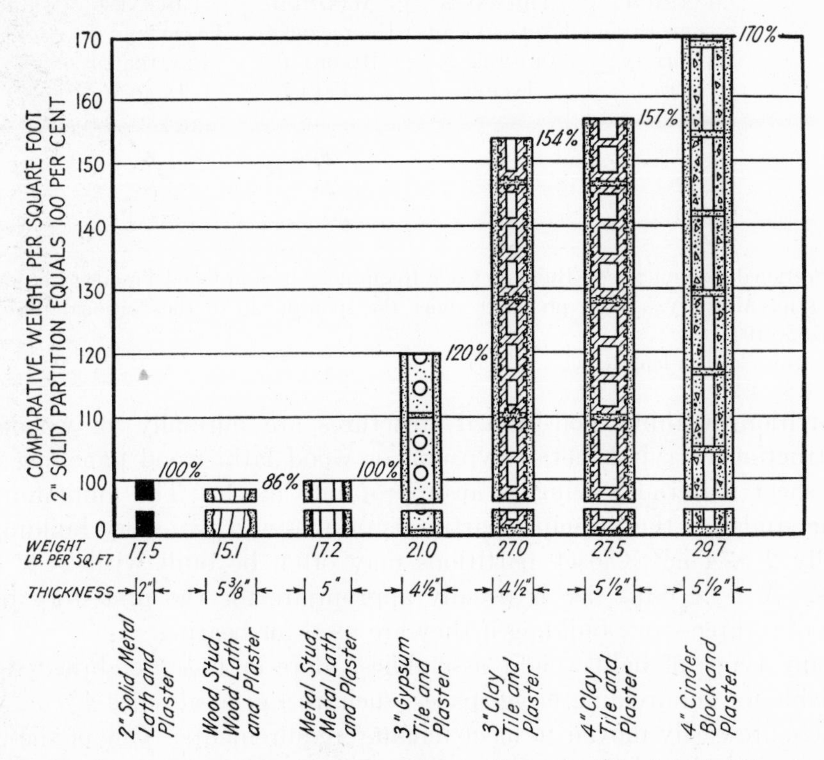

FIG. 5. Weights of Various Types of Partitions. Courtesy, Metal Lath Manufacturing Association.

types of occupancy. This subject is discussed on page 276 in its relation to such a choice. Surface finishes are likewise important and should be chosen to meet the conditions of occupancy as well as for their appearance. In order to insure adequate bond between plaster and tile or concrete-masonry units, surfaces should be wet to the extent necessary for proper suction. Even where scored tile have been used, neglect of this precaution has resulted in plaster separating from its base.

Bearing partitions are designed of sufficient thickness to support their vertical loads without exceeding the compressive stresses given on pages 310 and 319 for masonry walls, and the same requirements apply, as noted on page 352, for the lateral support of walls.

Nonbearing masonry partitions should be built solidly against floor and ceiling construction. The required thickness has a definite relationship to height, as indicated in the table.

MINIMUM THICKNESS OF NONBEARING MASONRY PARTITIONS

(From American Standard Building Code Requirements for Masonry) *

Maximum Unsupported Height in Feet	Thickness Exclusive of Plaster in Inches	Maximum Unsupported Height in Feet	Thickness Exclusive of Plaster in Inches
9 †	2	20	6
12	3	25	8
15	4		

* "Sectional Committee on Building Code Requirements, and Good Practice Recommendations for Masonry," A-41, prepared under the sponsorship of the National Bureau of Standards, 1944.

† Not over 6 ft in length.

Partitions within wood-framed structures are normally of wood-stud construction carrying metal, gypsum, or wood lath, wood panelling, tile, or a sheet material serving as an appropriate finish. The minimum size of the studs for the principal partitions of one- and two-story buildings is usually 2 × 4 in. Closet partitions may often be built with 2- × 3-in. studs. A 2- × 6-in. size is usually appropriate for the first-story partitions of a three-story building if they are used for bearing.

Many types of light-weight assemblies, more or less prefabricated, are available for subdividing large spaces, such as a general office area. Most of these are easily moved to meet tenants' requirements. One of the more permanent designs is in the form of panels composed of two or three ½-in. solid gypsum sheets. These panels are available in widths from 2 to 4 ft and in heights from 6 to 10 ft. They may be secured in place by wood mouldings. Wood is also used for the frames required around openings, floor, lintel, and ceiling runners. Channels are provided for conduit. The cream-colored surface of the panels may be left unfinished or painted. They have a broad application to many types of buildings where speed in erection and dry construction are demanded.

Article 4. Exterior Wall Surfaces; Impermeability and Durability

As the choice of wall construction may often be influenced by the desire to obtain a particular type of exterior finish, the various options are discussed in this article. Although such matters are primarily artistic, they merge into the structural, and the two aspects should be considered together. Within the bracket of good practice lies a wide choice of exterior wall finishes. These should be compared with a full knowledge of their advantages and disadvantages so that a design will be chosen to meet the particular conditions of exposure.

The quality of the surfacing materials should also insure reasonable durability under the expected conditions. This is exemplified by the practice of reducing the water: cement ratio of concrete mixtures in the colder climates when subjected to alternate freezing and thawing. The surface disintegration of some sandstones, when exposed to a deleterious atmosphere, is common knowledge. The softer grades of brick are not suitable for exterior use, as noted on page 293. The deterioration of paints, when applied to surfaces or subject to exposures for which they are not appropriate, implies the necessity for careful investigation on the part of the designer.

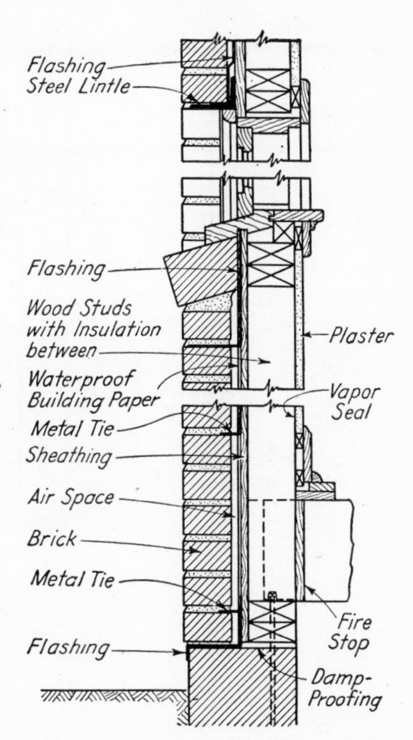

Fig. 6. Standard Construction for Brick Veneer over Wood-Stud Framing.

MASONRY AS A WALL SURFACING. An exterior finish of masonry is particularly appropriate where the body or backing of the wall is also of masonry. Brick and occasionally stone veneer are also used over wood frames. Reinforced-concrete walls have been faced with the same materials, but such an assembly is usually more expensive than one composed entirely of masonry units, employing common brick, hollow tile, or concrete block for backing. As many of the requirements for masonry surfacings are closely related to the character of the masonry units, quality of mortar, and workmanship, the subject is discussed under masonry walls in Chapter Eight.

BRICK VENEER OVER WOOD FRAMING. Designs of this type employ brick only as an exterior surfacing, all load being carried by the wood frame. Their application is limited to structures for which wood framing is appropriate and in particular to one- or two-family dwellings. The cost in most localities is less than that of a solid 8-in. brick wall, including the furring normally required for residential occupancy. Such designs have been built in many parts of the country where an exterior finish of brick is desired.

The brick are laid in a single wythe of 4-in. nominal thickness. The appearance of any desired bond is obtained by using half brick as headers. The principles applying to walls of solid brick masonry, as given in Chapter Eight, should be followed as far as applicable. Structural adequacy requires well-braced framing, ample support for the brick veneer, and firm

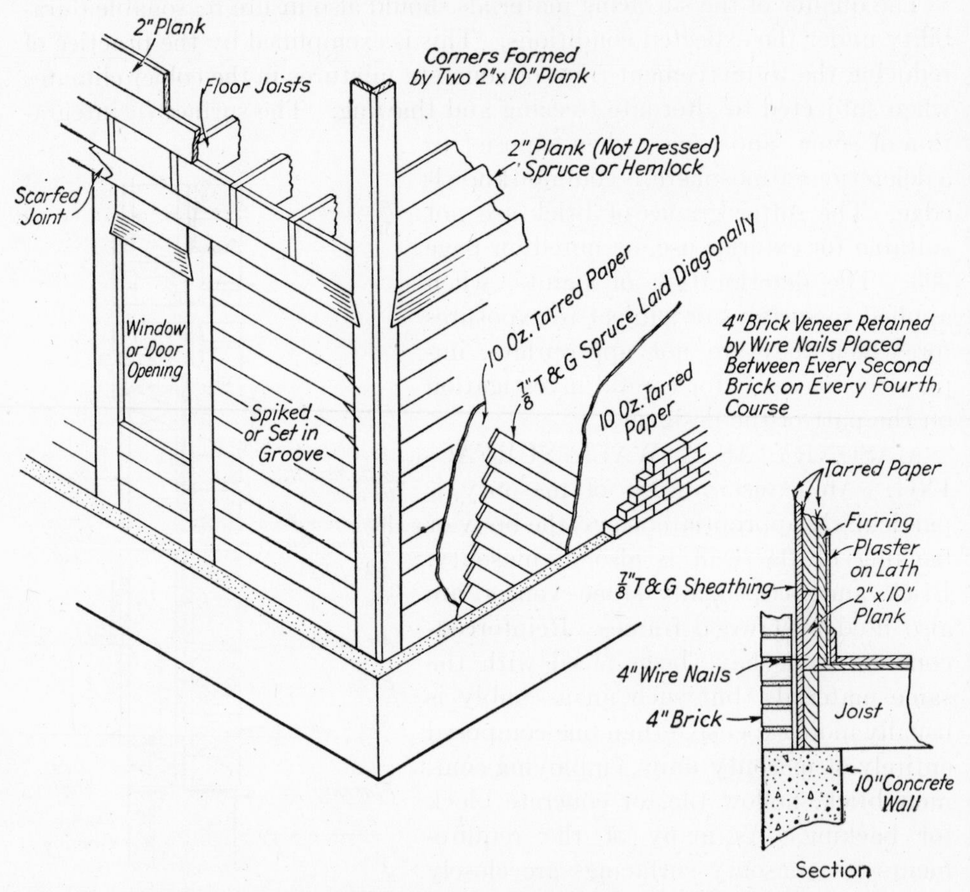

Fig. 7. Canadian Design for Brick Veneer over Plank. Courtesy, Nobbs and Hyde, Architects, Montreal, Canada.

anchorage of it into the wood sheathing. The proper bedding of the masonry units including sills, the complete filling of vertical joints, and thorough flashing are important. Figure 6 shows a typical section.

Support at the base of the veneer is obtained by extending foundation walls 5 in. outside the face of the wood sheathing. The brick work is retained in place by noncorrodible nails or metallic ties placed at intervals of not more than 16 in. vertically and 24 in. horizontally. The exterior face of the wood sheathing is protected with waterproof building paper. Over all openings steel angles are used to support the brick veneer.

Such designs offer a somewhat higher resistance to exterior fire exposure but are generally classed as wood-frame construction. If it is desired to reinforce the brick veneer, a fibrous-backed welded-wire mesh is sometimes nailed to the exterior surface of the wood sheathing. The space behind the brick is then filled with mortar. Interior finishes are applied as in the case of typical wood-framed assemblies.

Figure 7 shows an application of brick veneer over wood-framed construction which is popular in parts of southern Canada. The essential difference between this design and common practice in the United States is the use of 2-in. plank in addition to the ⅞-in. sheathing or a 3-in. plank without sheathing, which permits the elimination of studding. The availability of a satisfactory but comparatively cheap grade of pine, spruce, or fir lumber apparently justifies the choice of this design for much small residential work in the Montreal district.

STUCCO AS A WALL SURFACING. The term "stucco" generally signifies cement-aggregate mortar applied by hand to form an exterior surface. Coloring is usually incorporated in the final coat; plasticising and waterproofing agents may be used. The material is applied directly to a masonry base, as shown in Fig. 8, or to steel reinforcement, in the form of expanded metal or welded-wire mesh, attached to framed construction of wood or steel. Stucco is an appropriate surface treatment for many types of buildings. Although its use in this country is largely confined to rural and suburban dwellings, it is very popular in the cities of the Argentine and Brazil. The best recommendations now available are those given in "Standard Specifications for Portland Cement Stucco," approved by the American Standards Association in 1946.

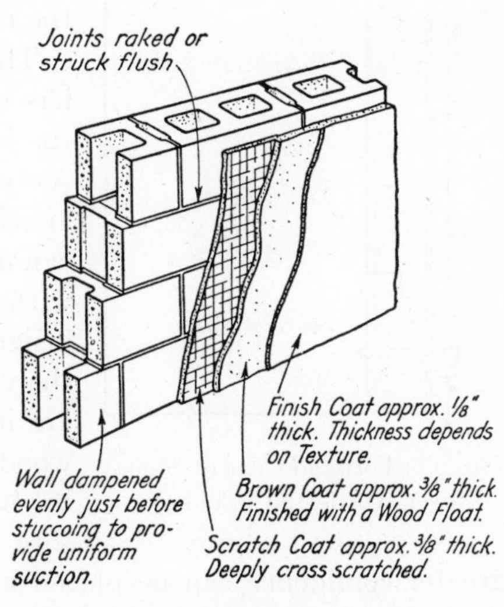

FIG. 8. Portland-Cement Stucco over Concrete-Masonry Units.

From an architectural viewpoint this material offers a wide range of colors and textures. When properly applied, portland-cement stucco is durable, impervious to wind-driven rain, and, although most colors fade somewhat over a period of years, may be even more attractive a decade or two after construction. The rougher textures supply sufficient bond for the adhesion of ivy. There is a very appreciable saving in upkeep of wall surfaces in comparison to those requiring periodic repainting.

These advantages should be weighed against the probability that a certain amount of surface cracking will occur in the colder climates under most conditions of exposure. Stucco applications involve rather extensive areas in the form of a comparatively thin, rather brittle mortar shell, continuous without joints. We are all familiar with the expansion and contraction of most building materials due to atmospheric variations. If appreciable, differential volumetric change occurs between the base over which the stucco is applied, and the enclosing envelope of stucco, stresses are developed which cause cracking of the surface. It is probably true that over a period of years most masonry-surfaced walls crack to a certain extent even when well designed, but such cracks are not usually conspicuous because of the fact that they are distributed among a large number of joints. Unfortunately, the surface cracking of stucco is usually all too evident and requires a difficult repair job if the original appearance must be restored.

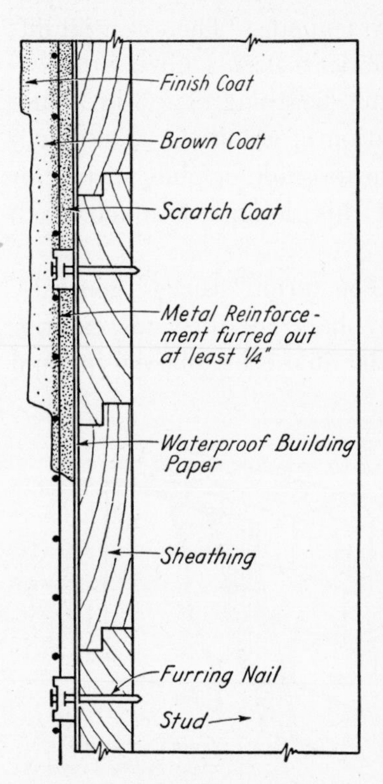

Fig. 9. Portland-Cement Stucco over Wood-Stud Framing.

This situation presents a problem which has not yet been satisfactorily solved but if the specification of the American Standards Association and the recommendations in this article are scrupulously followed, the designer can use stucco over masonry or steel framing with reasonable assurance that cracks will be insignificant and have little effect even from the viewpoint of appearance. Although there are instances of successful stucco work over wood-framed construction, even in districts having exposures as severe as those of Minnesota and Massachusetts, it is suggested that greater confidence can be placed in such assemblies when erected in more favorable climates.

The current specifications on stucco are sufficiently explicit in regard to the character of masonry surfaces acceptable as a base. Good practice has also been established in regard to type, weight, and installation details of the steel mesh used over wood or steel framing. Figure 9 shows such a design. Adequate emphasis is placed upon the extreme care necessary in detailing flashings, as a prime requisite is to prevent water from getting in behind the stucco. The advantage of using prepared mixtures for the surface coat, proper methods of application, and the necessity for most thorough curing have been publicized for many years.

From the viewpoint of the designer, a few additional matters should be noted. If it is desired to apply stucco over wood construction, the building frame should be designed to minimize cross-grain shrinkage, as mentioned on page 90, and braced adequately to avoid transmitting wind stresses or other applied loads to the stucco. Only thoroughly seasoned lumber should be used, and materials which will absorb moisture should be protected from rain during construction. If applied over steel framing, particularly the lighter-weight cold-formed assemblies, adequate bracing is again essential.

Particular care is necessary in foundation design, as the slightest settlement may result in unsightly surface cracks, which are far more difficult to repair than those caused in the interior plaster.

When concrete-masonry units are used for a base, as shown in Fig. 8, it is important, particularly in the colder climates, that the block be not only sufficiently cured but also sufficiently dried, before the application of stucco, to preclude future shrinkage when the building is eventually heated.

Stucco should be specified only for surfaces sufficiently pitched to drain freely. In freezing climates it is best to avoid its use upon any exterior surfaces exposed to rain except those that are practically vertical. This precludes stuccoing the tops of parapet walls, water tables, belt courses, or sills.

Stucco should be used with caution over particularly exposed surfaces subjected to high interior temperatures, such as the masonry of chimneys extended above a roof. To permit the expansion of the base material without transmission of stress to the stucco, some authorities recommend covering the masonry with steel-wire mesh furred out ⅜-in. to provide free support for the stucco. This procedure may be successful if carefully executed, but in severe climates it is far safer to specify suitable masonry and omit the stucco.

It is common practice to stop stucco at least 6 in. above finished grade. If stone masonry of suitable color is used for the exposed portion of the foundations, a careful treatment of joints, pointed with the same material as used for the finished coat of stucco, may provide a very pleasing relationship between the two surfaces.

GUNITE. This is the trade name of a portland-cement-sand mixture combined with water when discharged in the form of mortar from the nozzle of a cement gun. As it is practicable to use a very low water: cement ratio, such surfacings have a high structural strength and density. The process has a broad application for waterproofing and remedial treatment applied over deteriorated concrete or masonry. It may also be used advantageously as a means of constructing thin walls and partitions.

Over frames of wood or light-weight steel, such as is shown in Fig. 10, to which steel mesh is attached, Gunite may be shot against any solid backing such as a temporary wood panel or insulating board serving as a permanent part of the assembly. The nozzle of the hose delivering the mortar is held by hand a distance of 2 to 4 ft from the surface. When insulation is not desired, the mortar may be shot against a backing of heavy paper with reinforcing mesh attached to the steel or wood frame. The same treatment may be used to form an interior surface, resulting in a hollow wall. Normal proportions are 1 part portland cement: 4 parts by volume of sand. The thickness of the section usually varies from 1½ to 2 in., but thicker walls may be built when desired. The finished surface is of uniform, slightly rough texture.

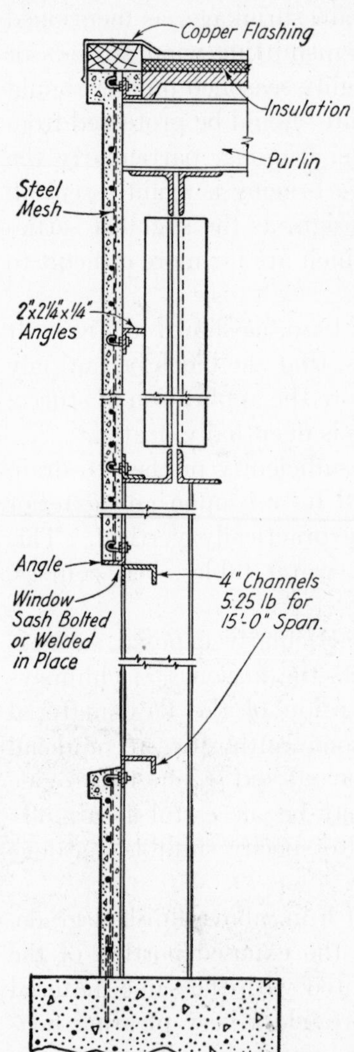

Fig. 10. Single Exterior Wall of Pneumatically Placed Cement-Mortar over Structural-Steel Framing. Courtesy, Gunite Concrete and Construction Company.

CEMENT-AGGREGATE PLANK. Light-weight concrete plank, composed of portland cement combined with slag, cinders, slag products, or a chemically expanded mixture of the same or similar materials, are used as an exterior wall surfacing for industrial buildings and have possibilities in other fields. Thoroughly reinforced with welded-wire, tongued and grooved on four sides, they may offer an economical choice for the lighter types of wall construction. Plank are usually bolted or clipped to T-bars or other appropriate structural shapes, spaced 6 to 8 ft on centers vertically or horizontally. A waterproofing treatment is applied to the exterior surface.

CEMENT-ASBESTOS, GYPSUM, PLYWOOD, AND CEMESTO BOARDS. The application of corrugated cement-asbestos boards to pitched and flat roofs has been mentioned. These boards are also appropriate as wall surfacings over structural steel for many types of industrial buildings and occasionally over wood framing. Either plain or corrugated sheets may be used. A typical size is 3 ft 6 in. × 8 ft, with a maximum length of 11 ft. Supports, usually in the form of steel girts, are required at a maximum spacing of 5 ft 6 in. on centers.

The assembly shown in Fig. 11 consists of ⅜-in. corrugated sheets backed by 1-in. insulating boards, to which the interior surface is veneered.

This design furnishes a very light-weight section with excellent heat insulation. The better materials in this group, such as Transite, are highly resistant to the attack of most acid fumes or gases, extreme temperature variations, and alternate wetting and drying. They are also fire resistant. Of a light gray color, cement-asbestos boards are usually left unpainted.

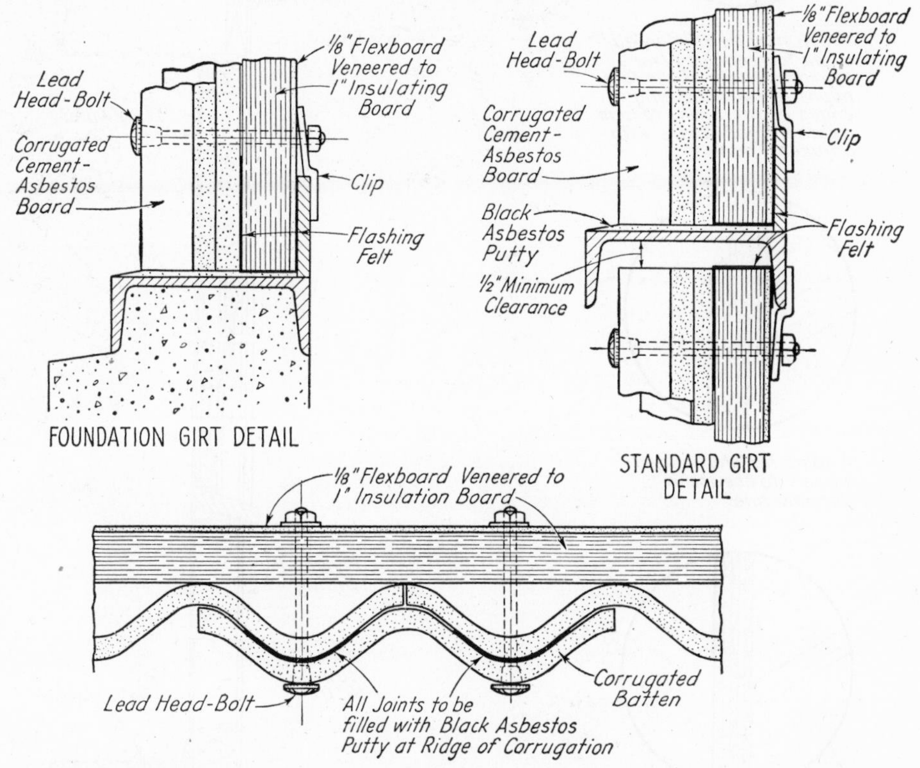

Fig. 11. Corrugated Cement-Asbestos Boards over Structural-Steel Framing. Courtesy, Johns-Manville.

Gypsum boards are also used for exterior walls but are appropriate only for temporary structures and must be protected from moisture by roll-roofing or rainproof fiber.

Plywood sheets suitable for exterior application are usually 3/8 to 5/8 in. thick, formed of three or five plies. Standard sizes are 4 to 8 ft in length with widths from 1 to 4 ft, but practically any size may be obtained for special purposes. For example, sheets 50 ft long and 8 ft in height have been supplied in thicknesses from 3/4 to 1 in. Joints may be of the V-type, shiplap or merely butted, with or without moulding. Except where a shiplap design is used, joints are caulked with white lead or mastic. Sheets are applied by means of noncorrodible nails. In light-weight wall construction, plywood is particularly appropriate as a surfacing material for service stations and small structures of a similar type but has been used to a limited

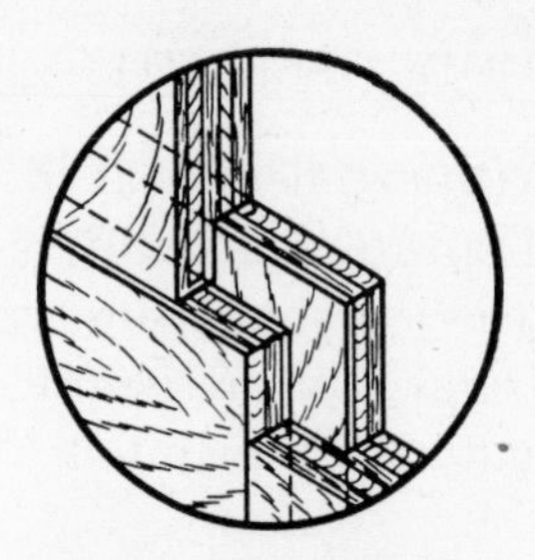
Panels may be shiplapped on all four edges (two adjoining edges of the face opposite two adjoining edges of the back) to form weathertight joints with adjacent panels.

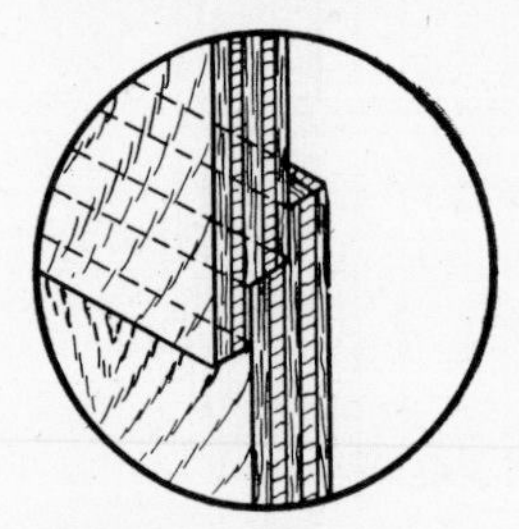
A joint for shiplapped panels to create a shadow line.

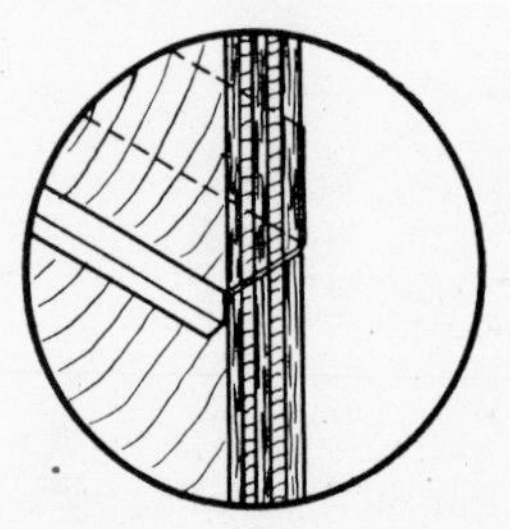
Butted panel joint with inserted metal flashing

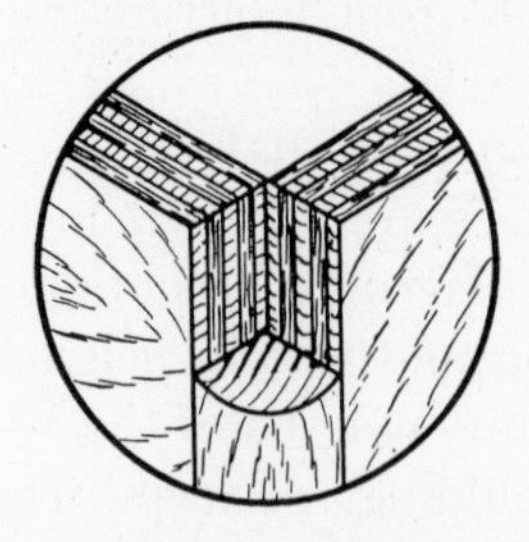
A simple corner treatment for flush walls

DETAILS OF EXTERIOR JOINTS

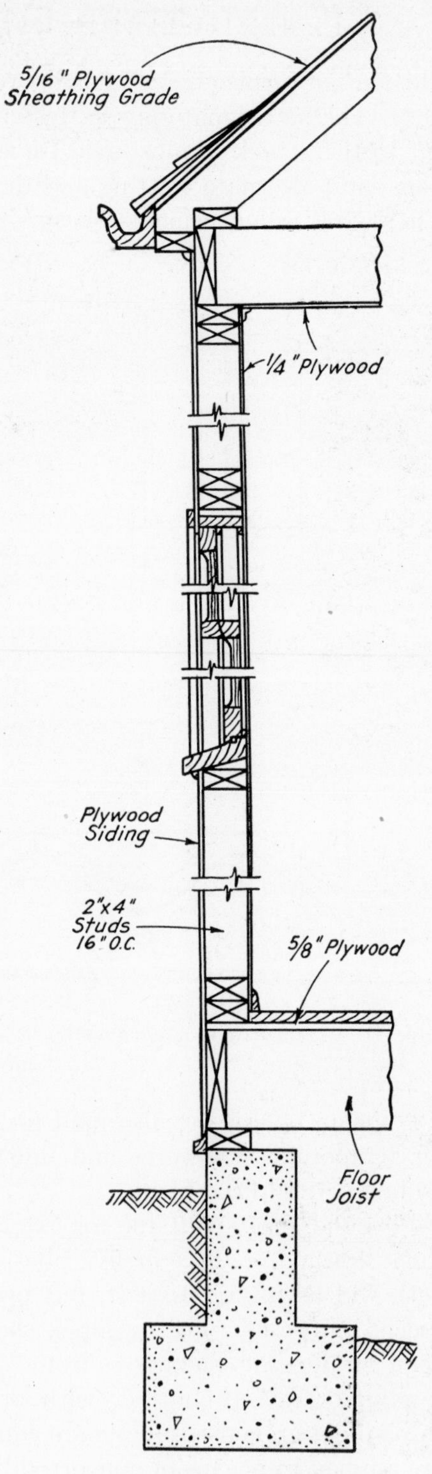

WALL SECTION

FIG. 12. Plywood over Wood-Stud Framing. Courtesy, Harbord Corporation.

extent on commercial and industrial buildings. Figure 12 shows a typical design. Plywood has an interesting application to wall panels in the prefabrication of small dwellings. The so-called "stressed-skin construction"

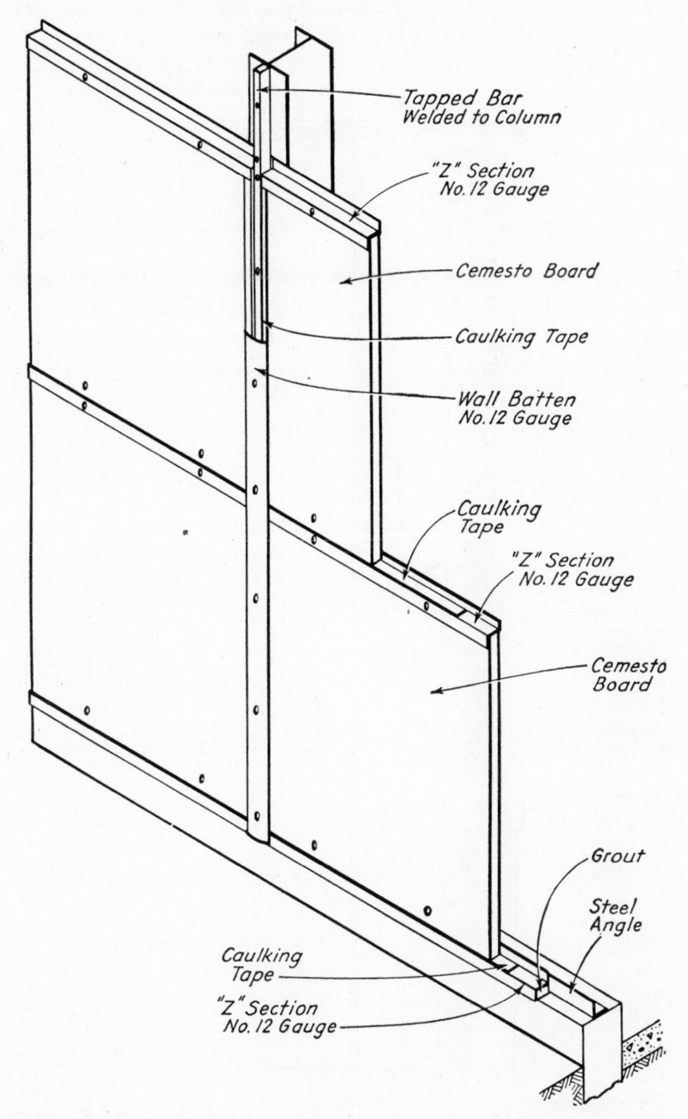

Fig. 13. Cemesto Board over Structural-Steel Framing. Courtesy, Celotex Corporation.

is composed of an outer and an inner sheet carried upon a light-weight wood frame to which they are glued, thereby obtaining continuity.

Cemesto board, defined on page 106, Fig. 13, provides a section, usually 2 in. thick, which has been used successfully in prefabricated designs for small dwellings. Many other excellent fiber and composition boards are available, some of which are weather resistant, others designed in attractive colors and textures for interior application.

SHEET METALS AS WALL SURFACINGS. For many years corrugated iron and, to a lesser extent, corrugated zinc and copper have been

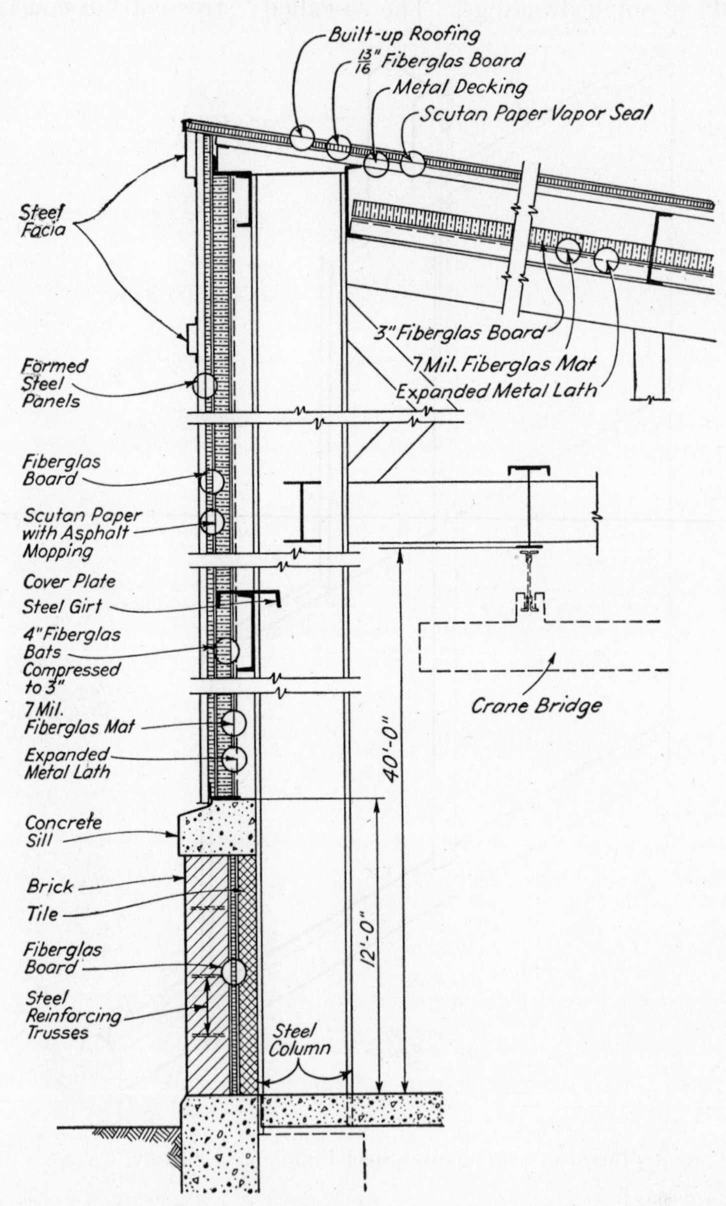

FIG. 14. Exterior Wall Section for a Windowless Factory. Design and Construction by the Austin Company.

applied to wood or steel frames to form wall surfaces. More recently, specially formed sections of steel have come into general use. Their particular application is for industrial buildings, but occasionally, with suitable surface treatment, they may be an acceptable choice for other types of occupancy.

An interesting design appropriate for industrial work is illustrated in Fig. 14. This is typical of the windowless factory or, more correctly expressed, the "controlled conditions" plant, which has been greatly developed during the past 15 years. Light and interior atmosphere are effectively regulated to meet the requirements of the occupants. Objectionable sound is largely eliminated. The wall and roof support is furnished by structural-steel framing. Up to the sill level the wall is of masonry, brick backed by

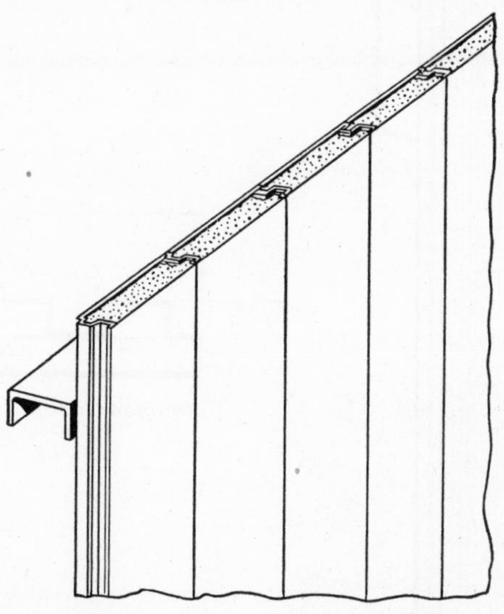

Fig. 15. Insulated, Sheet-Steel Wall Panels. Courtesy, Detroit Steel Products Company.

Fiberglas board with an interior finish of clay tile. Above the sill, steel panels are used for exterior finish. These panels are 30 in. wide, fabricated from 18-gage steel, and ribbed 10 in. on centers. They are designed to resist a 30-lb wind load when supported by girts or other framing on spans up to 12 ft. The shape of the panels, backed by the Fiberglas insulation board, results in the formation of vertical flues, which provide air circulation within the wall. A vapor seal is applied to the inner face of the board. Four-inch Fiberglas bats, compressed to 3 in. and covered by a 7-millimeter Fiberglas mat retained in place with expanded metal lath, serve as insulation and interior finish. This particular combination of materials was designed to obtain low heat transmission together with good sound absorption and light reflection.

A simple wall section comprising sheet steel, used on both exterior and interior with insulation between, is shown in Fig. 15. Figures 16 and 17 show a section and an elevation of a completed building where the fluted face of the panels is used upon the exterior. The flat surface may be similarly exposed if desired. The more recent installations made by the sponsors of this system employ aluminum sheets separated by an insulation of Fiberglas. Figure 18 shows the details of framing for a competing design furnished in galvanized copper-bearing steel. The advantage of dry-wall

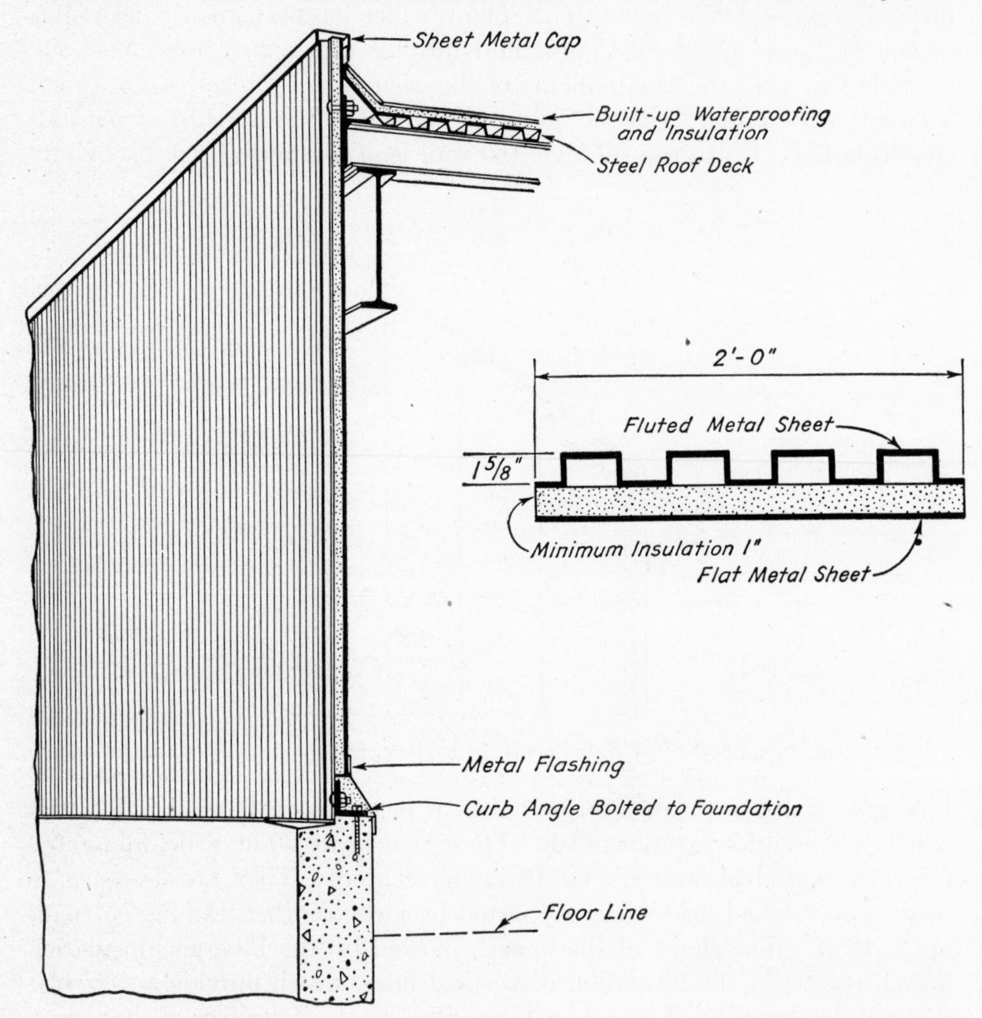

Fig. 16. Insulated, Fluted, Sheet-Metal Wall Panels. Courtesy, H. H. Robertson Company.

construction, combined with speed in erection, resulted in the wide acceptance of such designs for industrial buildings during World War II. They are also structurally appropriate for many other types of occupancy.

In addition to the purely utilitarian uses of formed-steel sheets in wall construction, several of the more expensive metals are now furnished in practicable shapes to serve as exterior surfaces. Such use has gradually developed from the acceptance of the metal spandrel, which was comparatively new when applied in the Empire State Building, New York City, in 1929. Outstanding among the "white metals" is stainless steel, composed of iron, chromium and usually nickel, together with small amounts of other

Fig. 17. Application of Fluted, Metal Wall Panels. Courtesy, H. H. Robertson Company.

elements. It has been used for many years principally in the form of mouldings and window and door frames. Designs are now available applying to its application in sheets, not only as a surface covering over masonry, but also in the form of panels which, with the addition of insulation, vapor seal, and interior finish, form a complete exterior wall section appropriate for steel-framed structures. A large variety of finishes is available. As stainless steel is one of the more durable metals, requiring a minimum of upkeep in the form of surface cleaning, it is appropriate from a utilitarian viewpoint and may often be used to produce very attractive architectural effects.

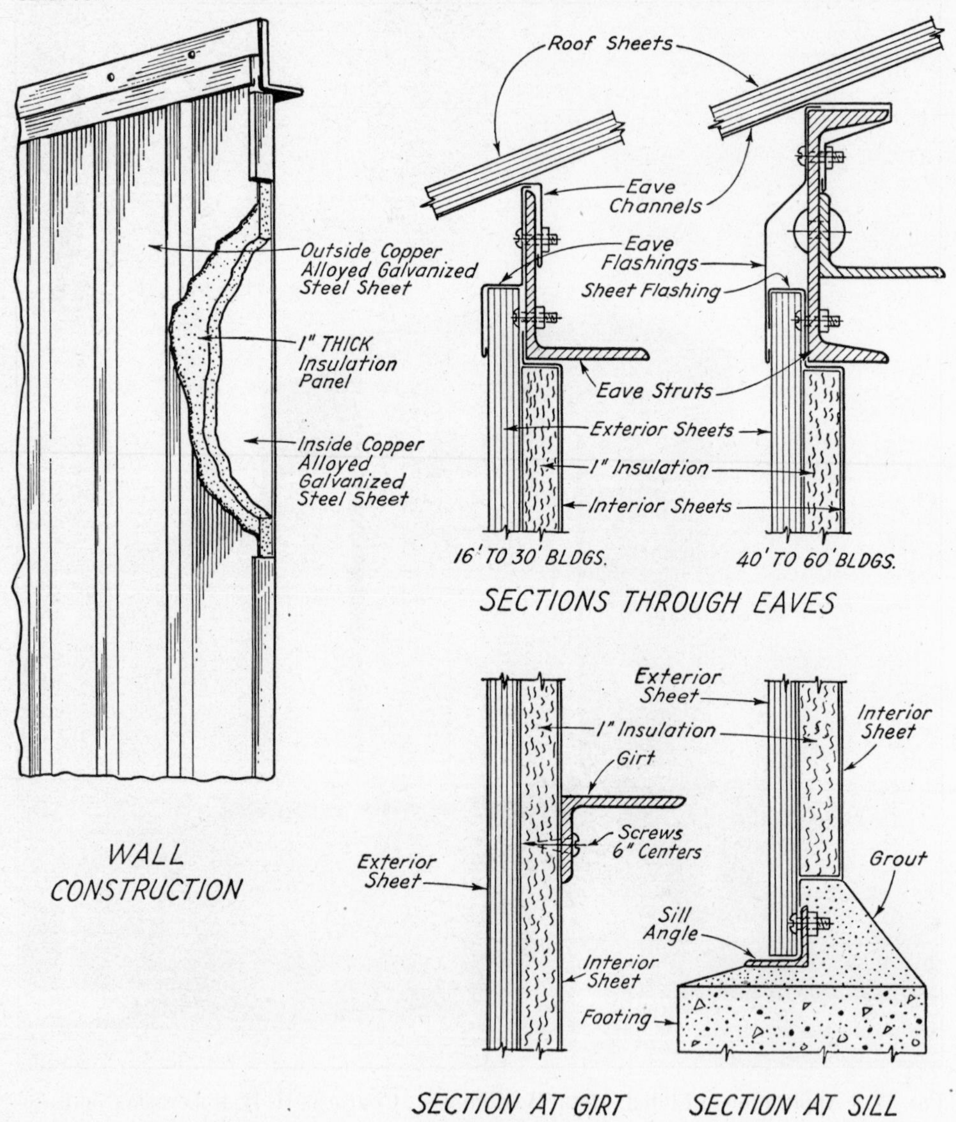

Fig. 18. Ribbed Panels of Galvanized, Copper-Bearing Steel. Courtesy, Blaw-Knox Company.

Aluminum is another metal which has excellent possibilities for wall surfacing in an assembly having a backing of Vermiculite or other material providing insulation against both the fire hazard and normal heat losses. Figure 19 shows typical details for its use in spandrels.

Copper panels composed of 16- to 24-oz hard copper are also designed to form weather-tight joints without the use of mastic. A size standardized by one manufacturer is 24 × 15 in. Surfaces may be left untreated, painted, lacquered, or enameled.

Supplementing these various designs, porcelain-enameled iron or steel sheets are available for both exterior and interior wall surfaces. The maximum dimension recommended by a number of manufacturers is 3 ft × 4 ft, the exact size depending upon architectural requirements.

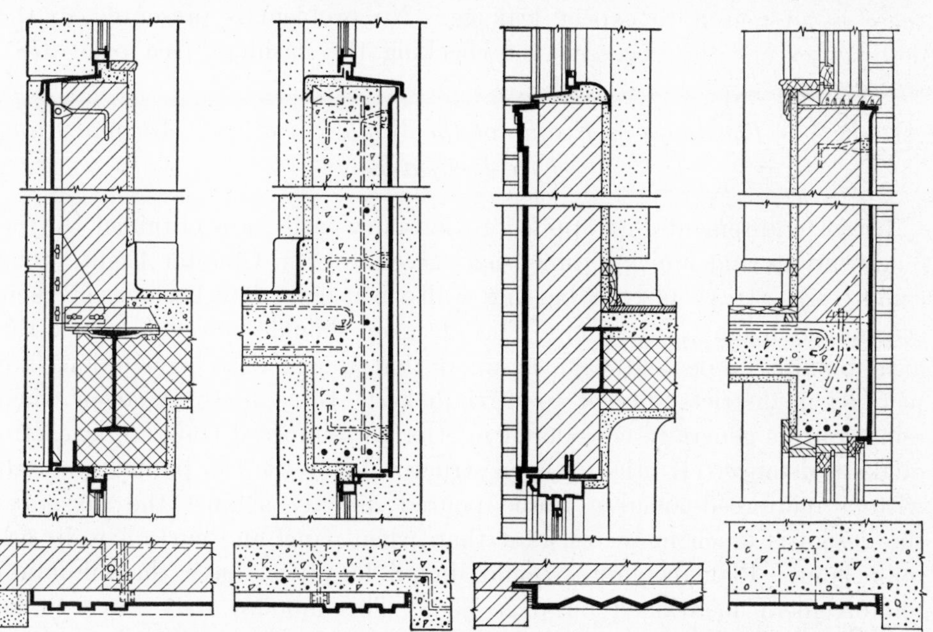

FIG. 19. Aluminum Spandrel Details. Courtesy, Aluminum Company of America.

Composed of 16- or 18-gage metal, panels may be backed with plywood, insulating board, or light-weight concrete. The enameled surface is an extremely thin application of a special composition of glass bonded to the metal base by fusion at high temperatures. A wide range of colors is available. A variety of plain sheets and special sections, which may often be appropriate as an exterior surfacing material for commercial buildings, are manufactured. Additional information in regard to such designs may be obtained from the Porcelain Enamel Institute.

Metallic wall surfacings offer many extremely interesting architectural possibilities. From the utilitarian viewpoint the problem is to obtain a section which can be easily applied to steel framing and which will provide the necessary heat insulation, together with an acceptable interior finish, without excessive cost. In considering the appropriateness of any proposed design, the fire rating should be checked where it is important, as many assemblies, unbacked by masonry, are classed merely as incombustible (see page 4). Since new designs are constantly being developed, it is recommended that no work of this type be planned without consultation with the manufacturers.

CLAPBOARDS, SIDING, AND SHINGLES AS WALL SURFACINGS. These and similar materials are generally appropriate only over wood-framed construction. For this reason they were mentioned on page 97 in connection with the conventional wood-stud assemblies. If standard materials are used and ordinary care is exercised in application, there is no reason to expect leakage. No problem is presented to the designer except the necessity for checking the flashings (see page 278).

Article 5. The Body or Frame of the Wall; Structural Adequacy and Fire Resistance

These requirements, as applied to masonry walls, are obtained by the qualifications and limiting dimensions given later in Chapter Eight. The compressive stress in even bearing walls is usually low because of their economical height limitation. The designer should, however, check the local building code and bear in mind that more severe restrictions are justified in districts subject to earthquakes. Brick masonry, even when reinforced, is generally considered inferior to reinforced concrete in earthquake resistance. If brick or even structural-clay tile can be incorporated with a reinforced-concrete frame poured directly against the masonry, the design is much more resistant than when panel and curtain walls are built later. Plain concrete should, in all localities, have the minimum reinforcement mentioned on page 338. This amount may have to be increased where there is probability of appreciable seismic disturbance.

For wood framing, the conventional practice illustrated on pages 97 and 98 provides ample strength except where exceptionally high winds may be expected. In such localities additional anchorage to foundations and more diagonal bracing than shown in the typical assemblies are necessary. From the viewpoint of fire resistance, wood-framed structures are frankly burnable and largely prohibited within the fire districts of many cities, but are almost universally used throughout this country for suburban and rural dwelling-house construction.

For prefabricated and partially prefabricated designs of both light steel and wood, the manufacturers provide a structure capable of carrying the imposed loads under normal conditions, but the structural adequacy should be checked for any exceptional exposure. This statement applies particularly to wind load in localities subject to hurricanes or tornadoes and to the fire rating of walls within congested districts.

Article 6. Heat Insulation and Vapor Seal

HEAT INSULATION. The subject of insulation against heat losses or heat gain was discussed in Chapter Five on roofing, together with various insulating materials and their appropriate use for roof construction. The same principles apply to walls, and most of the same materials are used.

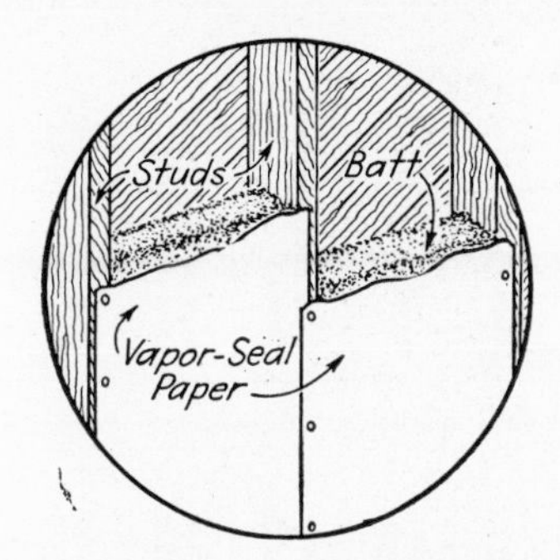

Installation of Flexible Insulation Between Wood Studs with Vapor-Seal on the Inside

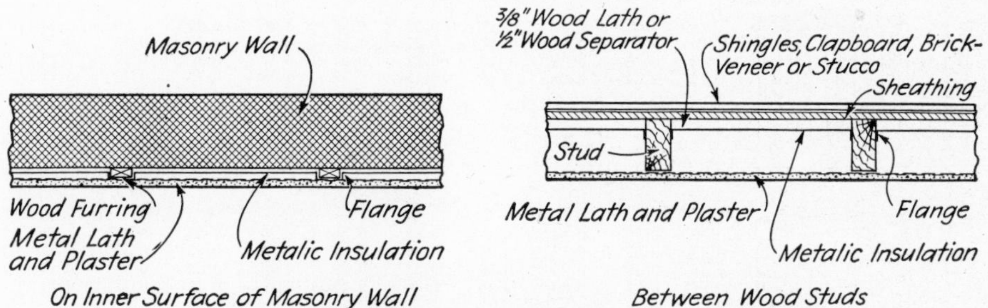

Installation of Metallic Insulation - Horizontal Sections

FIG. 20. Heat Insulation in Wall Construction. Courtesy, Johns-Manville and American Flange and Manufacturing Company.

The rigid, flexible, and reflective types have a broad application to exterior wall designs. The thinner styles of rigid insulation, commonly supplied in the form of wall boards of low density, are helpful in furnishing at least some degree of protection. The thicker units, such as the 2-in. blocks of pressed mineral wool or cork, are appropriate for the lining of cold rooms. Blocks are set in hot asphalt, from one to four layers being used according to the interior temperature to be maintained.

The flexible types, in the form of batts, blankets, or quilts composed of organic materials, mineral, or glass wool (see page 176) are usually more appropriate for new construction than are loose fills. Loose fills, however, are used very widely for insulating existing buildings, being installed by pneumatic means for this purpose.

COEFFICIENTS OF TRANSMISSION (*U*) OF MASONRY WALLS

(From *Heating Ventilating and Air-Conditioning Guide*, 1946)

Coefficients are expressed in Btu per hour per square foot per degree Fahrenheit difference in temperature between the air on the two sides, and are based on an outside wind velocity of 15 mph.

Type of Masonry	Thickness of Masonry, Inches	Interior Finish (Plus Insulation Where Indicated)									Wall Number
		Plain Walls—No Interior Finish	Plaster (½ in.) on Walls	Metal Lath and Plaster * Furred †	Gypsum Board (⅜ in.) Decorated—Furred †	Gypsum Lath (⅜ in.) Plastered ‡—Furred †	Insulating Board (½ in.) Plain or Decorated—Furred †	Insulating Board Lath (½ in.) Plastered ‡—Furred †	Insulating Board Lath (1 in.) Plastered ‡—Furred †	Gypsum Lath ‡ Plastered Plus 1 in. Blanket Insulation—Furred †	
		A	B	C	D	E	F	G	H	I	
Solid § Brick	8	0.50	0.46	0.32	0.31	0.30	0.22	0.22	0.16	0.14	67
	12	0.36	0.34	0.25	0.25	0.24	0.19	0.19	0.14	0.13	68
	16	0.28	0.27	0.21	0.21	0.20	0.17	0.16	0.13	0.12	69
Hollow ‖ Tile (Stucco Exterior Finish)	8	0.40	0.37	0.27	0.27	0.26	0.20	0.20	0.15	0.13	70
	10	0.39	0.37	0.27	0.27	0.26	0.20	0.19	0.15	0.13	71
	12	0.30	0.28	0.22	0.22	0.21	0.17	0.17	0.13	0.12	72
	16	0.24	0.24	0.19	0.19	0.18	0.15	0.15	0.12	0.11	73
Stone ¶	8	0.70	0.64	0.39	0.38	0.36	0.26	0.25	0.18	0.16	74
	12	0.57	0.53	0.35	0.34	0.33	0.24	0.23	0.17	0.15	75
	16	0.49	0.45	0.31	0.31	0.29	0.22	0.22	0.16	0.14	76
	24	0.37	0.35	0.26	0.26	0.25	0.19	0.19	0.15	0.13	77
Poured Concrete **	6	0.79	0.71	0.42	0.41	0.39	0.27	0.26	0.19	0.16	78
	8	0.70	0.64	0.39	0.38	0.36	0.26	0.25	0.18	0.16	79
	10	0.63	0.58	0.37	0.36	0.34	0.25	0.24	0.18	0.15	80
	12	0.57	0.53	0.35	0.34	0.33	0.24	0.23	0.17	0.15	81
Hollow Concrete Blocks		Gravel Aggregate									
	8	0.56	0.52	0.34	0.34	0.32	0.24	0.23	0.17	0.15	82
	12	0.49	0.46	0.32	0.31	0.30	0.22	0.22	0.16	0.14	83
		Cinder Aggregate									
	8	0.41	0.39	0.28	0.28	0.27	0.21	0.20	0.15	0.13	84
	12	0.38	0.36	0.26	0.26	0.25	0.20	0.19	0.15	0.13	85
		Light Weight Aggregate ††									
	8	0.36	0.34	0.26	0.25	0.24	0.19	0.19	0.15	0.13	86
	12	0.34	0.33	0.25	0.24	0.24	0.19	0.18	0.14	0.13	87

* Thickness of plaster assumed ¾ in.
† Based on 2 in. furring strips; one air space.
‡ Thickness of plaster assumed ½ in.
§ Based on 4 in. hard brick and remainder common brick.
‖ The 8 in. and 10 in. tile figures are based on two cells in the direction of heat flow. The 12 in. tile is based on three cells in the direction of heat flow. The 16 in. tile consists of one 10 in. and one 6 in. tile, each having two cells in the direction of heat flow.
¶ Limestone or sandstone.
** These figures may be used with sufficient accuracy for concrete walls with stucco exterior finish.
†† Expanded slag, burned clay or pumice.

COEFFICIENTS OF TRANSMISSION (*U*) OF FRAME WALLS WITH INSULATION BETWEEN FRAMING * †

(From *Heating Ventilating and Air-Conditioning Guide,* 1946)

Coefficients are expressed in Btu per hour per square foot per degree Fahrenheit difference in temperature between the air on the two sides, and are based on an outside wind velocity of 15 mph.

Coefficient with No Insulation between Framing	Coefficient with Insulation between Framing				Number
	Mineral Wool or Vegetable Fibers in Blanket or Bat Form ‡ (Thickness below)			3⅝ in. Mineral Wool between Framing §	
	1 in.	2 in.	3 in.		
	A	B	C	D	
0.11	0.078	0.063	0.054	0.051	33
0.12	0.083	0.067	0.056	0.053	34
0.13	0.088	0.070	0.058	0.055	35
0.14	0.092	0.072	0.061	0.057	36
0.15	0.097	0.075	0.062	0.059	37
0.16	0.10	0.078	0.064	0.060	38
0.17	0.10	0.080	0.066	0.062	39
0.18	0.11	0.082	0.067	0.063	40
0.19	0.11	0.084	0.069	0.065	41
0.20	0.12	0.086	0.070	0.066	42
0.21	0.12	0.088	0.072	0.067	43
0.22	0.12	0.089	0.073	0.068	44
0.23	0.12	0.091	0.074	0.069	45
0.24	0.12	0.093	0.075	0.070	46
0.25	0.13	0.094	0.076	0.071	47
0.26	0.13	0.096	0.077	0.072	48
0.27	0.14	0.097	0.078	0.073	49
0.28	0.14	0.098	0.079	0.073	50
0.29	0.14	0.10	0.080	0.075	51
0.30	0.14	0.10	0.080	0.075	52
0.31	0.14	0.10	0.081	0.076	53
0.32	0.15	0.10	0.082	0.077	54
0.33	0.15	0.10	0.083	0.077	55
0.34	0.15	0.10	0.083	0.078	56
0.35	0.15	0.11	0.084	0.078	57
0.36	0.15	0.11	0.085	0.079	58
0.37	0.16	0.11	0.085	0.080	59
0.38	0.16	0.11	0.086	0.080	60
0.39	0.16	0.11	0.086	0.081	61
0.40	0.16	0.11	0.087	0.082	62
0.41	0.16	0.11	0.087	0.082	63
0.42	0.16	0.11	0.088	0.082	64
0.43	0.17	0.11	0.088	0.082	65
0.44	0.17	0.11	0.089	0.083	66

* This table may be used for determining the coefficients of transmission of frame constructions with the types and thicknesses of insulation indicated in Columns A to D inclusive between framing. Columns A, B, and C may be used for walls, ceilings, or roofs with only one air space between framing but are not applicable to ceilings with *no* flooring above. (See table on page 178.) Column D is applicable to walls only. *Example:* Find the coefficient of transmission of a frame wall consisting of wood siding, 25/32 in. insulating board sheathing, studs, gypsum lath and plaster, with 2 in. blanket insulation between studs. According to the table on p. 272, a wall of this construction with *no insulation* between studs has a coefficient of 0.19 (Wall No. 4D). In Column B above, it will be found that a wall of this value with 2 in. blanket insulation between the studs has a coefficient of 0.084.

† Coefficients corrected for 2 x 4 framing, 16 in. o. c.—15 per cent of surface area.

‡ Based on one air space between framing.

§ No air space.

COEFFICIENTS OF TRANSMISSION (U) OF FRAME WALLS

(From *Heating Ventilating and Air-Conditioning Guide*, 1946)

Coefficients are expressed in Btu per hour per square foot per degree Fahrenheit difference in temperature between the air on the two sides, and are based on an outside wind velocity of 15 mph.

No Insulation Between Studs *

Exterior Finish	Interior Finish	Type of Sheathing				Wall Number
		Gypsum (1/2 in. Thick)	Plywood (5/16 in. Thick)	Wood † (25/32 in. Thick) Building Paper	Insulating Board (25/32 in. Thick)	
		A	B	C	D	
Wood Siding (Clapboard)	Metal lath and plaster ‡	0.33	0.32	0.26	0.20	1
	Gypsum board (3/8 in.) decorated	0.32	0.32	0.26	0.20	2
	Wood lath and plaster	0.31	0.31	0.25	0.19	3
	Gypsum lath (3/8 in.) plastered §	0.31	0.30	0.25	0.19	4
	Plywood (3/8 in.) plain or decorated	0.30	0.30	0.24	0.19	5
	Insulating board (1/2 in.) plain or decorated	0.23	0.23	0.19	0.16	6
	Insulating board lath (1/2 in.) plastered §	0.22	0.22	0.19	0.15	7
	Insulating board lath (1 in.) plastered §	0.17	0.17	0.15	0.12	8
Wood ‖ Shingles	Metal lath and plaster ‡	0.25	0.25	0.26	0.17	9
	Gypsum board (3/8 in.) decorated	0.25	0.25	0.26	0.17	10
	Wood lath and plaster	0.24	0.24	0.25	0.16	11
	Gypsum lath (3/8 in.) plastered §	0.24	0.24	0.25	0.16	12
	Plywood (3/8 in.) plain or decorated	0.24	0.24	0.24	0.16	13
	Insulating board (1/2 in.) plain or decorated	0.19	0.19	0.19	0.14	14
	Insulating board lath (1/2 in.) plastered §	0.19	0.18	0.19	0.13	15
	Insulating board lath (1 in.) plastered §	0.14	0.14	0.15	0.11	16
Stucco	Metal lath and plaster ‡	0.43	0.42	0.32	0.23	17
	Gypsum board (3/8 in.) decorated	0.42	0.41	0.31	0.23	18
	Wood lath and plaster	0.40	0.39	0.30	0.22	19
	Gypsum lath (3/8 in.) plastered §	0.39	0.39	0.30	0.22	20
	Plywood (3/8 in.) plain or decorated	0.39	0.38	0.29	0.22	21
	Insulating board (1/2 in.) plain or decorated	0.27	0.27	0.22	0.18	22
	Insulating board lath (1/2 in.) plastered §	0.26	0.26	0.22	0.17	23
	Insulating board lath (1 in.) plastered §	0.19	0.19	0.16	0.14	24
Brick Veneer ¶	Metal lath and plaster ‡	0.37	0.36	0.28	0.21	25
	Gypsum board (3/8 in.) decorated	0.36	0.36	0.28	0.21	26
	Wood lath and plaster	0.35	0.34	0.27	0.20	27
	Gypsum lath (3/8 in.) plastered §	0.34	0.34	0.27	0.20	28
	Plywood (3/8 in.) plain or decorated	0.34	0.33	0.27	0.20	29
	Insulating board (1/2 in.) plain or decorated	0.25	0.25	0.21	0.17	30
	Insulating board lath (1/2 in.) plastered §	0.24	0.24	0.20	0.16	31
	Insulating board lath (1 in.) plastered §	0.18	0.18	0.15	0.13	32

* Coefficients not weighted; effect of studding neglected.
† Nominal thickness, 1 in.
‡ Plaster assumed 3/4 in. thick.
§ Plaster assumed 1/2 in. thick.
‖ Furring strips (1 in. nominal thickness) between wood shingles and all sheathings except wood.
¶ Small air space and mortar between building paper and brick veneer neglected.

COEFFICIENTS OF TRANSMISSION (*U*) OF BRICK AND STONE VENEER MASONRY WALLS

(From *Heating Ventilating and Air-Conditioning Guide*, 1946)

Coefficients are expressed in Btu per hour per square foot per degree Fahrenheit difference in temperature between the air on the two sides, and are based on an outside wind velocity of 15 mph.

Typical Construction	Facing	Backing	Interior Finish (Plus Insulation Where Indicated)									Wall Number
			Plain Walls—no Interior Finish	Plaster (½ in.) on Walls	Metal Lath and Plaster *—Furred †	Gypsum Board (⅜ in.) Decorated—Furred †	Gypsum Lath (⅜ in.) Plastered ‡—Furred †	Insulating Board (½ in.) Plain or Decorated—Furred †	Insulating Board Lath (½ in.) Plastered ‡—Furred †	Insulating Board Lath (1 in.) Plastered ‡—Furred †	Gypsum Lath Plastered † Plus 1 in. Blanket Insulation—Furred †	
			A	B	C	D	E	F	G	H	I	
		6 in. hollow tile §	0.35	0.34	0.25	0.25	0.24	0.19	0.18	0.14	0.13	88
		8 in. hollow tile §	0.34	0.32	0.25	0.24	0.23	0.19	0.18	0.14	0.13	89
	4 in. Brick Veneer ‖	6 in. concrete	0.59	0.54	0.35	0.35	0.33	0.24	0.23	0.17	0.15	90
		8 in. concrete	0.54	0.50	0.33	0.33	0.31	0.23	0.23	0.17	0.15	91
		8 in. concrete blocks ¶ (gravel aggregate)	0.44	0.41	0.29	0.29	0.28	0.21	0.21	0.16	0.14	92
		8 in. concrete blocks ¶ (cinder aggregate)	0.34	0.33	0.25	0.24	0.24	0.19	0.18	0.14	0.13	93
		8 in. concrete blocks ¶ (light-weight aggregate) **	0.31	0.29	0.23	0.23	0.22	0.18	0.17	0.14	0.12	94
		6 in. hollow tile §	0.37	0.35	0.26	0.26	0.25	0.19	0.19	0.15	0.13	95
		8 in. hollow tile §	0.36	0.34	0.25	0.25	0.24	0.19	0.19	0.14	0.13	96
	4 in. Cut Stone Veneer ‖	6 in. concrete	0.63	0.58	0.37	0.36	0.34	0.25	0.24	0.18	0.15	97
		8 in. concrete	0.57	0.53	0.35	0.34	0.33	0.24	0.23	0.17	0.15	98
		8 in. concrete blocks ¶ (gravel aggregate)	0.47	0.44	0.30	0.30	0.29	0.22	0.21	0.16	0.14	99
		8 in. concrete blocks ¶ (cinder aggregate)	0.36	0.34	0.25	0.25	0.24	0.19	0.19	0.15	0.13	100
		8 in. concrete blocks ¶ (light weight aggregate) **	0.32	0.30	0.23	0.23	0.22	0.18	0.17	0.14	0.12	101

* Thickness of plaster assumed ¾ in.
† Based on 2 in. furring strips; one air space.
‡ Thickness of plaster assumed ½ in.
§ The hollow tile figures are based on two air cells in the direction of heat flow.
‖ Calculations based on ½ in. cement mortar between backing and facing except in the case of the concrete backing, which is assumed to be poured in place.
¶ Hollow concrete blocks.
** Expanded slag, burned clay or pumice.

The reflective types are also appropriate for wall work and may offer the added advantage of furnishing a vapor seal. As mentioned on page 177, they should be installed with an air space at least ¾ in. wide, and all sheets carefully lapped to form a tight, continuous surface. Figure 20 shows typical details illustrating some normal arrangements of wall insulation.

Transmission coefficients applying to the more conventional assemblies are given in the *Guide*, yearly publication of the American Society of Heating and Ventilating Engineers. The tables on pages 270 to 273 are abstracted from this excellent authority.

CONDENSATION AND VAPOR SEAL. These subjects, as applying to roofs, were discussed on page 184. They are also important in relation to walls. Proper provision to avoid condensation on the interior surfaces of exterior walls often requires insulation. Prevention of condensation of water vapor within the exterior wall assembly may require either a vapor seal on the warm side of the insulation or ventilation within the wall. This is particularly true if interior humidities are high. Lowering the vapor resistance on the exterior, or cold side, of the wall insulation by introducing vents open to the exterior air is effective; but, as we also have the requirement of preventing the entrance of wind-driven rain, such a provision is often impracticable.

In wood-framed walls, insulation such as mineral wool placed between the studs makes the danger of interstitial condensation actually greater than if no insulation were used, because of the fact that the temperature at the inner face of the sheathing, where condensation normally occurs, is much lower than in an uninsulated wall of the same design. Figure 21 shows two exterior wall sections applying to typical wood-stud construction: (*a*) is uninsulated; (*b*) has a loose-fill type of insulation.

For purposes of illustration an indoor temperature of 70° F and three outdoor temperatures of 20°, 0°, and −20° F are assumed. Indoor relative humidities are 40, 30, and 20 per cent. The three solid lines marked "temperature" show the temperature gradients from one side of the wall to the other for the three conditions chosen. The three dotted horizontal lines marked "dew-point temperature" locate the dew-point temperatures corresponding to the three indoor relative humidities. Water-vapor pressures are also shown for each of these lines.

If we compare sketches (*a*) and (*b*), we see that the temperature gradients within the stud space are much steeper in (*b*) than in (*a*) and the respective sheathing temperatures are lower. This difference is caused by the effect of the insulation, and condensation will occur on the sheathing with a lower room humidity than in sketch (*a*), where insulation was omitted. This fact makes it particularly necessary to install a vapor seal or provide ventilation within the walls of all well-insulated buildings.

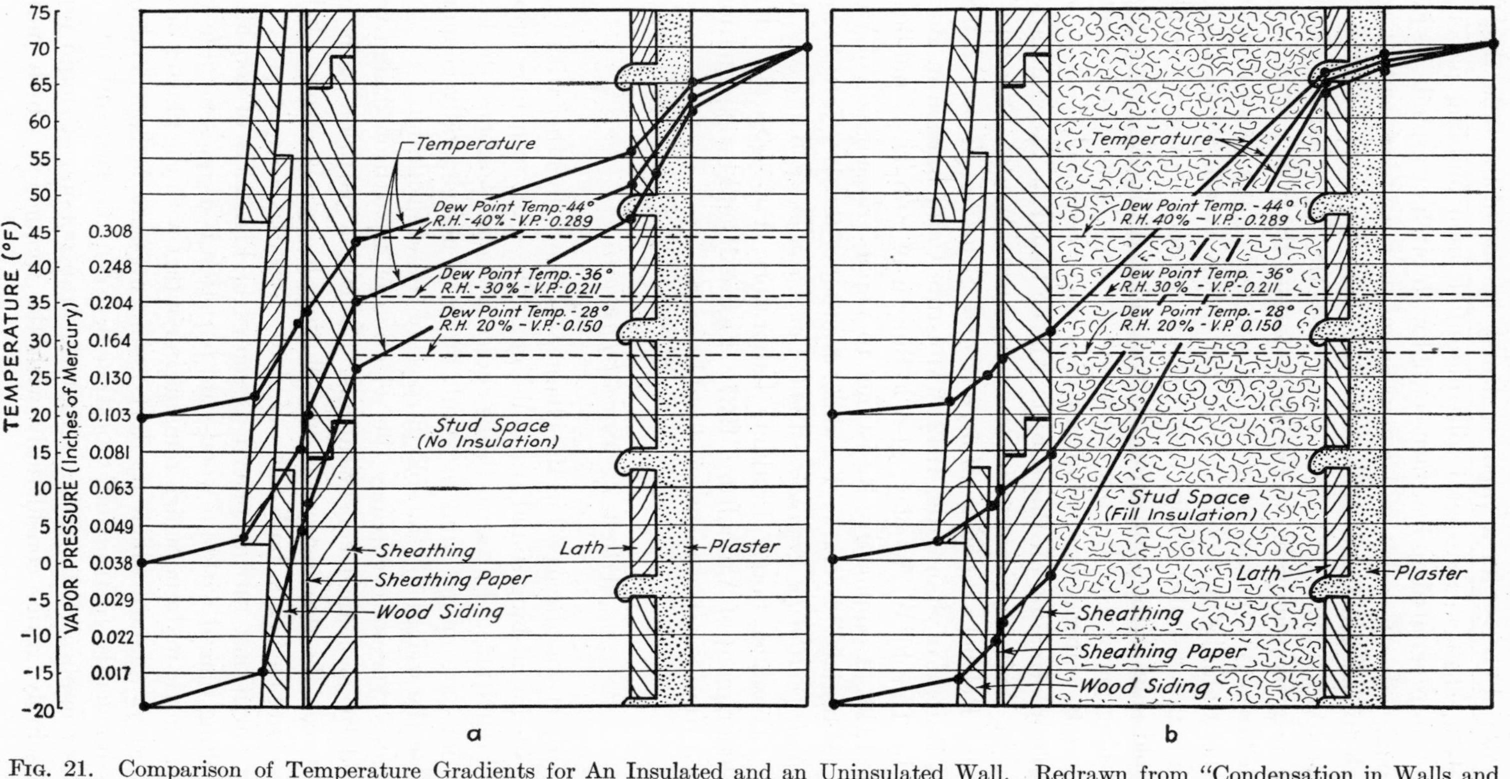

FIG. 21. Comparison of Temperature Gradients for An Insulated and an Uninsulated Wall. Redrawn from "Condensation in Walls and Attics," by L. V. Teesdale, Forest Products Laboratory, Forest Service, U. S. Department of Agriculture.

The material chosen for a vapor seal may be one of the reflective types of insulation, such as the metal foils mounted upon building paper or a roofing felt impregnated and surface-coated with pitch or asphalt, as identified on page 185. For dry-wall construction, two coats of asphalt paint, or enough to make a bright, shiny surface, may be applied to the outer face of an interior plywood finish. In all cases the vapor barrier should be placed as near as practicable to the inside face of the wall.

In order to permit easier escape to the exterior of any moisture forming within the wall, bituminous coatings or other waterproofing materials offering a high resistance to the passage of water vapor should not be placed on the cold side of the insulation. For example, in wood-framed designs the sheathing paper usually applied outside the sheathing should be similar to slaters' felt, water resistant but not very vapor resistant.

Valuable information on this subject will be found in "Accumulation of Moisture in Walls of Frame Construction during Winter Exposure," by Weber and Reichel, *Building Materials and Structures Report BMS* 93, National Bureau of Standards, 1942; "Moisture Condensation in Building Walls," by Harold W. Wooley, also a Bureau of Standards publication, *BMS* 63, 1940; "Comparative Resistance to Vapor Transmission of Various Building Materials," by L. V. Teesdale, *Journal of the American Society of Heating and Ventilating Engineers*, 1943; *Condensation in Walls and Attics*, by L. V. Teesdale, Forest Products Laboratory, Forest Service, United States Department of Agriculture, 1937. Figure 21 and its explanation are abstracted from this last-mentioned publication.

Article 7. Sound Insulation

This subject was discussed in the chapter on floors, together with various methods of diminishing sound transmission. The same principles apply to walls and partitions. In regard to the choice of such assemblies, the heavier constructions are more sound resistant, but it is not generally economical to increase the weight for the sole purpose of sound insulation.

For many types of occupancy the selection of a partition design will be influenced by acoustical considerations. A double partition with an air space between the two sections is one solution; but, if the space is bridged by supporting elements, both faces tend to vibrate as a single unit. With masonry partitions, furring placed as shown in Fig. 22 is of considerable help. Filling placed within a wood-stud partition is of questionable value. A porous, elastic material which remains in contact with the plaster or other surface layers against which it exerts some pressure is beneficial unless packed sufficiently to transmit vibration between the two surfaces. The subject is complicated by the fact that the transmission of sound for any given assembly varies considerably with the frequency, which indicates

SOUND TRANSMISSION LOSS FOR VARIOUS WALL ASSEMBLIES IN DECIBELS FOR FIVE FREQUENCIES FROM 256 TO 1,024

Design	Loss	Design	Loss
3"x12"x30" gypsum tile; brown coat of gypsum plaster; smooth, white finish.	37.8	Two-inch solid plaster partition; 3/4" channel studs; perforated gypsum lath; gypsum plaster; smooth, white finish.	33.9
3"x12"x30" gypsum tile; United States Gypsum resilient clip; metal lath and gypsum plaster on one side; gypsum plaster applied directly to tile on the other side, smooth, white finish on both sides.	52.7	Two-inch solid plaster partition; 3/4" channel studs; expanded metal lath; gypsum plaster; smooth, white finish.	34.1
(a) – Hollow clay tile panel constructed of 4"x12"x12" partition tile, three cells; plastered on both sides with brown coat of gypsum plaster; smooth, white finish. (b) – Hollow clay tile panel constructed of 3"x12"x12" partition tile, three cells; plastered both sides with brown coat of gypsum plaster; smooth, white finish.	(a) 40.9 (b) 40.0	Wood studs; Steeltex lath with paper backing nailed to studs with special nail; scratch and brown coats of gypsum plaster; smooth, white finish; thickness of grounds 3/4".	33.2
(a) – Cinder-block panel constructed of 4"x8"x18" standard Straub hollow cinder blocks; plastered on both sides with 5/8" of brown-coat gypsum plaster; smooth, white finish. (b) – Cinder-block wall panel constructed of 3"x8"x16" cinder blocks; plastered on both sides with 5/8" of brown-coat gypsum plaster; smooth, white finish.	(a) 38.6 (b) 43.0	Wood studs staggered; expanded metal lath; scratch and brown coats of gypsum plaster; smooth, white finish; thickness of grounds 3/4".	48.5

Reprinted from "Sound Insulation of Wall and Floor Construction," by V. L. Chrisler, *Report BMS* 17 (1939) and Supplement (1940), National Bureau of Standards, U. S. Department of Commerce.

that a suggested design should be checked for the character of the sound which it is expected to intercept.

In considering the use of sound-absorbent materials, it should be remembered that they are appropriately employed for the control within a room of sound originating in the same room, rather than for the formation of a barrier against its transmission to other rooms. A modification of this principle is the use of acoustical surfaces in corridors to prevent them from conducting sound through open doors.

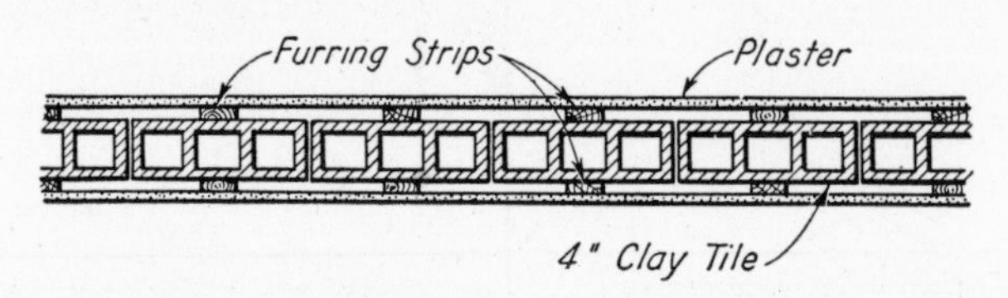

FIG. 22. Application of Furring Strips Decreases Sound Transmission through Tile Partitions. Redrawn from "Sound Insulation of Wall and Floor Construction," by V. L. Chrisler, *Report BMS* 17 (1939) and Supplement (1940), National Bureau of Standards, U. S. Department of Commerce.

Sound-insulating values of various assemblies are presented in the table on page 277 as sound-transmission losses. The transmission loss is given in decibels for an average of five or more frequencies. Additional information will be found in the references from which these data were abstracted.

Article 8. Flashing and Caulking

The basic principle in the design of flashing is to provide a means of shedding water before it can enter the exterior surface of the building or, accepting the possibility that some water will seep in, to lead it out of the wall, where it can do no harm. These two cases are illustrated by the cap-and-base flashing and the through-parapet flashing, respectively, shown with other typical details in Fig. 23. The all-too-common practice of applying bituminous or metallic materials to the inside faces of parapet walls is generally undesirable, as such surfaces should not be treated in any way to prevent free evaporation of moisture. An obvious exception is the very low parapet, where a sufficient flashing height could not otherwise be obtained, as shown in Fig. 24. Neither is it desirable that the exterior of parapet walls be surfaced with impervious materials, as this practice causes the same result unless the entire wall is protected from moisture penetration.

LOCATIONS WHERE FLASHINGS ARE REQUIRED. It is a definite obligation of the designer to study the exterior surfaces of his proposed building and to indicate on the drawings or in the specification the location of all flashings, the material to be used, and the design. Flashings built into the structural wall are generally necessary in the following places, which may be identified in Figs. 23 and 25.

a. Wherever a parapet, chimney, or wall intersects a roof surface.

b. Directly beneath the coping of parapets, chimneys, and moat walls or other masonry courses which form the top surface of walls or piers, except where a continuous metal coping is installed. It is also good practice to place a through flashing, in other than very low parapets, at the level of the cap flashing, or just above the flashing block.

c. Beneath or over masonry cornices and belt courses, in order to guard against leakage through the vertical joints separating the masonry units of which the projection is composed; the same statement applies to recesses.

d. Usually across the top of basement walls. This provision is necessary where the wall carries a timber sill, typical of wood-framed designs, and is desirable beneath walls composed of masonry units such as brick, stone, and tile. The purpose is to prevent ground moisture absorbed by the basement wall from travelling upward by capillary action. It is known as a "damp check" and, if metal is used, may be designed to form a termite shield.

e. Over spandrel beams in skeleton construction at every floor and roof level, with particular care around columns.

f. At heads and sills of all window, door, or other openings penetrating exterior walls unless the sill is both impervious to moisture and made in one piece without joints. Careful study of flashing requirements is particularly necessary in cavity-wall design (see page 324), around dormer windows, and in buildings where wood-framed construction is superimposed on masonry walls, such as a

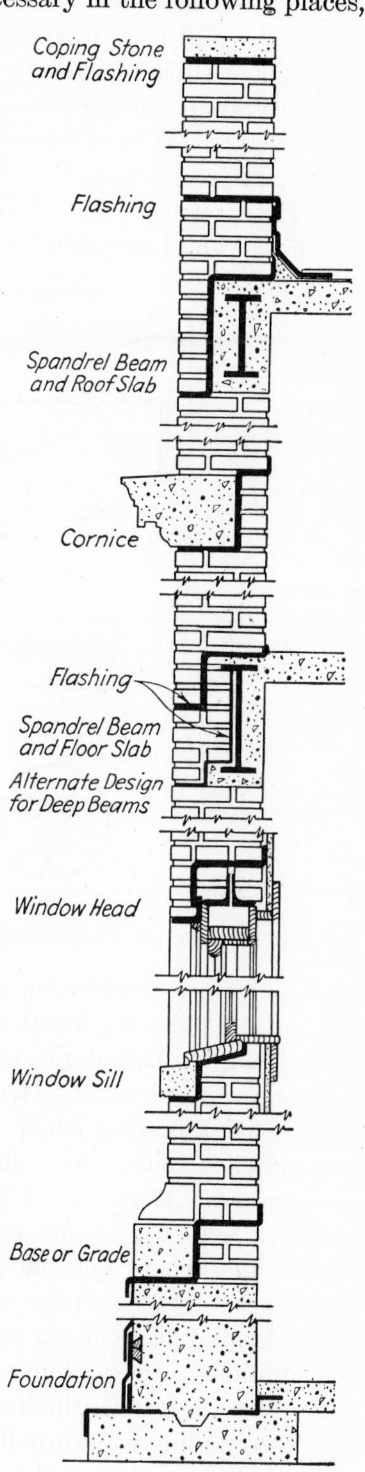

Fig. 23. Flashings in Exterior Masonry Walls. Based upon Designs by Wasco Flashing Company.

wood-framed half-story, often used in residential work when the lower portion of the wall is of masonry.

g. Where stucco forms the exterior wall surface, along the sides as well as at heads and sills of openings. This is usually necessary where projecting trim occurs. Where stucco extends over flashings, it should be carried by metal reinforcement.

h. Except where eaves have a considerable overhang, between the top of the wall and lower surface of the roof.

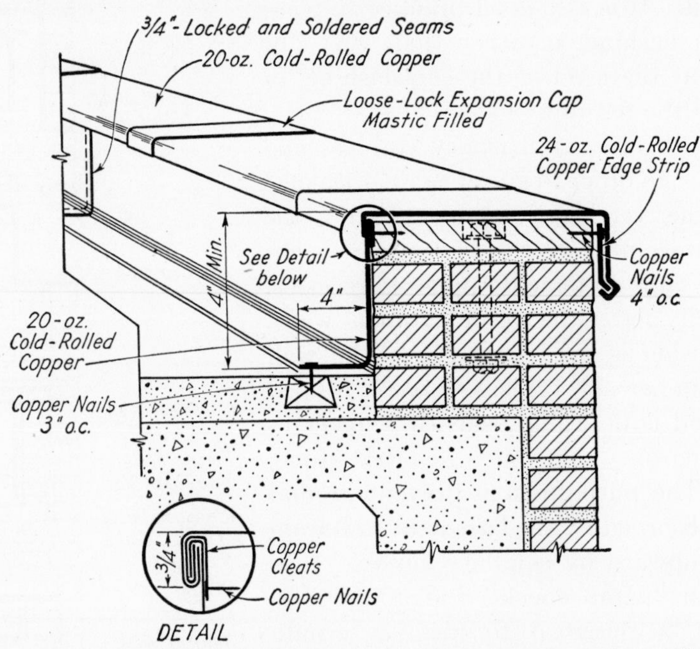

Fig. 24. Low-Parapet Flashing Details. Courtesy, Revere Copper and Brass Company, Inc.

In writing a specification for flashings, the designer would also give attention to the following locations, but they do not affect the structural work.

i. Along the boundaries of flat roofs without parapets and surfaced with built-up waterproofing. Here gravel stops are required and are often combined with a flashing which protects the eaves.

j. Pitched roofs. All valleys formed by the intersection of roof surfaces are flashed. Hips and ridges are designed in conformity with common practice applying to the particular roof-surfacing material. Along horizontal lines where a change occurs in the slope of a pitched roof, flashing is necessary. These sections are shown in Fig. 25.

k. Around all elements penetrating a roof surface, such as pipes or flues, in addition to the various wall locations previously mentioned. On comparatively flat roofs, the gutters and drainage connections are flashed into the surrounding waterproofing.

l. Built-in gutters, which require particular attention.

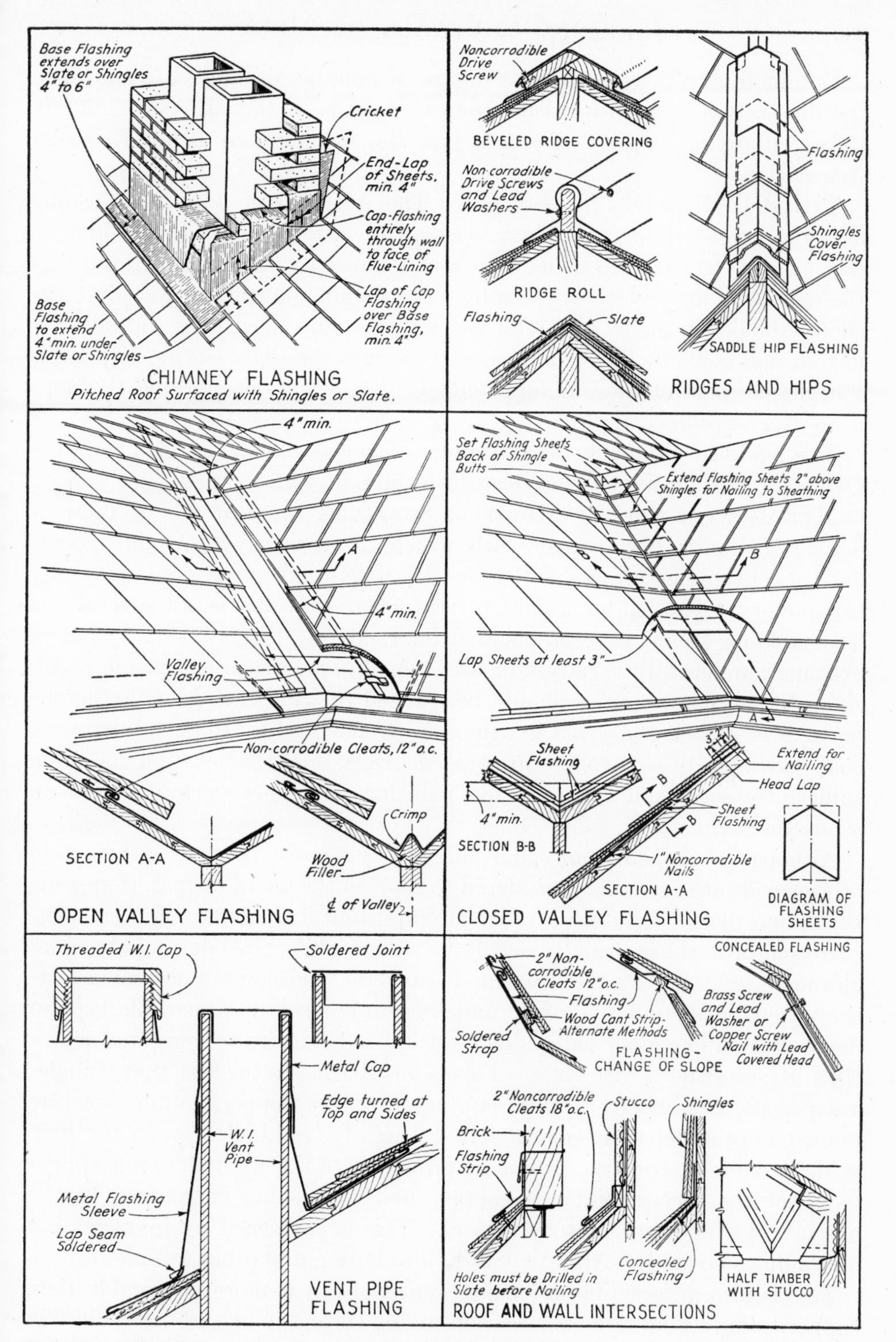

FIG. 25. Miscellaneous Flashing Details. Based upon designs by the Copper and Brass Research Association.

Details illustrating the correct design of metallic flashings are shown in the illustrations. Additional information may be obtained from manufacturers supplying roofing materials and the Copper and Brass Research Association.

THE CHOICE OF FLASHING. The selection of a proper flashing material is more important than is usually realized. The obvious ideal is to select a type that will be as permanent, under its particular exposure, as the assembly into which it is built. This is not always possible, but the choice should be made without too much thought of cost, as the labor of installation is about the same for any type and the slight saving in price is a negligible part of the building budget. Repairing deteriorated flashings is an expensive operation.

As a guide to making a suitable choice, flashings may be divided from the viewpoint of their appropriate uses into the following groups:

METALS WITH SMOOTH METALLIC SURFACES. Except where there is danger of staining from copper wash, which may seriously injure the appearance of contiguous surfaces, soft-rolled 16- to 24-oz sheet copper is generally satisfactory. The lighter weight is used where exposure is not severe. At least a 20-oz weight is recommended for relatively long runs subjected to extreme temperature variation or uses where permanence is a prime requisite. In this connection it should be realized that even copper may deteriorate after a period of years in atmospheres polluted by the combustion of coal, particularly soft coal. In some districts this deterioration has been sufficiently serious to warrant the painting of copper flashings with an asphaltic compound.

Although the wash from cedar shingles and moist contact with certain other woods are generally considered to shorten the life of copper, it appears that atmospheric pollution is often an important contributory factor. The corrosion of flashings usually occurs in valleys along the edges of the shingles or slate and along the drip line in gutters. Accelerated corrosion tests show that both sulphur dioxide and sodium chloride produce this type of line corrosion in copper valleys used with wood shingles to a greater degree than in copper used with slate. This is largely due to the fact that shingles are porous and, where in close contact with the copper, retain moisture immediately under their edges. The lifting of the shingles by a cant strip is of considerable benefit. The mere proximity of the ocean does not appear to affect the serviceability of copper used as flashing or roofing, in the absence of other contributory factors. This is confirmed by investigation of buildings erected at Atlantic City, New Jersey, and other seaside resorts.

Zinc is also an acceptable flashing material but is more vulnerable than copper to industrial atmospheres containing sulphuric or carbonic acid. It has the advantage, however, of not staining and is normally about one-third cheaper than copper of equal thickness. For ordinary flashing purposes an

11-gage zinc is suitable; 13-gage should be used for monumental work. Because of the rather high coefficient of thermal expansion of zinc and its tendency to become brittle when subjected, over a period of years, to wide temperature changes, designs should be carefully studied and the recommendations of the American Zinc Institute followed. When the zinc is placed in contact with mortar containing lime, a heavy coating of paint or a bituminous compound free from acid is essential.

The lead and antimony alloy, generally called "hard lead," contains 6 to 7½ per cent antimony. It can be used for flashings in weights of 2, 2½, and 3 lb per sq ft. It is particularly resistant to industrial atmospheres containing sulphuric acid and will not stain light-colored stones or other materials injured by copper. As lead also has a high coefficient of thermal expansion and very little elasticity, large sheets tend to "creep" and maintain a permanent set after wrinkles have developed. This danger requires a definite limitation on the size of sheets. Designs should be carefully studied and the recommendations of the Lead Industries Association followed. An asphaltum coating is recommended where lead is placed in contact with fresh mortar or concrete.

Lead-coated copper is popular where copper staining would be objectionable or the color of copper inappropriate. There is also a general belief that the lead coating increases the permanence of copper. This is not always true. For a few years after installation such a surface diminishes deterioration but does not entirely prevent it under most conditions which would attack the bare copper. After the lead coating is worn down in spots sufficiently to become porous, corrosion is apparently accelerated, as would be expected from electrolytic action, to a degree greater than that in plain copper.

Aluminum, used more or less as sheet roofing, also has possibilities as a flashing material but is not yet employed to any extent for this purpose. As the coefficient of expansion due to temperature changes is nearly twice that of steel and approximately 50 per cent greater than that of copper, it must obviously be used with caution. If brought in contact with mortar or concrete, a coating of lacquer is necessary to prevent corrosion.

As a class, the metallic flashings are appropriate for standard cap and base designs and for through flashings, as shown in Fig. 23. Galvanized steel sheets and the cheaper grades of tin plate should not be used except where their probable life will equal that of the roof-surfacing material. They are appropriate for wood- and asphalt-shingled roofs. Certain iron alloys have been found very satisfactory where the cost of more expensive materials is not justified. As even the partial failure of flashings may result in very serious leakage, the choice of a material should be based upon authentic records of its performance under similar exposure or accelerated tests of a conclusive nature.

Metals with Surfaces Especially Formed to Provide a Bond with Masonry. These metals are particularly appropriate for through flashings such as those laid in the masonry of parapets. Copper designs are the most popular, usually of 16-oz or heavier weight.

Thin Copper Sheets Surfaced with Asphalt-Saturated Fabric. These are very flexible, as the copper is of only 2- to 5-oz weight. This type of flashing is particularly appropriate for spandrel waterproofing. See Fig. 23.

Membrane and Composition Flashings. Fabrics saturated with bitumen and laid in a bituminous waterproofing compound are appropriate for a damp-check across the top of masonry walls. Such flashings are also used for spandrel waterproofing as an alternate to the material described in the preceding paragraph. For this purpose two layers of fabric are laid with three coats of a cold-troweled asphalt mastic. Such procedure is superior to the common practice of using merely a bitumen-saturated and surface-coated fabric. Bituminous materials also serve as a cheaper but inferior substitute for the metal flashings of window sills and lintels. They are the usual choice around the boundaries of flat roofs surfaced with built-up waterproofing, as shown on page 172. Even where one of the metals is employed as a cap flashing, fabric laid with hot mastic may be used as a base flashing.

Caulking. This term identifies the use of a plastic compound resembling putty, instead of mortar, for filling joints between masonry or other building units and for sealing the cracks around window frames and other wood or metal elements built into masonry walls. The material may be applied by extruding from a caulking gun, thereby forming a bead along the joint, or by the use of a trowel or knife. Consistencies suitable for either type of application are furnished by the manufacturers. These caulking compounds usually contain a vehicle of blown oils, such as soybean, cottonseed, linseed, and fish. The solid materials, called pigments, are calcite, talc, asbestine, etc., with asbestos fibers. A number of colors are available, but coloring pigments must be limited in amount, as too great a quantity causes too rapid hardening and crazing.

A plastic caulking compound should be very carefully selected to provide low shrinkage, slow rate of hardening, tenacity, adhesiveness, and ability to retain the vehicle. It must be of a consistency to work easily but not to flow after placement. Excessive shrinkage is undesirable, because it places the joint filler in tension even when there is no structural movement. Excessive shrinkage also causes separation from the materials on either side. Hardening reduces the ability of the compound to function under service conditions and causes higher bonding stresses when the joint is in tension. Since the value of caulking is dependent on its remaining soft, compounds with a low hardening rate are likely to be more durable. When a joint is in tension, caused by either shrinkage of the compound or structural movement, it is desirable that the caulking stretch without breaking the bond upon the sides. The quality of tenacity, or cohesive strength, is therefore necessary.

The adhesion or bonding value is very important, as the caulking compound must maintain contact with the materials on either side of the joint. In fact, this is the most common type of failure. Bond varies considerably with the type of adjacent material, being much better against porous surfaces than those of low porosity.

The consistency of the caulking material should be chosen to suit its use. For example, along the junction of a masonry wall with a window or door frame, a bead is run with a caulking gun, requiring what is called a "gun consistency." If it is necessary to fill the joints between masonry units on the horizontal or nearly horizontal surface of a wall coping, such as that forming the top of a roof parapet, a "knife consistency" is appropriate. The joint in this case is filled to a depth of about ½ in. and finished flush with the surface.

The width of the joint, or the size of the bead covering the joint, also influences the choice of consistency, as wider joints naturally tend to sag if the material is too plastic. In this regard it should be noted that, if masonry joints are to be caulked with plastic compounds, they should have a width of at least ⅜ in. The porosity of the material in contact with the caulking is also a factor; a stiffer material should be used against metallic or other nonabsorbent surfaces than in contact with stone or brick. Work of this type should be inspected after a few hours; if any sagging has occurred, a stiffer consistency is indicated.

If operations are carried out in cold weather, it is not desirable to add a thinner for the purpose of obtaining greater workability; the proper procedure is to warm the material by setting the container in hot water. For the purpose of reducing the absorption of masonry surfaces on either side of a joint, it is a common practice to coat the sides of the joints with a primer. This is not considered essential, provided that the joint is cleaned of all dust, but thinned varnishes and tong-oil paint have been found to reduce the shrinkage of certain compounds without seriously affecting their other desirable properties. If a primer is used, it is necessary that it be allowed to dry thoroughly before the joint is filled.

As certain types of caulking compounds have been found to stain porous materials because of the fact that they contained oils of too low viscosity or too much thinner, this possibility should be checked before deciding upon the use of a specific product. In fact, the subject should receive serious attention, as there are many trade preparations on the market which vary greatly in quality as affecting durability. If the proper material is chosen, it is to be expected that caulking compounds will serve their purpose for at least 8 years, but their probable renewal after that time should be accepted as a matter of upkeep.

Much additional information on this subject will be found in "Plastic Caulking Materials," by Tregoning, Milliken, Hockman, Sligh, and Kessler, *Building Materials and Structures Report BMS* 33, National Bureau of Standards, 1940.

Article 9. Design Procedure

The problem is to select a type of wall construction which fulfills the desired functions at the least ultimate cost for a building of known architectural design and use, to be erected in a specific locality at a definite time.

Commencing with what might be identified as the architectural, rather than structural, requirements, the designer will find that certain preferences will be apparent, or a tentative choice can be made for the exterior and interior finishes. Such preliminary selection will apply to the material, color, and texture. Each possibility should be checked and perhaps modified by the utilitarian requirements of an exterior treatment reasonably durable without costly upkeep and interior finishes suitable for the type of occupancy. The need for the wall to be rain- and windproof will also be considered; but, as these qualities can be obtained with any of the customary wall-surfacing materials by careful detailing, specification, and supervision, the choice of surface finishes is not affected.

Passing to the structural requirements, which concern both the backing or body of the wall and its bonding or anchorage to the exterior surface finish, the designer should refer to the standards of his mandatory code or follow those which he has accepted as representing good practice for the geographical locality, particular location, size of structure, and type of occupancy. From the first he will check the possibility of seismic disturbance, hurricane damage, or torrential rains. From his knowledge of the location or site, he will be concerned with exposure to wind above grade and to earth or water pressure below grade.

From the size of the structure, as well as the location and type of occupancy, are derived very definite limitations imposed by building codes or good practice. Those limitations concerned with the character and quality of the materials and workmanship will be considered principally in the specifications, but the dimensional limitations, as well as the stress values and bonding or anchorage of the individual units comprising the wall assembly, apply to the design. As mentioned in Chapter Eight on masonry walls, such requirements are for the purpose of assuring adequate strength, stability, and fire resistance.

Well-standardized methods have long been established for accommodating electric conduit, plumbing, and heating pipes within the outer surfaces of the conventional wall assemblies. Chases and recesses are limited as later noted, but an increase in the thickness of the furring can be made where required. When walls are prefabricated, however, such provision deserves attention in the early stages of the work. The "building in" of frames of wood or hollow or rolled metallic sections for doors and windows should also be carefully studied when considering any type of construction which departs from conventional practice.

From the locality will be obtained the probable outdoor-temperature range, solar intensity, and relative humidity for the various seasons. These data, in relation to the type of occupancy, will not only make possible a decision concerning the desirable extent of heat insulation, but may favor one wall surface over another as having a higher reflection of radiant heat or a greater time-lag in heat transmission. For the small residential and commercial buildings such matters are comparatively unimportant. In this type of work the designer is concerned merely with obtaining a wall section having as low a heat-transmission coefficient as practicable and detailing the construction around openings or other critical places, such as at sills and eaves in wood-framed designs, to avoid heat loss by convection. For large, air-conditioned structures, however, these considerations may influence the wall design, and in particularly humid climates or where a manufacturing process causes or requires a high interior humidity its possible effect should be considered. The subject of heat insulation and the purpose of a vapor seal were discussed on page 269.

The comparative sound transmission of various exterior wall designs has little significance for most buildings, but this factor should be considered in connection with the choice of partition construction for many types of occupancy.

The weights per square foot of the different wall assemblies will seldom be important for low buildings but should be considered for comparatively high structures or in localities where a low soil-bearing capacity demands an appreciable increase in foundation cost to carry an increased dead load. The thickness of walls obviously affects the usable floor area. This is quite important for partitions in multifamily dwellings and was one of the chief reasons for using a thin, solid plaster partition on several large housing developments. For exterior walls, however, the relative loss of floor area between two different types will only occasionally be sufficient to warrant consideration.

Having checked the requirements suggested by the preceding paragraphs for each of the probable designs, the architect should secure estimates of those which are acceptable. Only by using the material prices and labor rates applying to the time and place of construction, and with the local standard of man-hour production, can a valid estimate be obtained. Unit prices in cents per square foot of wall area may serve as a general guide but are valueless on borderline cases. Detailed estimates should be made by a competent builder for typical panels, including an evaluation of all contiguous and related work, such as the accommodation of pipes or flues and the placing of frames for openings. Such an estimate will enable the designer to make a final decision.

Chapter Eight

MASONRY WALLS

The design, specification, and supervision of masonry walls are seldom given adequate attention by the architect or architectural engineer. New materials and new characteristics of old materials present problems that cannot be met by routine methods. Widespread trouble has resulted in matters as elementary as the prevention of rain penetration. It therefore seems desirable to present this subject from the viewpoint of the designer, who must choose the material, determine the wall assembly, and specify and supervise the construction.

Article 1. Definitions

The following definitions are given as they appear in "American Standard Building Code Requirements for Masonry," by the Sectional Committee on Building Code Requirements, and "Good Practice Recommendations for Masonry," A41, prepared under the sponsorship of the National Bureau of Standards, 1944, and issued as *Miscellaneous Publication* M174. This report was approved by the American Standards Association as *American Standard* A41.1–1944.

A comparison with the more recent publications selected from the voluminous bibliography on the subject of masonry construction, supplemented by personal experience, has led to the inclusion of considerable material from this report as representing good practice. The definitions, specifications for materials, and structural requirements for masonry, the last being in effect a revision and amplification of "Recommended Minimum Requirements for Masonry Wall Construction," prepared by the Building Code Committee of the Department of Commerce in 1925, with modifications in 1931 and 1939, have been abstracted and printed in smaller type in this chapter.

These standards should be useful to the designer as specification references and as a guide in the supervision of masonry work. The quotations applying to minimum wall thicknesses and lateral support are of value in comparing competing designs. The maximum allowable working stresses for different types of masonry have been included in order to make the text complete for reference purposes.

Fig. 1. Folger Shakespearean Library, Washington, D. C. *Arch.:* Paul P. Cret; *Sculptor:* John Gregory. Courtesy, Georgia Marble Company.

ARCHITECTURAL TERRA COTTA is plain or ornamented (modeled or moulded) hard-burned building units, larger in size than brick, consisting of mixtures of plastic clays, fusible minerals, and grog,[1] with glazed or unglazed ceramic finish.

ASHLAR FACING is a facing composed of solid rectangular units of burned clay or shale, or natural or cast stone, larger in size than brick, having sawed, dressed, or squared beds, and joints laid in mortar.

ASHLAR MASONRY is masonry composed of rectangular units of burned clay or shale, or natural or cast stone, larger in size than brick and properly bonded, having sawed, dressed, or squared beds, and joints laid in mortar.

BRICK is a material of construction in small, regular units, formed from inorganic substances and hardened in a shape approximating a rectangular prism, approximately $2\frac{1}{4} \times 3\frac{3}{4} \times 8$ in. in size,[2] the net cross-sectional area of which, in any plane parallel to the bearing surface, is not less than 75 per cent of its gross cross-sectional area measured in the same plane.

CAVITY WALL is a wall built of masonry units or of plain concrete, or a combina-

[1] Dried, pulverized clay.

[2] At the present time, the standard size of brick is $2\frac{1}{4} \times 3\frac{3}{4} \times 8$ in. Brick and tile manufacturers are, however, in the process of converting to modular sizes. These are listed in "American Standard Sizes of Clay and Concrete Modular Masonry Units," American Standards Association, *American Standard* A62.3, which includes the following nominal sizes of brick and solid masonry units: $2\frac{2}{3} \times 4 \times 8$, $3 \times 4 \times 8$, $4 \times 4 \times 8$, $5\frac{1}{3} \times 4 \times 8$, $4 \times 4 \times 12$, and $5\frac{1}{3} \times 4 \times 12$. In California and parts of the East, nominal sizes $2 \times 4 \times 8$, $2 \times 4 \times 12$, and $2\frac{2}{3} \times 4 \times 12$ are also manufactured. It should be remembered that these nominal dimensions are from center line to center line of mortar joints (see page 54). Standard dimensions are equal to the nominal dimensions less the thickness of the mortar joint with which the unit is designed to be laid.

tion of these materials, so arranged as to provide an air space within the wall, and in which the facing and backing of the wall are tied together with metal ties.

CONCRETE-MASONRY UNIT is a building unit made from cement and suitable aggregates, such as sand, gravel, crushed stone, cinders, burned clay, or shale, or blast-furnace slag.

FACED WALL is a wall in which the masonry facing and backing are so bonded as to exert common action under load.

HOLLOW MASONRY UNIT is a masonry unit whose net cross-sectional area in any plane parallel to the bearing surface is less than 75 per cent of its gross cross-sectional area measured in the same plane.

MASONRY means architectural terra cotta, brick, and other solid masonry units of clay or shale, concrete-masonry units, glazed building units, gypsum tile or block, plain concrete, stone, structural-clay tile, structural-glass block, or other similar building units or materials, or a combination of same, bonded together with mortar.

PIER means an isolated column of masonry; a bearing wall not bonded at the sides into associated masonry shall be considered a pier when its horizontal dimension measured at right angles to the thickness does not exceed four times its thickness.

PILASTER is a part of a wall that projects not more than one-half of its own width beyond the outside or inside face of a wall, acting as an engaged pier.[3]

COURSED RUBBLE is masonry composed of roughly shaped stones fitting approximately on level beds and well bonded.

RANDOM RUBBLE is masonry composed of roughly shaped stones laid without regularity of coursing, but well bonded and fitted together to form well-defined joints.

ROUGH OR ORDINARY RUBBLE is masonry composed of unsquared or field stones laid without regularity of coursing but well bonded.

SOLID MASONRY UNIT is a masonry unit whose net cross-sectional area in every plane parallel to the bearing surface is 75 per cent or more of its gross cross-sectional area measured in the same plane.

SOLID MASONRY is masonry consisting of solid masonry units laid contiguously with the joints between the units filled with mortar, or consisting of plain concrete.

STRUCTURAL-CLAY TILE is a hollow masonry unit composed of burned clay, shale, fire clay, or mixtures thereof and having parallel cells.

VENEERED WALL is a wall having a masonry facing which is attached to the backing but not so bonded as to exert common action under load.

Article 2. Specification of Masonry Materials

The materials used in wall construction should fill the requirements for strength and durability demanded by good practice or mandatory code. Obviously, they should meet architectural demands in qualities such as color and texture. The designations of the various standards, such as those of the American Society for Testing Materials, are given in "American

[3] This definition is taken from "A Glossary of Housing Terms, Building Materials, and Structures," *Report BMS* 91, National Bureau of Standards, 1942.

Standard Building Code Requirements for Masonry," 1944. As constant changes are being made, no revision would have more than temporary significance. The designer may either obtain the current designation from the secretary of the corresponding society or merely state that the latest revision shall apply.

FIG. 2. State Capitol, Salem, Oregon. *Arch.:* Trowbridge and Livingston and Francis Keally; Whitehouse and Church, Associates; *Sculptor:* Leo Friedlander. Courtesy, Vermont Marble Company.

SOLID MASONRY UNITS (CLAY OR SHALE). a. Brick subject to the action of weather or soil, but not subject to frost action when permeated [4] with water, shall

[4] When water is in contact with the surface of a dry unit, the tendency is for it to enter the unit by capillary action. If there is enough water and the time of contact is sufficiently long, the water will strike through from face to face of the unit, giving a degree of saturation equaling or exceeding that resulting from a 24-hour submersion. This wetting through from face to face is the condition of being "permeated" referred to in the description of grades SW and MW. Bricks exposed in parapets, in horizontal surfaces, and as retaining walls may become permeated. When properly protected from above by flashings or overhanging eaves, ordinary exposure in the vertical face of an exterior wall is unlikely to result in permeation except in the case of defective workmanship or faulty drainage.

conform to the requirements for grade MW brick of the "Tentative Specifications for Building Brick (Made from Clay or Shale)," *ASTM* [5] C62–41T.[6] When not subject to the action of weather or soil, brick shall conform to the requirements for grade NW brick. Grade SW of the above specification should be required where brick may be subject to temperatures below freezing while permeated with water. In localities where brick conforming in physical properties to the requirements of this specification is not readily obtainable, the use of other brick should be permitted if suitable evidence of resistance to weathering is presented.

b. Other solid masonry units of clay or shale shall meet the requirements for physical properties of brick as specified above.

Sand-Lime Brick. Sand-lime brick subject to the action of weather or soil, but not subject to frost action when permeated with water, shall conform to the requirements for grade MW brick of the "American Standards Specification for Sand-Lime Building Brick," *ASA*[7] A78.1–1942 (*ASTM* C73–39). When not subject to the action of weather or soil, sand-lime brick shall conform to the requirements for grade NW brick. Grade SW of the above specification should be required where brick may be subject to temperature below freezing while permeated with water.

Concrete Brick. Concrete brick subject to the action of weather or soil shall conform to the requirements for grade A brick of the "American Standard Specifications for Concrete Building Brick," *ASA* A75.1–1942 (*ASTM* C55–37). When not subject to the action of weather or soil, concrete brick shall conform to the requirements for grade B brick.

Structural-Clay Tile. a. Structural-clay tile subject to the action of weather or soil shall conform to the requirements for grade LBX tile of the "American Standard Specifications for Structural Clay Load-Bearing Wall Tile," *ASA* A74.1–1942 (*ASTM* C34–41).

b. Structural-clay tile used in load-bearing masonry but not subject to the action of weather or soil shall conform to the requirements for grade LB tile of the above specification.

c. Structural-clay tile used in interior non-load-bearing masonry shall conform to the requirements of the "American Standard Specifications for Structural Clay Non-Load-Bearing Tile," *ASA* A76.1–1942 (*ASTM* C56–41).

Concrete-Masonry Units. a. Hollow-concrete-masonry units used in load-bearing masonry or subject to the action of weather or soil shall conform to the requirements of the "American Standard Specifications for Hollow Load-Bearing Concrete-Masonry Units," *ASA* A79.1–1942 (*ASTM* C90–39).

b. Hollow concrete-masonry units used in non-load-bearing masonry not subject to the action of weather or soil shall conform to the requirements of the "American Standard Specifications for Hollow Non-Load-Bearing Concrete-Masonry Units," *ASA* A80.1–1942 (*ASTM* C129–39).

c. Solid concrete-masonry units shall conform to the requirements of the "American Standard Specifications for Solid Load-Bearing Concrete-Masonry Units," *ASA* A81.1–1942 (*ASTM* C145–40).

[5] American Society for Testing Materials.

[6] The more recent designation, *ASTM* C62–44, was issued subsequent to this report.

[7] American Standards Association.

CAST STONE. Cast stone shall conform to the requirements of the "Specification for Cast Stone," *ACI*[8] 704–44.

NATURAL STONE. Stone for masonry shall be sound and free from loose or friable inclusions. It shall have sufficient strength, durability, and resistance to impact for the proposed use.

ARCHITECTURAL TERRA COTTA. Architectural terra cotta shall have a strong homogeneous body and give a sharp, metallic, bell-like ring when struck. All units shall have the necessary anchor holes and shall be so formed as to engage properly with the supporting structure.

GLAZED BUILDING UNITS. Glazed building units shall conform to the requirements of the "Tentative Specifications for Glazed Building Units," *ASTM* C126–39T except that the requirements for finish shall not apply to salt-glazed building units.[9]

Gypsum Tile and Block. a. Gypsum partition tile or block shall conform to the requirements of the "Standard Specification for Gypsum Partition Tile or Block," *ASTM* C52–41.

b. Gypsum partition tile or block shall not be used in bearing walls or in exterior walls, or where subject to continuous dampness.

STRUCTURAL-GLASS BLOCK. Glass blocks may be solid or hollow. All mortar-bearing surfaces of the blocks shall be precoated with a material to improve adhesion between mortar and glass.

MORTAR MATERIALS. a. Cementitious materials used in mortars shall conform to the requirements of the following applicable standard specifications:

"Quicklime for Structural Purposes," *ASTM* C5–26.

"Hydrated Lime for Structural Purposes," *ASTM* C6–31.

"Hydraulic Hydrated Lime for Structural Purposes," *ASTM* C141–42.

"Natural Cement," *ASTM* C10–37.

"Masonry Cement," *Federal Specification* SS–C–181b.

"Portland Cement," *ASTM* C150–42.

b. Aggregate for mortar shall conform to the requirements of the "Tentative Specifications for Aggregate for Masonry Mortar," *ASTM* C144–42T.[10] Materials which have been found in practice to cause harmful volume changes should not be incorporated in masonry.

c. Water used in mixing mortar shall be clean and free from deleterious amounts of acids, alkalis, or organic materials. Water suitable for drinking purposes is satisfactory.

[8] American Concrete Institute.

[9] For a more complete specification refer to that of the Facing Tile Institute, Washington, D.C.

[10] The more recent designation, *ASTM* C144–44, was issued subsequent to this report. Its recommendations, supplemented by *ASTM Specification* C33–44, applying to grading of aggregate, should be followed.

Article 3. Provision against Moisture Penetration; Remedial Treatments

When determining the general type and construction of a wall, this provision is one of the more vital considerations. Many of the other important requirements, such as stability and fire resistance, are largely controlled by building ordinances or common practice, but there is no law in this country against designing and constructing a building with walls through which wind-driven rain can easily pass. Experience in many localities, particularly with the upper stories of our higher buildings in New York City and exposures such as those presented by the seaside hotels in Atlantic City, New Jersey, has amply demonstrated that this matter deserves the most careful consideration.

The recommendations in the following articles have a general application to all masonry assemblies when used in exterior wall construction. The materials not only should meet the mandatory or accepted standards previously given, but also should be chosen for the purpose of obtaining a wall section impervious to wind-driven rain. This choice is important, as there are usually several options, all of which would meet the requirements of any building code or the standards of the American Society for Testing Materials. For example, in the case of mortar (see page 306) a type of lime should be chosen that will produce, with the selected proportions, at least a medium and preferably a high water retentivity. This requirement would favor the better grades of pulverized quicklime made into putty or type S mason's hydrate, rather than the standard variety of hydrated lime which is identified as type N. Each would meet any common requirement of code or standard, but the proper choice greatly facilitates laying a watertight wall.

CONTROLLING THE SUCTION OF MASONRY UNITS. The suction [11] of the bricks when laid, rather than their total absorption when dry, affects the impermeability of the wall. The optimum suction rate of brick depends both upon the ingredients, their proportion and quality, and upon the flow of the mortar. For different mortars and different flows, optimum suctions range from 5 to 20 grams; however, if the mortar is mixed with the maximum amount of water consistent with workability, satisfactory results can be obtained with bricks laid dry when their suction rates do not exceed 20 grams per minute. If brick show a suction greater than 20 grams,[12] wetting should always be demanded. This requirement is commonly covered in the specification by stating that "all brick shall be thoroughly wet immediately before laying." This statement is not sufficient

[11] "Brick suction" is defined as the amount of water, in grams or ounces, absorbed by a brick (30 sq in.) placed on the flat side in water to a depth of ⅛ in. for 1 minute.

[12] One ounce (avoirdupois) equals 28.35+ grams.

for such an important matter. Harm can be done by overwetting brick as well as by underwetting them, although this fault occurs much less frequently. The following quotation, taken from the authority mentioned on page 289, gives a simple test for use on the job and a suggested method for wetting the brick.

A rough but effective test for determining what bricks give improved bond by wetting consists in sprinkling a few drops of water on the flat of the brick and noting the time required for these drops of water to be absorbed completely. If this time exceeds 1 minute, wetting is not needed. A refinement of this method consists in drawing a circle 1 in. in diameter on the flat of the brick with a wax pencil (using a 25-cent piece as a guide provides a circle of almost the exact dimension). One milliliter of water (20 drops) is applied to the surface thus limited and the time for complete absorption is noted. If this time exceeds 1½ minutes, the bricks need not be wetted; if less than 1½ minutes, wetting is recommended.

Wetting of vitrified and semivitrified bricks or excessive wetting of other bricks is undesirable because of resultant floating of the bricks and "bleeding" of the mortar. A satisfactory procedure consists in playing a stream of water on a pile of bricks until water is observed to run from each individual brick visible in the pile. Unless the bricks are exposed to conditions favoring the rapid evaporation of moisture, one wetting per day is sufficient.

Although it is necessary to forbid the use of brick which do not conform to the requirements for grade SW (*ASTM Specification* C62–44) in locations where they may be frozen when saturated, those having an absorption as high as 17 to 20 per cent [13] have been used successfully in exposed walls in both Chicago and New York City. It is essential, however, that their suction rate be reduced to the limit given on page 295 and that they be not overwet when laid, or it will be difficult to keep them in alignment. Brick with a high absorption, if of adequate strength, can be used satisfactorily in the interior of a wall. Structural clay tile and concrete masonry units also vary considerably in absorption and the speed with which water will rise by capillary action when the face shell is immersed. In the case of structural clay tile, the more absorptive units should be sufficiently wet to prevent other than slight suction. Concrete masonry units (*ASTM Specification* C90–44) are laid dry, as wetting causes expansion.

The usual specification to the effect that "brick shall not be wet in freezing weather" is also inadequate. The same test should be applied as for warm-weather construction, and excessive suction reduced by sprinkling with warm water immediately before laying. A brick that does not require wetting is obviously preferable.

COLD-WEATHER CONSTRUCTION. All masonry materials should be stored on the site in a manner that will protect them from ice or snow. This provision normally requires placing sand and masonry units, such as

[13] Percentage by weight after 5-hour boiling. See *ASTM Specification* C62–44.

brick, on platforms covered with tarpaulins or similar material. The mortar should be at a temperature between 70° and 120° F when used. To obtain this temperature, the mixing water should be heated to the necessary temperature up to a maximum of 160° F. If the atmospheric temperature is actually below freezing when the work is executed, the sand should also be heated. For lower temperatures, from 1½ to 2 lb of calcium chloride may be added per sack of portland cement, but the protection mentioned below should not be reduced. If masonry cements are used, the manufacturer's recommendations should be followed, as nonfreezing compounds may be harmful.

The protection necessary to provide against injury of the masonry after placement depends to a certain extent upon the type of mortar employed. If type A is used (see page 307) the period should be 48 hours when standard portland cement is employed and may be reduced to 24 hours for high-early strength cement. If type B is used, the protection should be extended for a period of 72 hours for standard portland cement and for 48 hours for high-early strength cement. Protection, which means maintaining a temperature over 40° F, is accomplished by covering the masonry and, if necessary, by the use of artificial heat. For temperatures below 18° F hollow masonry units should be heated to at least 40° F when laid. If work must be carried out at temperatures approaching zero, both solid and hollow masonry units should be similarly heated.

WORKMANSHIP. From the viewpoint of preventing moisture penetration, the most important requirement is good workmanship. Joints should not be too thin or too wide; recommendations are given later in articles applying to the various masonry units.

In modular design the joint thickness is controlled. As bond is important, masonry units should be placed on mortar beds with pressure to assist in developing complete contact between unit and mortar. Provided that sufficient mortar is used to cover the bed, National Bureau of Standards tests show no significant difference in permeability where the mortar for the bed joints is levelled and where it is furrowed before placing the brick, but a level bed of mortar, not furrowed, does increase the strength.

The sand, or other fine aggregate, should pass a No. 8 sieve for a joint thickness of ⅜ to ½ in., except for glass block, which is laid in sand passing a No. 16 sieve. For joints thicker than ½ in., the aggregate should meet the standard specification for fine concrete aggregate (see page 41) containing not less than 10 per cent of material passing a No. 50 sieve. This specification requires that 100 per cent pass a ⅜-in. sieve, and 95 to 100 per cent pass a No. 4 sieve. In walls composed of solid masonry units it is imperative that all joints be thoroughly filled with mortar and that each unit, such as an individual brick or stone, be well bedded. Figures 3, 4, 5, and 6 illustrate good practice.

(a)

An adequate thickness of mortar should be evenly spread for the horizontal or "bed" joints. The furrow in the center, parallel to the wall, should be shallow so that the excess mortar will fill it and insure a full joint.

(b)

Mortar should be spread over only a few bricks at a time so that it will still be plastic when the bricks are bedded. If allowed to dry, a good bond is impossible.

(c)

To make certain of filling the vertical or head joints, plenty of mortar should be "thrown" on the end of the brick to be placed or on the end of the adjoining brick already laid. The new brick is then pushed or shoved into place so that mortar oozes out at the top of the joint.

(d)

An alternate and excellent method, employed where appropriate, is shown above. A deep bed of mortar is thrown on the wall and the brick shoved into place so that mortar oozes out at the top of the joint.

FIG. 3. Laying Stretcher Courses in Brick Masonry. Courtesy, Louisville Cement Company.

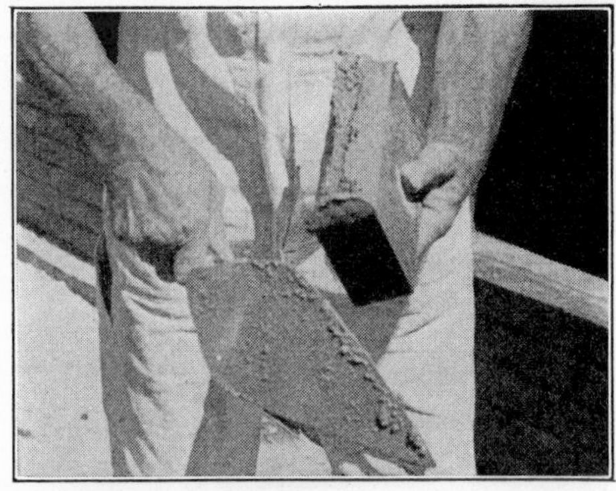

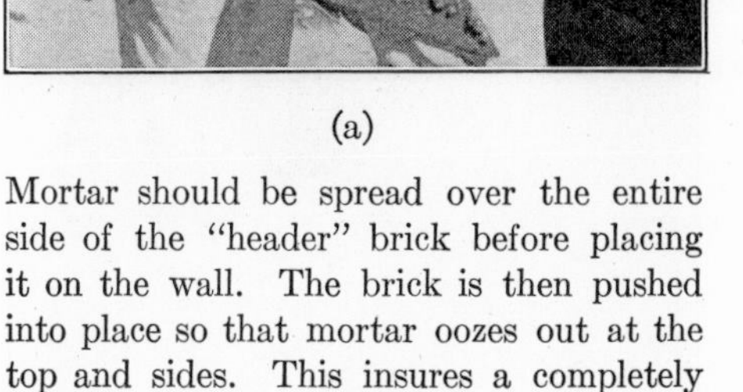

(a)

Mortar should be spread over the entire side of the "header" brick before placing it on the wall. The brick is then pushed into place so that mortar oozes out at the top and sides. This insures a completely filled cross-joint.

(b)

An alternate method is to spot mortar on both corners of the header brick and then work mortar into the remaining space. This operation is called "slushing." It seldom succeeds in entirely filling the joint and is not recommended.

FIG. 4. Laying Header Courses in Brick Masonry. Courtesy, Louisville Cement Company.

(a)

The front of the back-up units, when placed first, should be parged with at least ⅜ in. of mortar before the face units are laid. If the face units are placed first, they should be similarly treated before the back-up units are laid.

(b)

Face joints are finished before the mortar hardens. The concave or rodded type, formed with a round-ended tool, is the best, as this operation forces the mortar tightly against the brick on both sides of the joint.

FIG. 5. Parging and Finishing Joints. Courtesy, Louisville Cement Company.

With the exception of rare cases where porous building units have been used, almost all the difficulty experienced in the passage of rain through exterior masonry walls has been due to improper filling of the joints, particularly the vertical joints. The surface of exposed joints should be thoroughly compacted and not left rough for artistic effect. The application of a ½-in. mortar coat to the inner surface of an exterior vertical layer of brick or stone (see Fig. 6) or to the outer face of the backing forms a helpful

(a)

A full head joint is thrown on one edge of the adjacent tile or brick already in place and on the opposite edge of the unit to be laid.

(b)

An alternate method is to throw full head joints on both edges of the tile or brick to be laid.

Fig. 6. Laying Hollow Clay Tile and Concrete-Masonry Units. Courtesy, Louisville Cement Company.

water barrier but will not be effective unless all joints adjacent to headers are filled. Mortar used in this manner and the operation of applying it are called "parging."

The resistance of composite walls formed with a surfacing of brick or stone backed by clay tile or concrete masonry units, such as solid brick walls, is largely a function of workmanship and depends primarily upon the effectiveness of the exterior surface as a water stop. The same principles apply to the choice of mortar and the necessity for filling the joints as apply in the case of solid brick masonry, except that the manufacturer's directions should be followed in laying tile of special design. Concrete-masonry units should be protected by surface facings or coatings. Much valuable information on the subject of this article will be found in the two reports identified below:

"Water Permeability of Masonry Walls," by Fishburn, Watstein, and Parsons, *Building Materials and Structures Report BMS* 7, National Bureau of Standards, 1938.

"Water Permeability of Walls Built of Masonry Units," by Cyrus C. Fishburn, *Building Materials and Structures Report BMS* 82, National Bureau of Standards, 1942.

REMEDIAL TREATMENTS. Because of the inadequacy of the usual masonry specification and the poor quality of workmanship so common in this country, considerable remedial work has been necessary upon even our monumental buildings. The choice of treatment is a serious obligation for the architect, often complicated by the advice of engineers representing proprietary methods.

If there is actual penetration of water through exterior masonry walls above ground, the first step is to identify the cause of leakage. This may be inadequate or faulty flashings or the omission or poor performance of caulking, but in this discussion we will assume that the water comes through the masonry itself. It must be determined, then, whether the water passes by way of the joints or through the masonry units. As previously mentioned, the joints are usually to blame. If they are, the most effective remedy is to cut out the joints and refill them.

Repointing is a costly operation when carried out after the completion of a building. It will be effective except where water is passing through the actual units, such as the brick or stone, of which the wall is composed. It should be done with a mortar of high water retentivity and low volumetric change during hydration. A good mixture, proportioned by volume, is 1 part nonstaining portland cement: 2 parts lime putty: 5 parts screened sand. "Waterproof" quicklime, slaked for a period of at least a week, is recommended.

The procedure is to cut out the joints to a depth of about ¾ in. and to fill in, two operations which may be done several days apart. The first filling is made to a depth of only about ¼ in., and the face of the mortar roughened. After complete filling, the face is finished as a "rodded" or "concave" joint. Thorough compacting of the mortar is essential. Thorough cleaning of the recess before repointing is obviously necessary. If very porous, the faces of the adjoining masonry should be moistened. Some years ago the practice arose of mixing the mortar 1½ to 2 hours before use. By so doing, some of the shrinkage after placement is eliminated. During this period it is covered with a piece of canvas or burlap bags. This method has been applied successfully on many comparatively recent operations. When first mixed, the mortar should be a little overwet. At the expiration of the period mentioned above, it is reworked until thoroughly plastic, but no additional water should be added.

An alternate method, which may succeed under favorable conditions, consists in scrubbing a thin mortar into the leaky joints by means of a stiff brush. A mixture by volume of 1 part portland cement: ¼ part lime putty: 2 parts sand passing a No. 50 sieve was used in this manner on a large housing project about 1940. A template was employed to protect the masonry units from discoloration. This is a much less expensive process than the far more reliable method described above. It is reported, however, to have been successful.

If the masonry units are pervious to rain, which has happened with some brick and stone of poor quality, exterior surface treatments are appropriate. Application of the better colorless waterproofing compounds over the entire exterior surface of a masonry wall will have at least a temporary value in diminishing water penetration, but the probable permanence of any proposed method should be checked by a study of past performance upon other buildings. Some proprietary materials containing molten paraffin and various types of paints have been found beneficial, but no treatment of this type will take the place of repointing open joints. Furthermore, all surface waterproofings, if really efficient, have the disadvantage of preventing evaporation from the surface, which is the natural outlet for any moisture entering the exterior face of the wall or formed by condensation of water vapor within the wall.

Article 4. Furring Masonry Walls

Between the body or backing of a masonry wall and the interior finish, an air space is often provided. This may be formed by tile furring block, a free-standing tile partition, light-weight steel sections, wood furring strips or steel rods supporting some type of plaster base, or interior surfacing material. The tile may be of clay or cement aggregate. Gypsum tile is appropriate only where there is no probability of moisture. Metal lath is widely used over both wood and metal furring strips. Some types provide ribs which furnish support and hold the lath away from the wall, as shown in Fig. 7. In damp locations metal is obviously inferior to masonry furring. Wood lath is seldom employed today except in districts where it is locally produced, and there only for the less fire-resistant types of construction. The various plaster boards, often referred to as "plaster lath," compete with metal lath as a plaster base. When lapped and wired at intersections and reinforced at corners, however, metal lath gives greater protection against plaster cracks. Types of plaster lath injured by moisture should not be used in damp locations.

The purpose of the furring is to provide a more or less dead air space within the interior of the wall. This air space assists in preventing the direct passage of wind-driven rain and increases the resistance of the wall to the transmission of heat. As in the case of applied insulating materials, such an air space reduces the heating load of the building and helps to protect the inner surface of the wall from becoming sufficiently cold to condense the humid air of the interior. Where furring is used, a clear air space at least ¾ in. wide is desirable.

Exterior walls of solid masonry, including concrete, should ordinarily be furred. The exceptions may be summarized as follows: (1) in localities having a dry climate and not subject to extremely low temperatures at times when interior humidity is high; (2) for buildings where the heat loss by conduction through the walls is not an important factor; (3) for buildings where the danger of condensation upon the interior surface can either be accepted or is obviated by plenty of ventilation. The third situation

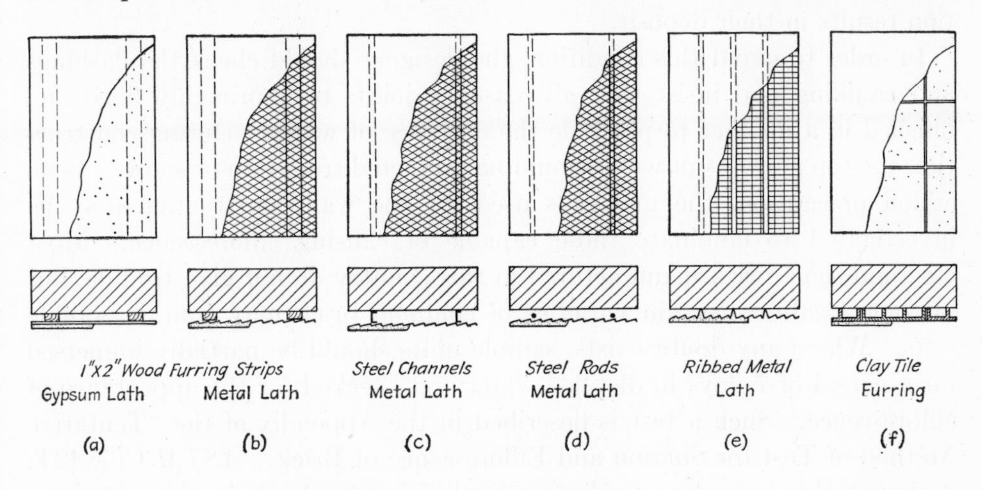

Fig. 7. Exterior Masonry-Wall Furring.

exists in many garages and factories where solid walls of concrete or brick have been found satisfactory.

The question often arises as to the necessity of furring exterior walls formed of a single tier of hollow units, such as clay tile and cellular cement-aggregate block. If furring is omitted, plaster is generally applied directly to the interior surface, occasionally over a brush application of damp-proofing. The exterior surface is left without finish, is painted, or stuccoed. Although tests performed upon hollow masonry units surfaced with portland-cement stucco have shown excellent resistance against moisture penetration in experiments simulating an exposure to wind-driven rain, it is recommended that furring be used except for the conditions mentioned in the previous paragraph. This applies particularly to residential buildings.

Article 5. Efflorescence and the Staining of Building Stones

EFFLORESCENCE. The prevention of efflorescence on brick walls deserves particular consideration in the specification and flashing details. In some sections of the country, notably parts of New England, this white powdery deposit frequently appears on exterior masonry surfaces. It is caused by the action of water penetrating the wall and dissolving salts contained in the mortar or masonry units. These salts may be calcium sulphate, magnesium sulphate, sodium chloride, sodium sulphate, or potassium sulphate. In order for efflorescence to occur, soluble salts must be present in the wall materials, and the construction must permit water to enter the wall, dissolve the salts, and then carry them to the surface, where evaporation results in their deposit.

In order to avoid this condition, the designer should check the flashings and caulking and insist that all masonry joints be thoroughly filled and finished in a manner to preclude the entrance of water. During construction the top surfaces of walls should be protected from rain or snow. As an added precaution, the materials used for the wall construction may be investigated to eliminate those capable of causing efflorescence. Most clay and shale brick manufactured in this country do not give trouble, but in some localities certain varieties of common brick may contain soluble salts. Where any doubt exists, sample units should be partially immersed for a period of 7 days in distilled water and checked for the appearance of efflorescence. Such a test is described in the Appendix of the "Tentative Method of Test for Suction and Efflorescence of Brick," *ASTM* C67–42T. Although this procedure applies particularly to brick, it should be remembered that other types of masonry units may also contain soluble salts, the presence of which may be detected in the same way.

Efflorescence can be removed from the face of a wall by applying, with fiber brushes, a solution of 1 part commercial muriatic acid mixed with 10 parts of water. The walls should be thoroughly washed with clean water both before and after scrubbing with this solution. Such treatment is seldom of more than temporary value.

STAINING OF BUILDING STONES. As most varieties of light-colored stones commonly used for wall facing or veneer become discolored or otherwise injured when in contact with standard portland cement, such masonry units should be set in a mortar containing a white or nonstaining cement. The lime should also be of a type incapable of causing injury to the stone. Stearate compounds are often added for waterproofing. As the masonry backing of the wall is normally laid in an ordinary mortar, some provision is necessary to prevent its contact with the stone facing. Although waterproofing is often applied to the unexposed surfaces, this practice is not recommended, as it is seldom effective and may diminish the bond between facing and backing. The best means of preventing injury is to coat the backsides of the facing units, including bond stones, with a ¾-in. layer of the same nonstaining mortar, which, as previously noted, is called "parging." This method is satisfactory, but the difficulty of doing it properly may be sufficient to warrant the laying of both facing and backing in a nonstaining mortar.

Article 6. The Choice of Mortar

WATER RETENTIVITY AS A GAGE OF WORKABILITY. Provided that the ingredients of the mortar and the proportions of the mixture meet the mandatory or accepted standards for structural strength, the designer is primarily concerned with determining a specification which will facilitate the laying of the masonry units so that they may be thoroughly bedded and all horizontal or vertical joints completely filled, except those which may intentionally be left open for interior drainage. In order that the wall assembly exclude wind-driven rain, it is imperative that mortars have the characteristic of "workability," a requirement which prohibits a mixture such as 1 part portland cement: 3 parts of sand by volume, as being too harsh or "short."

We have not as yet developed a laboratory method for evaluating this most essential quality, but we know that workability is closely related to the water retentivity of the mixture, which can be determined by the water-retention test of *Federal Specification for Masonry Cement*, SS–C–181. This specification contains the following requirement: "Standard mortar after suction for 60 seconds shall have a flow greater than 65 per cent of that immediately after mixing." The "flow after suction" is a function of the water retentivity and can be used as a gage of workability. A mortar with low water retentivity stiffens rapidly when in contact with a porous building unit, is much more difficult to bond properly with the unit, and may cause bleeding or weeping of the joint when used with one of low suction.

PROPORTIONS. The proportions of the mortar should be selected for its particular use. In the following recommendations all proportions are by volume, and sand or other aggregate is measured in a damp and loose condition which conforms with usual practice on the job.

If the essential requirement is structural strength or durability to resist alternate thawing and freezing in the presence of moisture, a mortar containing a comparatively high proportion of portland cement is desirable. Such a mortar is also appropriate for foundation walls laid with hollow masonry units and for the thinner cavity wall designs. A good mixture is:

1 part portland cement: ¼ part lime putty: 3 parts sand

This mortar has a somewhat lower water retentivity than that which would be chosen when less strength is demanded, but it is still workable. The cost is generally more than for a mortar containing higher proportions of lime and sand, which is preferable where high strength is not demanded.

If the essential requirement is impermeability to wind-driven rain, which is the usual criterion for exterior walls above grade, a mortar having greater workability is desirable. A good mixture is:

1 part portland cement: 1 part lime putty: 5 to 6 parts sand

Such a mortar is appropriate for foundation walls laid with solid masonry units, isolated piers, and load-bearing walls of solid units. In work above grade it may be used for hollow masonry units, hollow walls of masonry, and cavity walls more than 10 in. in nominal thickness. Such a mortar is, in fact, suitable for all general purposes except where one of higher strength is definitely required. This would be the case in districts where the earthquake hazard demands that masonry have a higher structural strength than is needed elsewhere. It should also be remembered that gypsum block are laid in gypsum mortar, and special mortar mixtures are used with refractory cements.

It is important that the lime be chosen for high plasticity, and, with the exception of specially processed hydrates, which have a high plasticity immediately after mixing with water, the lime should be made into the form of putty. This is, of course, necessary in the case of the quicklimes and should be done when using the ordinary hydrates. Whatever lime is chosen should meet a plasticity rating of 500 or better, as determined by *Federal Specification* SS–L–351. For mixtures having these proportions it is recommended that the mortar show a flow after suction of at least 70, as determined by *Federal Specification* SS–C–181b, instead of 65, as this can easily be obtained with the better limes.

As an alternate to this last specification, the designer has the option of using a masonry cement such as that identified by *Federal Specification* SS–C–181b–Type II or a natural cement conforming to *ASTM Specification* C–10–37. As the natural cements may be included in the general classification "masonry cements," they are not specifically mentioned in the table on page 307. The usual mixture is:

1 part cement : 3 parts sand

Such mortars have been used successfully over a period of many years. In making a comparison with the portland cement-lime-sand mixtures, they should be evaluated on the basis of compressive strength and water retentivity. Water retentivity is important, as some brands of cement produce only about two-thirds of that produced by the portland cement-lime-sand proportions previously noted.

The cement and lime used for laying all exterior masonry should be of a type to preclude any possibility of staining or disintegration through chemical action with the material used for facing. Unless it is thoroughly established that no injury will result from contact with the standard portland cement, a nonstaining cement should be used, as mentioned on page 304. Several nonstaining portland cements are manufactured in this country. At least one variety of cement similar to pozzuolan has been used successfully in laying light-colored stones which would have been injured by standard portland cement. Some of the masonry cements are also suitable for this purpose. The nonstaining portlands and those of the pozzuolan variety should be mixed with lime and sand in the proportions previously noted.

The following table gives six different sets of proportions for mortar. The first three correspond to the mixtures mentioned in the foregoing discussion. The two types identified as C are not recommended in locations where mortar is in contact with soil. Their use may be permitted in exterior and interior walls of solid masonry, in interior non-load-bearing walls or partitions of hollow units, and in other locations for which types A or B are not specifically required.[14]

VOLUMETRIC PROPORTIONS FOR MASONRY MORTARS

(From "American Standard Building Code Requirements for Masonry")

Mortar Type	Cement	Hydrated Lime or Lime Putty, Allowable Range	Aggregate, Measured in a Damp and Loose Condition
A	1 (portland)	0 to ¼	Not more than 3
B	1 (portland)	1 to 1¼	Not more than 6
B	1 (masonry FS type II)	....	Not more than 3
C	1 (portland)	2 to 2½	Not more than 9
C	1 (masonry FS type I)	....	Not more than 3
D	0 to ½ (portland)	1 to 1¼	Not more than 3 parts for each part of cementitious material

Mortar of type D hardens very slowly and may soften if kept wet. It is not recommended for parapet walls, rubble-stone walls, or uses where it will be in contact with soil. When this type is used, lower limits should be set for height and the spacing of lateral supports than for walls built with stronger mortars (see page 352).

The only advantage of using either type C or D would be economy, and the designer should very carefully check the requirements of his building, as well as local code restrictions, before making such a decision. In districts subject to earthquakes, proportions may be definitely controlled by code. For example, many West Coast cities require that cement-lime mortar be mixed in the volumetric proportions of 1 part portland cement: ½ part lime putty: not more than 4½ parts sand. Where a so-called "cement mortar" corresponding to type A in the table is required, many

[14] This and the following paragraph have been adopted but not directly quoted from "American Standard Building Code Requirements for Masonry."

codes in various parts of the country limit the permitted amount of lime to less than the maximum allowed by this standard. Such limitation is seldom justified but may be mandatory.

As noted on page 249, gypsum partition tile or solid gypsum masonry units are laid in gypsum mortar. Fire brick may be laid in fire clay or air-setting mortar.

COMPRESSIVE STRENGTH. The following table gives the minimum compressive strength which the mortars mixed in the corresponding proportions may be assumed to develop at an age of 28 days when tested in 2-in. cubes. Such tests should be performed as described in the *Federal Specification for Masonry Cements*, SS–C–181b. Except for type D mortar, the entire curing should be in laboratory air at 70° F plus or minus 5°.

CLASSIFICATION OF MASONRY MORTARS ON A BASIS OF STRENGTH

(From "American Standard Building Code Requirements for Masonry")

Type	Minimum Compressive Strength of 2-in. Cubes at 28 Days, in Pounds per Square Inch
A	2500
B	600
C	200
D	75

MORTAR COLORS. These colors should be in the form of inorganic compounds free from acids or soluble salts and of a type that will not react with calcium hydroxide, which results from the hardening of mortar. With the exception of carbon black and other colors of specific gravity less than 3.0, a quantity up to about 10 [15] per cent by weight of the cement may be used without harmful result. Carbon black should be limited to 2 per cent of the weight of the cement.

ADMIXTURES. Experience in the field and laboratory tests indicate that the desirability of some mortars is increased by incorporating certain proprietary compounds. Some of these are designed to diminish the absorption of surface water. Others serve to accelerate hydration, diminish initial shrinkage of the mortar, or increase workability. Manufacturers' directions should be followed in the use of such admixtures. As no nationally accepted standard has as yet been developed for gaging the value of these materials, the designer has little guide in their selection other than tests sponsored by the manufacturers and the history of their performance.

Antifreeze compounds of a proprietary type are not recommended. If masonry is erected in cold weather, the procedure given on page 296 should

[15] "American Standard Building Code Requirements for Masonry" permits 12 per cent.

be followed. The use of salt for lowering the freezing point of mortar or of sugar for retarding the set should be prohibited.

REFERENCES. Much valuable information on the general subject of mortars will be found in "Recommended Mortar for Clay Products Masonry," published by the Structural Clay Products Institute, 1942, and "Watertightness and Transverse Strength of Masonry Walls," by Douglas E. Parsons, published by Structural Clay Products Institute, 1939.

Article 7. Solid Brick Masonry

This classification applies to masonry composed of clay or shale brick, sand-lime or concrete brick. Brick masonry has its particular application for walls above grade in localities where brick are produced locally or to which they may be transported at competitive prices. There is no structural objection to the use of hard-burned brick below grade, and reinforced-brick walls (see page 313) can be designed to resist earth pressure. In most localities, however, reinforced concrete is a better choice. Plain concrete also competes with brick masonry and is usually cheaper for cellar walls where satisfactory aggregates are locally available. Likewise, if an acceptable quality of rough building stone can be cheaply obtained, rubble masonry may prove a more economical selection for comparatively shallow cellars or basements.

Because of its excellent fire-resistance properties and neat appearance, brick masonry is widely used for interior bearing walls, fire walls, and fire-division walls in locations where the application of plaster is unnecessary. It is also structurally satisfactory and often the most economical choice for many miscellaneous uses, such as piers and chimneys. The particular application of reinforced-brick masonry, illustrated on page 314, is for wall construction in districts subject to earthquakes. Reinforced brickwork has also been used quite extensively in some parts of the world for structural elements such as floor slabs, but in this country such application is seldom economical except in locations where reinforced concrete is unusually expensive.

The term "face brick" or, preferably, "facing brick," as applied to the product, identifies types of brick manufactured especially for use on exposed surfaces. The desired characteristics may be obtained by adding admixtures to the clay or by special processing designed to furnish a particular color or texture. The term "common brick" signifies a unit made of clay or shale, without admixtures other than those required for burning or for obtaining the desired plasticity for molding. Neither are common brick given any special surface treatment. The better grades of common brick may, however, be used for wall facings. In this case they are called "facing brick," when referring to the wall assembly, in order to distinguish them from the backing, which may be composed of brick of inferior quality. In the New England states and some other localities, well-burned common brick are frequently used for facing purposes.

ALLOWABLE WORKING STRESSES. The matter of load, so important in floor construction, has less significance in the choice between types of walls intended for use above grade. The arbitrary minimum thicknesses imposed by code or common practice for fire resistance and stability generally result in comparatively low compressive stresses for walls of solid masonry when built within the height limitations for which they are economical. The obvious exceptions are for eccentric loads or concentric loads beneath supported beams and girders or where a large part of the wall section is replaced by openings. In the case of piers or pilasters, direct compressive stresses or provision for an eccentric load may control the thickness.

Wall assemblies composed of clay tile, concrete-masonry units, or sand-lime brick, should be checked for their safe load in direct compression when supporting other than their own weight. In this connection it should be remembered that, when different kinds or grades of building units or mortars of different strengths are combined in the same wall section, the maximum allowable stress used in design should be that of the weakest component. Allowable compressive stresses in pounds per square inch of gross cross-sectional area are given below for solid masonry composed of solid units.

COMPRESSIVE STRESSES IN SOLID BRICK MASONRY

(From "American Standard Building Code Requirements for Masonry")

Brick and other solid units of clay or shale, sand-lime or concrete brick.

Average Compressive Strength of Units Tested in the Position Taken in the Masonry, in Pounds per Square Inch	Allowable Compressive Stresses, in Pounds per Square Inch, Corresponding to Mortar Types			
	A	B	C	D
8000 plus	400	300	200	100
4500 to 8000	250	200	150	100
2500 to 4500	175	140	110	75
1500 to 2500	125	100	75	50

THICKNESS: SOLID MASONRY BEARING WALLS. a. The thickness of solid masonry bearing walls shall be sufficient at all points to keep the combined stresses due to live, dead, and other loads for which the building is designed within the limits given in the preceding table.

b. Except as otherwise provided in this section, the minimum nominal thickness of solid masonry bearing walls shall be 12 in. for the uppermost 35 ft of their height and shall be increased 4 in. for each successive 35 ft, or fraction thereof, measured downward from the top of the wall.

c. Where solid masonry bearing walls are stiffened at distances not greater than 12 ft apart by cross walls, or by internal or external offsets or returns at least 2 ft deep, or by reinforced-concrete floors, they may be of 12-in. nominal thickness for the uppermost 70 ft, measured downward from the top of the wall, and shall be increased 4 in. in thickness for each successive 70 ft or fraction thereof.

d. In buildings not more than three stories in height, solid masonry bearing walls of the top story may be of 8-in. nominal thickness when the total height of the wall does not exceed 35 ft, provided that such 8-in. walls do not exceed 12 ft in height and that the roof beams are horizontal.

e. In residential buildings not more than three stories in height, solid masonry bearing walls may be of 8-in. nominal thickness when not over 35 ft in height. Such walls in one-story single-family dwellings and one-story private garages may be of 6-in. nominal thickness when not over 9 ft in height, provided that when gable construction is used an additional 6 ft is permitted to the peak of the gable.

f. Solid masonry walls above roof level, 12 ft or less in height, enclosing stairways, elevator shafts, penthouses, or bulkheads may be of 8-in. nominal thickness and may be considered as neither increasing the height nor requiring any increase in the thickness of the wall below, provided that the requirements for allowable stresses are met.

Requirements for lateral support are as given on page 352.

THICKNESS: SOLID MASONRY NONBEARING WALLS. Nonbearing walls of solid masonry may be 4 in. less in thickness than required for bearing walls, but the nominal thickness shall be not less than 8 in., except where 6-in. walls are specifically permitted.

BOND. The facing and backing of solid masonry walls shall be bonded, either with at least one full header course in each seven courses, or with at least one full-length header in each 1.5 sq ft of wall surface. The distance between adjacent full-length headers shall not exceed 20 in. either vertically or horizontally. In solid brick walls of more than 8-in. nominal thickness, the inner joints of header courses shall be covered with another header course which shall break joints with the course below.

The preceding recommendations relative to bond represent the opinion of the committee preparing this report, but it should be noted that they are somewhat more liberal than those in many existing building codes, which often require that brick walls have a course of headers at least every sixth course and at least one full-length header in every 72 sq in. of wall surface. The designer should also note that many of the West Coast codes require a header course at least every fourth course, with a supplementary requirement to the effect that there shall be not less than one header in every 48 or 50 sq in. of wall surface.

The more common types of brick bonds are shown in Fig. 8. The method by which this effect is produced through overlapping the individual bricks is shown in Fig. 9. The selection of the bond is usually governed by archi-

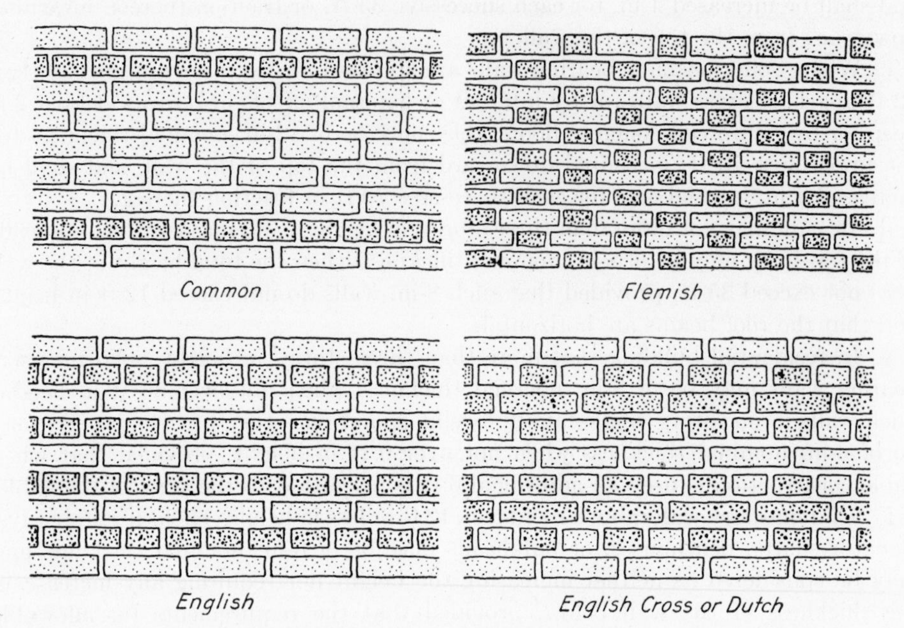

Fig. 8. Popular Types of Brick Bonds.

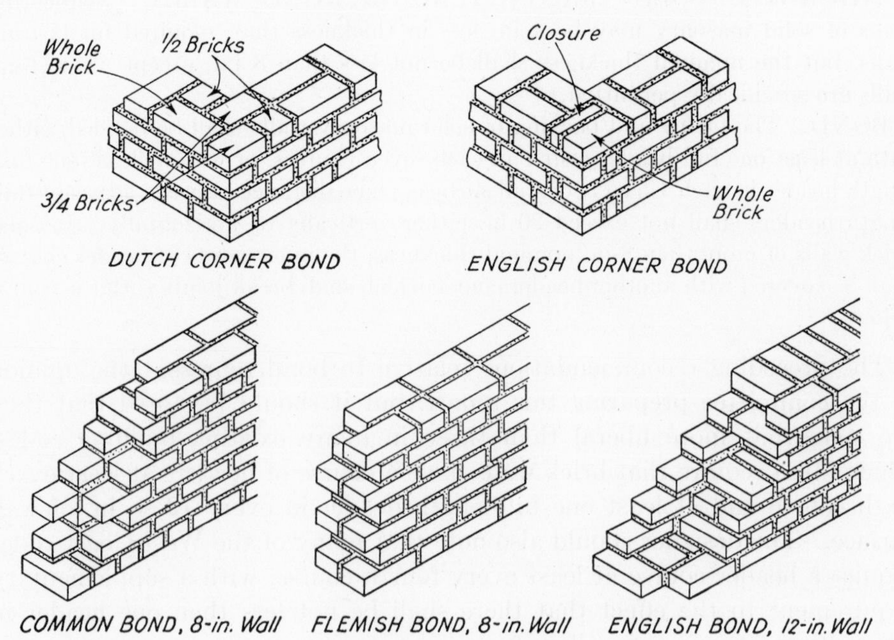

Fig. 9. Typical Methods of Bonding Bricks.

tectural considerations, as the strength of any of these standard designs is sufficient for all normal requirements.

JOINTS. The more common methods of finishing the exposed surfaces of mortar joints are shown with their corresponding designations in Fig. 10. The raked joint should never be used on the exterior of a wall exposed to rain. The flush or plain cut joint is difficult to make watertight and requires careful supervision. The struck joint is very simply formed and popular with masons. It can be made weathertight but is usually slighted and not recommended for use on exterior surfaces.

Among the several possibilities illustrated, the concave or rodded joint is the best, as it requires a special tool and particular attention on the part of

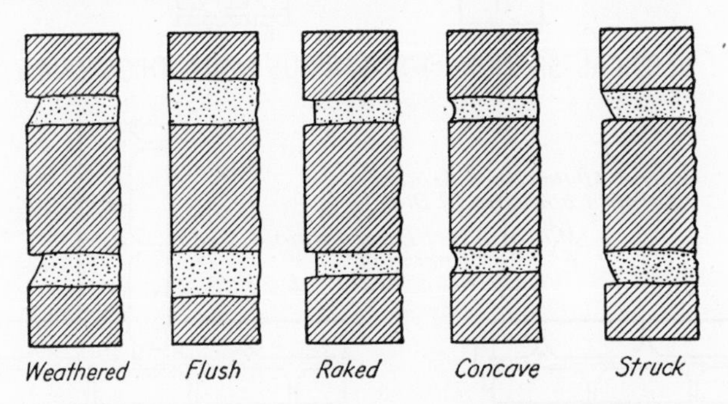

FIG. 10. Common Types of Exposed Joints.

the mason to make it; the probability of water impermeability is thereby increased. The second choice is the weathered joint, which tends to shed water and can easily be made tight if care is exercised. For standard brickwork, a ½-in. joint thickness is usually satisfactory with a normal variation between ⅜ in. and ⅝ in. A ¼-in. joint may be used for certain types of face brickwork. If the principles of modular design are to be applied, these dimensions will be fixed as noted on page 54.

REINFORCED-BRICK MASONRY. This subject, as applied to floor construction, was mentioned on page 133. In brick walls and piers the use of small steel rods, inserted in the mortar joints, has a much wider application than in floor slabs or beams. Because of the fact that masonry, although strong in compression, is comparatively weak in tension, this type of construction has a valuable application in walls which may be subjected to stresses induced by seismic disturbance. Figure 11 illustrates a typical assembly which has been used successfully on the West Coast.

A suitable mortar for this purpose is 1 part portland cement: ¼ part lime putty: 3½ parts sand. Proportions are by volume; water is added to obtain a flowing consistency but not in sufficient quantity to cause separation of the ingredients. When the grouting method is used, brick or other masonry units should be of a type sufficiently absorptive and laid sufficiently dry to draw some water from the grout. This matter is covered in the Uniform Building Code, Pacific Coast Building Officials Conferences, to the effect that such units, when immersed in water for 5 minutes, are

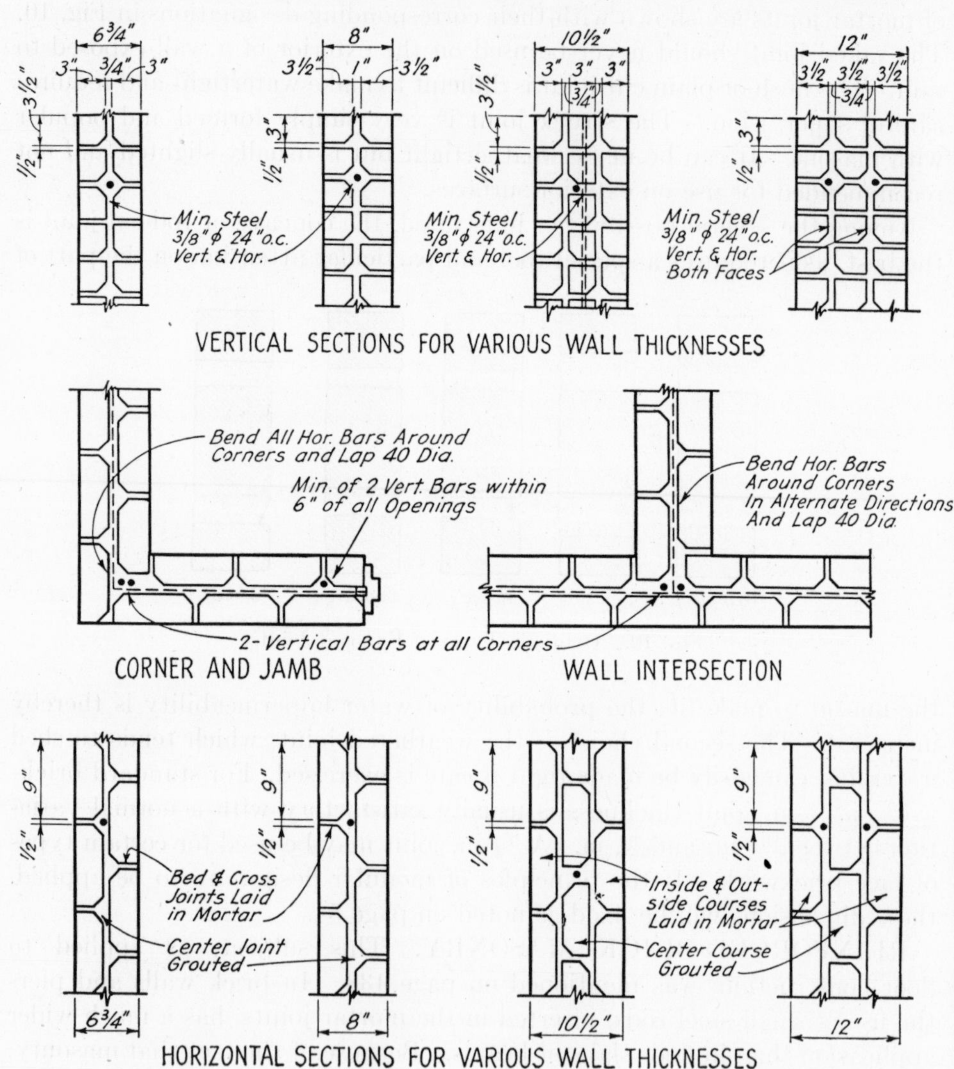

FIG. 11. Reinforced-Groutlock Bearing and Filler Walls. Courtesy, Simons Brick Company, Los Angeles, Cal.

required to absorb at least 5 per cent and not more than 10 per cent of the dry weight of the unit. An excellent article on this subject will be found in *Principles of Brick Engineering*, by H. C. Plummer and L. J. Reardon, published by the Structural Clay Products Institute, 1943. Additional references appear in many West Coast building codes, ordinarily included under the heading, Reinforced Grouted Masonry.

Article 8. Solid Stone Masonry

With the exception of rubble masonry, which is usually employed for the entire structural thickness of the wall, solid stone masonry, composed of natural or cast stone, is used principally in the form of facings combined with a cheaper backing material. Definitions of ashlar masonry and the various types of rubble were given in Article 1 of this chapter. In Fig. 12 are shown the more common designs with their corresponding designations.

ALLOWABLE WORKING STRESSES. The allowable stresses in compression in pounds per square inch of gross cross-sectional area are given in the following table.

COMPRESSIVE STRESSES IN SOLID STONE MASONRY

(From "American Standard Building Code Requirements for Masonry")

Material	Allowable Compressive Stresses, in Pounds per Square Inch, Corresponding to Mortar Types			
	A	B	C	D
Granite, ashlar	800	640	500	400
Limestone, ashlar	500	400	325	250
Marble, ashlar	500	400	325	250
Sandstone, ashlar	400	320	250	160
Cast stone	400	320	250	160
Rubble stone	140	100	80	...

THICKNESS. a. The thickness of stone walls shall be sufficient at all points to keep the combined stresses due to live, dead, and other loads for which the building is designed within the prescribed limits.

b. The minimum thickness of walls of stone ashlar shall be not less than that required for solid masonry walls on pages 310 and 311.

c. Rubble-stone walls shall be 4 in. thicker than is required for solid masonry walls of the same respective heights, but in no case less than 16 in. thick. Requirements for lateral support are as given on page 352.

Occasionally it is possible to lay a rubble wall 12 or 14 in. in thickness. Such a wall may be practicable for certain types of residential work when the size and shape of the available stone are particularly favorable but is seldom permitted by building ordinances.

BOND. a. In ashlar masonry bond stones uniformly distributed shall be provided to the extent of not less than 10 per cent of the area.

b. Rubble-stone masonry 24 in. or less in thickness shall have bond stones with a maximum spacing of 3 ft vertically and horizontally, and if the masonry is of greater thickness than 24 in., shall have one bond stone for each 6 sq ft of wall surface on both sides.

This requirement should not be confused with that applying to the bond between ashlar facing and the backing (see page 327). As in the case of brick masonry, such regulations may be more severe in districts subject to earthquakes.

JOINTS. Stone facing and veneer, if of a type showing excessive suction, should be well moistened immediately before setting. The stone

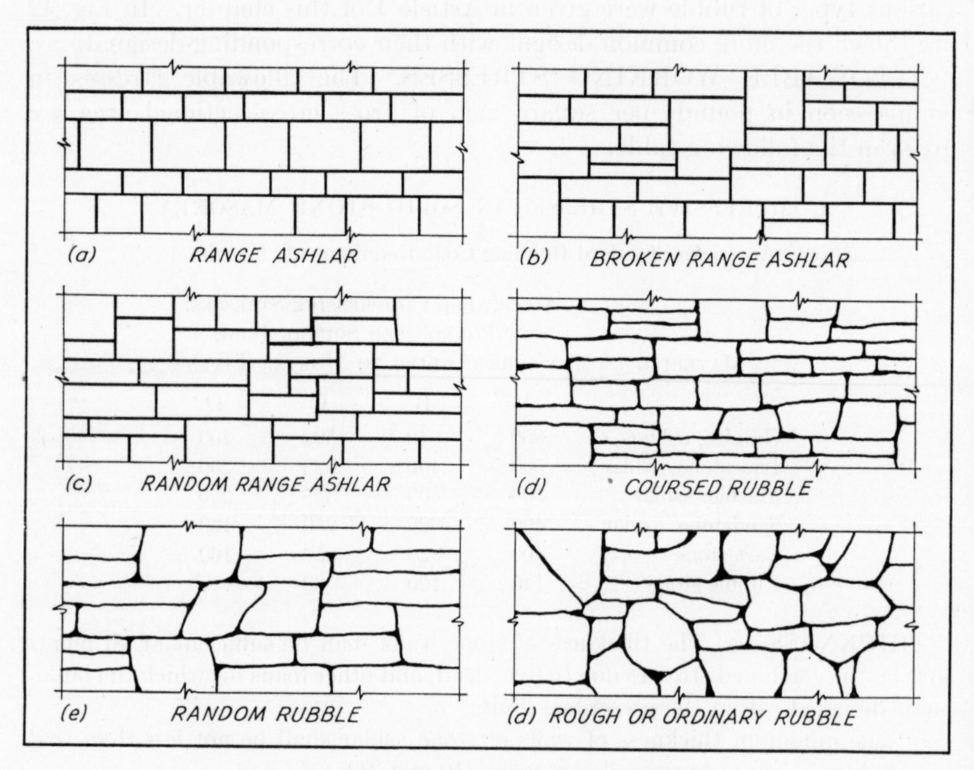

FIG. 12. Stone Ashlar and Rubble Masonry.

when laid should have sufficient suction to bond well with the mortar but not enough to leave the mortar too dry for proper hydration. The thickness of both the vertical and horizontal joints, the latter identified as "beds," is usually ¼ or ³⁄₁₆ in. In order to provide for secondary stresses, corrugated lead pads enclosed in a sheet-lead cover are often placed in the horizontal joints between windows at the alternate stories of high buildings.

When the stone is laid, the mortar is either kept back from the face or raked out to a depth of ¾ in. At some later period, often after all the exterior stone has been placed, joints are "pointed" or filled and finished to the required surface appearance. The usual types are the same as those shown on page 313. Considerable variation exists in the recommendations of different authorities for the proportions of the pointing mortar. The Indiana Limestone Institute recommends a mixture of 1 part nonstaining cement: 2 parts white sand, to which sufficient lime putty is added to form as stiff a mixture as can be worked. Proportions are by volume. Sand is required to pass a screen having 6 meshes to the inch. Some excellent work has been done employing larger quantities of lime and sand. The exact proportions of the mortar are not as important as the workmanship. The procedure given on page 301 for remedial work can be used. Most authorities agree that even the rapid-slaking limes improve by being slaked

FIG. 13. Court House, Shelbyville, Ind. *Arch.:* D. A. Bohler and Son. Courtesy, Ingalls Stone Company.

for a period of at least a week. "Waterproofed" quicklime, mixed well in advance, is desirable.

Vertical joints in cornices, copings, and belt courses require particular attention. The stones comprising these elements are set with vertical joints dry. The exterior profile is then caulked with picked oakum, and the joint poured with as thick a mortar grout as can be worked into it. Recommended proportions are 1 part cement: $1\frac{1}{2}$ parts fine white sand. The grout is stopped $\frac{3}{4}$ in. below the surface. After it has hardened, the caulking is removed, and the face joints are pointed. Plastic caulking compounds are often appropriate for the joints of parapets and copings (see page 284). A discussion of their uses and of other materials, such as lead wool and molten lead, may be obtained from the Indiana Limestone Institute, Vermont Marble Company, and Georgia Marble Company.

When rubble masonry is laid, the face joints should be fairly well filled and the mortar thoroughly compacted. After the mortar has stiffened sufficiently, joints can be finished by rubbing off the excess material with a short stick having a rounded end. The use of a steel pointing trowel for this purpose is not recommended. As the appearance of the wall is greatly affected by the depth to which the joints are cut back from the face of the stone, samples should be prepared in advance.

Article 9. Walls of Hollow Masonry Units

This classification applies to walls built of structural-clay tile or hollow concrete-masonry units. Clay tile is used very widely for back-up purposes

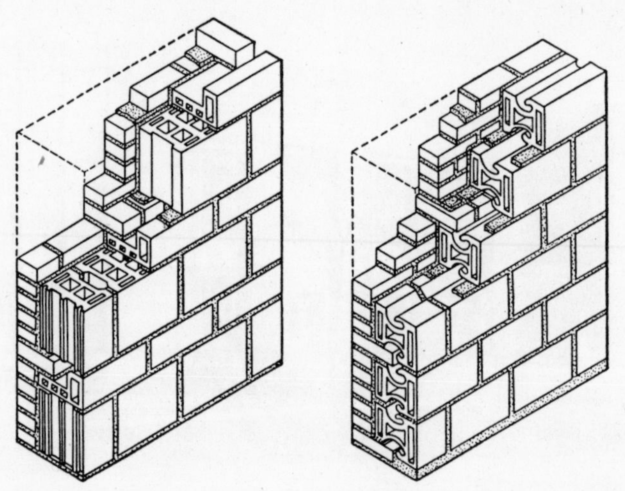

Fig. 14. Brick Facing with Clay-Tile Back-up. Courtesy, National Fireproofing Company.

with stone or brick facings. An assembly of this type (see Fig. 14) has the advantage of eliminating or at least lessening the need for furring, which would be desirable for most classes of occupancy if a backing of solid masonry were used. The better types of clay-tile backing units are especially formed to provide drainage. The joint thickness is usually ½ in. Hollow concrete masonry is also employed for the same purpose, as shown in Fig. 15.

Both clay tile and hollow concrete block have a wide application for the exterior bearing walls of low structures, such as one- or two-family residential buildings. Figure 16 shows typical details for the support of the floor construction when hollow concrete-masonry units are used for this purpose. The joint thickness is usually ⅜ in. Portland-cement stucco is normally applied as an exterior finish over the standard block. An alternate finish is two coats of cement paint. Special concrete-masonry units are also manufactured to serve as a wall-surfacing material and are laid in various patterns, as shown in Fig. 17. Structural-glass block, which fall under this general classification, may be used for both exterior and interior nonbearing walls or in openings where windows would be permitted but should carry no load other than their own weight.

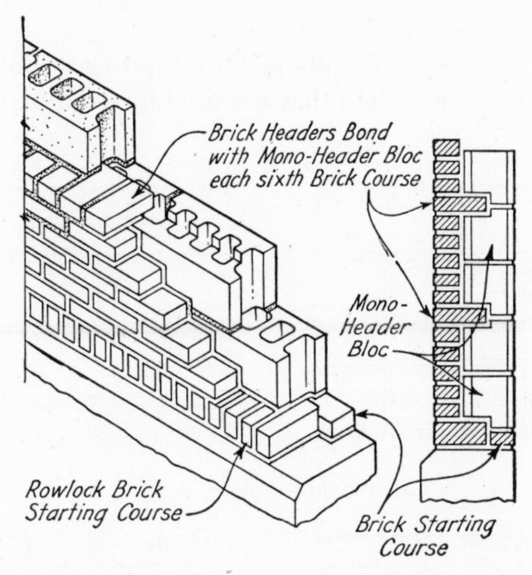

FIG. 15. Brick Facing with Hollow Concrete-Masonry Back-up. Courtesy, Portland Cement Association.

ALLOWABLE WORKING STRESSES.[16] The allowable compressive stresses in pounds per square inch of gross cross-sectional area in masonry of hollow units of structural-clay tile or of hollow concrete masonry should

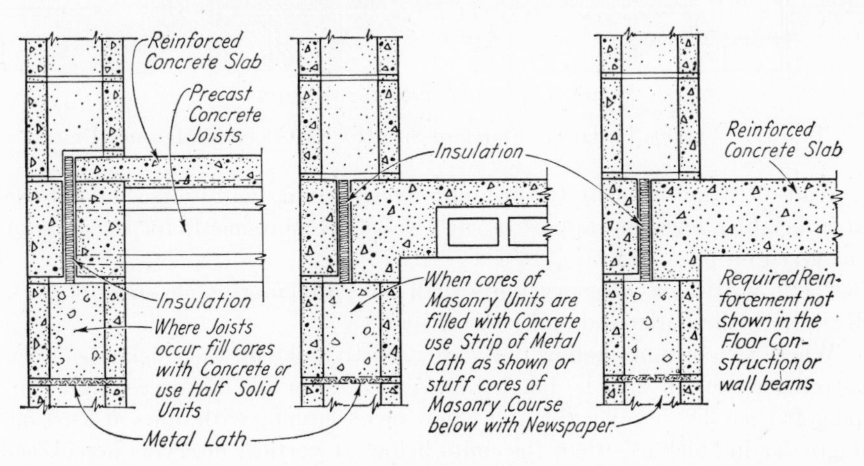

FIG. 16. Detail of Edge-Bearing for Floors Supported by Walls of Hollow Concrete Masonry.

not exceed 85 lb per sq in. when laid in type A mortar nor 70 lb per sq in. when laid in type B mortar.

[16] Also quoted from "American Standard Building Code Requirements for Masonry."

THICKNESS AND HEIGHT. a. The thickness of walls of structural-clay-tile or hollow concrete-masonry units shall be sufficient at all points to keep the combined stresses due to live, dead, and other loads for which the building is designed within the allowable stresses.

b. The minimum thickness of walls of structural-clay tile or hollow concrete-masonry units shall be not less than that required for solid masonry walls, as given on pages 310 and 311.

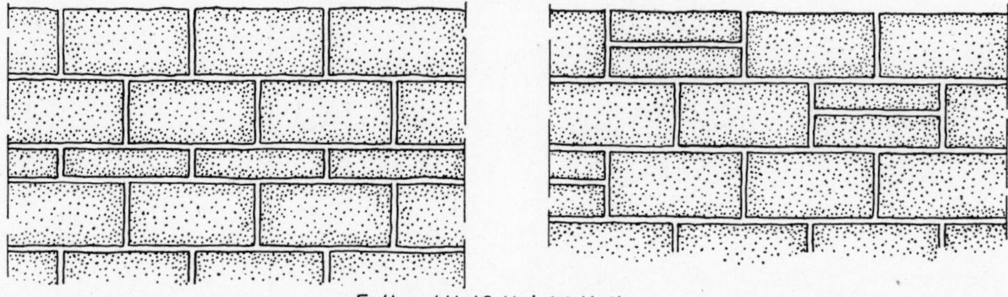

Full and Half-Height Units

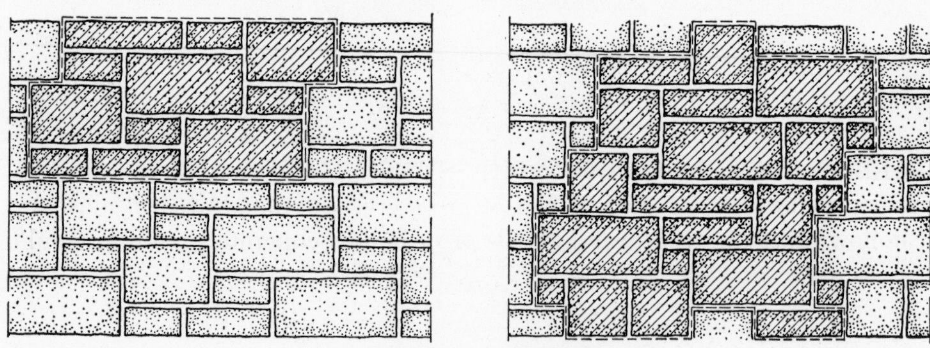

Full, Half and Fractional Size Units

FIG. 17. Various Designs of Standard-Size Hollow Concrete-Masonry Units.

c. Walls of structural-clay tile or hollow concrete-masonry units shall not exceed 50 ft in height above the support of such walls. Requirements for lateral support are as given on page 352.

BOND. a. Hollow masonry units shall have full mortar coverage of the face shells in both the horizontal and vertical joints.

b. Where two or more hollow units are used to make up the thickness of a wall, the stretcher courses shall be bonded at vertical intervals not exceeding 34 in. by lapping at least 3¾ in. over the unit below or by lapping with units at least 50 per cent greater in thickness than the units below at vertical intervals not exceeding 17 in.

c. Where walls of hollow masonry units are decreased in thickness, a course of solid masonry shall be interposed between the wall below and the thinner wall above.

STRUCTURAL-GLASS BLOCK. The usual thickness is 3⅞ in. with sizes 5¾ × 5¾, 7¾ × 7¾, and 11¾ × 11¾ in. Mortar-bearing surfaces are corrugated and coated with an alkali and moisture-resistant aggregate material to insure proper bond. Noncorrodible wire ties are placed in the

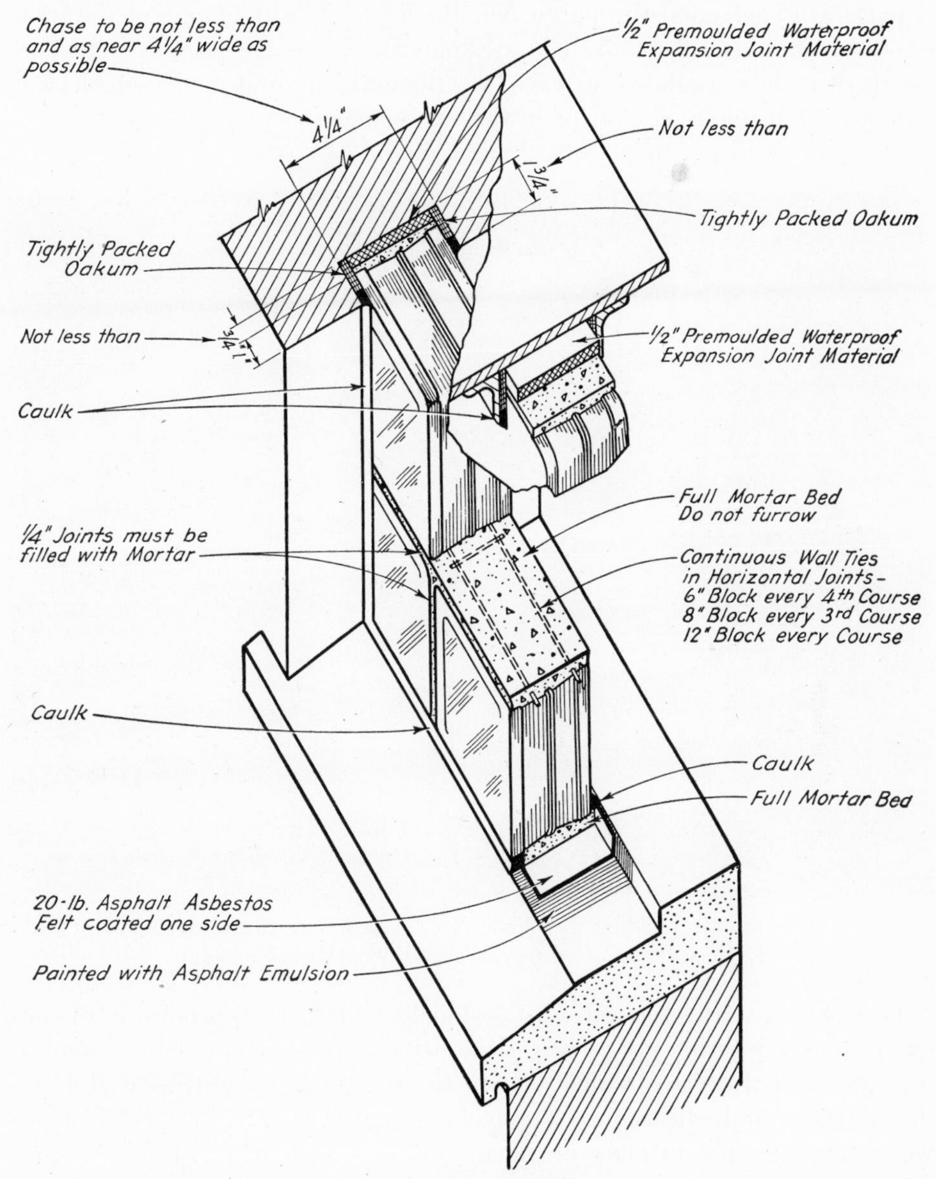

Fig. 18. Installation Details for an Exterior Glass-Block Panel. Courtesy, Pittsburgh Plate Glass Company.

joints as required to reinforce the assembly. Where panels are not set into chases, they are anchored to adjoining walls with perforated steel strips.

If panels have an area greater than 144 sq ft, a length over 25 ft, or a height over 20 ft, the horizontal dimension is divided by mullions, and the vertical dimension by shelf angles. Glass block are usually laid in mortar of volumetric proportions 1 part white portland cement: 1 part lime putty: 4 parts sand screened through a No. 16 sieve. The thickness of the joints should be between 3⁄16 and 3⁄8 in. Expansion strips are used at jambs and heads of panels, as shown in Fig. 18. Beneath the first course of block an asphalt emulsion is spread over the sill which serves to break the bond between sill and panel.

Fig. 19. Mergenthaler Building, Brooklyn, N. Y. *Arch. and Engrs.:* Lockwood, Greene, Engineers, Inc. Courtesy, Owens-Illinois Glass Company.

In addition to the general-purpose blocks which are appropriate for both exterior and interior use, many decorative types are available, together with functional designs which control the direction of light, as well as the distribution and diffusion. Some manufacturers supply prefabricated wood strips for use in place of mortar joints. Such strips are appropriate for temporary interior partitions, permitting dismantling and re-erection without injury to the materials.

The weight of the general-purpose block laid in mortar is about 17½ lb per sq ft of wall surface. The overall coefficient of heat transfer, U,[17] varies

[17] Coefficients are based on a wind velocity of 15 mph and are expressed in British thermal units per hour per square foot per degree Fahrenheit difference in temperature between the atmosphere inside and outside the wall.

slightly for different designs but is about 0.48, as compared with 1.13 for single-thickness common glass. The sound-transmission loss is indicated by a sound-reduction factor of about 40 decibels over a range of 9 frequencies. The manufacturers supplying structural-glass block have devoted considerable study to their installation. It is recommended that

Fig. 20. Recreation Pool, Shrine Hospital, San Francisco, Calif. *Arch.:* Whitehouse and Price. Courtesy, Owens-Illinois Glass Company.

the designer follow their instructions in design and specification. Figures 19 and 20 show appropriate exterior and interior uses.

Although not a structural material, a type of heat-absorbing plate glass is also available where the exclusion of solar heat is essential. It has its particular application in reducing the cooling load on the sides of buildings exposed to the direct rays of the sun. If it is desirable to admit the solar heat and at the same time reduce the normal heat transmission from the inside to the exterior atmosphere, a type of glass having the characteristics of Thermopane is appropriate. Such glass has its particular application to the Solar House and many types of occupancy for which we would have formerly used storm sash to reduce the loss of interior heat by conduction through the glass. If this advantage is desired in combination with the exclusion, rather than the admission, of solar heat, still another type of glass is available which is referred to as "heat absorbing." All types greatly reduce the condensation upon the glazed surfaces characteristic of high interior humidities during the heating season.

Article 10. Cavity Walls and Hollow Walls of Solid Units

CAVITY WALLS. This term identifies a hollow assembly formed by two wythes, in which the brick or other solid masonry units are separated by an air space of about 2 in. No through headers are employed, the two wythes being bound together by noncorrodible metal ties. Such designs were popular in England and Australia during the years immediately preceding World War II and have gained general acceptance in this country. Their chief application is for the exterior bearing walls of low structures, such as one- or two-story residential buildings, but they have also been used for panel and curtain walls in skeleton designs.

An example is a large apartment house in New Jersey. A recent report indicates that this building is satisfactory from the viewpoint of occupancy, but it has been considered necessary to install furring, originally omitted, on some of the wall surfaces which were subjected to an unusual rain exposure. Where such unfurred designs are employed, extreme care in supervision would appear to be essential.

The more important matters are complete filling of all joints with mortar, except those left open for drainage; careful placing of metal ties; and adequate flashing. The cavity must be kept free of mortar. Drainage is obtained by means of weep holes placed in the vertical joints of the bottom course of the outer wythe. Holes are usually spaced 2 ft apart and may be formed with ⅜-in. oiled steel rods left in the joint and removed after the mortar has set. Flashings placed over openings should extend 6 in. beyond the face of the jamb on each side of the opening. The flashing at the bottom of the cavity is continuous.

Ventilation of the cavity is furnished gratuitously by the weep holes, although it may be desirable in warm climates to augment this feature by leaving additional openings through the outer wythe near the top of the wall. In cold climates circulation should be diminished, as the heat-insulating value of the wall is materially reduced by air movement within the cavity. For this purpose airstops are often employed. Figure 21 illustrates a typical section of a cavity wall, as described in *General Ruling No.* 90, Technical Division, Federal Housing Administration, 1940. This document offers the design for dwellings with exterior walls not exceeding two stories in height. Recommendations from the viewpoint of British practice are given in *Principles of Modern Building*, Vol. 1, by R. Fitzmaurice, published by His Majesty's Stationery Office, 1939.

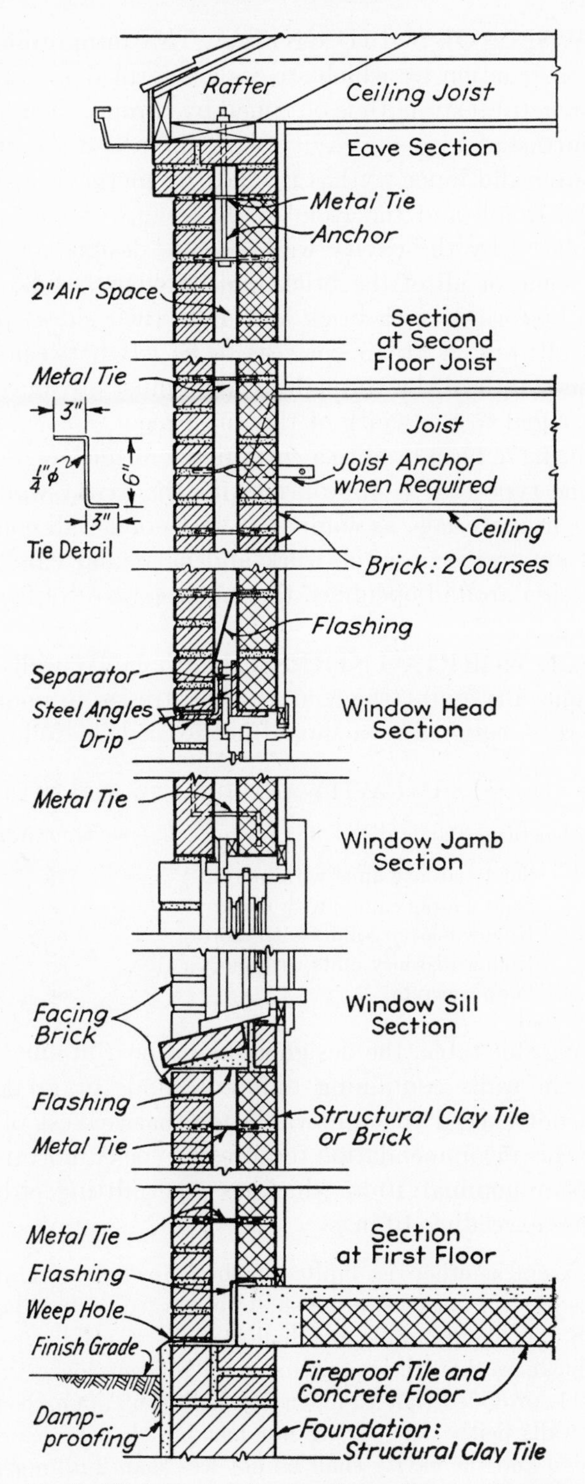

Fig. 21. Exterior Cavity-Wall Design for Small Dwellings. Courtesy, The Producers' Council, Inc.

HOLLOW WALLS OF SOLID UNITS. This term ordinarily identifies a method of construction by which spaces are formed within the thickness of a wall and structural strength is obtained by through-bonding of masonry headers, as contrasted with the cavity wall, for which the only connection between the outer and inner wythes is made by metal ties. Typical examples are the All-Rolok and the Rolok-Bak designs, which have now been practically replaced by the cavity wall. These designs are generally constructed with some or all of the brick laid on edge. Hollow walls of this type may also be formed with brick laid upon their sides, as is customary for the solid wall; but, if an air space is to be left between the outer and inner faces, the length of the through headers must obviously be increased by an amount equal to the width of the air space.

These designs have been used to a certain extent for low residential buildings of the same type that is appropriate for the cavity-wall. There is an obvious saving in materials, as compared with solid wall construction, but unless masons are trained for the work and particular care is exercised to simplify the design around openings, the increased cost of labor may cancel any such saving.

ALLOWABLE WORKING STRESSES. In cavity walls and in hollow walls of solid masonry units, the compressive stresses in pounds per square inch of gross cross-sectional area should not exceed the following:

COMPRESSIVE STRESSES IN CAVITY AND HOLLOW WALLS OF SOLID UNITS

(From "American Standard Building Code Requirements for Masonry")

Solid masonry units with mortar A	125
Solid masonry units with mortar B	100
Hollow masonry units with mortar A	60
Hollow masonry units with mortar B	50
Plain concrete	300

In interpreting this table, the designer should bear in mind that the compressive stress in walls containing different kinds or grades of units or mortar should not exceed that allowable for the weakest of the combinations and that this recommendation requires a type A mortar to be used for cavity walls of a nominal 10-in. thickness, permitting either type A or type B for those exceeding 10 in.

HEIGHT. Except as otherwise limited in the following paragraph, cavity walls and hollow walls of solid masonry units shall not exceed 35 ft in height.

THICKNESS. a. Cavity walls and hollow walls of solid masonry units shall be not less in thickness than the requirement for solid masonry walls, as given on pages 310 and 311, provided that 10-in. cavity walls shall not exceed 25 ft in height.

b. In cavity walls neither the facing nor backing shall be less than $3\frac{3}{4}$ in. in nominal thickness, and the cavity shall be not less than 2 in. nor more than 3 in. in width. The requirements for lateral support are as given on page 352.

BOND. a. In hollow walls of solid masonry units, the facing and backing shall be securely tied together with headers or bonding units, as required for solid masonry walls, so that the parts of the wall will exert common action under the load.

b. Where such walls are decreased in thickness, a course of solid masonry shall be interposed between the wall below and the thinner wall above.

c. In cavity walls the facing and backing shall be securely tied together with suitable bonding ties of adequate strength. A steel rod 3/16 in. in diameter or a metal tie of equivalent stiffness coated with a non-corrodible metal or other approved protective coating shall be used for each 3 sq ft of wall surface. Where hollow masonry units are laid with the cells vertical, rectangular ties shall be used; in other walls the ends of ties shall be bent to 90° angles to provide hooks not less than 2 in. long. Ties shall be embedded in horizontal joints of the facing and backing. Additional bonding ties shall be provided at all openings, spaced not more than 3 ft apart around the perimeter and within 12 in. of the opening. Cavity walls of plain concrete shall be reinforced as specified for solid walls of plain concrete on page 338.

DRAINAGE. In cavity walls the cavity shall be kept clear of mortar droppings during construction. Approved flashing shall be installed, and adequate drainage provided to keep dampness away from the backing.

Article 11. Faced and Veneered Walls

GENERAL REQUIREMENTS. Ashlar masonry of natural or cast stone, face brick, architectural terra cotta, structural glass, and occasionally other materials are used as a facing or as a veneer over a backing of cheaper masonry units. As will be seen from the definitions given on page 291, a faced wall is one in which the masonry facing and backing are so bonded as to act together under load, whereas a veneered wall is one in which the masonry facing is not so bonded, being merely attached to the backing. These definitions represent a common use of the two terms and imply that the designer should, except in the case of the thinner materials such as structural glass and 1¼-in. or 2-in. stone, meet the requirements for a faced wall in order that the surfacing may be included as part of the structural thickness demanded by code or good practice.

FACED WALLS.[18] In conventional wall assemblies the minimum thickness of the facing should be not less than 2¼ in. nor less than one-eighth of the height of the unit. The full cross-section of both the facing and the backing is then included when computing the unit stresses, which should not exceed those allowed for the weaker of the two materials. The total structural thickness of faced walls should not be less than that required for masonry walls of either of the types forming the facing and backing. Brick facing should be bonded to the backing, as noted on page 311 for solid

[18] The requirements applying to masonry for faced walls have been adopted but not directly quoted from "American Standard Building Code Requirements for Masonry."

masonry walls. Ashlar facing of either natural or cast stone should have at least 20 per cent of the superficial wall area extending not less than 3¾ in. into the backing to form bond stones, which should be uniformly distributed throughout the wall.

Substantial noncorrodible metal anchors with a cross-section of not less than 0.2 sq in. should be required for every projecting stone, and, except

Fig. 22. City Hall Faced with Cast Stone, Santa Ana, Calif. *Arch.:* Austin and Wildman.

when alternate courses are full bond courses, every stone not a bond stone should be similarly anchored. Each stone more than 2 ft in length and 3 sq ft in superficial area should have two anchors. Facing stones not over 12 sq ft in area should have at least one anchor to each 4 sq ft of superficial face area. The bond required between a backing of structural-clay tile or hollow concrete masonry and a facing of hollow units is the same as previously shown on pages 318 and 319.

Where a stone facing is used over a reinforced-concrete backing, special methods are necessary. Figure 22 shows the city hall built in Santa Ana, California, which was faced with cast stone; Fig. 23, details of the wall construction.

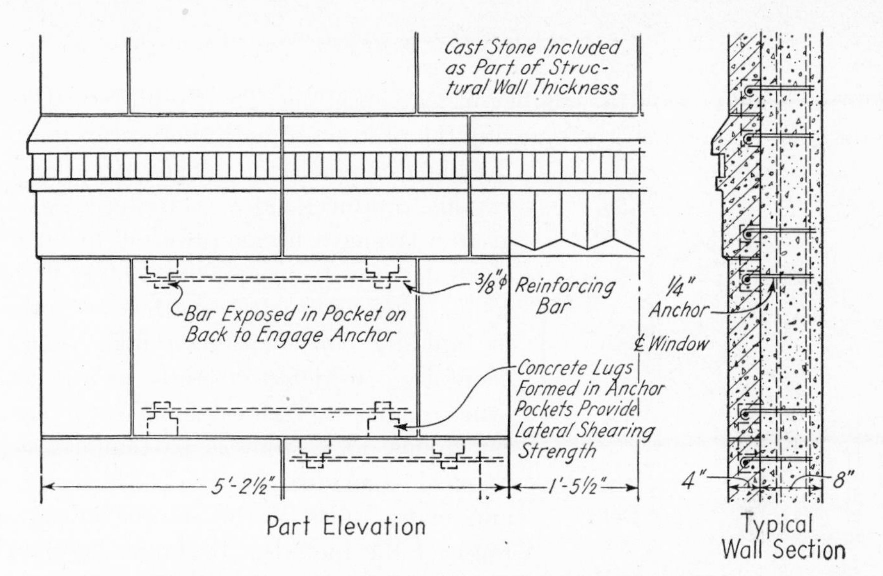

Fig. 23. Exterior Wall Section of Santa Ana City Hall.

Fig. 24. Magnin Store Building Surfaced with Marble Veneer, Los Angeles, Calif. *Arch.:* Myron Hunt and H. C. Chambers.

During recent years the quality of cast stone has greatly improved, but the designer should insist upon using the product of only those firms having the highest reputation. The better organizations produce today a material which gives a strength in compression, at an age of 28 days, of from 8000 to 10,000 lb per sq in. Although such strength is not needed in building construction, a high value is generally considered desirable as a gage of other qualities. As compared to the natural stones, cast stone is particularly economical when curved surfaces are required, and many units of the same size permit reuse of the moulds. It should be chosen not merely as a cheaper substitute for the natural product, but with full realization of texture, color, and the general architectural effects which may be obtained.

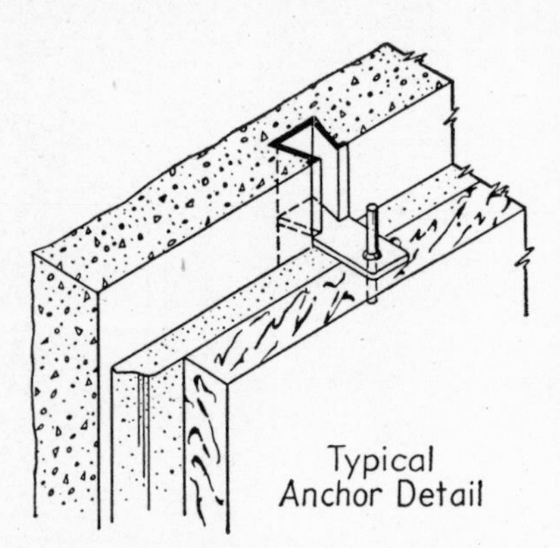

Fig. 25. Attachment of Marble Veneer to Concrete Walls of Magnin Building. Courtesy, Vermont Marble Company.

VENEERED WALLS. The minimum thickness of the masonry materials commonly used as wall veneer varies from a maximum of 3 in. for natural stone to 1 in. for flat tile. As it cannot be considered a part of the structural wall thickness, the allowable compressive stress on sections of this type is that permitted for the backing material. The height of veneered surfaces should be limited to 35 ft above foundations or other support. Stone veneer, when of 3-in. thickness, may be bonded into the masonry backing by a header projecting at least 3¾ in. into the backing for every

Fig. 26. Bakery Surfaced with Terra Cotta Veneer in New Jersey. *Arch.:* The McCormick Company. Courtesy, Federal Seaboard Terra Cotta Company.

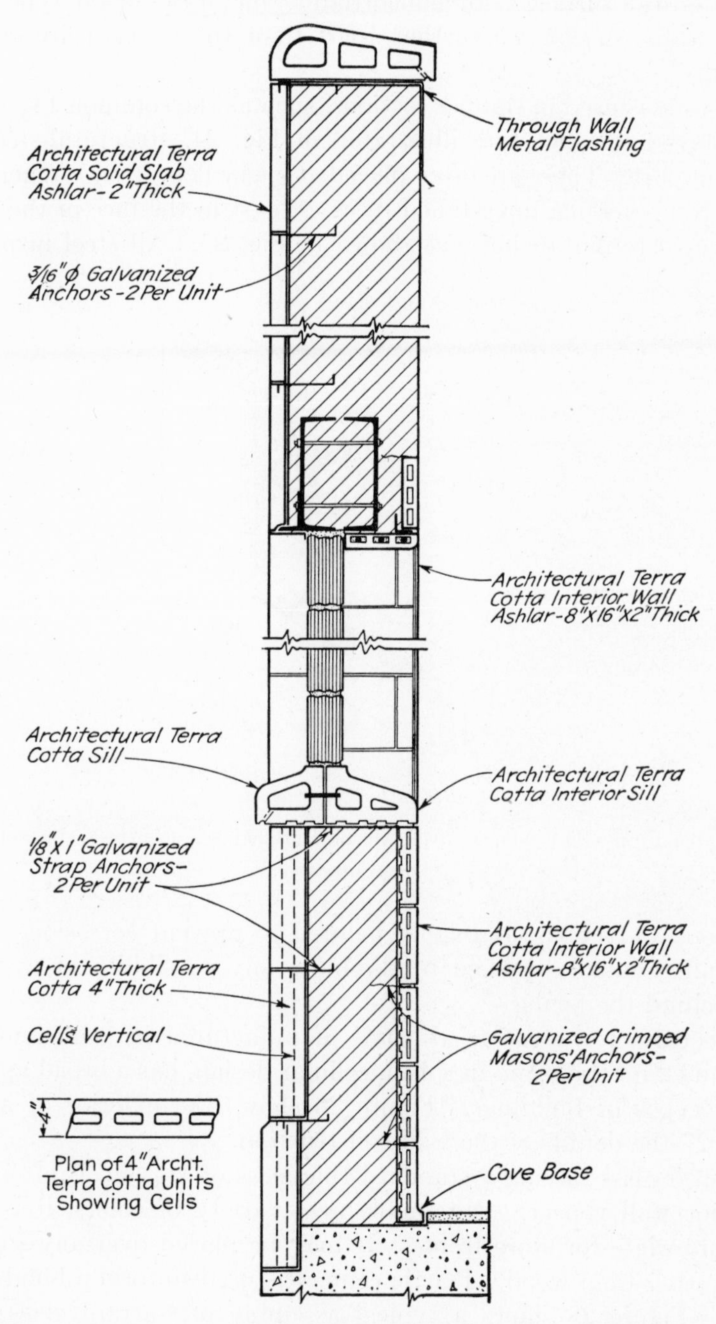

Fig. 27. Exterior Wall Section of New Jersey Bakery. Courtesy, Federal Seaboard Terra Cotta Company.

300 sq in. of wall surface or by noncorrodible metal ties of the type required for faced walls, spaced not further apart than 16 in. vertically and 24 in. horizontally.

When stone is used in thinner sections, such as the common 1¼-in. thickness employed for the store illustrated in Fig. 24, structural-steel angles serve as support. These are often placed at every floor level. When applied over concrete backing, dove-tailed recesses, cast in the face of the concrete wall, serve to retain anchors, as shown in Fig. 25. All steel in proximity

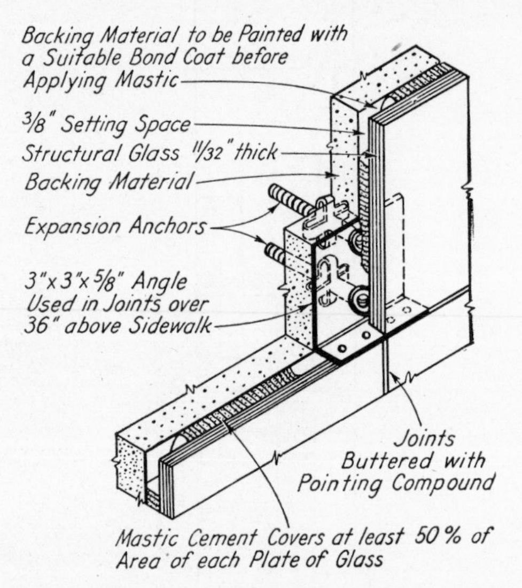

FIG. 28. Structural Glass Veneer over Masonry Backing. Courtesy, Pittsburgh Plate Glass Company.

to the stone should be thoroughly painted to prevent corrosion. The top of the wall should be flashed to eliminate any possibility of water penetrating behind the facing.

Architectural terra cotta, which is manufactured in solid and cellular ashlar units 2 in. thick and in a 4-in. cellular design, has a broad application to many types of buildings. Figure 26 shows the exterior of a bakery, and Fig. 27 the details of the wall construction.

Structural glass having a standard thickness of 11/32 in. is often used as an exterior wall veneer. Obtainable in a variety of colors, it is particularly appropriate for store fronts. It may be placed over any substantial material other than wood. Plastic cement is used to form a bond with the backing. Figure 28 shows a typical assembly of Carrara glass installed over masonry with concealed supports.

VENTILATED MASONRY WALLS. This type of construction has its particular application to industrial buildings. In the design illustrated, Fig. 29, brick veneer is used for the exterior surfaces. The backing is flue tile with rear faces perforated, laid with cells vertical. Rigid insulation is placed against the tile, the insulation separated by a vapor seal from another layer of brick, which forms the interior finish. A light-colored brick is normally used in order to reflect artificial light into the working area.

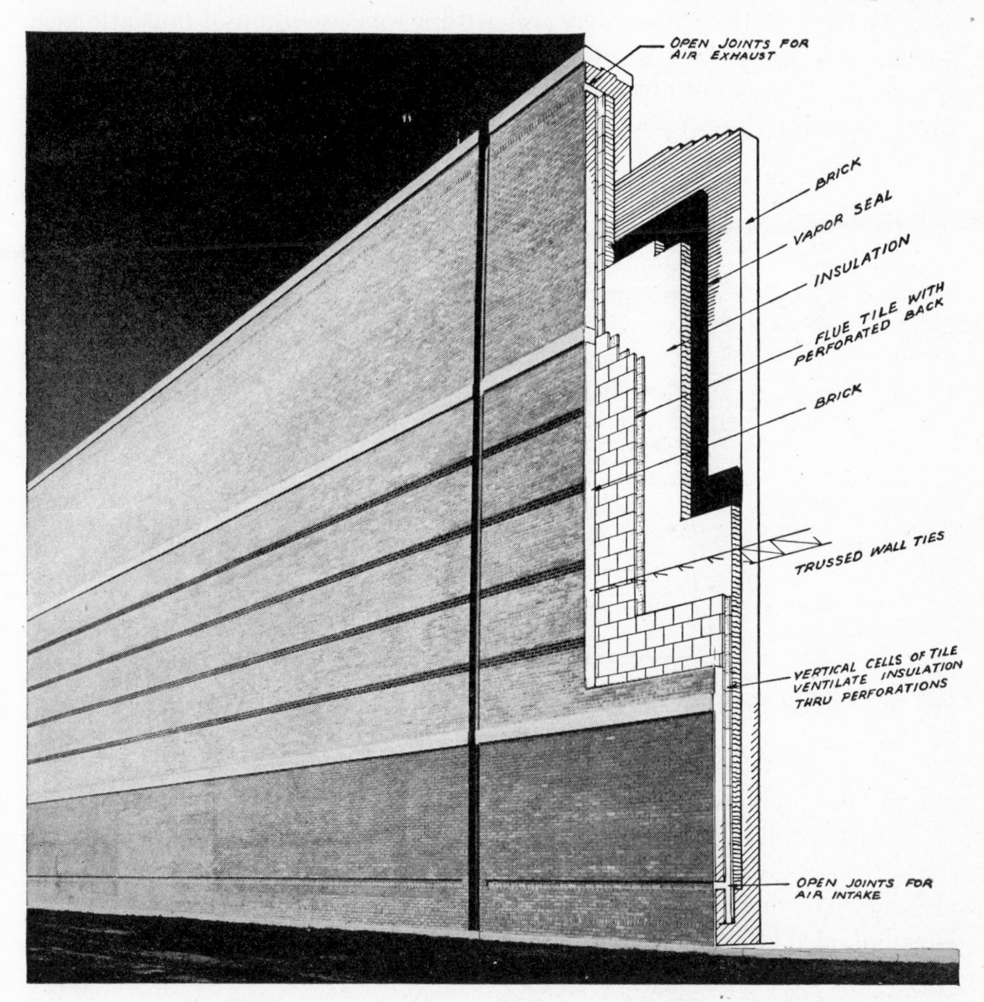

Fig. 29. "Ventilated" Masonry-Wall Design as Used for a Large Aircraft Factory. Design and Construction by the Austin Company.

Vents near the top and bottom of the wall equalize inside and outside air pressure, preventing the passage of moisture.

PRECAST CONCRETE PANELS. An important application of cast stone is its use in large panels serving as both an exterior wall surface and a form for concrete backing cast-in-place. The design shown in Fig. 30 was used for the model-testing basin built for the United States Navy at Carderock, Maryland, in 1939. The panel section, precast in a factory, is composed of standard portland-cement concrete surfaced with white portland cement combined with a carefully selected aggregate graded to provide an attractive finish. Panels are only 2 in. thick, although they range up to 8 × 10 ft in area. All are heavily reinforced. Shortly after casting, the exterior faces of the panels were wet with a weak solution of muriatic acid mixed with water and scrubbed with brushes to expose the aggregate. Excellent surfaces are obtained by this means, and, where desired, aggregates of an appropriate color may be used or other methods employed to

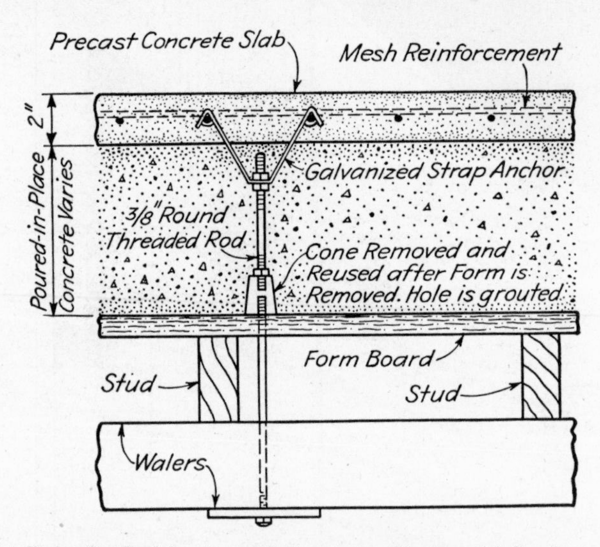

Fig. 30. Precast Slabs Backed by Poured Concrete; Horizontal Section of Exterior Wall. Courtesy, Mo-Sai Associates.

obtain the required appearance. An interesting description of the Carderock project was written by Admiral Ben Morell and published in *Architectural Concrete*, Vol. 6, No. 1.

Somewhat similar cast-stone panels were used for facing the Bethesda Hospital, also built for the navy in 1942, but in this structure 8 in. of brick were employed as back-up instead of concrete cast-in-place. Colored aggregates give interest and variety to the spandrels. Figure 31 shows a design precast with lugs, which rest upon spandrel beams or cantilevered floor slabs, and are backed with masonry. Most of the slabs are only 2½ in. thick, although the detail shows 3¼ in. They are faced with white portland cement combined with a white quartz aggregate. This wall assembly was used in a research laboratory built in New Jersey.[19]

Precast concrete wall facings of this type have a wide application to many classes of occupancy. They were used on the Idaho Falls Temple,

[19] See article entitled "Research Laboratory for Hoffman-LaRoche, Inc.," by Stewart Wagner, architect, *Architectural Concrete*, Vol. 12, No. 1 (1946).

completed in 1946. Joints between slabs are pointed with either a plastic compound or a nonstaining, cement-lime mortar. The choice should be carefully considered with the manufacturers. Such designs can be accepted with confidence, but it is essential that the panels be thoroughly cured before placement. The structural assembly should be arranged to prevent

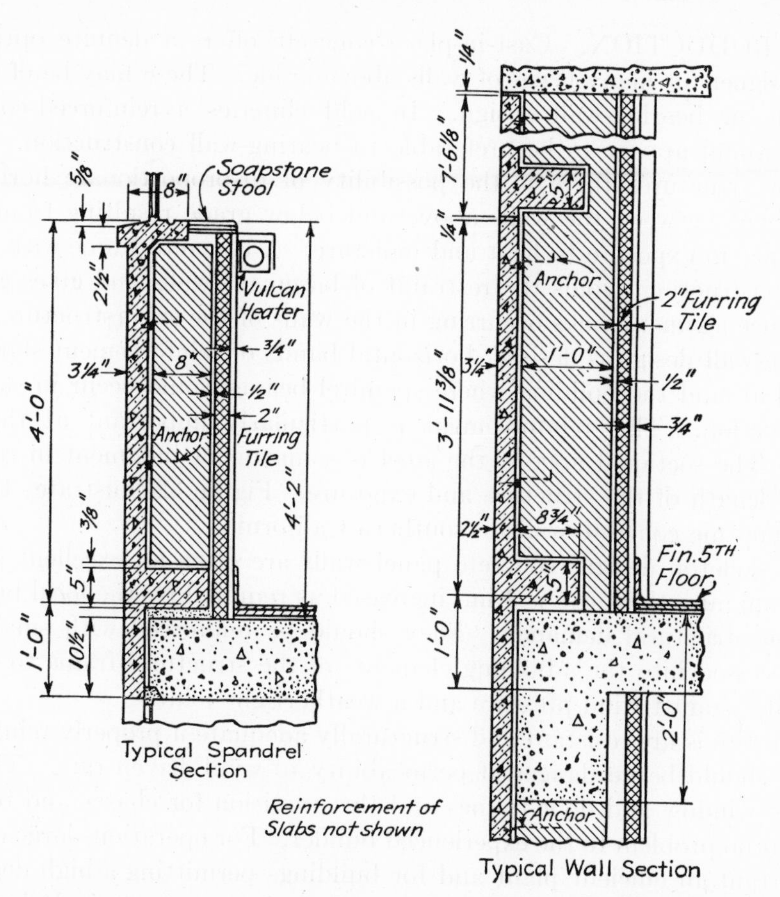

FIG. 31. Precast Slabs Backed by Masonry; Vertical Sections of Exterior Wall. *Arch.:* Fellheimer and Wagner.

any appreciable stress from being transmitted to the facing. Lack of such provision has resulted in the cracking of panels.

STUCCO-SURFACED MASONRY WALLS. Exterior walls of concrete-masonry units or structural-clay tile may be surfaced with portland-cement stucco, as discussed on page 255. Concrete-masonry units should have a rough, coarse texture. Scored clay tile provide a mechanical bond. Brick with a rough or moderately rough surface are also acceptable as a base. Joints are raked out to a depth of ½ in. from the face of the wall. Both clay tile and brick should be well burned but not vitrified. Stone masonry is occasionally surfaced in the same manner; but, where an exterior stucco finish is desired, it is usually more economical to use structural-clay tile or concrete-masonry units. For further discussion of this subject see page 255.

Article 12. Concrete Walls above Grade

INTRODUCTION. Cast-in-place concrete offers a definite option to the designer for many types of walls above grade. These may be of panel, curtain, or bearing-wall design. In cold climates a reinforced-concrete frame would appear to be preferable to bearing-wall construction. Even for low structures there is the possibility of disproportionate horizontal movement between the walls above and below grade resulting from their difference in exposure to heat and moisture. A concrete frame with panel-wall construction avoids the restraint of basement walls and gives greater assurance against cracks occurring in the walls of the superstructure. If a bearing-wall design is desired, horizontal bands of reinforcement should be placed around the building where spandrel beams would occur in skeleton construction. This reinforcement is particularly important at the roof level. The sectional area of the steel is a matter of judgment in relation to the length of the structure and exposure. Figure 32 illustrates the use of monolithic concrete walls in southern California.

For skeleton designs concrete panel walls are often an excellent choice. The minimum thickness is 4 in., increased as required by the local building code or structural demands. They should be reinforced with small rods and recessed into the adjoining elements of the structural frame to obtain stability against wind pressure and a weathertight joint.

Concrete is fire resistant and structurally adequate if properly reinforced. There should be no danger of permeability to wind-driven rain. The setting of window and door frames and the provision for chases and recesses present no problem to the experienced builder. For operations large enough to warrant an efficient plant and for buildings permitting a high degree of standardization in form work, concrete may be an economical choice for the walls. These considerations are important and have particular significance in small, isolated structures, for which the cost of forms or the expenditure of too much labor in placing the concrete may cancel all economy in its use.

The problem of adapting monolithic construction to small dwellings has received considerable attention for about 40 years. After many less ambitious designs, a number of comparatively large private residences, club houses, and other buildings were constructed in this manner between 1905 and 1915. Throughout this period and during the following decade many ingenious attempts were made to reduce the cost of form work by standardization in both wood and steel. Although some designs were used for commercial, public, and industrial buildings, the principal object was to produce single- and two-family dwellings of a substantial type at a comparatively low cost. These operations were scattered widely throughout the United States. Of the hollow-wall systems the Van Guilder is an example. Those furnishing a solid wall section are represented by the Metaforms and Morrill Systems. Many of these designs had considerable merit, and some

Fig. 32. School in Hollywood, Calif., with Monolithic Concrete Walls.

have been applied to the erection of a large number of buildings. From the viewpoint of the designer who contemplates the use of concrete for the bearing walls of low structures, however, they are of little more than historical interest.

The solid concrete wall, furred when required and built by conventional methods, is usually the logical solution if this material is to be used in monolithic construction. The choice of form material and details of erection should be decided by the builder, provided that they are such as to produce surfaces acceptable architecturally. As previously mentioned, the comparative economy between plain concrete and other types of masonry construction depends upon the size of operation, the adaptability of the design to standardization of form work, and the local prices for labor and material. Only authoritative estimates for a particular project can answer this question.

PLAIN CONCRETE WALLS. Cast-in-place concrete is now generally classed as masonry when reinforced only for the purpose of distributing secondary stresses caused by volumetric change occurring during hydration of the cement or later by reason of variations in atmospheric temperature or moisture. If the sectional area of the reinforcement in each direction is equal to or more than 0.0025 of the cross-sectional area of the wall, in addition to that placed around openings, the wall is generally classed as reinforced concrete. For walls classed as masonry, "American Standard Building Code Requirements for Masonry" limit the allowable compressive stress to 25 per cent of the 28-day compressive strength of the concrete. The allowable tension in the extreme fiber in flexure is limited to 3 per cent. When the ratio of height to thickness of structural members of plain concrete exceeds 10, the foregoing percentage for compression is reduced proportionately to 18 per cent for a ratio of height to thickness of 20. This same standard contains the following recommendations:

> The minimum thickness of walls of plain concrete may be 2 in. less than given on pages 310 and 311 for walls of solid masonry, but not less than 8 in., except that 6-in. walls of plain concrete may be permitted where 6-in. walls are specifically allowed (see page 311).
>
> Reinforcement symmetrically disposed in the thickness of the wall shall be placed not less than 1 in. above and 2 in. below openings and extend not less than 24 in. each side of such openings or be of equivalent length with hooks. The reinforcement both above and below shall consist of one ⅝-in. round rod for each 6 in. in wall thickness or fraction thereof.

These requirements are less severe than those of some building codes. Modern practice tends toward the use of thinner concrete sections reinforced as may be necessary. Even in walls of the type referred to as "plain concrete," it is recommended that reinforcement in the form of small rods, bars, or welded-steel fabric be placed, as shown in Fig. 33. If rods are used, they should be of ⅜-in. diameter and in cold climates should be spaced as indicated in the following table.

SPACING OF ⅜-IN. ROUND STEEL-ROD REINFORCEMENT IN EXTERIOR CONCRETE WALLS

Wall Thickness in Inches	Horizontal Reinforcement	Vertical Reinforcement
6	8-in. centers in outside face of wall	8-in. centers in outside face of wall
8	6-in. centers in outside face of wall	8-in. centers in outside face of wall
10	10-in. centers in both faces of wall	12-in. centers in both faces of wall
12	8-in. centers in both faces of wall	12-in. centers in both faces of wall

For a comparatively thin wall, 6 to 8 in. in thickness, one layer is placed at a clear distance of 2 in. from the exterior face. For a thicker wall, the required amount is divided about equally into two layers, the inner layer being placed at a clear distance of 1 to 3 in. from the interior face. In districts subject to earthquakes, concrete walls should always be reinforced throughout their entire area. Some standards [20] demand as much as 0.03 times the thickness of the wall in inches, per linear foot in each direction. The requirements for lateral support given in Article 15 apply equally to walls of plain concrete. The limiting ratio of unsupported length or height may generally be taken as 20 times the structural wall thickness. In districts subject to earthquakes good practice may demand a somewhat lower ratio or an increase in the reinforcement for bearing walls supporting floors.

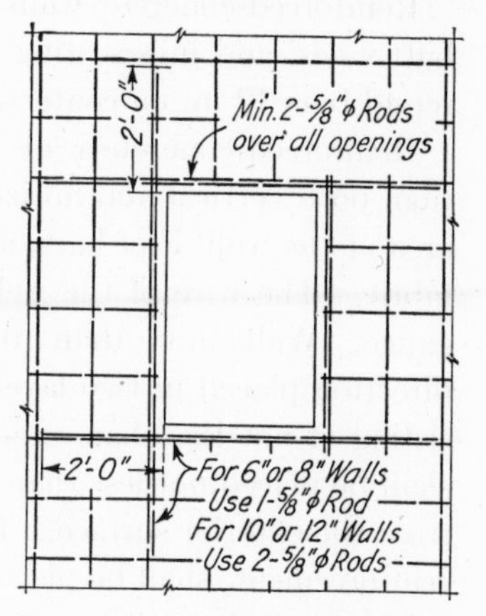

Fig. 33. Arrangement of Reinforcing Rods in Walls of "Plain" Concrete.

REINFORCED-CONCRETE WALLS. Detailed recommendations in regard to the structural design of reinforced-concrete walls are given in "Building Regulations for Reinforced Concrete," American Concrete Institute, 318–1941, from which the following paragraphs are abstracted:

Walls shall be designed for any lateral or other pressure to which they are subjected. Proper provision shall be made for eccentric loads and wind stresses. In such designs the allowable stresses shall be as given in preceding sections.[21]

Panel and enclosure walls of reinforced concrete shall have a thickness of not less than 5 in. and not less than one-thirtieth the distance between the supporting or enclosing members.

Bearing walls of reinforced concrete in buildings of fire-resistive construction shall be not less than 6 in. in thickness for the uppermost 15 ft of their height; and for each successive 25 ft downward, or fraction thereof, the minimum thickness shall be increased 1 in. In two-story dwellings the walls may be 6 in. in thickness throughout.

In buildings of non-fire-resistive construction bearing walls of reinforced concrete shall not be less than one and one-third times the thickness required for buildings of fire-resistive construction, except that for dwellings of two stories or less in height the thickness of walls may be the same as specified for buildings of fire-resistive construction.

Exterior basement walls, foundation walls, fire walls, and party walls shall not be less than 8 in. thick whether reinforced or not.

[20] Appendix A, "Rules and Regulations Relating to the Safety of Design and Construction of Public School Buildings, State of California," 1941.

[21] This reference applies to the American Concrete Institute Building Regulations.

Reinforced-concrete bearing walls shall have a thickness of at least one-twenty-fifth of the unsupported height or width, whichever is the shorter; provided, however, that approved buttresses, built-in columns, or piers designed to carry all the vertical loads may be used in lieu of increased thickness.

Reinforced-concrete walls shall be anchored to the floors, columns, pilasters, buttresses, and intersecting walls with reinforcement at least equivalent to ⅜-in. round bars 12 in. on centers, for each layer of wall reinforcement.

Reinforced-concrete walls shall be reinforced with an area of steel in each direction, both vertical and horizontal, at least equal to 0.0025 times the cross-sectional area of the wall, if of bars, and 0.0018 times the area, if of electrically welded wire fabric. The wire of the welded fabric shall be of not less than No. 10 W. & M. gauge. Walls more than 10 in. in thickness shall have the reinforcement for each direction placed in two layers parallel with the faces of the wall. One layer, consisting of not less than one-half and not more than two-thirds the total required, shall be placed not less than 2 in. nor more than one-third the thickness of the wall from the exterior surface. The other layer, comprising the balance of the required reinforcement, shall be placed not less than ¾ in. and not more than one-third the thickness of the wall from the interior surface. Bars, if used, shall not be less than the equivalent of ⅜-in. round bars, nor shall they be spaced more than 18 in. on centers. Welded-wire reinforcement for walls shall be in flat-sheet form.

In addition to the minimum reinforcement prescribed above, there shall be not less than two ⅝-in.-diameter bars around all window or door openings. Such bars shall extend at least 24 in. beyond the corner of the openings.

Where reinforced-concrete bearing walls consist of studs or ribs tied together by reinforced-concrete members at each floor level, the studs may be considered as columns, but the restrictions as to minimum diameter or thickness of columns shall not apply.

SURFACE FINISHES. If concrete walls are properly poured between well-designed and well-built forms, an exterior surface acceptable for many types of occupancy may be obtained without facing or applied finish. If such a surface is desired, the designer should review the specifications applying to the entire operation. A change in aggregate size or brand of cement may result in variations of appearance. The day's run of concrete should be deposited, as far as practicable, in continuous, level layers of such depth that none is placed against surfaces already hardened. Construction joints separating the work of successive days should be located where the line of demarkation will be the least noticeable. This objective requires careful planning between designer and builder in relation to daily output of the construction plant. When any type of applied finish is used, forms should not be greased or oiled.

The water content of the mixture should be adjusted to prevent the accumulation of free water on newly deposited surfaces. Forms should have well-cleaned, even faces. They should be mortar-tight and built in a manner to facilitate early removal.[22] Tie-rods should be of a type which will not needlessly mar the surface. All details should conform with the recommendations given in the Report of the Joint Committee, already mentioned on page 41 as a basis for the specification of concrete.

As the surface treatment of concrete walls is often an integral part of the construction and the various possibilities may influence the decision for or against concrete as a wall material, the subject is of importance to the designer. The treatments applicable to concrete cast-in-place may be broadly classified as follows:

a. Concrete walls may be veneered with brick, terra cotta, natural stone, or other surfacing materials, but these are seldom used for extensive areas, as masonry is generally cheaper than concrete as a backing material. There are, however, certain conditions which present exceptions. If large, precast, reinforced-concrete units are desired as exterior surfacing, these units can serve also as exterior forms for concrete walls and piers, thereby obtaining an economy which may favor concrete in place of other materials. This design was described on page 334. Where medium-sized field stone is available, rubble-stone facing may be laid in rough forms and backed by poured concrete. This design has been used for one- and two-story dwellings in New England.

b. Precast ornamental units may be set into the form work. These units require positive anchorage to the concrete backing. Monolithic ornament may also be formed by setting negative moulds into the forms and filling them with concrete cast monolithically with that of the wall. Such designs require particular attention to the reinforcement, form construction, and method of pouring. Information on this subject, known as the "waste-mould" method, will be found in "Forms for Architectural Concrete," published by the Portland Cement Association. Figure 34 shows such a design.

c. Types of special linings can be used as the contact surface of forms to produce simple types of ornament in low relief as shown in Figure 35. When planning work of this type, the designer should realize that projections from the face of the wall greatly complicate forming, whereas indentations can be easily made.

d. Special mixes with selected aggregates can be used for comparatively thin monolithic facings in order to save the expense of employing the surfacing material for the entire thickness of the walls. When applied to vertical sections, this operation demands expert supervision to prevent the two types of concrete from blending and still obtain a satisfactory bond between them. It is standard shop practice for facing precast units poured with faces horizontal, for which it is more appropriate.

[22] An excellent and comprehensive treatment of this subject is presented in "Forms for Architectural Concrete," published by the Portland Cement Association.

e. Well-hardened concrete surfaces may be tooled or sand-blasted in a manner similar to natural stone. Although used somewhat in England,

Fig. 34. Ornamental Designs Appropriately Cast by the Waste Mold Method; School in Joliet, Ill.

finishes such as that obtained by the bush-hammer are comparatively expensive in this country and are not generally to be recommended.

f. Another type of finish which can be applied much more cheaply to a hardened wall is the "rubbed finish" which results from wetting and grind-

Fig. 35. Ornamental Designs Easily Obtained by Inserts or Linings Placed upon the Inner Surfaces of Forms; School in Venice, Calif.

ing with carborundum or another abrasive. Fins are removed, and cement mortar is used to fill holes left by form ties, honeycomb, or other imperfections, and to assist in bringing the entire surface to a uniform appearance.

Such a treatment is appropriate for conditions that prevent the removal of forms before the hardening of the concrete.

g. A "sand-floated finish" is produced by wetting and rubbing the surface of an unhardened wall with fine sand beneath a wood float. For this method to be successful, the wall should be stripped just as soon as security permits. In this connection it should be remembered that if forms are promptly removed there is danger of drying the wall too quickly, and it may be necessary to provide moisture for proper curing. Samples should be prepared in advance to determine the schedule for stripping.

h. An exposed-aggregate finish, often called a "scrubbed-out finish," results from treating the unhardened surface with wire or fiber brushes and a solution of hydrochloric acid and water in volumetric proportions of 1 part acid: 5 or 10 parts water. Walls are thoroughly washed with plain water both before and after the acid application. Because of the use of acid, this type of finish may be obtained on a wall somewhat harder than that on which the preceding sand-floated treatment is used, but extreme care is required in controlling the periods elapsing between the pouring of the concrete and the removal of forms. Considerable variation in texture results if all surfaces are not treated at the same age. This requirement is often difficult to meet because of uncertainties of weather, time lost over week-ends, and the need of retaining some elements of the forms longer than others to facilitate erection. These matters should be considered before deciding upon an exposed-aggregate finish, and samples should be prepared in advance.

i. A stucco finish composed of mortar may be applied with a float but requires that the surface of the concrete be previously roughened. If forms can be stripped when the concrete has attained an age of about 48 hours, the operation of roughening can probably be performed with wire brushes and plain water or with the help of the acid solution previously mentioned. When forms must be kept in place for a longer period, the contact faces may be coated with a brush application of a chemical compound which retards the setting of the cement upon the surface. After forms are stripped, a thorough washing of the wall with water, applied by means of a hose, will then remove the mortar to a depth of about 1/8 in., leaving the surface sufficiently roughened to provide a bond for the stucco.

In California cast-in-place concrete has been successfully stuccoed over a base coat applied as described in the following paragraph. In order to improve the bond, forms are built of rough lumber, unoiled and soaked in water to raise the grain. Some authors have suggested the use of burlap or wire mesh placed on the contact surfaces of the forms and removed after stripping to obtain a roughened surface. This procedure is not recommended. Roughening the face of the wall by means of an electric hammer or hand tooling is satisfactory but expensive.

j. A cheap and often permanent finish may be obtained by dashing or throwing a mortar of heavy creamy consistency against the face of a wall. This is done by means of a whisk broom or fiber brush after the wall has been evenly moistened. Mortar dashed or thrown will adhere to a hardened concrete surface too smooth for trowel or float applications. Volumetric proportions of the finishing material should be 1 part portland cement: 1½ parts screened sand. Excess material is removed by light brushing, but the surface should not be trowelled or floated. This method has been used successfully for finishing the exposed surfaces of reinforced-concrete columns and beams in skeleton construction. As mentioned above, it has also been employed as a base for subsequent stucco applications but is not generally recommended for such a purpose.

k. Concrete surfaces may be painted. Walls should be well cured, clean, and dry at the time of application. Many excellent paints are available. Only those approved by the manufacturers for the specific conditions presented by the work should be used. Considerable trouble has occurred through either an incorrect choice of material or faulty application. Selections should be based upon investigation of performance on previous jobs presenting a similar exposure. The specification should follow the manufacturer's recommendations.

COLORING CONCRETE. Dry pigments for coloring mortar were mentioned on page 308. Such pigments may also be used for precast concrete-masonry units employed for wall surfacings and concrete cast-in-place, but more permanent color and more attractive finishes may often be obtained by means of colored aggregates.

Pigments used for coloring concrete should be insoluble in water, free from acid of soluble salts, and of a type not to affect calcium hydroxide, which results from the hardening of concrete. Those comprising inorganic compounds are preferable, as they are usually more permanent in color and more likely to meet the foregoing requirements. The heavier pigments, having a specific gravity of at least 3.0, may be used in amounts up to 10 per cent by weight of the cement; lighter materials, such as lampblack, should be limited to much smaller amounts, and tests made to check their possible deleterious effect upon the strength, abrasive resistance, or volumetric change produced in the concrete. Crushed natural stones and various ceramics are suitable provided that they meet the standard specifications identified on page 41 for concrete aggregates.

Article 13. Foundation, Basement, and Cellar Walls

GENERAL REQUIREMENTS. The function of a wall below grade is primarily structural. This consideration and the comparative cost of competing designs ordinarily determine the choice. The upper portion, however, is usually above grade, and in some cases extensive areas are exposed to view. If appearance is a factor, a type should be selected that presents an acceptable exterior surface or to which a desired finish can be economically applied.

Below grade, the requirement of impermeability to wind-driven rain is replaced by impermeability to ground water. This requirement dictates choosing as moistureproof a design as practicable and providing facilities for draining off the ground water, installing waterproofing, or both. The resistance to atmospheric conditions required above grade is replaced by the need to withstand contact with the soil or ground water, carrying perhaps alkali or other chemicals in solution.

Structural adequacy demands a design having sufficient strength to resist the applied forces without resorting to an excessive wall thickness. The fire resistance would be adequate for any otherwise appropriate choice. Where panels of masonry or reinforced concrete are built between steel or concrete framing, the structural members are fireproofed and dampproofed in accordance with the exposure.

SHALLOW BASEMENTS. In the case of a cellar wall for a two-story, wall-bearing structure, there is the vertical load imposed by the supported floors and roof, together with the dead load of the wall. There is also the horizontal load due to the soil pressure or soil plus surcharge, if the surface of the ground is loaded. The stresses caused by these loads are low unless the cellar is unusually deep for this type of structure. Concrete, plain, or reinforced where necessary, rubble masonry, solid brick, or solid ashlar are all acceptable structurally unless the depth below grade is sufficient to favor reinforced concrete. Hollow masonry units of structural-clay tile or hollow concrete-masonry units can also be used for shallow cellars in dry soil where there is no probability of dampness and building codes permit.

Although all reinforcement is often omitted from the concrete basement walls of low buildings when stress requirements do not demand it, the same steel should be placed around openings as is used above grade. Where there is any possibility of unequal settlement, a band of two rods, such as ⅝-in. rounds, should also be placed near the top and bottom of the wall and run continuously around the building.

The following recommendations are quoted from "American Standard Building Code Requirements for Masonry."

a. Foundation walls shall be of sufficient strength and thickness to resist lateral pressures from adjacent earth and to support their vertical loads without exceeding the specified stresses, provided that in no case shall their thickness be less than the walls immediately above them, except as provided in paragraph c below.

b. Foundation walls shall be of not less than 12-in. nominal minimum thickness, except as follows:

1. Solid masonry walls reinforced with at least one ⅜-in. round deformed bar,

continuous from footing to top of foundation wall, for each 2 ft of length of the wall, may be of 8-in. nominal thickness.

2. Solid foundation walls of solid masonry units or of coursed stone that do not extend more than 5 ft below the adjacent finished ground level, and hollow walls of masonry and walls of hollow units that do not extend more than 4 ft below the adjacent finished ground level, may be 8 in. in nominal minimum thickness. These depths may be increased to a maximum of 7 ft with the approval of the building official when he is satisfied that soil conditions warrant such increase. The total height of the foundation wall and the wall supported shall not exceed that permitted by these requirements for 8-in. walls.

3. Foundation walls of rubble stone shall be at least 16 in. thick. Rough or random rubble without bonding [23] or level beds shall not be used as foundations for walls exceeding 35 ft in height, nor shall coursed bonded rubble walls be used as foundations for walls exceeding 50 ft in height.

4. Foundation walls of cast-in-place concrete shall be at least 8 in. thick; provided that, when supporting one-story structures, and the area within the foundation walls is not excavated, they may be 6 in. thick if the total height of the foundation wall and the wall supported is within the allowable height of 6-in. walls (see page 311).

c. Foundation walls of 8-in. nominal thickness and conforming to the provisions of this section may be used as foundations for single-family dwellings with walls of brick veneer on frame walls, or with nominal 10-in. cavity walls, provided that the dwelling is not more than one and one-half stories in height and the total height of the wall, including the gable, is not more than 20 ft. Foundation walls of 8-in. nominal thickness supporting brick veneer or cavity walls shall be corbelled with solid units to provide a bearing the full thickness of the wall above. The total projection shall not exceed 2 in. with individual corbels projecting not more than one-third the height of the unit. The top corbel course shall be not higher than the bottom of floor joists and shall be a full header course.

d. Foundation walls shall extend below the level of frost action.

DEEP BASEMENTS. Such basements are customary for large structures and should generally be enclosed by concrete walls reinforced as required to resist the vertical and lateral loads. For depths more than about 8 ft. below grade, stone or unreinforced-brick walls become too bulky when designed to resist soil pressure. Where masonry is very cheap, a gravity-retaining wall may sometimes be used to advantage. Reinforced-brick work, employing small steel rods embedded in the joints, can be made structurally adequate for moderate spans, but reinforced concrete is usually more economical.

Concrete designs may be in the form of vertical panels cast-in-place between structural-steel or reinforced-concrete columns and extending from

[23] In the author's opinion all rubble-masonry walls should be well bonded, and such a requirement is mentioned for each class of rubble in "American Standard Building Code Requirements for Masonry" in the definitions quoted on page 291.

a basement floor to a spandrel beam at the first or next floor level above the basement. The lateral load due to soil pressure is carried by the panel either horizontally to the adjacent columns or vertically to the supports supplied by the floor construction. The choice depends upon the dimensions of the wall panel, the load being carried in the shorter direction unless

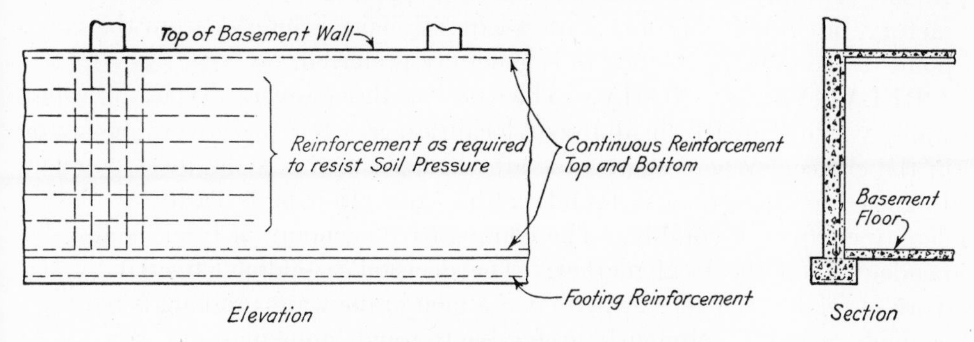

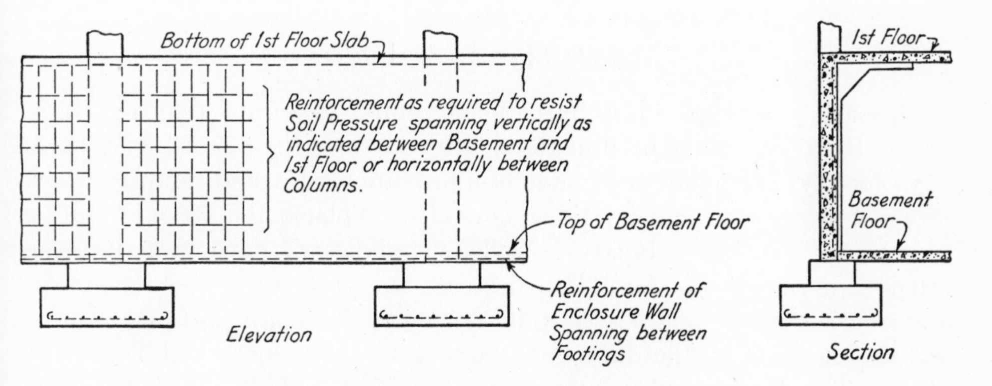

FIG. 36. Arrangement of Reinforcement for Concrete Basement Walls.

windows or other features control the design. A two-way distribution is sometimes economical where the horizontal span between columns or piers is approximately equal to the vertical span between the supports at floor levels. Occasionally, for structures of only moderate height, the steel or concrete exterior columns are supported by the basement wall and not carried down to separate footings. In this case, the wall distributes and carries with its own footing the concentrated loads of the exterior columns as well as its own dead load, the loads transmitted from any supported floor or superimposed wall, and the lateral pressure resulting from soil, water, or surcharge. Figure 36 shows the arrangement of reinforcement for typical conditions.

FURRING. Furring is generally necessary for the exterior walls of occupied rooms. Hard-burned hollow clay tile or cement-cinder block are appropriate. Gypsum is undesirable. If insulation is required, it should be of a type not injured by dampness. In spaces used only for storage and building equipment, walls are usually left without furring or finish. In this case any of the masonry materials previously mentioned are satisfactory, but rubble masonry, unless carefully laid, is inferior from the viewpoint of cleanliness. Concrete is generally preferred.

RELATIVE ECONOMY. The cost of these several types of cellar walls, varying greatly in different localities, is often the governing factor in the choice. Where aggregates are cheap, concrete is the most popular. If good building stone is found in the excavation or is easily available, it may compete favorably. The comparative economy of brick is also dependent upon the local market. The decision is seldom affected by the work of related trades, except that if a membrane waterproofing is required concrete or brick is obviously preferable to rough stone masonry, and where moisture is present any hollow masonry unit is inappropriate.

Article 14. Adobe Walls

Masonry composed of unburned-clay units, generally referred to as adobe, has been widely used in the Southwest since the Spanish Conquest. The older type of adobe was made of a mixture of clay and sand, to which chopped straw was added. Fiber now often replaces the straw. During recent years various admixtures called "stabilizers" have been incorporated with the clay and sand to decrease the absorption and render the construction more weather-resistant. Among these are portland cement and bitumen. If portland cement is added, the units are called Terracrete block. The most popular bitumen is emulsified asphalt, which has been used with apparent success in southern California. According to tests performed by the Bureau of Standards, the addition of this material lessens the water permeability of the construction.

Adobe block are structurally appropriate for the walls of comparatively low buildings and well adapted to the climate prevailing in many parts of the Southwest. Sizes are not standardized. Units $4 \times 10 \times 14$ in. are popular in New Mexico; $4 \times 7\frac{1}{2} \times 16$ in. in California. They are usually laid in either adobe clay or cement-sand mortar, the mortar being preferred when blocks contain an asphalt compound. In this case emulsified asphalt is also added to the mortar, which varies from $2\frac{1}{2}$ to $3\frac{1}{2}$ parts by volume of sand to one part of portland cement. The addition of lime, up to one-fourth of the cement volume, is permitted by the Uniform Building Code but not allowed by some authorities.

Although heat transfer is about equal to that of concrete walls having the same thickness, 10 to 16 in., the heat capacity is greater, thus aiding in reducing fluctuations of interior temperature. Adobe walls also provide good sound insulation. The comparative cost, in relation to competing materials, is so dependent upon local labor and material prices that no general statement can be made. The chief difficulty, from a practical viewpoint, is the deterioration of adobe surfaces exposed to the weather.

FIG. 37. California Bungalow with Exterior Walls of Adobe Block. Courtesy, American Bitumals Company, Los Angeles, Calif.

In locations where walls are subject to low temperatures or driving rains, considerable upkeep in the form of periodic surface repair is usually necessary. For this reason it is recommended that protection be furnished by overhanging eaves. Stucco supported by wire fabric may be used as a surface finish, but it is not practicable to stucco directly upon the adobe blocks because of lack of bond between them and cement mortar. The following recommendations, published by the Federal Housing Administration, Santa Fe, New Mexico, 1939, under the title, "Minimum Construction Requirements for New Dwellings," identify characteristics of such designs:

1. Adobe construction may be used not to exceed two stories or 30 ft in height. The adobes shall be made from adobe-clay soil, practically free of gravel, loam, or other deleterious matter, except clean straw, and shall be not less than approximately 10 by 14 by 4 in. in size, and shall have an ultimate compression strength

equal to 350 lb per sq in. Adobes shall be thoroughly sun dried for a period of not less than 30 days before laying in the walls; 60 days is preferred.

2. Adobe walls shall have poured-concrete or rubble-stone masonry foundation walls, full thickness of the supported wall and resting upon poured concrete footings. Foundation walls of concrete or masonry shall extend above the finished grade not less than 8 in.

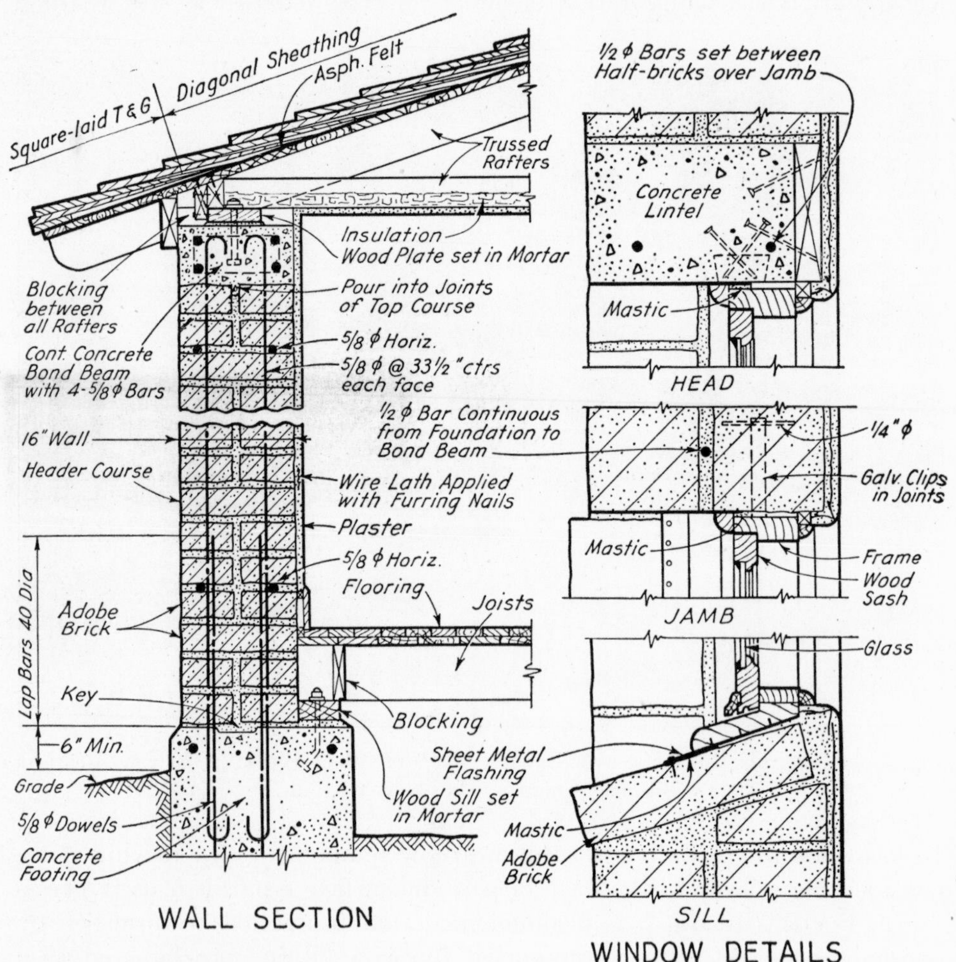

Fig. 38. Typical Adobe-Wall Construction. Courtesy, Foster and Kleiser, San Diego, Calif.

3. All walls of adobe shall be not less than 10 in. thick. All adobes shall be laid up in adobe or lime mortar (adobe mortar preferred) with full slush joints. All adobes shall be bonded not less than 6 in. For thick walls, adobes shall be bonded in both directions with special long bricks if necessary. In structures over one story or 12 ft in height, the first-story walls shall be not less than 20 in. thick and shall have a continuous 8-in.-thick concrete belt course reinforced with not less than two ⅜-in. bars in the bottom, over all the adobe walls directly under the second-floor joists.

4. All openings in adobe walls shall be spanned with structural-iron, steel, reinforced-concrete, or heavy-timber lintels with a bearing at each end of not less than 12 in.; metal lintels to have bearing plates full width of wall. All joists, rafters, or vigas shall have at least an 8-in. bearing upon the concrete belt course, or on a 2 × 8-in. continuous wood plate embedded in the wall. Care is to be taken to keep adobe dry with waterproof paper under concrete lintels and beams while pouring concrete. Wood nailing blocks cut from 2 × 10's shall be provided for anchoring all frames, etc. Steel sash shall be set in wood subframes, or have long brick anchors set into the wall.

5. Adobes shall not be used for narrow, isolated piers or columns. Wall sections less than 24 in. shall be considered as isolated piers, in which case the lintel shall be designed to span the distance of both openings and the pier. All chimneys in adobe shall be lined with fire-clay flue linings and be enclosed in at least 8 in. of adobe.

6. Interior stud partitions shall be anchored to the adobe wall with not less than two bolts or perforated strap anchors with hooked ends embedded in the adobe wall.

7. All exterior adobe walls less than 14 in. thick shall be covered with a minimum ¾-in. thickness of portland-cement stucco applied over galvanized wire mesh, not less than 20-gage wire and not more than 1-in. mesh opening, stretched tightly and thoroughly nailed to the adobe at least 12 in. each way, carried in vertical bands up and over the parapet walls and down to the roof flashings.

8. Mud plaster or other approved treatments may be used on all interior adobe walls and on exterior adobe walls that are 14 in. or over in thickness. Mud plaster may be used on interior stud partitions over scratch and brown coats of hard plaster only.

9. All adobe hardeners, stabilizers, and other so-called preservatives shall be approved by the Chief Architectural Supervisor, but their use in adobes or adobe plaster will not in any way vary the above requirements as to wall thicknesses, exterior stucco, plaster, etc.

10. Flashings into adobe parapets shall be carried through the wall.

The Uniform Building Code adopted by the Pacific Coast Building Officials Conference, 1943, contains a short and more restrictive standard. For example, the height of walls built of unburned-clay units is limited to 10 times their thickness, which is required to be at least 16 in. This code further prohibits their use for structures over one story in height. Additional requirements for both the quality of the soil and physical characteristics of the adobe units are given in both this code and that of Los Angeles, 1944. A very interesting discussion of the entire subject will be found in "Structural, Heat-Transfer, and Water-Permeability Properties of Five Earth-Wall Constructions," by H. L. Whittemore and associates, *Building Materials and Structures Report BMS* 78, National Bureau of Standards, 1941. This publication contains advice pertaining to both design and construction for monolithic walls formed of earth rammed in place, as well as for block walls.

Article 15. Miscellaneous Structural Requirements for Masonry Walls

FIRE RESISTANCE. The general requirements for fire resistance merge into those for structural strength. For example, the limiting horizontal distance between lateral supports, such as buttresses or cross-walls, diminishes the tendency for the wall to bulge when subjected to intense heat, and the proper anchorage or bonding of the elements comprising a wall assembly helps in fire resistance. The quality of materials identified in Article 2 and the construction details shown in many of the illustrations also help to lessen fire hazard. The ratings accorded various wall assemblies are not the same in the codes of different cities. The designer will have to follow those of his local ordinance or obtain a special ruling for new types of construction.

EARTHQUAKE RESISTANCE. In districts subject to earthquakes, the design is influenced by requirements for stability and structural integrity. If the local code is not sufficiently explicit, excellent recommendations will be found in the Uniform Building Code mentioned above, the Los Angeles City Code, and "Minimum Design Loads in Buildings and Other Structures," sponsored by the National Bureau of Standards, approved and published by the American Standards Association. Such regulations do not, in general, prohibit the use of any otherwise satisfactory type of wall construction but often contain more severe requirements in regard to the strength of mortar and bonding of masonry walls. The maximum height for unreinforced-masonry walls may also be considerably less than in localities comparatively free from this hazard. The object is to obtain, as far as practicable, complete structural unity of the entire building assembly. The walls, because of their rigidity, constitute with the assistance of the floors, acting as horizontal distributing diaphragms, the principal earthquake-resisting elements. The design of walls in relation to other parts of the structure should consequently be given attention in any district subject to seismic disturbance.

The following recommendations, completing the text of this chapter, are quoted from "American Standard Building Code Requirements for Masonry." They conform with the most modern practice in this field, but it should be remembered that they are more liberal in some respects than those of many building codes.

LATERAL SUPPORT. Solid masonry walls shall be supported at right angles to the wall face at intervals not exceeding 20 times the nominal wall thickness if laid in type A, B, or C mortar and not exceeding 12 times the nominal wall thickness if laid in type D mortar.

Walls of structural-clay tile or hollow concrete-masonry units and hollow walls of masonry shall be supported at right angles to the wall face at intervals not exceeding 18 times the nominal wall thickness.

Cavity walls shall be supported at right angles to the wall face at intervals not exceeding 14 times the nominal wall thickness.

Lateral support may be obtained by cross-walls, piers, or buttresses, when the limiting distance is measured horizontally, or by floors and roofs, when the limiting distance is measured vertically. Sufficient bonding or anchorage shall be provided between the walls and the supports to resist the asumed wind force, acting either inward or outward. Piers or buttresses relied upon for lateral support shall have sufficient strength and stability to transfer the wind force, acting in either direction to the ground. When walls are dependent upon floors or roofs for their lateral support, provision shall be made in the building to transfer the lateral forces to the ground.

Except for window-panel backs and permissible chases and recesses, walls shall not vary in thickness between their lateral supports. When a change in thickness, due to minimum thickness requirements, occurs between floor levels, the greater thickness shall be carried up to the higher floor level.

Bonding of Walls at Intersections. Masonry walls shall be securely anchored or bonded at points where they intersect and where they abut or adjoin the frame of a skeleton frame building. When two bearing walls meet or intersect and the courses are built up together, the intersections shall be bonded by laying in a true bond at least 50 per cent of the units at the intersection.

When the courses of meeting or intersecting bearing walls are carried up separately, the perpendicular joint shall be regularly toothed or blocked with 8-in. maximum offsets, and the joints provided with metal anchors having a minimum section of $\frac{1}{4} \times 1\frac{1}{2}$ in. with ends bent up at least 2 in. or with crosspins to form anchorage. Such anchors shall be at least 2 ft long, and the maximum spacing shall be 4 ft. Meeting or intersecting nonbearing walls shall be bonded or anchored to each other in an approved manner.

Anchoring of Walls. Masonry walls shall be securely anchored to each tier of wood joists or wood beams bearing on them at maximum intervals of 6 ft in one- and two-family dwellings, and 4 ft in other buildings, by metal anchors having a minimum cross-section of $\frac{1}{4} \times 1\frac{1}{4}$ in. and at least 16 in. long, securely fastened to the joists or beams and provided with split and upset ends or other approved means for building into masonry. Girders shall be similarly anchored at their bearings. Anchors shall be attached in a manner to be self-releasing.

Masonry walls parallel to wood joists or wood beams shall be provided with similar anchors at maximum intervals of 8 ft in one- and two-family dwellings, and 6 ft in other buildings, engaging three joists or beams. Upset and T-ends on anchors shall develop the full strength of the anchor strap.

Cast-in-place concrete slabs bearing on masonry walls shall be considered as sufficient anchorage for the supporting walls.

Chases and Recesses. There shall be no chases in walls of less than 12-in. nominal thickness or within the required area of any pier, and no chase in any wall shall be deeper than one-third the wall thickness, except that in dwellings not over two stories in height vertical chases may be built in 8-in. walls under the following limitations:

In 8-in. bearing walls the chases shall not exceed 4 in. in depth, 30 in. in width, and 2 ft in height, and shall not extend below the level of joist bearing, provided that where such chases occur below window sills the width may be not in excess of the width of the window opening above. In any case, not less than 4 in. of masonry shall remain between the back of chase and exterior surface of wall, and the backs and sides of all such chases in exterior walls shall be waterproofed and insulated. Masonry directly over chases wider than 12 in. shall be supported on lintels. Chases permitted in 8-in. walls shall not be cut but shall be built in as construction progresses.

No horizontal chase shall exceed 4 ft in length, nor shall the horizontal projection of any diagonal chase exceed 4 ft in length. There shall be at least 7¾ in. of masonry between chases and the jambs of openings.

Recesses for stairways or elevators may be left in walls, but in no case shall the walls at such points be reduced to less than 12 in. unless reinforced by additional piers or by columns or girders of steel, reinforced masonry, or concrete, securely anchored to the walls on each side of such recesses. Recesses for alcoves and similar purposes shall have not less than 8 in. of material at the back. Such recesses shall be not more than 8 ft in width and shall be arched over or spanned with lintels.

The aggregate area of recesses and chases in any wall shall not exceed one-quarter of the whole area of the face of the wall in any story. Chases and recesses shall not be cut in hollow walls, cavity walls, or walls of hollow masonry units, but when permitted may be built in.

LINTELS AND ARCHES. The masonry above openings shall be supported by arches or lintels of metal or masonry, plain or reinforced, which shall bear on the wall at each end for not less than 4 in. Stone or other nonreinforced-masonry lintels shall not be used unless supplemented on the inside of the wall with iron or steel lintels or with suitable masonry arches or reinforced-masonry lintels carrying the masonry backing.

Steel or reinforced-masonry lintels shall be of sufficient strength to carry the superimposed load without deflection of more than $1/360$ of the clear span. Masonry arches shall have at least 1-in. rise for each foot of span and shall be designed to carry the superimposed load. Proper provision shall be made for resisting lateral thrust.

SEPARATION OF COMBUSTIBLE STRUCTURAL MEMBERS. No wall of 8-in. nominal thickness shall be broken into, subsequent to building, for the insertion of structural members. A separation of at least 4 in. of solid masonry shall be provided between combustible members which may enter walls from opposite sides.

When unprotected steel or combustible structural members frame into hollow walls of thickness not greater than 12 in., they shall project not more than 4 in. into the wall and shall be so spaced that the distance between embedded ends is not less than 4 in. The space above, below, and between such members shall be filled solidly with burned-clay materials, mortar, concrete, or equivalent fire-resistive material to a depth of not less than 4 in. on all sides of the members.

All open cells in tiles or blocks occurring at wall ends shall be filled solidly with concrete for a depth of at least 6 in., or closure tiles set in the opposite direction shall be used.

BEAM SUPPORTS. Beams, joists, girders, or other concentrated loads, supported by a wall or pier, shall have bearing at least 3 in. in length upon solid masonry not less than 4 in. thick or on a metal bearing plate of adequate design and dimensions to distribute safely the loads on the wall or pier.

Parapet Walls. Parapet walls shall be at least 8 in. in nominal thickness. They shall be not higher than 4 times their thickness unless laterally supported, provided that, when reinforced both horizontally and vertically with not less than ¼-in. rods spaced not more than 2 ft on centers, the height shall be not more than six times the thickness. All parapet walls shall have a coping of incombustible material.

Piers. The unsupported height of piers shall not exceed 10 times their least dimension. When structural-clay tile or hollow concrete-masonry units are used for isolated piers to support beams and girders, the cellular spaces shall be filled solidly with concrete of type A mortar, and when so constructed the allowable stresses may be increased 25 per cent, provided that unfilled hollow piers may be used if their unsupported height is not more than 4 times their least dimension.

Chapter Nine

CHOOSING THE TYPE OF FOUNDATION

The purpose of a structural foundation is to transmit the weight of the superstructure of the building and any other loads to underlying strata of soil or rock capable of furnishing support without objectionable settlement. Spread foundations, pile foundations, or concrete piers offer the three broad possibilities for accomplishing this purpose. The choice of the particular type of foundation obviously depends upon subsurface conditions and the structural requirements of the building.

INTRODUCTION. Foundations are a particularly vital part of most structures. They represent an appreciable portion of the building cost. Injury caused by settlement is expensive to repair. As building records indicate that such settlement is almost invariably due to an incorrect evaluation of soil conditions, rather than error in structural design, the need for adequate subsurface information is clearly apparent.

For the superstructure of a building a correct choice of structural assemblies can often be made by the architect and is one of the chief functions of the architectural engineer. The quantitative design which follows is based upon generally accepted standards of stress analysis and stress values for materials such as steel, concrete, and lumber. These have known or safely assumed properties.

For the foundations of a building, an entirely different situation exists. Here we are depending upon the bearing capacity of the underlying material, and the subsoil strata assume a definite structural function. They become, in effect, one of the structural materials upon the behavior of which, under the imposed loads, the very success or failure of the design depends. We cannot expect to verify definite values for compressibility and the other characteristics affecting the stresses, nor can we be any too certain of the stress distribution beneath the future foundations. We have, however, certain means at our disposal which, if intelligently applied, will give the best results possible within the limits of our present knowledge.

Subsurface investigation, the study of settlement records from other structures erected over similar soil conditions, loading tests, and laboratory investigation of soil samples are the principal methods employed. A proper interpretation of such data should make possible an appropriate choice of foundation assemblies and the determination of allowable bearing values for use in design.

This is not a responsibility to be lightly assumed. The subject of soil mechanics is complicated by the many and vastly different combinations of soil underlying building foundations. Although important advances have been made, particularly during the last generation, soil mechanics is at present far from an exact science. Experience and judgment, supplemented by a thorough knowledge of the already extensive literature on this subject, are the only safe guides. This chapter is consequently written to assist the designer in correlating his procedure with the service of a foundation engineer rather than to present a definite program for his own use.

Article 1. Subsurface Materials

TYPES OF SOIL.[1] Soil is the unconsolidated material formed by the disintegration of rock or organic substances. The two principal classes are sand and clay. Sand is often referred to as a cohesionless soil; clay, as a cohesive soil. Sand is composed of comparatively large grains, and clay of very small grains. The percentage of voids by volume (volume of voids divided by total volume) in sand seldom exceeds 45 per cent. For clays this figure may vary from 25 per cent to a maximum of about 93 per cent. The corresponding void ratios (volume of voids divided by volume of soil particles) for clays would then vary between 0.33 and approximately 13.00.

Sand is highly permeable to water; clay is comparatively impermeable. Sand is inelastic. Clay may have considerable elasticity, that is, ability to regain its original form and dimensions when an applied load, which has caused deformation, is released. Sand is not plastic, whereas clay has this characteristic, which means that it may change in shape without appreciable change in volume when subjected to continued loading.

The following definitions, applying to the more commonly encountered soils, are such as are used in field identification. They are based on an analysis given by H. A. Mohr in "Exploration of Soil Conditions and Sampling Operations," *Soil Mechanics Series No.* 21, published by the Graduate School of Engineering, Harvard University, 1943.

CLAY is an inorganic sedimentary deposit consisting largely of very fine mineral grains ranging down to colloidal sizes and displaying, between certain water contents, the characteristic of plasticity previously mentioned. One very crude basis of differentiation is the use of the terms "hard," "medium," and "soft." The behavior of clays under building loads requires very careful consideration, often warranting the obtaining of undisturbed samples (see page 364) upon which laboratory tests can be made. The

[1] See also classification of Boston Building Code on page 377.

color of a clay found in any particular locality may often be of help in identifying it as a type encountered and tested upon previous operations.

FILL applies to all man-made deposits of natural or waste materials. As such fill is usually placed in low areas to improve the value of property, peat or organic silt often lies below. The character of a fill should always be determined by subsurface investigation. Seldom will any type furnish adequate support for a permanent structure.

"HARDPAN," as the term is used in foundation engineering, identifies a degree of hardness resulting from consolidation, cementation, or induration, rather than any definite soil composition. It may consist of highly consolidated clay, mixed with sand, gravel, and boulders or a cementated combination of sand and gravel. In restricted areas its removal usually requires the use of tools operated by compressed air or a resort to explosives. Hardpan often furnishes an excellent support for building foundations.

INORGANIC SILT, or ROCK FLOUR, is a fine-grained material lacking plasticity and possessing only slight cohesion when dried. All types of inorganic silt are dangerous from the viewpoint of foundation engineering. If the structure of silt is destroyed by the disturbance of established ground-water conditions, serious settlement may result. Furthermore, when subjected to an unbalanced hydrostatic head, producing flow through the material in an upward direction, the component grains may go into a condition of suspension, creating what is commonly known as quicksand.

ORGANIC SILT is a sedimentary deposit resulting from frost- and heat-weathering of the earth's surface. The color ranges from a light to a very dark gray. Often mixed with peat, it may contain sand or shells. If sand predominates, it is classified as a silty sand; if silt predominates, it may be identified as a sandy silt. Organic silt is highly compressible. Only when the sand is greatly in excess of the silt and vegetable content will any appreciable load be supported.

Peat is partially carbonized vegetable matter. It varies from light brown to black in color and is composed of leaves, grass, and often limbs of trees, which give it a fibrous texture. It is generally odoriferous and will seldom support any permanent load, even in the form of a fill, without considerable reduction in volume.

ROCK. As used in building construction, the term "rock" identifies the solid material forming the earth's crust and often referred to as "bed-rock" or "ledge rock" to distinguish it from boulders. Sound, hard rock is the best known support for the foundations of a structure. The various classifications and their characteristics may be obtained from any textbook of geology. If the quality or depth of a rock stratum is in doubt, core drills or well drills are used for investigation. As some rocks disintegrate rapidly when placed in contact with water, a geologist should be consulted if the proposed construction will effect a change in ground-water level.

SAND, GRAVEL, and BOULDERS are formed from rocks on the earth's surface through disintegration by weathering or other natural causes. The three groups are differentiated arbitrarily by grain size. These materials, either alone or in combination, have neither plasticity nor cohesion. Except along the seacoast and occasionally in the beds of streams, sand, gravel, and boulders are generally mixed with other soils. Coarse sand and gravel often furnish an excellent support for building foundations. Fine sand is less reliable (see page 377).

SHALE is an intermediate stage between clay and slate, having been highly consolidated by pressure but without essential change having occurred in the original minerals. In contrast with slate, in which the original clay minerals have been altered, shale may be reduced to a plastic condition by moderate grinding and the addition of water. When considered for the support of foundations, the characteristics of any particular shale should be thoroughly checked.

GROUND WATER. Below a certain level all soil is saturated with water. This level is often called the "water table" and roughly follows surface contours but may be lowered by dry seams, by pumping, or by covering the surface with buildings and pavements. It has special significance as affecting the bearing capacity of some soils, particularly fine sand and clay; as determining the level of "cut-off" for wood piles; and as necessitating increased cost of excavation and eventual provision for either waterproofing or the relief of water pressure, as described on page 141.

Article 2. Subsurface Exploration

PRELIMINARY CONSIDERATIONS. Subsurface investigations should always be made well in advance of the structural design. When there is a choice between two or more building sites, such investigations may determine the selection. The architect should arrange with the owner for the services of a foundation engineer, whose advice should be sought in selecting the methods to be used as well as in analyzing the results. Such services are normally paid directly by an owner.

It would seem needless to emphasize the necessity for thorough subsurface investigation except for the fact that incompetent engineers often assume an allowable bearing value equal to the maximum permitted by the local building code for the type of soil encountered at the level of the footings. In many cases no objectionable settlement has been recorded, but in other instances serious trouble has occurred, which could have been easily avoided at a comparatively negligible expense. Even where rock underlies the entire site of the future building, an investigation of its character, by means of core borings, may be necessary. An excellent illustration of a log of borings is published in *Bulletin* 208, Graduate School of Engineering, Harvard University.

For all important work "dry-sample" borings (see page 362) should be made not only as a preliminary step toward determining the most economical type of foundation assembly, but also as a guide when choosing the construction methods. In most cases this type of soil sampling gives sufficient data for design purposes, but over plastic soils, such as clay, where the structural characteristics of the material, as well as the depth of the strata, may be in doubt, laboratory tests performed upon "undisturbed samples" (see page 364) may be desirable. Occasionally, where foundations are to be founded upon rock overlain by soil offering particular difficulties, it has even been considered necessary to sink an open caisson. Such a procedure enables inspection of the practically undisturbed material.

The number of borings, or other type of subsoil exploration, obviously depends upon site conditions, the amount of supplementary information available, and the degree to which it seems necessary to develop a subsoil profile. In the general case, at least one boring should be made at points corresponding to the corners of the future structure. Additional borings are desirable where subsoil conditions are variable. Particularly within the glaciated region, there is a possibility of encountering peat, organic or inorganic silt, and soft clay. This area lies north of a line extending through Long Island, northern New Jersey, and Pennsylvania, along the Ohio and Missouri rivers into Kansas, thence northwesterly roughly parallel to and a little west of the Missouri River to the Rocky Mountains, thence westerly south of the Canadian border to the Pacific Coast.

At least one, and preferably several, of the borings should be carried down to a definitely identified stratum of rock or to a depth of not less than 1½ times the width of the structure. For very wide buildings, where this depth appears excessive, judgment based on the available information may warrant a lesser depth. Where heavy loads are involved, the investigation of rock by means of core borings is often desirable, but the crushing strength of most rocks equals or exceeds that of the materials used for the substructure.

The amount of water to be encountered in the excavation may be estimated from the boring record and is of importance in both its affect upon soil characteristics and the planning of the operation. If there is a possibility of using piles, the water should be checked for the presence of chemicals destructive to wood, concrete, or steel. After the completion of the borings a subsurface profile is prepared. When borings are carried to rock, a contour map of the rock surface is often of great value. Depths below grade are referred to well-established datum levels. Samples of soil are retained in containers identifying the various strata shown on the profile.

The records of foundation experience during construction and the subsequent settlement of adjacent structures known to be supported by similar types of soil often furnish very valuable information. Geological advice will occasionally be helpful. All available records should be checked to identify underground obstacles such as sewers, water and gas pipes, electrical conduit, old foundations, pier heads, and stumps below the surface of wet soils. Stumps have been encountered beneath the meadows east of Newark, New Jersey. Of large size and well preserved, they have interfered considerably with pile driving. Old pier heads, buried in fill for a generation or more, have been found along the Manhattan side a considerable distance from the present shore line of the Hudson River.

The designer should also obtain legal advice in regard to the possibility of claims arising by reason of injury to adjoining structures if the proposed construction is likely to cause disturbance in the soil beneath their foundations. Unless a building occupies an isolated position, it is desirable to make a thorough investigation of all adjacent structures which would identify their structural condition by means of notes and photographs. If this is not done, an unscrupulous neighbor may make a claim for settlement or other injury which already exists. In this connection it should be remembered that buildings at some distance from the site may be injured by the lowering of the ground-water level through pumping or drainage if such measures are required in connection with the new work.

METHODS EMPLOYED FOR SUBSURFACE EXPLORATION. The following means are those most generally used for investigating the character of the materials underlying building sites.

TEST PITS. These pits have an occasional application for very important investigations where it is essential to examine the soil in its natural and, as far as possible, undisturbed condition. They present a satisfactory but usually expensive method, as deep pits, excavated to a size sufficient to accommodate a man, generally require shoring and lining to prevent the caving-in of loose soil. On small operations, however, pits may often be an inexpensive and useful means of making comparatively shallow investigations. For example, a pit may be dug to the level of the future footings, and an auger or post-hole digger employed to obtain samples of soil to a depth of 10 or 15 ft below this level.

SOUNDING RODS. These are usually in the form of a solid steel rod or pipe, the pipe being driven in lengths of about 5 ft and provided with a point at the lower end. Driving is often done by hand, occasionally with a hammer operated by a gasoline engine. Provided that boulders or other obstacles are not mistaken for ledge rock, sounding rods may have a useful but limited application for the purpose of determining the depth to rock or other satisfactory bearing, such as gravel. The results of such tests, however, should not be relied upon except in special cases where the character of the soil is already known and the only object of the investigation is to determine the depth to a firm stratum at various points upon the site.

AUGER BORINGS. These borings have very little application to the determination of subsoil conditions beneath future building foundations but are occasionally used for preliminary survey. The auger is rotated by hand or power. The object is to raise samples of soil. Its effective use is limited to cohesive materials, such as clay, a sand containing sufficient clay to make it somewhat plastic, or noncohesive soils above ground-water level. Augers may be operated either with or without an exterior metal casing. Post-hole diggers may be useful up to depths of about 15 ft provided that no obstacles are encountered.

WASH-SAMPLE BORINGS. These borings are obtained by driving a steel pipe casing, usually 2 or 2½ in. in diameter, in 5-ft lengths by means of a hand-operated or power-driven drop hammer. Inside the casing a 1-in. wash pipe, usually fitted at the lower end with a chopping bit, is churned up and down and rotated by hand to advance the hole. Figure 1 shows a typical installation.

The purpose of the casing is to provide an opening through which the boring operation can progress. After a few lengths have been driven, the hole is advanced without additional lengths of casing if the walls stay in place. A hand or power pump circulates the wash water down through the wash pipe and back to the surface through the annular space between the pipe and the casing. The water is then drained into a tub, from which it is again recirculated. In its upward flow the water carries the loosened soil in suspension. As it is emptied into the comparatively still water of the tub, this material is partially deposited in the form of sediment.

The boring foreman handling the wash pipe depends upon the "feel" of the pipe as he rotates it and the color and consistency of the wash water returned to the tub for the detection of any change of soil as the hole progresses downward. Samples of each type of soil, in the form of sediment, are then obtained by scraping a receptacle along the bottom of the tub. Such samples are referred to as "wash samples." As the finer particles of soil remain in suspension in the wash water and any individual sample may contain material from every stratum penetrated up to that time, the results are of so little value that this method is not recommended.

DRY-SAMPLE BORINGS. This method employs the same procedure for drilling the hole except that, as soon as the foreman detects a change in the soil as he turns the wash pipe at the end of the stroke, he raises the pipe off the bottom of the hole and continues pumping until the water flowing from the casing shows a substantial reduction in suspended soil.

The wash pipe is then removed from the casing, and a sampling spoon or a piece of open 1-in. pipe is substituted for the chopping bit. The spoon or pipe is then extended to the bottom of the hole and driven for a sample.

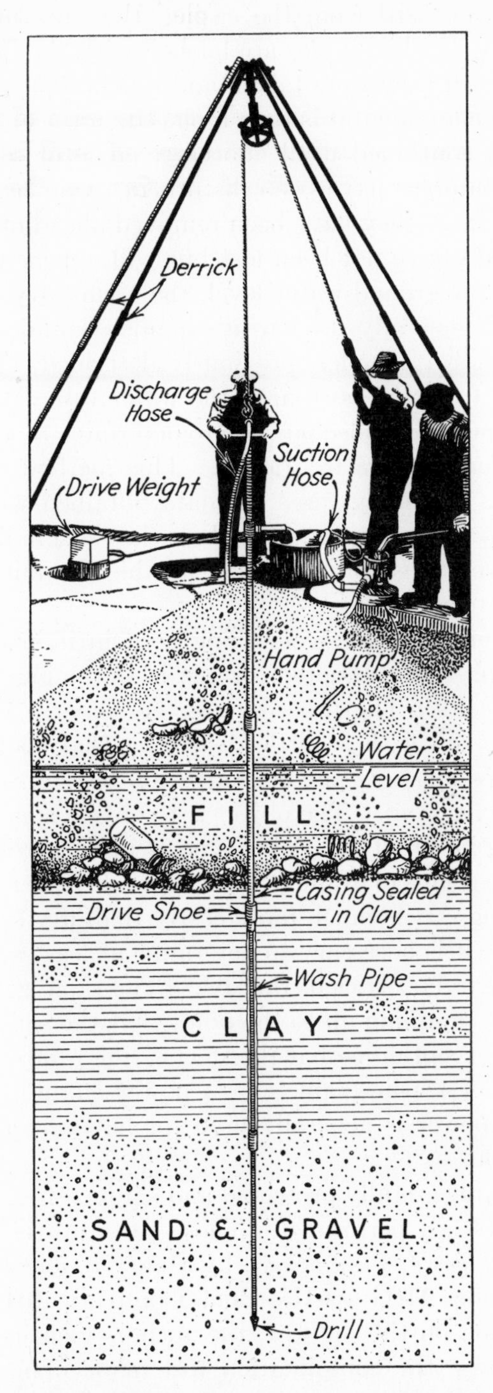

Fig. 1. Wash-Boring Outfit at Work. Redrawn from "Exploration of Soil Conditions and Sampling Operations," *Soil Mechanics Series No.* 21, by H. A. Mohr, Graduate School of Engineering, Harvard University, Cambridge, Mass.

After the pipe is removed from the casing, the sample is reclaimed and placed in a bottle. These samples are labeled with the boring number and the depth from which they were taken, and a field identification of the soil is appended. The chopping bit is then replaced on the end of the wash pipe and the operation continued until another change of soil is encountered.

Although such samples have been disturbed, as far as the natural state of the soil is concerned, they have been removed ahead of the washing, and the smaller particles have not been lost but will appear in natural proportion. If taken below ground-water level, the term "dry sample" is hardly appropriate but is generally used to distinguish samples obtained in this manner from the wash samples, previously described, taken by means of scraping sediment from the bottom of the water tub. When the sampling pipe is being advanced, it is also possible to determine roughly the resistance to penetration offered by each stratum. This method of sampling has a broad application. In many cases the data obtained will furnish an adequate basis for foundation design. In others they will indicate the necessity for more expensive investigations, such as the obtaining of undisturbed samples for laboratory analysis.

A special type of seamless steel tubing used in industry and known as "Shelby tubing" has been adopted for use in obtaining samples of plastic soils or inorganic silts. The procedure is the same as the foregoing, and samples may be taken with so little distortion that they can be used for unconfined compression tests and consolidation tests of small diameter.

UNDISTURBED SAMPLING. The object is to obtain a sample with as little change as possible in structure. This type of investigation applies only to plastic soils, as the grains of granular soils suffer displacement in any known method of sampling. It is much more costly than dry sampling but is the best method where it is necessary to determine at least approximate values for the physical characteristics of the soil.[2] The same general procedure is followed as for dry sampling up to the point that the soil specimens are obtained. The only exception is that the steel casing is often of 6-in. diameter to permit samples of 4¾-in. diameter. A power pump is usually employed for washing, and power is generally used for handling the heavier casing and sampling spoon.

Samples of soil are carefully protected and shipped to a laboratory, where the necessary tests are performed. These tests are clearly described in *Foundations of Bridges and Buildings*, by Henry S. Jacoby and Donald P. Davis, Third Edition, McGraw-Hill Book Company, 1941. In conformity with general opinion on this subject, the authors identify the more important tests as follows: the consolidation test made upon samples laterally confined, water-permeability test, direct shearing test, and compression

[2] "Undisturbed Clay Samples and Undisturbed Clays," by Karl Terzaghi, *Journal of the Boston Society of Civil Engineers*, July, 1941.

test made upon unconfined or partially confined samples. From the consolidation test some indication of the probable amount of settlement may be obtained. In combination with the permeability of the sample, it indicates the probable rate of settlement. The shearing and unconfined or partially confined compression test indicate the relative strength of the soil.

Core Borings. These are samples in the form of a more or less continuous core cut from rock. A casing is sunk to refusal with earth-boring tools and tightly sealed to the rock. It is of a size to permit an appropriate rotary drilling tool, such as a diamond or shot drill; a 1⅜-in. diameter is popular. Well drills are sometimes used to extend earth borings in order to determine whether ledge rock or a boulder forms the obstruction, but as the chopping bits cut the rock into small pieces, the information obtained by core drilling is more definite.

Article 3. Spread Foundations

The various types may be classified as wall footings, isolated or independent column and pier footings, combined footings, cantilever footings, continuous footings, and raft or mat and rigid-frame foundations. The surface of soil or rock upon which the foundation directly rests is called the "foundation bed."

WALL FOOTINGS. Wherever suitable aggregates can be obtained at a reasonable cost, plain or reinforced concrete is the most appropriate material. For basement walls of masonry beneath wood-framed construction,

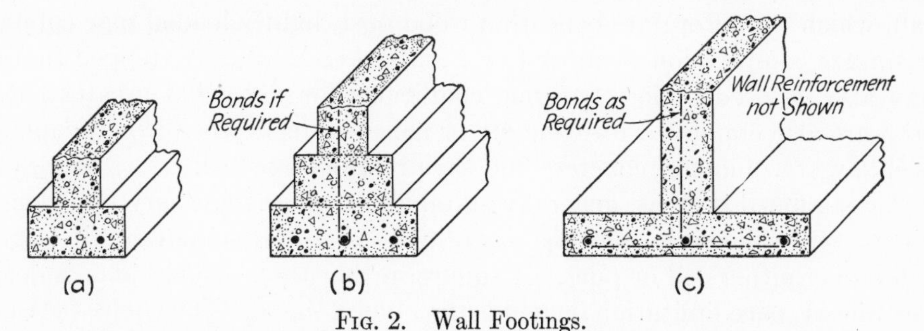

Fig. 2. Wall Footings.

or as a support for low wall-bearing designs, footings may be built of plain concrete. Often a single rectangular section such as that shown in Fig. 2, sketch (*a*), is adequate. The depth is made twice the projection from the face of the wall in order to prevent stresses that may rupture the unreinforced section. In footings of this type some longitudinal steel may be desirable if the character of the soil forming the foundation bed is variable. It should be placed about 4 in. from the bottom and run continuously with adequate splices entirely around the building.

If the load per linear foot of footing, when divided by the allowable bearing value of the soil per square foot, results in a required projection of over 6 to 8 in., the single rectangular block shown in sketch (*a*) becomes too bulky, and another step may be introduced as shown in sketch (*b*). This procedure could be carried on indefinitely and footings of any size designed in this manner, but it is usually cheaper, where widths over about 3 ft are required, to use a reinforced-concrete slab as shown in sketch (*c*). Where the stepped footing is used, each block may be poured separately after the one below has hardened just enough to eliminate the need for a form across the top. In order to increase the bond between the slabs comprising the footing, the surface of the underslab should be left rough. If this is considered inadequate, short lengths of vertical rods with hooked ends may be used as bonds, or the forms built to permit pouring the entire depth in a continuous operation.

The reinforced-concrete spread footing, sketch (*c*), is not a particularly economical section, as the design requirement for bond stress usually demands that a large number of small rods be used at a comparatively close spacing. Fortunately, it is seldom necessary to use this type, as the loads beneath walls are normally low because of the economic limit for wall-bearing designs noted on page 41. An exception would occur where allowable soil pressure is also low. In such cases the reinforced-concrete spread footing may be the best solution, as the weight is less and the amount of excavation reduced in comparison to the stepped footing.

ISOLATED OR INDEPENDENT COLUMN AND PIER FOOTINGS. The simplest type of column footing is an unreinforced-concrete slab, which is appropriate beneath a wood post, lightly loaded pipe column, or similar compression member [see Fig. 3, sketch (*a*)]. A stepped footing may also be used under the same conditions for somewhat greater loads. Both are also employed for concrete or masonry piers when it is cheaper to use a larger volume of concrete and save reinforcing steel.

The standard designs, generally suitable for other than very light loads, are the types shown in sketches (*b*), (*c*), and (*d*). These designs are appropriate over either soil or piles. A square, rather than oblong, plan is desirable unless space limitation demands the oblong shape. The choice between a single slab, sketch (*b*), and a stepped design, sketch (*c*), is merely one of economy. The single slab is wasteful of concrete; the stepped design, more costly to form. A sloped-top design, simulating the shape of the fustrum of a pyramid, always requires top forming and, although it saves concrete, is seldom economical. Adjacent to elevator wells, footings are dropped to avoid interference. The area of the footing slab is located concentrically with the supported column or pier. A two-way reinforcement, placed 3 in. or 4 in. from the bottom of the slab, is customary; the addition of diagonal rods is usually uneconomical. The ends of rods, protected by 3 in. or 4 in. of concrete, should be hooked, as bond stresses are generally critical.

Pedestals are often used to reduce the unit compressive stress, transferred from the column to the footing, by distributing the load over an increased area. Where a computation for "punching shear" is required, pedestals may be of use in reducing the depth of the footing slab. In designs where the upper surfaces of footings are at variable heights, they are also

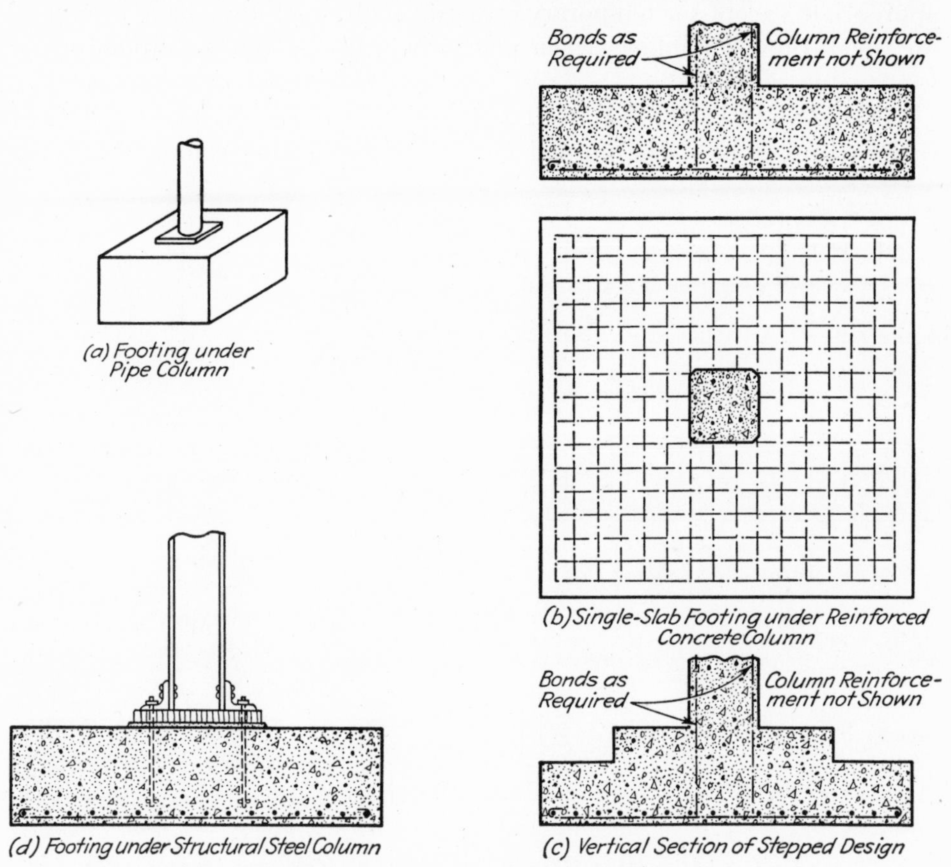

FIG. 3. Independent Column Footings.

very helpful as a means of obtaining a uniform level at the base of all columns. Short lengths of vertical rods serve as bonds to obtain continuity between footing and pedestal or between footing and superimposed concrete column.

Beneath structural-steel columns, supported by either soil or piles, a steel slab is used to distribute the column load as shown in sketch (*d*), except beneath very heavily loaded columns, for which both a steel slab and a grillage, the latter composed of I-beams, placed between the bottom of the steel slab and the top of the concrete footing, may furnish a more economical method of load distribution. The cost of the grillage and in particular the expense of accurate leveling generally limit such a choice to column loads well over a million pounds. Steel grillages, composed of I-beams enclosed in concrete, are also used in place of reinforced-concrete slabs over a rock foundation bed and are brought to level by means of grouting. In the past, such designs were employed over soil but are very seldom found in present-day American practice. Various timber assemblies are hardly appropriate except for temporary structures, although they have been used for wood-framed buildings when placed beneath permanent ground-water level.

COMBINED FOOTINGS. The isolated footing described in the preceding paragraphs is the normal method of supporting column loads but

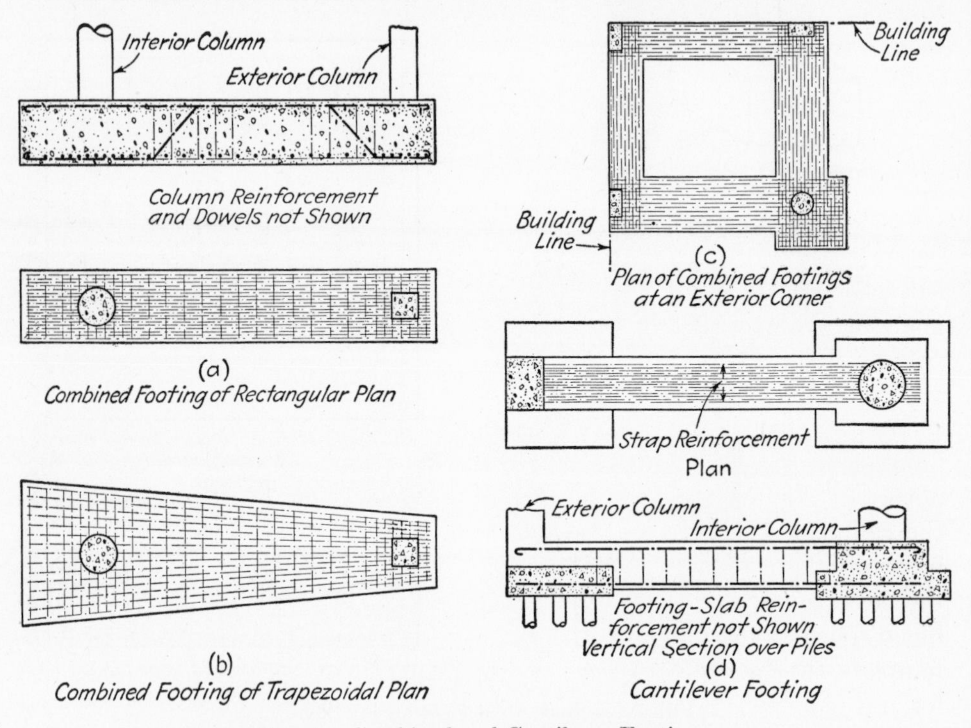

Fig. 4. Combined and Cantilever Footings.

can be used for wall columns only when sufficient space is available beyond the exterior face of the column to permit the footing and column to be built concentrically. As exterior columns are often placed adjacent to property lines where space is not available, some method must be employed to overcome the eccentricity. The common solution is to combine the footing of the exterior column with that of the adjacent interior column. The shape of the footing slab to support the two columns is then determined so that, under the assumed condition of loading, the centroid of the area corresponds to the line of action of the resultant of the two-column loads. Figure 4, sketches (*a*), (*b*), and (*c*), shows such designs.

Sketch (*a*) is the normal shape, as a rectangular section is easier to design and construct. The trapezoidal plan, sketch (*b*), is used only when it is impracticable to extend the length of the projection beyond the heavier of the two columns a sufficient distance to supply the necessary area located so as to fulfill the requirement of the preceding paragraph. In this case the only alternative is to increase the width beneath the more heavily loaded column, resulting in the trapezoidal shape.

Many building codes permit the footings of exterior columns facing upon public streets and alleys to project beyond the property line a distance which is a function of the depth below the sidewalk. In some cases a specific distance of 1 ft is allowed, provided that the top of the footing is 8 ft or more below the surface of the sidewalk. This allowance is often of considerable help and in some cases will influence the choice of the footing type, as discussed on the following page.

Sketch (*c*) shows a typical plan for combined footings at the corner of a building where little or no projection is allowed beyond the faces of columns on two adjacent sides. All combined footings are designed as inverted beams with or without cantilever projections. As footing slabs are of considerable width, some transverse reinforcement is required, particularly beneath columns. The typical arrangement of the steel is shown in sketches (*a*) and (*b*).

CANTILEVER FOOTINGS. This design, shown in Fig. 4, sketch (*d*), serves the same purpose as the combined footing but in a somewhat different manner. In this case, as the name implies, the wall column is supported by a beam or strap, as it is often called, which is assumed to rest on the center of the exterior footing as upon a fulcrum. The weight of the interior column, resting upon the other end of the connecting beam, holds the beam horizontal. Such a design is less dependable than that of a combined footing, and the entire analysis becomes so uncertain, when we contemplate the possibility of unequal settlement, that it is not recommended for use over soil. When carried by piles adequately supported by point bearing (see page 396), cantilever footings may be accepted as an alternate for the combined footing and will often prove somewhat cheaper. As in the isolated column footings, steel grillages composed of I-beams enclosed in concrete are also infrequently used in place of reinforced concrete.

CONTINUOUS FOOTINGS. These footings may be used for the support of interior columns but have their particular application for exterior columns. They are often economical when a foot or two is available between the exterior face of the column and the property line. This distance is seldom sufficient for the concentric slab footing described on page 366 but may be adequate to permit a continuous footing beam of the necessary width to be built on the column center line, as shown in Fig. 5. If, for example, the dimensions are as indicated and the accepted soil-bearing capacity is 3 tons, each column can have a footing of this design capable of carrying:

$$3 \text{ ft } 6 \text{ in.} \times 20 \text{ ft } 0 \text{ in.} \times 6000 \text{ lb} = 420{,}000 \text{ lb}$$

(less the weight of the footing)

Unless the allowable soil pressure is comparatively low, the typical footing beam is seldom sufficiently wide to require transverse reinforcement. When the section is similar to sketch (*c*) of Fig. 2, such reinforcement is necessary, but it is always costly, as it comprises small-diameter rods at a comparatively close spacing. A continuous footing may be more economical than a combined footing over either soil or piles. Continuous footings are not

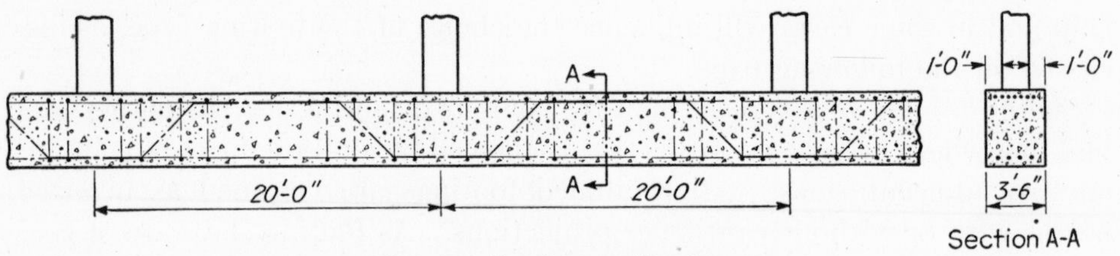

FIG. 5. Continuous Footing.

ordinarily as appropriate as isolated footings for the support of interior columns but may be used, where it is desired to tie the entire foundation assembly together, in districts subject to earthquakes.

RAFT OR MAT AND RIGID-FRAME FOUNDATIONS. The raft or mat foundation is an inverted slab of reinforced concrete, often several feet in thickness, which covers the entire foundation area of the building. The design may be similar to that of an inverted flat slab (see page 40), or comprise inverted T-girders placed beneath the columns and connected by a reinforced-concrete slab. One purpose of such a foundation is to employ the entire area of the basement for support when the soil-bearing capacity is so low that any partial coverage obtained by the more economical types of footings is inadequate.

Such designs have apparently been the most economical solution for certain cases, but there is always the danger of excessive soil pressures occurring beneath heavily loaded columns. To avoid such a condition, which may result in serious differential settlement, the mat must be sufficiently rigid to distribute the loads over the soil between columns. Even if the design is made on this basis, a mat foundation may be uneconomical, as the load from individual footings, beneath columns at normal spacings, will often be spread over the entire basement area at a depth of less than 20 ft below the level of the foundation bed. Any foundation of this type, placed over a cohesive soil of low bearing capacity, requires a very careful study of the actual column loads and subsurface information.

Rigid-frame designs are also occasionally used below grade to furnish a foundation assembly of sufficient rigidity to distribute the concentrated loads beneath columns. These designs have their application over soils of low bearing capacity extending to a depth so great as to make the use of piles impracticable. The approach to the problem is to determine the maximum load to which the stratum of soil, at the level of the proposed foundation bed, has been previously subjected. This load is generally that due to the weight of the overlying soil before the commencement of operations. The excavation is then carried to such a depth that the weight of the material removed approximates that of the structure to be erected. Although the elastic swelling of the soil as excavation progresses, and before the reinforced-concrete foundation is constructed and loaded, tends to cause unequal settlement, such designs have been built successfully when sufficiently rigid to distribute the loads and avoid excessive concentrations beneath individual columns.

Portions of the Back Bay district of Boston furnish an example of soil conditions adapted to this type of substructure. Beneath the New England Mutual Life Insurance Company's building [3] rock was about 150 ft below the surface. Above it lay 30 ft of hardpan, 70 ft or more of glacial clay, and a 20-ft layer of alluvial silt extending up to mean tide level. Above the silt was about 20 ft of man-made fill. Experience with other buildings in the same locality indicated that the upper 8 or 10 ft of clay was satisfactory as a distributing layer for moderate loads, although the clay beneath was comparatively soft.

A preliminary design considered a single basement and piles driven through the silt to the hard layer of clay, but it was believed that even the comparatively light increase of load, equal to only about 1 ton per sq ft over the entire building area, would cause sufficient consolidation of the soft clay beneath to result in excessive settlement. This possibility was consequently discarded in favor of a basement and subbasement, which carried the excavation down to the hard clay, upon which spread foundations were built. The total weight of the excavated material then approximated that of the building, resulting in practically no increased loading. The entire substructure was designed as a reinforced-concrete box employing continuous, wide footings, heavy walls, and partitions of reinforced concrete, as shown in Fig. 6.[4] Because there was thought to be danger of continued subdrainage causing settlement of adjoining buildings, the foundations were planned to resist the hydrostatic head, about 30 ft at the level of the subbasement floor, rather than relieving the pressure by the use of a sump pit.

Recent reports indicate that the design was a good solution for this par-

[3] "Application of Soil Mechanics in Designing Building Foundations," A. Casagrande and R. E. Fadum, *Transactions of the American Society of Civil Engineers*, Vol. 109, 1944.

[4] From "Building on Soft Clay," *Engineering News Record*, Vol. 123, November 23, 1939.

ticular building over the soil conditions existing at this site. Its success should not, however, lead to the unconsidered acceptance of such a design as normally safe and economical over all deep strata of low bearing capacity. Every building must be studied as an individual problem. Some of our more experienced engineers consider foundations of this type hazardous from the viewpoint of potential, differential settlement, which may occur even after many years. Where conditions permit a foundation to be carried to rock bearing, this procedure is structurally preferable and should

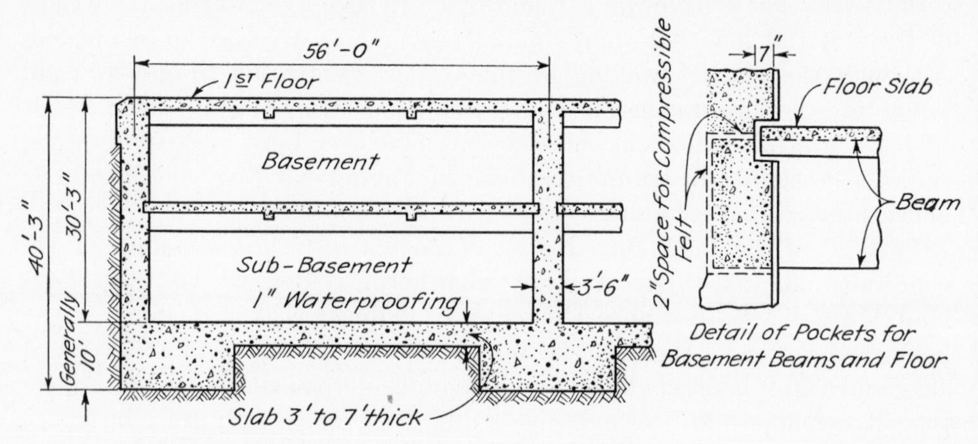

FIG. 6. Vertical Section through Reinforced-Concrete Box Forming Substructure of Building Supported on Soft Clay. Courtesy, *Engineering News-Record.*

generally be accepted unless prohibitive in cost. This statement applies particularly to buildings of considerable height and to those of tower design.

Article 4. Soil Pressure under Spread Foundations

INTRODUCTION. The design of spread foundations often involves a study of pressure distribution in the underlying soil. Such pressure distribution has been measured by actual investigation both in laboratory experiments and beneath existing structures, but the amount of reliable information is still all too meager. Soil mechanics was accepted as a definite branch of civil engineering only about 30 years ago, and the complicated character of soils makes a mathematical analysis so difficult that theory is little more than a guide for field observations. Only recently has the subject begun to receive the attention which it merits. The First International Conference of Soil Mechanics and Foundation Engineering was held at Harvard University in 1936. In 1940 a conference on the applications of soil mechanics was held at Purdue University, Lafayette, Indiana. At that time sixty-two engineering schools in the United States were giving courses pertaining to this field.

CONTACT PRESSURES. Among the arbitrary assumptions generally accepted by building codes and common practice is that of uniform pressure over the entire loaded area. This is a crude approximation but has been widely and successfully employed in designs based on conservative loads, as identified on page 377. Some indication of the actual stress variation believed to exist at the contact surfaces under smooth, rigid, foundation slabs is illustrated in Fig. 7.[5] Sketch (*a*) applies to a cohesive elastic clay; sketch (*b*), to a cohesionless soil, such as sand or gravel. As the depth of the foundation slab below the surface of the ground increases, the stress distribution becomes more uniform.

A number of mathematical solutions have been offered in an attempt to devise a method of evaluating pressure distribution beneath flexible

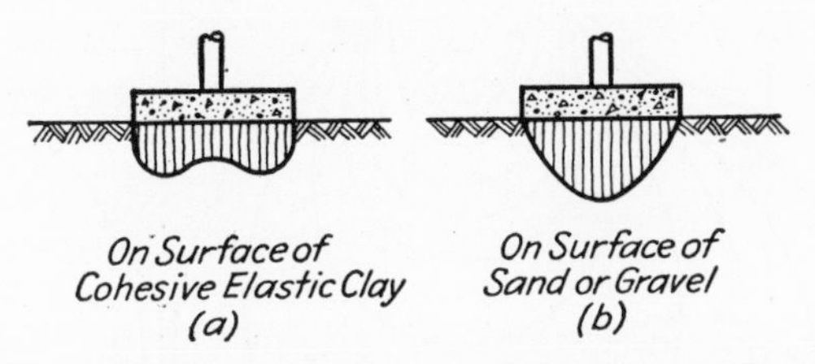

FIG. 7. Contact Pressures beneath Rigid Foundation Slabs. Following Dr. Franz Kögler.

foundation slabs, but they present the difficulty of making specific assumptions which, because of the great diversity in soil composition, are either too limited for general application or too complicated for practical use.

PRESSURE BULBS. The load transmitted to soil by a spread foundation causes pressure within the soil, extending laterally beyond the sides of the foundation and to a considerable depth below the contact surface. Figure 8[6] shows a typical "pressure bulb," presented in 1927 by Professors Kögler and Scheidig, and based upon a combination of the Boussinesq theory and empirical data. Since that time similar drawings have been published by many other authorities. The curves are called isobars and are formed by connecting points of equal vertical pressure. The percentages given on the curves are in terms of the average unit load on the contact surface of the bearing area.

Although the contact pressure mentioned above for sand is quite different from that for clay, and this fact would affect the upper segments of the curves, Fig. 8 would otherwise apply to either material. The

[5] Taken from "Stress Distribution in Soils," by Prof. Franz Kögler, *Proceedings of the International Conference on Soil Mechanics and Foundation Engineering*, Graduate School of Engineering, Harvard University, 1936. See also *Baugrund und Bauwerk*, by Prof. Franz Kögler and Dr. Alfred Scheidig, Berlin, 1938.

[6] "Druckverteiling im Baugrund," by Prof. Franz Kögler and Dr. Alfred Scheidig; *Die Bautechnik*, Berlin, 1927.

values shown, however, should be considered only approximate. They vary with the size of the loaded area, the depth of the loaded area beneath the surface, the rigidity of the footing or foundation assembly, and any of the many differences in soil composition affecting the stress distribution.

This type of analysis has, nevertheless, considerable significance for the architect and architectural engineer. It presents a widely accepted concept of pressure distribution and indicates that the volume of earth which

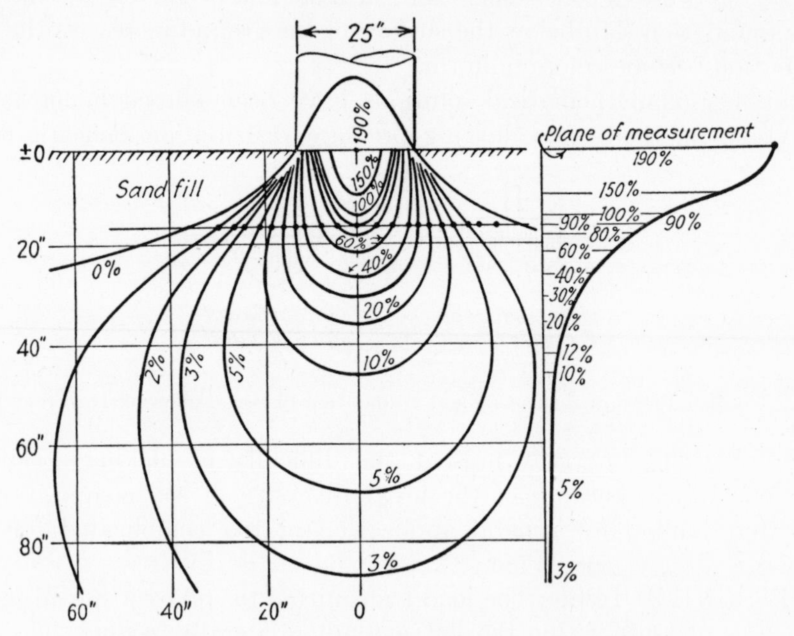

FIG. 8. Bulb of Pressure by Kögler and Scheidig.

should be considered definitely affected by the imposed load probably extends to a depth of 1½ to 2 times the width of the footing. Furthermore, in some types of soil, at least, an appreciable increment of load above that due to natural conditions of overburden would be transmitted to a considerably greater depth. It also indicates the probability of considerable variation in unit pressures at points upon horizontal planes within a short distance of each other.

There is likewise the probability of the individual pressure bulbs of adjoining footings overlapping unless the footings are separated by a considerable distance. This overlapping may cause an excessive load upon some critical subsurface stratum. Increasing the size of the footings will obviously lessen the contact pressures on the foundation bed, but may be of little value in relieving the subsurface pressure on a lower plane if the load is already spread fairly uniformly over the entire available area. As pointed out by Prentis and White in their very practical work, *Underpin-*

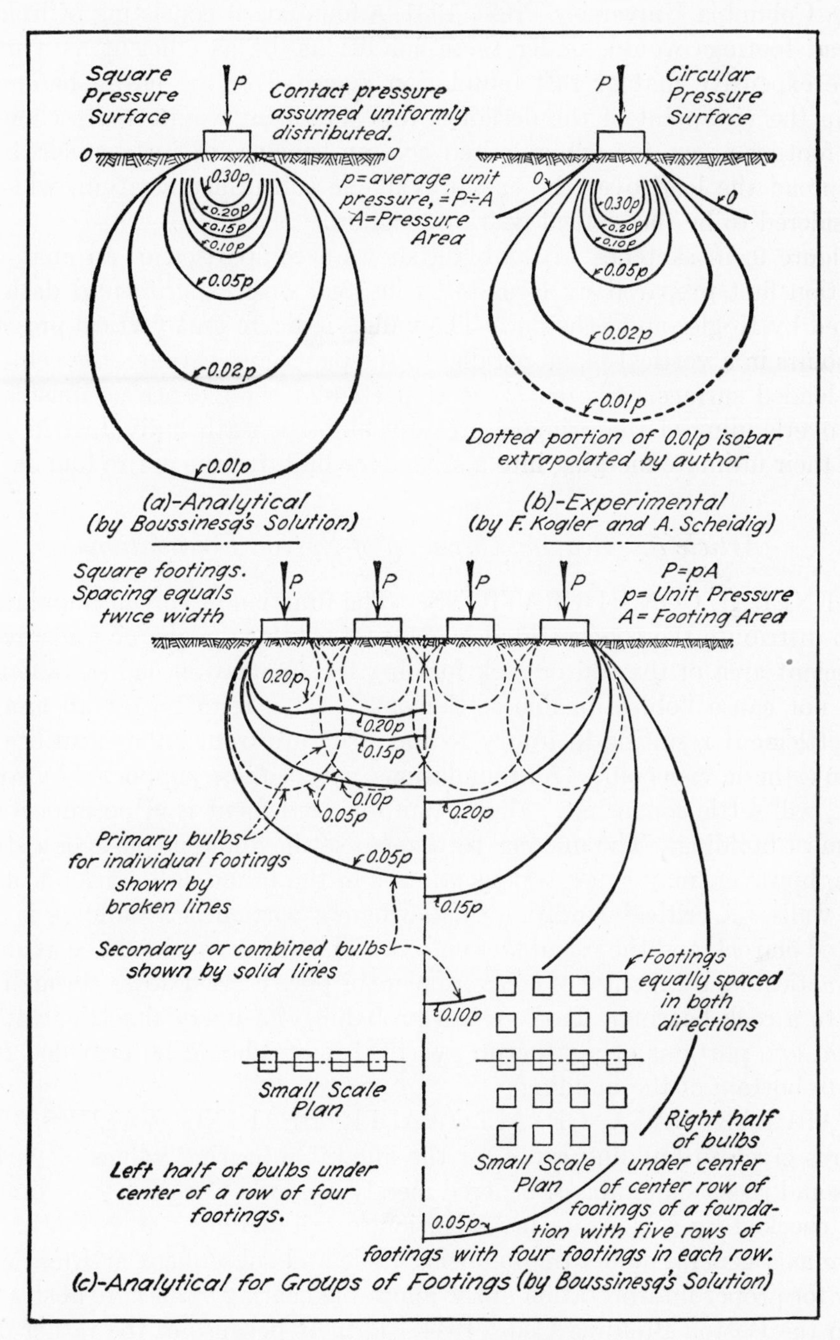

FIG. 9. Bulbs of Pressure for Spread Footings. From *Building Construction*, by Whitney C. Huntington, Second Edition, John Wiley & Sons.

ning, Columbia University Press, 1931, a foundation consisting of isolated spread footings would, under these conditions, be as efficient as a much more expensive mat or raft foundation placed over the entire basement. From the viewpoint of the designer, this statement would imply choosing the footing areas, for any required column spacing, of just sufficient size to spread the load over the entire available subsurface stratum, which is considered to be the critical bearing medium.

Figure 9, in sketches (*a*) and (*b*), shows a comparison of an analytical solution first prepared by Boussinesq in 1885 with experimental data obtained by Kögler and Scheidig. The values indicate unit vertical pressures at points in a vertical plane parallel to the paper and through the center of the loaded surface. Sketch (*c*) is of particular significance as illustrating the overlapping of the primary pressure bulbs beneath individual footings and their ultimate merging into a secondary bulb for the entire foundation.

Article 5. Bearing Capacity of Spread Foundations

GENERAL CONSIDERATIONS. The function of spread foundations is to distribute the concentrated loads from columns, piers, or walls over a sufficient area of the soil or rock forming the foundation bed so that they will not cause "objectionable settlement." This term means an amount of settlement resulting in injury to the structure from either a utilitarian or an esthetic viewpoint. All foundations, except those supported by sound rock, will settle somewhat. Slight, uniform settlement is of no importance for most building. The unequal settlement of the different parts of a structure, however, may cause serious stresses in the frame and cracks in floors and walls. A critical condition exists where a portion of a building is supported on rock and the remainder on soil. This situation should be avoided, if practicable, by the use of concrete piers or piles carried down through the soil to a rock bearing. If there is a probability of unequal settlement between two portions of a structure, vertical joints should be provided from top to bottom of the building.

TABULAR DATA OF ALLOWABLE BEARING VALUES. The figures given in building codes for the allowable bearing values of various soils and rocks should be considered merely somewhat arbitrary maximums and checked by subsurface investigation, a soil-loading test, or both. To serve as a general guide, the following table and subsequent articles necessary for proper interpretation of the allowable bearing values are abstracted from the Boston Building Code, 1944. Largely because of the rather difficult soil conditions existing within the Boston metropolitan area, the requirements are more severe than in many other cities but represent a consideration of potential foundation settlement which might well be emulated in other districts. These rules should also be of interest to the designer as illustrating a practical application of several principles discussed in the preceding articles.

ALLOWABLE BEARING VALUES FOR VARIOUS SOILS AND ROCKS

(Boston Building Code, 1944)

Class	Material	Allowable Bearing Value in Tons per Square Foot
1	Massive bedrock without laminations, such as granite, diorite, and other granitic rocks; gneiss trap rock, felsite, and thoroughly cemented conglomerates, all in sound condition *	100
2	Laminated rocks, such as slate and schist, in sound condition *	35
3	Shale in sound condition *	10
4	Residual deposits of shattered or broken bedrock of any kind except shale	10
5	Hardpan	10
6	Gravel, sand-gravel mixtures, compact	5
7	Gravel, sand-gravel mixtures, loose; sand, coarse, compact	4
8	Sand, coarse, loose; sand, fine, compact	3
9	Sand, fine, loose	1
10	Hard clay	6
11	Medium clay	4
12	Soft clay	1
13	Rock flour, shattered shale, or any natural deposit of unusual character not provided for herein	†

* Minor cracks allowed.

† Value to be fixed by the Commissioner.

DEFINITIONS AND RULES APPLYING TO THE INTERPRETATION OF THE BOSTON CODE

IDENTIFICATION OF ROCK AND SOIL TYPES. The terms used in the following classification shall be interpreted in accordance with generally accepted geological and engineering nomenclature. Certain terms shall, for the purposes of this chapter, have more specific interpretations, as follows:

a. *Rocks.*

SHALE. A laminated, fine-textured soft rock composed of consolidated clay of silt, which cannot be moulded without the addition of water, but which can be reduced to a plastic condition by moderate grinding and mixing with water.

SLATE. A dense, very fine-textured, soft rock which is readily split along cleavage planes into thin sheets and which cannot be reduced to a plastic condition by moderate grinding and mixing with water.

SCHIST. A fine-textured, laminated rock with a more or less wavy cleavage, containing mica or other flaky minerals.

b. *Granular Soil.*

GRAVEL. An uncemented mixture of mineral grains 1/4 in. or more in diameter.

SAND. A type of soil possessing practically no cohesion when dry, and consisting of mineral grains smaller than 1/4 in. in diameter.

COARSE SAND. A sand consisting chiefly of grains which will be retained on a 65-mesh sieve.

FINE SAND. A sand consisting chiefly of grains which will pass a 65-mesh sieve.

COMPACT GRAVEL, COMPACT SAND. Deposits requiring picking for removal and offering high resistance to penetration by excavating tools.

LOOSE GRAVEL, LOOSE SAND. Deposits readily removable by shoveling only.

c. *Cohesive soil.*

HARDPAN. A thoroughly compact mixture of clay, sand, gravel, and boulders, for example, boulder clay; or a cemented mixture of sand or of sand and gravel, with or without boulders, and difficult to remove by picking.

CLAY. A fine-grained, inorganic soil possessing sufficient cohesion when dry to form hard lumps which cannot readily be pulverized by the fingers.

HARD CLAY. A clay requiring picking for removal, a fresh sample of which cannot be moulded in the fingers.

MEDIUM CLAY. A clay which can be removed by spading, a fresh sample of which can be moulded by a substantial pressure of the fingers.

SOFT CLAY. A clay which, when freshly sampled, can be moulded under relatively slight pressure of the fingers.

ROCK FLOUR (INORGANIC SILT). A fine-grained, inorganic soil consisting chiefly of grains which will pass a 200-mesh sieve, and possessing sufficient cohesion when dry to form lumps which can readily be pulverized with the fingers.

RULES.

a. The maximum pressure on soils under foundations shall not exceed the allowable bearing values set forth in the preceding table [page 337] except when determined in accordance with the provisions specified for loading tests, and in any case subject to the modifications of subsequent paragraphs of this section.

b. The tabulated bearing values for rocks of classes 1 to 3 inclusive shall apply where the loaded area is less than 2 ft below the lowest adjacent surface of sound rock. Where the loaded area is more than 2 ft below such surface, these values may be increased 20 per cent for each foot of additional depth but shall not exceed twice the tabulated values.

c. The allowable bearing values of materials of classes 4 to 9 inclusive may exceed the tabulated values by 2 1/2 per cent for each foot of depth of the loaded area below the lowest ground surface immediately adjacent, but shall not exceed twice the tabulated values. For areas of foundations smaller than 3 ft in least lateral dimension, the allowable bearing values shall be one-third of the allowable bearing values multiplied by the least lateral dimension in feet.

d. The tabulated bearing values for classes 10 to 12 inclusive apply only to pressures directly under individual footings, walls, and piers. When structures are founded on or are underlain by deposits of these classes, the total load over the area of any one bay or other major portion of the structure, minus the weight of excavated material, divided by the area, shall not exceed one-half the tabulated bearing values.

e. Where the bearing materials directly under a foundation overlie a stratum having smaller allowable bearing values, these smaller values shall not be exceeded at the level of such stratum. Computation of the vertical pressure in the bearing materials at any depth below a foundation shall be made on the assumption that the load is spread uniformly at an angle of 60° with the horizontal, but the area considered as supporting the load shall not extend beyond the intersection of 60° planes of adjacent foundations.

f. Where portions of the foundation of an entire structure rest directly upon or are underlain by medium or soft clay or rock flour, and other portions rest upon different materials, or where the layers of such softer materials vary greatly in thickness, the magnitude and distribution of the probable settlement shall be investigated as specified in paragraph f, page 382, and, if necessary, the allowable loads shall be reduced or special provisions be made in the design of the structure to prevent dangerous differential settlements.

g. Whenever, in an excavaticn, an inward or upward flow of water develops in an otherwise satisfactory bearing material, special methods satisfactory to the commissioner shall be immediately adopted to stop or control the flow to prevent disturbance of the bearing material. If such flow of water seriously impairs the structure of the bearing material, the allowable bearing value shall be reduced to that of the material in loose condition.

The common practice of many building codes, after assuming a uniform pressure distribution on the foundation bed, is to neglect the distribution of load upon underlying strata even if these strata are of a lower bearing value. This practice has so often resulted in excessive settlement that it is covered by the requirements of paragraph e, quoted above. Although merely an approximation, this regulation is a definite advance in the right direction. Figure 10 illustrates the condition to which paragraph e applies.

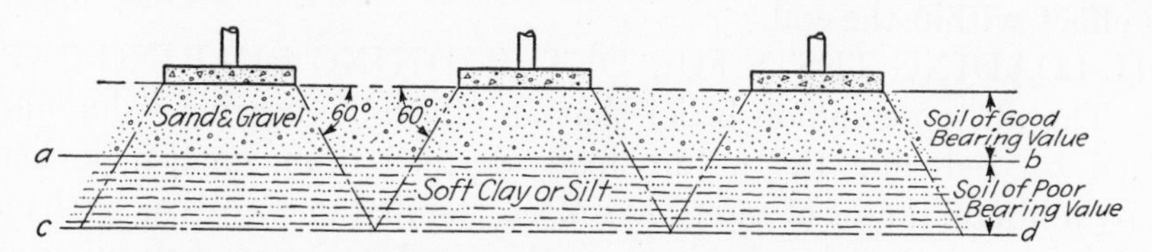

The Lower Bearing Value of the Soil on the Horizontal Plane a-b must not be Exceeded when the Footing Load is Divided by the Area which, at this Level, is Bounded by the 60° planes. The Bearing Capacity of Each Footing is Also Limited by the Product of the Area, Included Between the 60° Planes, and the Bearing Value of the Soil at the Level c-d

Fig. 10. An Assumption of Pressure Distribution beneath Footings. Following Building Code of Boston, Mass., 1944.

SETTLEMENT OF FOUNDATIONS. The physical characteristics of the various types of soil are important in relation to their load-carrying capacity. These should be studied particularly as affecting the compressibility of soils and their tendency to fail in shear, moving laterally from beneath a superimposed load. As the actual grains of soil, whether of sand or clay, cannot be compressed by the loads used in foundation design, consolidation occurs by a diminution of void content. For sand and gravel, subjected to loads such as those identified on page 377, this is not usually of an order to cause objectionable settlement, except with loose sand, where vibration may effect a rearrangement of the grains. The lateral displacement of either sand or gravel may be caused by adjoining excavations, but if confined it furnishes good bearing. This is true, to a lesser extent, of even fine, wet sand. Below water level, however, fine sand may easily flow a considerable distance, resulting in serious settlement.

Clay generally contains a higher percentage of voids than sand, and these are normally either partly or completely filled with water. As clay is more impermeable to the passage of water, consolidation takes place slowly, often continuing over a period of years. Gradually, as the water is pressed out, very serious settlement may take place even under comparatively light loads. This fact has been the reason for avoiding construction methods which might result in draining such soils beneath adjoining buildings. In some instances the uplift caused by ground-water pressure has been considered a help in resisting the weight of a building, but it should be remembered that prolonged pumping or future drainage will cancel this factor.

Although settlement can generally be assumed as practically independent of the size of the loaded area for foundations supported by sand or gravel, settlement over clay apparently increases with the size of the loaded area, even when the load per square foot is the same. On the other hand, the bearing capacity of any particular homogeneous stratum of considerable thickness increases with the depth below the surface. It should be remembered, however, that the larger the footing or foundation, the deeper will be its effect within the soil.[7]

SOIL-LOADING TESTS FOR DETERMINING BEARING CAPACITY. The all-too-common belief that an allowable bearing value may be obtained by reducing the failure load, derived from small-scale loading tests, by a liberal factor of safety has often resulted in excessive settlement.[8] In many cases the results obtained by this method form a helpful addition to the subsurface investigation, but their value should be carefully considered in relation to the following limitations.

The depth of the pressure bulb increases with the width of the loaded area, and any settlement record derived from a small-scale test depends upon the properties of only that soil which lies within the shallow bulb of pressure produced by the loading block or platform. Unless the material is uniform and homogeneous for the entire depth to which the pressure bulb would extend for the entire building, the relationship between test results

[7] See *Theoretical Soil Mechanics*, by Karl Terzaghi, John Wiley & Sons, Inc., 1943.

[8] "Application of Soil Mechanics in Designing Building Foundations," by A. Casagrande and R. E. Fadum, *Transactions American Society of Civil Engineers*, Vol. 109, 1944.

and future settlement is questionable.[9] Furthermore, even if the soil conditions are similar beneath the entire foundation bed, the pressure effect from adjacent footings will often overlap, as noted on page 374. Both these considerations affect the validity of small-scale soil tests. For example, under a test load applied to 4 sq ft of area, the soil would be stressed severely to a depth of only about 3 ft, whereas beneath a footing 12 ft square an appreciable stress might be transmitted to a depth of about 18 ft. Under this condition the loaded area would also be extended laterally.

Experiments have indicated, as mentioned on page 380, that the amount of settlement of a footing which transmits pressure to a cohesionless soil is not affected by the size of the loaded area, but settlement over a cohesive soil may increase with the linear dimensions of the footing. Still another matter bearing upon the use of data obtained from loading tests is the varying resistance to compression of soils, even of the same apparent characteristics, at different depths below the surface. Consequently, the common assumption that the settlement of footings placed over the same type of soil will be equal, provided that the unit pressures are equal, is far from true, particularly for cohesive soils, and tends further to complicate comparison between the settlement of a small loading block or platform and that of a full-sized footing.

In conclusion it may be said that allowable bearing values derived from small-scale tests of this nature should always be studied in relation to other available data and not considered conclusive in themselves. Dry-sample borings should be obtained unless soil conditions are definitely known. Settlement records of other buildings where conditions were similar are also very helpful. If no decision seems justified by a study of these records, laboratory tests upon undisturbed samples may be necessary in the case of cohesive soils.

The following requirements for a soil-loading test are also taken from the Boston Building Code, 1944.

a. For bearing materials of classes 1 to 5 inclusive, the loaded area shall be at least 1 sq ft and for other classes at least 4 sq ft. For materials of classes 6 to 13 inclusive, the loaded area shall be the full size of the pit and at such depth that the ratio of the width of the loaded area to its depth below the immediately adjacent ground surface is the same as the larger of the following two values:

1. Ratio of the width of any footing to its depth below the immediately adjacent ground surface.

2. Ratio of the width of the entire foundation or group of footings to its depth below the average surrounding ground surface.

[9] "Settlement of Structures" by Karl Terzaghi, Opening Discussion of the International Conference on Soil Mechanics and Foundation Engineering, Graduate School of Engineering, Harvard University, 1936.

b. When loading tests are made on bearing materials of classes 10 to 13 inclusive, suitable methods shall be used to prevent evaporation from the materials being tested.

c. A test load shall be applied which will produce a unit pressure equal to that for which the proposed foundations are designed. This load shall be allowed to remain undisturbed until no measurable settlement occurs during a period of 24 hours. The load shall then be doubled in increments not exceeding 25 per cent of the design load. At least 4 hours shall elapse between the application of successive increments. The total load shall be allowed to remain undisturbed until no measurable settlement occurs during a period of 24 hours.

d. Measurements of settlement shall be accurate to $\frac{1}{32}$ in. and shall be taken and recorded every hour during the first 6 hours after the application of each increment, and at least once every 12 hours thereafter.

e. When the design load upon bearing materials of classes 1 to 10 inclusive causes settlement of less than $\frac{3}{8}$ in. and twice the design load causes settlement of less than 1 in., the design load shall be allowed; but if medium or soft clay underlies these materials, the vertical pressure in such clay shall not exceed that allowed in the table.

f. Whenever the proposed foundation rests on or is underlain by bearing materials of classes 11 to 13 inclusive, the results of loading tests must be interpreted in conjunction with accurate soil profiles showing magnitude and variation of the thickness of these strata. If this information, in the opinion of the commissioner, is not sufficient to determine whether the design load will cause excessive settlement, as might occur due to a thick stratum of clay, or dangerous differential settlement, as might occur when the underlying clay stratum varies considerably in thickness, the commissioner may require an analysis to be made of the probable magnitude, rate, and distribution of settlement of the proposed structure. Such analysis may be based upon:

1. A study of settlement records of near-by structures having essentially the same foundation conditions.

2. Consolidation tests and other investigations of undisturbed samples of the compressible materials.

Article 6. Types of Piles and Pile Driving

INTRODUCTION. When designing a pile foundation for the support of a building, we are concerned only with bearing piles which are normally driven in a vertical position. Batter piles, fender piles, and anchor and sheet piles are not considered in this text. Batter piles are driven at an inclination for the purpose of resisting lateral forces; fender piles are used to absorb shock and receive abrasion due to impact. Anchor piles are used to resist upward or lateral forces, and sheet piles are driven to resist lateral soil or water pressure.

Bearing piles are of the following types: wood piles; concrete piles, both precast and cast-in-place; structural-steel piles; metal-pipe piles; and composite piles, composed of wood or steel superimposed by concrete. Ordinarily driven in groups, called clusters, for the support of columns and piers, a staggered arrangement of two or more parallel lines may be appropriate beneath bearing walls. Piles may also be distributed over an entire basement area beneath a reinforced-concrete mat. In the more usual cases the superimposed footings, known as pile caps, are similar in plan to those employed over soil. The depth is somewhat greater, allowing for an embedment of the pile heads or butts to a depth of 4 to 6 in. The quantitative design is based upon a series of concentrations, because of the pile reactions, rather than a uniform load or appropriate modification of a uniform load, as would be the case over soil. Figure 11 shows a typical design

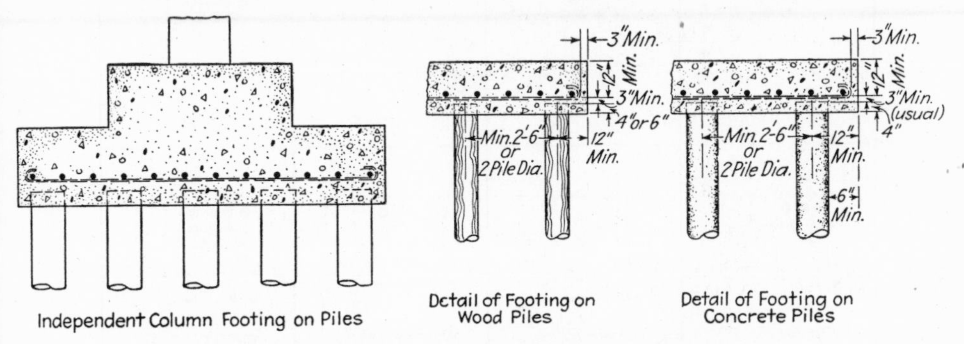

FIG. 11. Column Footing Supported by Piles.

for an independent column footing, and Fig. 12 the most economical arrangements for grouping piles.

Although the pile cap rests upon the soil, it should not be considered to transmit any load except to the piles themselves. Although recent investigations indicate that over sand some load may be directly transmitted to the soil, the data available on this subject are very scant, and the ultimate bearing capacity of every pile comprising a cluster would generally be reached or approximated before any appreciable pressure could be exerted by the cap. In districts subject to earthquakes it may be necessary to design pile foundations against uplift. This has been done on the Pacific Coast.

WOOD PILES. These are usually tree trunks, normally driven with the small end down. In comparison with other types of piles, they are more appropriate for light than heavy loads.[10] Practically any kind of sound timber, particularly Douglas fir, southern pine, spruce, and white and red oak, may be used.[11] Where driving is difficult, a metal point with a shoe is employed. The lengths are determined to suit soil requirements.

[10] "Survey of Foundation-Construction Methods," by Ralph H. Chambers, *Civil Engineering*, January, 1941.

[11] Specifications of the American Society for Testing Materials and those of the American Railway Engineering Association.

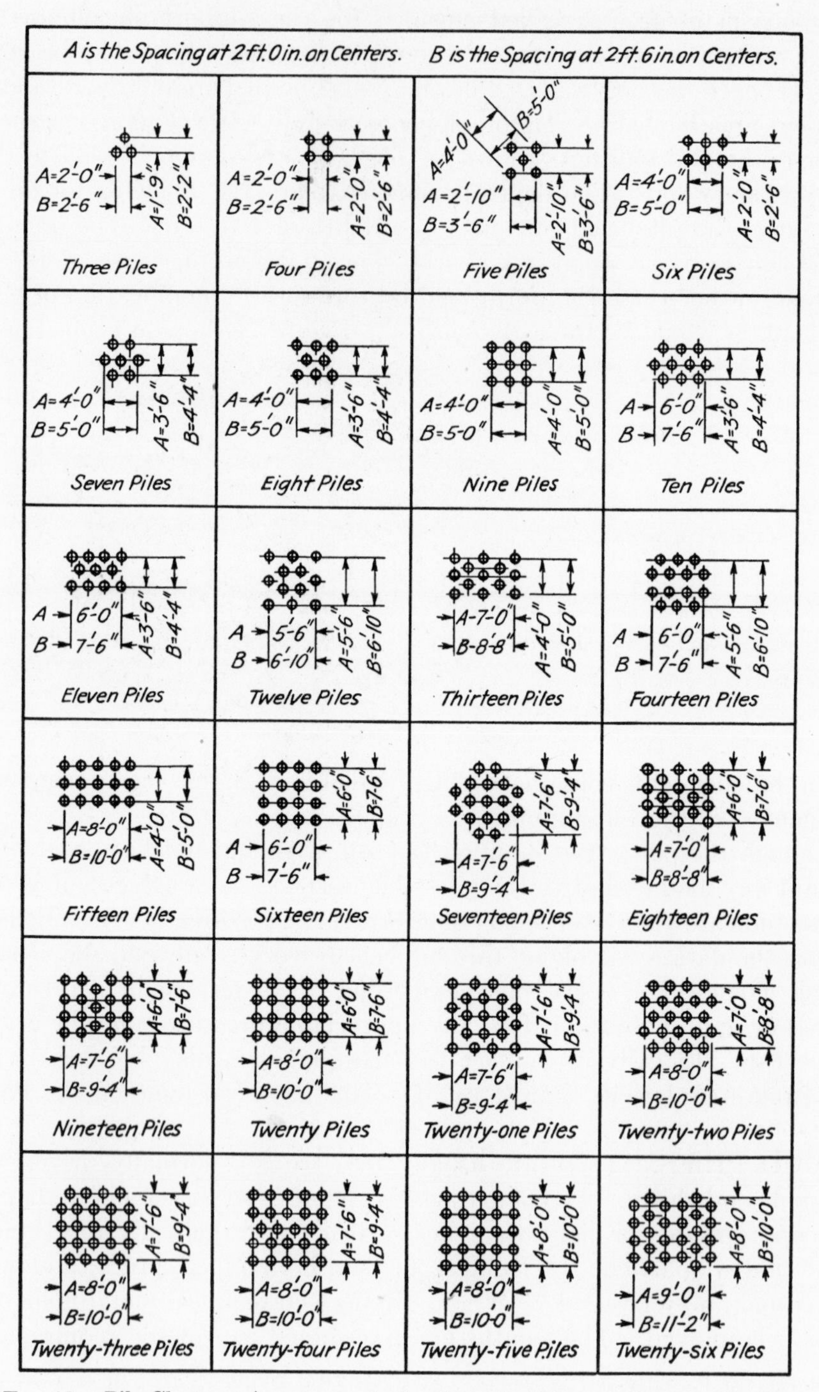

Fig. 12. Pile Clusters: Arrangements for Grouping Three to Twenty-Six Piles.

The diameter at the tip usually varies from 6 to 8 in.; the diameter at the butt is seldom less than 12 in.; the taper should be uniform. For building foundations, untreated wood piles should be used only below permanent ground-water level. Except for temporary structures, even treated wood piles should be used with due consideration of the possibility of future replacement, when not entirely below ground-water level. This requirement alone may involve deep excavation with consequent expense for sheathing and pumping. In comparing the cost of wood piles with other types, these items may be important. It should also be remembered that, although the cost of wood piles is generally much less per linear foot than that of other types, their bearing capacity is also much lower. This means that more piles are required in each cluster, and the superimposed concrete footing is larger.

If entirely embedded in soil and cut off below the lowest present or future ground-water level, or entirely submerged in fresh water, untreated timber piles may be considered permanent.[12] When exposed to unfavorable conditions, durability can be greatly increased by the use of coal-tar creosote impregnated by standard methods.[13] Either a treated or untreated pile, particularly the latter, may be injured by ground water containing alkali or acids, but the principal danger to untreated timber piles is an unexpected lowering of the ground-water level, which causes the upper part of the pile to decay. Where there is even a remote possibility of this condition occurring in future years, the design should be based upon such a contingency.

CONCRETE PILES. These piles fall into two broad classifications: precast and cast-in-place. The fact that they are immune to attack by biological organisms permits their use where untreated wood piles would be inappropriate. If entirely embedded in soil, concrete piles may be considered permanent, irrespective of ground-water level, unless destructive acids, alkalis, or chemical salts are present.[14] If the piles are extended above the surface, as they often are in the precast design, they are subject to weathering and the effect of deleterious atmospheres to the same extent as

[12] The statements in this article regarding the permanence of various types of piles follow the opinions expressed in "Pile Foundations and Pile Structures," *Manual of Engineering Practice No.* 27, American Society of Civil Engineers, 1946. This manual is an excellent reference on the entire subject identified by the title and has been quoted in several portions of this chapter.

[13] "Timber Piles and Construction Timbers," *Manual of Engineering Practice* No. 17, American Society of Civil Engineers.

[14] "Pile Foundations," by A. E. Cummings, *Proceedings of the Purdue Conference on Soil Mechanics and Its Applications,* sponsored by the Society for the Promotion of Engineering Education, Purdue University, Lafayette, Indiana, 1940. This is a very practical treatment of the subject, with particular reference to concrete piles. Reprints are available from the Raymond Concrete Pile Company.

concrete columns. Each type of concrete pile has its particular advantages and disadvantages, which should be considered in relation to the soil conditions and duty to be performed.

PRECAST CONCRETE PILES. Although generally octagonal or square with chamfered corners (see Fig. 13), these piles are occasionally of circular section. Parallel sides and pointed ends are the more common,

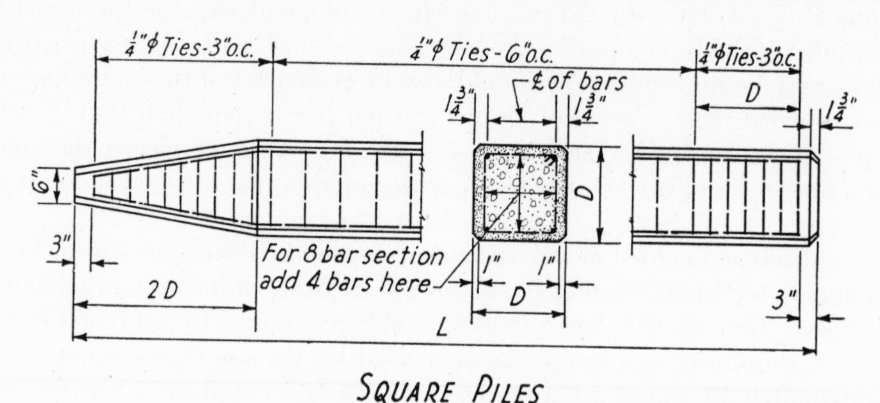

D	16"	20"	24"
SIZE	#5	#4	#3

FIG. 13. Precast Concrete Piles.

but tapered designs are used in lengths up to about 40 ft. Where support is furnished by skin-friction (see page 396), the carrying capacity of a tapered pile is increased in comparison to one having parallel sides. When the pile is used for end-bearing, this factor is negligible.

The parallel-side type has been cast with diameters up to 30 in. and in lengths over 100 ft. The particular application of these piles is for highway viaducts and locations where a part of the pile extends above the ground or above water level, acting as a column for the superstructure. They are always reinforced internally to resist stresses caused by handling and driving. If the pile is serving as a column or is required to resist horizontal forces, additional steel may be necessary. As this type of pile is usually cast on or near the site of the future building, space is required for manufacture and storage, but these piles have the advantage of permitting inspection before driving. Pipes are occasionally placed in precast concrete piles to permit jetting (see page 393) while they are being driven.

CAST-IN-PLACE CONCRETE PILES. These are of two types: those in which a steel shell is left in the ground, and those which are shell-

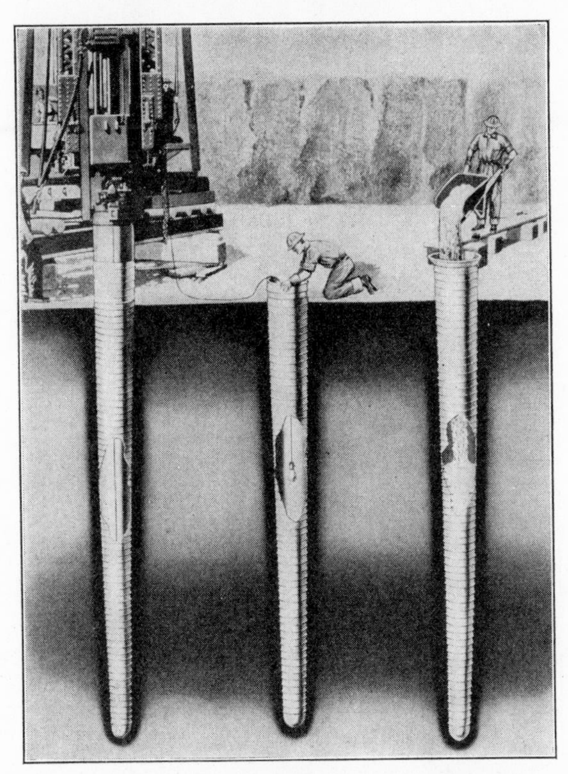

Fig. 14. Cast-in-Place Uniformly Tapered Concrete Shell-Pile. Courtesy, Raymond Concrete Pile Company.

less or unencased. In the first type the shell is usually of thin steel with a boot at the bottom, designed for driving with a heavy steel core called a mandrel. When sufficient resistance has been obtained, the core is collapsed and withdrawn. The driven shell is then inspected by means of an electric light and filled with concrete. Figure 14 shows the procedure. Alternate designs feature steel pipe, heavy enough to be driven without a core.

A standard design for the type shown in Fig. 14 has an 8-in. point diameter, the thickness increasing at the rate of 0.4 in. for each foot of pile length. As the practicable limit of the uniformly tapered type is about 37 ft, a "step-taper" design, shown in Fig. 15, was developed, which has been driven in lengths up to nearly 100 ft. For greater depths a pipe-step-taper pile is available in lengths up to about 150 ft. This design is shown in Fig. 16.

Typical of the unencased type is the use of a heavy steel shell or tube in combination with a steel core. After sufficient driving resistance has been

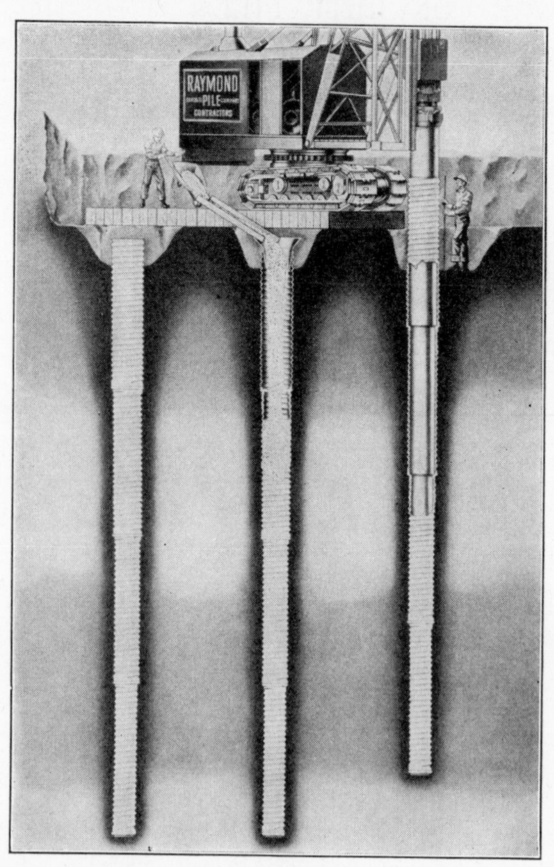

Fig. 15. Cast-in-Place Step-Taper Concrete Shell-Pile. Courtesy, Raymond Concrete Pile Company.

obtained, the core is withdrawn, and the tube filled with concrete. In this case, however, the core is then placed on top of the newly deposited concrete at the upper end of the tube, and remains in this position while the tube is pulled out of the ground, leaving the concrete in contact with the soil.

A modification of this procedure results in what is termed a "pedestal" pile, which is formed in the following manner. After the lower portion only of the tube has been filled with concrete to a depth of 5 or 6 ft, the core is replaced, and the tube lifted from 18 in. to 3 ft while the pressure of the core and hammer rests on the concrete. The charge of concrete is then rammed down and flows out of the lower end of the tube. The next step is to remove the core and completely fill the tube. The last operation is to replace the core in the upper end of the tube, which is then withdrawn while the concrete is still held under pressure by the weight of the core.

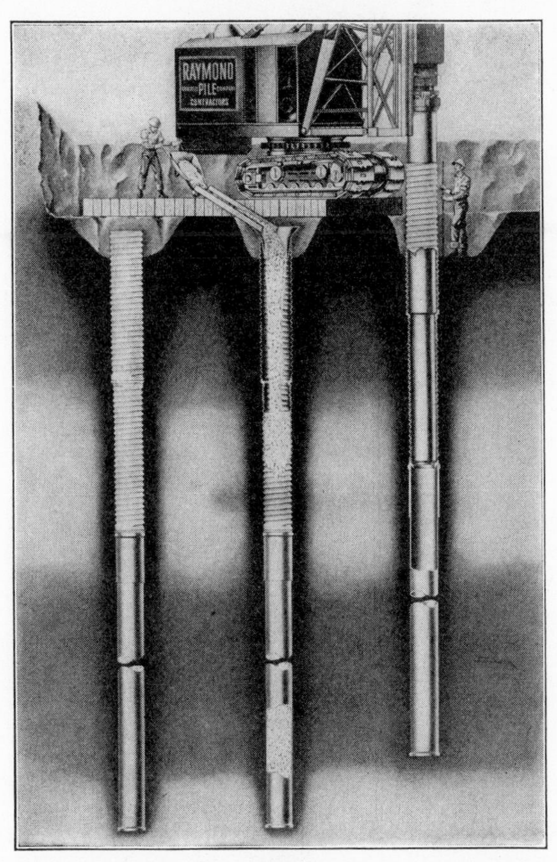

FIG. 16. Cast-in-Place Pipe-Step-Taper Concrete Pile. Courtesy, Raymond Concrete Pile Company.

Figure 17 shows these operations for both the straight-shaft and pedestal types.

The cast-in-place pile is the usual choice, rather than the precast type, for ordinary building foundations. It can be more rapidly installed, as no time is lost in driving test piles for the purpose of determining pile lengths, and no delay is caused by waiting for the piles to be properly cured. Furthermore, there is no need to establish a casting yard. Cast-in-place piles are not generally reinforced internally except where subject to the probability of seismic disturbance or under special conditions where resistance to bending is required. The piles which include a steel shell left in the ground permit inspection of the shell before it is filled with concrete and provide protection for the concrete while it is hardening. Where soil conditions are favorable, the shell-less design may be more economical but is of less general application, as in many soils there is danger that subsurface pressures or the driving of adjacent piles will reduce or otherwise injure the concrete section.

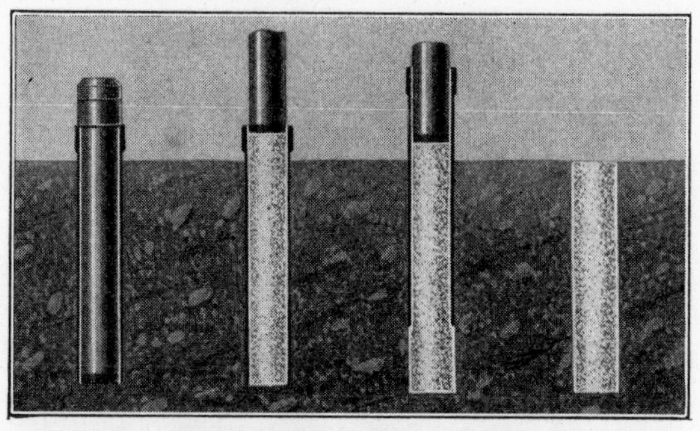

FIG. 17. Straight Shaft and Pedestal Type Shell-Less Concrete Piles. Courtesy, MacArthur Concrete Pile Company.

STRUCTURAL-STEEL PILES. Rolled steel H-sections are designed with wide flanges for use as piles. Their strength permits driving through dense gravel, which would be difficult, even with the aid of jetting, for either a wood or precast concrete pile. Because of their smaller cross-sectional area, steel H-piles cause less compaction of the soil and, when driven in cohesive soils, cause less swelling of the ground. They are consequently less likely to force adjacent piles to rise than are timber or concrete piles, even when supporting heavier loads. The comparatively small end-area and slight volume displacement of steel piles adapt them to deep driving, which permits carrying the load to a lower stratum. Their particular application is to extend the foundation to rock.

Steel piles were used for this purpose beneath an addition to the John Hancock Mutual Life Insurance Company's building in Boston's Back Bay area, where soil conditions were similar to those described on page 371. Because of the weight of this structure, approximating 140,000 tons, a rigid-frame or "floating foundation," such as that used for the New England Mutual Life Insurance Company's building, was not considered practicable. Steel piles were chosen in preference to a caisson design or metal-pipe piles, as their driving was less likely to cause settlement of adjacent buildings resulting from disturbance of the underlying soft clay stratum. The piles are approximately 120 ft long and serve as support for a reinforced-concrete slab 10 ft thick, upon which rests the steel-framed structure of twenty-six stories. An interesting description of this design is given in "Welded Steel Piles Support 26-Story Skyscraper," *Civil Engineering*, March, 1947.

If entirely embedded in comparatively impervious soil, steel piles may be considered permanent. When extended above the ground, there is the probability of rusting at the surface and for a short distance below grade. To avoid this danger the steel piles may be encased in concrete or coated with coal tar, extending from 6 in. above grade to 2 ft or more below the surface. If corrosive materials are present in the soil or ground water, such protection should be carried to a greater depth. Where coal pockets, alkali soils, cinder fills of comparatively recent deposit, or waste from certain manufacturing plants occur in the immediate locality, an analysis of the soil should be made.

METAL PIPE PILES. These piles are usually in the form of heavy open-end cylindrical shells. Common sizes are 10 to 18 in. in diameter. The thickness of the shell is usually ¼ to ½ in., although a ⅞-in. thickness has been used for 12-in. pipe where it was necessary to drive through obstructions. When driven with a hammer, which is the usual procedure except when working beneath a structure, sections are sunk in lengths of about 20 ft. This type of pile is normally driven to rock, as it can be designed to carry up to 150 tons. Lengths up to 100 ft have been used. After driving, the soil contained within the pipe is blown out by means of compressed air, and the pipe filled with concrete. If overhead clearance is restricted, short lengths of pipe can be sunk by jacks. They offer the same advantages as steel H-sections to the extent that soil enters the pipe during driving. In some cases the lower end of the pile is closed by means of a steel shoe. Such designs are often classed as concrete piles poured-in-place, and the carrying capacity is greatly reduced.

COMPOSITE PILES. These may be of two types. In both, the upper portion is a concrete pile; it may be superimposed upon either wood or steel. The more common design is the wood-and-concrete combination. The wood portion is used only below permanent ground-water level. The connection between concrete and wood is usually made by forming a tenon in the upper end of the wood pile, which projects into the concrete above; some type of fastening is also provided to prevent the two sections from separating. The concrete portion is usually cast-in-place but may be precast. If it is cast-in-place, a sealing ring of heavy sheet metal prevents the entrance of soil or water into the interior of the shell before it is filled with concrete. The type shown in Fig. 18 consists of a cast-in-place step-taper pile above a wood pile, which may be of any practicable length. After the core, or mandrel, is used as a follower in driving the wood pile, it is removed,

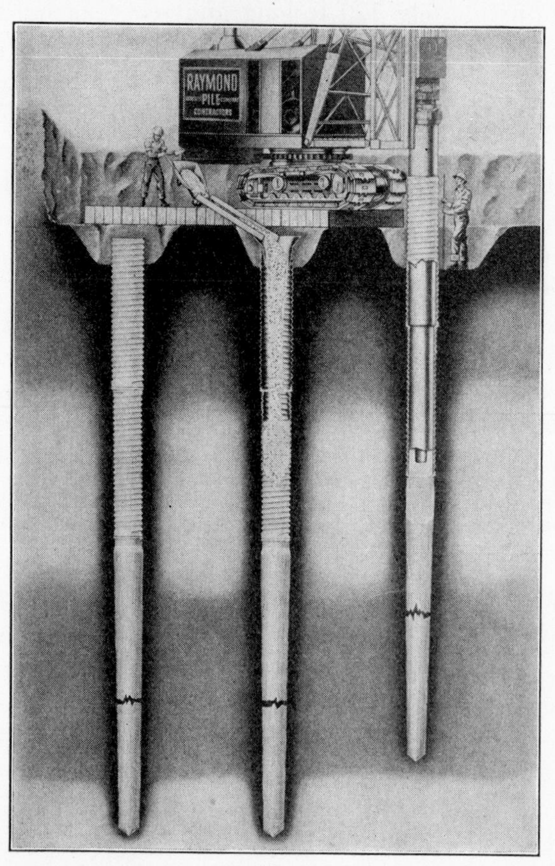

Fig. 18. Composite Piles. Courtesy, Raymond Concrete Pile Company.

and the shell filled with concrete, as in the all-concrete design. The advantage of such a combination is the comparatively low cost of the wood pile and the elimination of deep excavation, often necessitating sheathing and pumping, which would be required if the cut-off elevation were to be dropped below permanent water level.

The steel-and-concrete combination, less frequently used, consists of a steel pipe or H-section below ground-water level.

PILE DRIVING. The selection of suitable pile-driving equipment, and in particular the type, weight, and velocity at impact, or equivalent gravity fall, of the hammer, is extremely important. Selection should be made only by a competent engineer who is familiar with the soil conditions and probable pile loads. Inappropriate equipment, as well as the "over driving" of piles, can seriously impair their bearing value.

A drop hammer is essentially a heavy metal weight, raised by a hoisting line and allowed to fall on top of the pile by gravity. A single-acting steam hammer is a freely falling weight with steam pressure applied only to the underside of the piston for the purpose of raising the ram. The ram of the double-acting steam hammer is likewise raised by steam, but at the top of the stroke steam is admitted to the upper side of the piston, and its pressure, added to the weight of the ram, increases the driving force.

Piles are occasionally sunk by means of hydraulic jacks. Placed on top of a short pile, they force it down with resistance against the superstructure of a building, a temporary rig, or previously driven piles. This method was employed successfully in the driving of steel cylinder piles for piers along the Hudson River in New York City. Short lengths were successively added and jacked down as the superstructure was raised.

A water jet is often used when it is necessary to penetrate a considerable depth of sand or gravel, particularly if the entire depth is not needed for support. Normally employed in connection with hammer driving, the water jet is occasionally used by itself. If it is, the results should be checked by loading tests. In every case, however, jetting should be used with discretion. When piles support their loads by skin-friction (see page 396), their bearing value depends upon the soil settling back into place around the pile. This may or may not occur after jetting. There is also danger of loosening adjoining piles, particularly in silty sands. If any doubt exists in regard to the bearing capacity of piles driven by means of jetting, they should be checked with additional hammer blows or loading tests after all work within 25 ft has been completed.[15]

When piles are driven into soil, the material is either compacted or displaced to an amount equivalent to the solid volume of the pile. This fact is reflected in the term "displacement piles," applied to those which displace a considerable quantity of material. Wood, concrete, and closed-end pipe piles would be included in this group, as contrasted with steel H-sections and open-ended pipe piles.

Vibration due to driving tends to compact cohesionless granular soils whether above or below ground-water level. In such soils the surface of the ground after pile driving may be either lowered or raised. Fine, loose sand may be consolidated through vibration from driving to an amount that causes settlement of adjacent structures. Comparatively dry clay and silt or other cohesive soils are generally compacted by driving. Saturated clays and silts are practically incompressible during the short period required for this operation, as the pore spaces between particles are of

[15] For a description of air jetting and the use of compressed air combined with water see "Air Jetting Aids Pile Sinking," by Ernest E. Howard, *Civil Engineering*, September, 1946.

capillary size, and considerable time under pressure is required to force out the water. Consequently upward displacement, even equal to that of the volume of the piles, may occur and may cause serious heaving beneath adjoining foundations.

When piles are driven through soft clay or silt to a firmer material, such as coarse sand or gravel, it is important that sufficient penetration be obtained in the firmer soil, and driving should often be continued even after adequate resistance has apparently been reached. The compression of the soil due to driving may raise piles already in place to such an extent that they no longer bear properly. If this condition is suspected, the levels of all pile heads should be checked after each cluster is completed, and those that have risen appreciably should be redriven. Cast-in-place concrete piles of the unencased types may be seriously injured by adjacent driving. Composite piles may be pulled apart or deflected unless the two sections are strongly joined.

Article 7. Determining Bearing Capacity of Pile Foundations

GENERAL CONSIDERATIONS. "Allowable safe load" and "bearing capacity" are terms ordinarily used to identify that load which can be sustained by a pile foundation without objectionable settlement. A vital consideration is the carrying capacity of the subsoil strata underlying the points of the piles, as these strata must support the load placed upon the piles, in addition to the weight of soil above this level plus any other loads. This fact requires a study of the results obtained from subsurface investigation, supplemented by the information mentioned on page 361, in order to choose the substratum which provides the best support at the lowest cost.

A type of pile should be chosen which is of ample strength and character to meet the particular soil conditions, is durable, and involves the lowest cost for the entire foundation design. From the descriptions previously given, it will be remembered that wood piles are more applicable to the lighter than the heavier load requirements and are often more economical than other types, but untreated piles should never be used in permanent building foundations except below ground-water level. Cast-in-place concrete piles are generally more practicable for building foundations than the precast type and have the advantage of adjustment in length to meet variations in the bearing capacity of soil strata. The structural-steel and open-end pipe piles, with their greater carrying capacity, are particularly appropriate for deep driving to rock or other sound foundation. The selection is often influenced by the character of the soil and by other factors involved in handling and driving. For example, if a pile obtains its support in a stratum of sand or gravel lying beneath a considerable depth of clay or silt, it should be of a type to penetrate adequately into the supporting material. Experience indicates that large piles of the displacement type, in contrast to the steel piles, drive with difficulty through any considerable depth of dense clay.

Where piles are to be driven to rock or other well-defined hard bottom, a study of the soil profile may definitely indicate the required length. In other cases, the length of the piles may be approximated from the results of driving test piles distributed over the building area. It should be remembered, however, that actual lengths may vary considerably from such results. As mentioned on page 380, the bearing capacity of a homogeneous stratum of considerable thickness increases with the depth below grade. Consequently, an advantage corresponding to deepening a spread foundation is obtained if piles are chosen as long as practicable. If a mat foundation is placed over cohesive soil, friction piles should be at least as long as the width of the mat. Shorter piles may fail to carry the load appreciably deeper than would be the case if they were omitted. Under comparatively narrow structures, it is often necessary to use a length of pile at least equal to the width of the building.

MEANS BY WHICH PILES SUPPORT LOAD. Piles may transfer their loads by point-bearing to an underlying stratum or by skin-friction to the mass of soil in which they are embedded. Figure 19 shows a typical bulb of pressure beneath a single friction pile. The skin-friction may be supplemented by any bearing due to the taper of the pile. Frequently piles furnish support by a combination of these two means, but all types may be roughly classified as either "end-bearing" or "friction" piles, depending upon the way in which they obtain their chief resistance. It should be remembered, however, that in either case the load is eventually imposed upon the soil around and beneath the points of the piles, and upon the load-carrying capacity of these strata depends the resistance of the piles to settlement. At this level the condition of load upon the soil is analogous to that immediately below the foundation bed of a spread footing. When the piles are driven to rock of suitable character and thickness, this consideration is obviously unimportant.

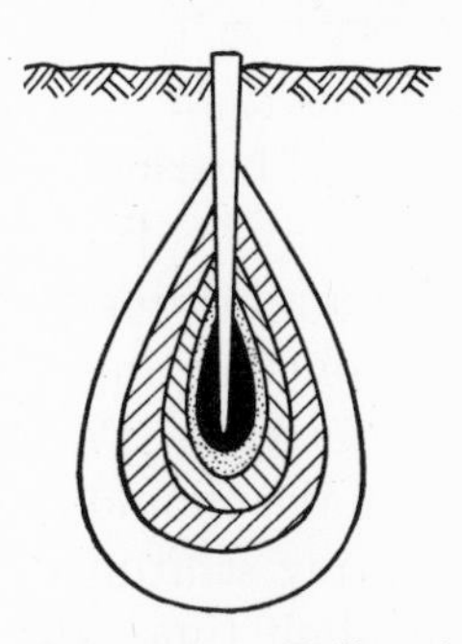

Fig. 19. Bulb of Pressure beneath a Single Friction Pile.

In Fig. 20, sketch (*a*) illustrates the case where the load of an end-bearing pile is practically all transmitted by point bearing to the rock or hardpan upon which it rests. The pile acts as a column with an indeterminate amount of lateral support from the material through which it is driven. Piles functioning in this manner must be strong enough to support the design load without injury to the tip. When the piles are driven to rock or into a material furnishing adequate point resistance, their spacing in the various clusters may be as close as convenient from the viewpoint of driving. Sketch (*b*) illustrates the case where the points of the piles are embedded in a firm stratum, such as dense sand or gravel, without clay or other soft strata below, and the piles support load by friction through the lower portion aided by end-bearing. As the load is transferred to the sand at the level of the pile points, the bearing capacity of such stratum would limit the bearing capacity of the pile for any particular spacing. Settlement can be controlled by conservative design, and no laboratory tests are necessary.

Sketch (*c*) illustrates a similar condition, except that a stratum of soft clay or other material of low bearing capacity is assumed to exist beneath

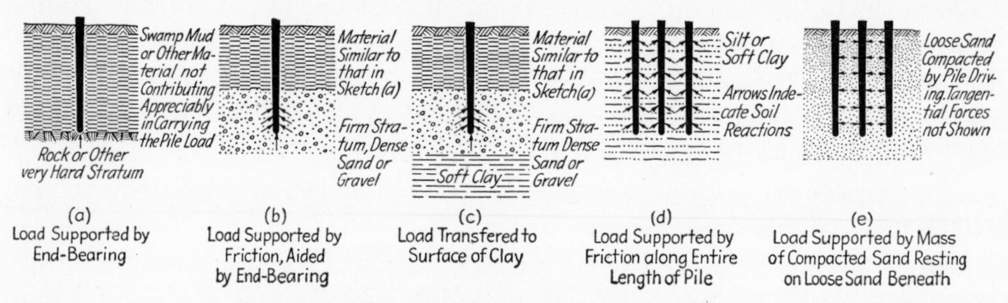

FIG. 20. Means by Which Piles Support Load.

the stratum of sand or gravel. In this case the surface of the clay is the critical bearing area. The load from a single pile, or even that of one cluster, may be distributed over a sufficient area to cause only slight settlement when a loading test is applied; but, when the entire foundation is in place, the overlapping of the pressure bulbs may result in excessive and continued settlement. Piles transmitting their load to any deposit of compressible material should be spaced so that the load-carrying capacity of the selected bearing stratum and any underlying strata, to a depth of at least one and one-half times the width of the entire foundation, is not exceeded. This consideration may require limiting the load to that imposed by the original overburden. As a help in estimating the probable amount of settlement, laboratory tests on undisturbed samples of the compressible soil may be desirable.

Sketch (*d*) illustrates the case where piles are supported by friction throughout their full length. Where such piles are embedded in silt or soft clay, the assembly is often referred to as a "floating" pile foundation. The segment of soil surrounding a pile, to which the load is transmitted, is known as the "bearing body." For an entire cluster the same term is applied to the mass of soil lying within the perimeter of the group and closely surrounding it, comprising the volume to which load is distributed. Again, in this case, the load-carrying capacity may be limited by the bearing value of the undisturbed soil beneath the level of the pile points, as the general downward displacement of the bearing bodies of soil around pile clusters is a common type of failure where a compressible stratum lies below.

Two additional considerations applying to this same case are the strength of the bond between soil and pile, generally referred to as "skin-friction," and the strength of the soil in shear. If the bond is inadequate, the pile will fail by slipping through the surrounding material. The value of the ultimate shearing stress in the soil is a measure of the tangential resistance which the earth can transmit. The forces indicated diagrammatically by the arrows in sketch (*d*) are the resultants of the tangential (vertical) and the normal (horizontal) soil reactions for a loaded pile.

In some types of saturated clays pile driving may eventually cause a remoulding of the soil located between the piles above the level of their points. This remoulding may result in either greater compressibility of the material or the formation of a slippery layer around each pile, which reduces its frictional value. On the other hand, some clays apparently become denser after pile driving. The subject is extremely involved, and the results of additional research must be available before definite statements can be made in regard to the value of piles driven in many types of saturated clays and silts.

Sketch (*e*) illustrates piles driven their entire length into a stratum of loose sand and having the primary function of consolidating the material by vibration and lateral displacement. When these piles are driven in sufficient number and at proper spacing, the result is the formation of a more or less solid block bounded approximately by the perimeter of the pile cluster. Provided that there is no underlying stratum of lower bearing value, the bearing capacity of such a design is limited by the adequacy of the loose sand below the pile points to support the entire bearing body of consolidated sand.

FORMULAS FOR COMPUTING BEARING CAPACITY. As the following quotations from "Pile Foundations and Pile Structures," *Manual of Engineering Practice No.* 27, American Society of Civil Engineers, 1946, well point out, the limitation of data obtained solely by driving records is all too apparent. Dynamic formulas have, however, been used for many years and with comparative success when the results have been applied with discretion. This is particularly true when driving through noncohesive soils such as sand. The formulas are far less helpful when applied to clay and silt. Although static formulas would appear to offer a logical solution, they have not as yet been used to any extent.

DYNAMIC PILE FORMULAS. The object in using a dynamic pile-driving formula is to determine from the measured movement of the pile against the soil resistance, under the impact of the hammer blow, what safe static load a single individual pile may transmit to the surrounding earth. It must be emphasized that the formula has nothing whatsoever to do with the capacity of the soil below the points of a group of piles to carry safely the total load of the foundation of the future structure; furthermore, it takes no account of loads transmitted from adjoining piles to the same surrounding soil mass, that is, the group effect; and lastly, it takes no account of the temporary disturbance to the soil through which the pile is driven nor of any subsequent short- or long-time readjustments of that soil due to natural causes. Obviously, therefore, even in a case where the formula yields fairly reliable results for a single pile, it gives only a part of the information necessary to determine the safe bearing value for that pile as a part of a group.

However, keeping constantly in mind all of the limitations and uncertainties involved, a pile formula may still serve as a guide or "yardstick" to help the engineer obtain reasonably safe and uniform results over the entire job. Adjustments may be indicated in the field as to length and number of piles to support the required foundation loads. On a large undertaking where the soil conditions, the type of driving equipment, and the type of piles are uniform, test piles should be driven and subjected to actual load tests. Then a factor may be applied to some suitable formula, and allowable loads obtained empirically that are sufficiently correct. When many piles are driven, the effect on the soil mass and the resulting effect on the empirical factor in the formula must be taken into account through additional load tests.

Almost any formula of the many that have been devised for determining the bearing value of piles from dynamic data may be adapted empirically to a given site with uniform conditions and uniform driving equipment. This is practicable only as a result of experience with these conditions or as a result of tests on the site. It does not make much difference what formula is used so long as all data are observed carefully during driving of test piles and if, after loading them to failure, the engineer puts suitable factors in whatever formula he selects so that it is correlated to the test results.

Illustrating the more simple type of formula are the following:[16]

Engineering News—drop hammers: $R = \dfrac{2Wh}{s + 1.0}$.

Engineering News—single-acting steam hammers: $R = \dfrac{2Wh}{s + 0.1}$.

Modified *Engineering News* formula: $R = \dfrac{2Wh}{s + 0.1P/W}$.

Hiley formula (simplified) for drop hammers: $R = \dfrac{3Wh}{s + k} \times \dfrac{W}{W + P}$.

Hiley formula (simplified) for

single-acting steam hammers: $R = \dfrac{3.6Wh}{s + k} \times \dfrac{W}{W + P}$.

[16] For a discussion of these and other pile formulas, see *Proceedings of the American Society of Civil Engineers*, May, 1941, and September, 1941.

R = allowable safe static load on pile in pounds.
W = weight of a drop hammer or striking parts of a single-acting steam or air hammer in pounds.
P = weight of pile as driven in pounds.
h = height of fall of a drop hammer or length of stroke of a steam or air hammer, in feet.
s = penetration of pile per blow in inches (either the last blow or the average of the last few blows).
k = half the total rebound of pile hammer used in Hiley formula and expressed in inches.

The following references will be found particularly helpful in connection with the application of pile-driving formulas:

Pile-Driving Handbook, by Robert D. Chellis, Pitman Publishing Corporation, 1944.

"Dynamic Pile-Driving Formulas," by A. E. Cummings, *Journal of the Boston Society of Civil Engineers*, January, 1940.

STATIC PILE FORMULAS. Because of the uncertainty that exists as to the relationship between the dynamic driving resistance and the subsequent static carrying capacity of a pile, formulas have been developed for determining the bearing capacity of the pile on the basis of purely static considerations. The existing static formulas may be divided into two classes: (*a*) purely empirical formulas, and (*b*) scientific or theoretical formulas.

To use these static formulas, it is necessary to know the shape and size of the pile and the physical properties of the surrounding soil. The necessary information about the pile itself is always available. The determination of the physical properties of the surrounding soil is a problem which is still unsolved. The pile must be either driven or jetted into the ground, and either process produces a profound change in the state of stress in the soil and in some cases alters the physical properties of the soil itself. It is necessary, therefore, to know the soil characteristics after the pile is in place to determine its bearing capacity by means of a static formula.

From the standpoint of practical usefulness, the present position of static formulas is no better than that of the dynamic formulas. The weakness of the theoretical formulas is in the fact that the pile does not necessarily develop its bearing capacity, nor does the soil provide resistance to distortion in accordance with the assumptions on which such formulas are based.[17]

The chief weakness of the purely empirical formulas, as noted in the manual, is that sufficient information is not available to enable the designer to select satisfactory numerical values for the ultimate bearing capacity of the soil below the pile point and the friction per unit of area between the pile and the soil.

[17] Quoted from "Pile Foundations and Pile Structures," *Manual of Engineering Practice No.* 27, American Society of Civil Engineers, 1946.

PILE-LOADING TESTS. The settlement of pile clusters cannot be accurately determined from preliminary loading tests made upon single piles. Even a well-conducted test made under favorable conditions does not alone constitute an adequate basis for determining the allowable safe load. Results must be considered in relation to the soil profile. the driving record, and all other available data.

The principal value of a load test is to determine the resistance which the pile offers to slipping through the surrounding soil when subjected to a

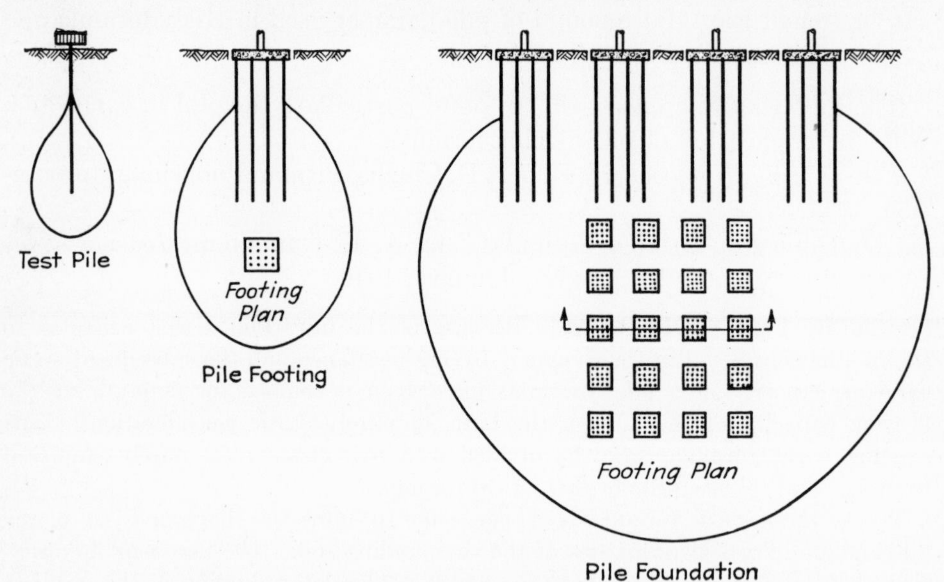

FIG. 21. Diagrammatic Comparison of the More Highly Stressed Zones beneath a Single Pile, a Pile Footing, and a Complete Pile Foundation.

static load for a specified period. This information assists the engineer in choosing suitable factors for use in a dynamic formula, as mentioned on page 398, but does not establish any definite relationship between the settlement of a single pile and that of a complete pile foundation. The overlapping of the bearing bodies of the individual piles comprising a single cluster, or a similar overlapping of the bearing bodies of the pile clusters comprising the entire foundation, may cause the settlement of the foundation to be far greater than that of an isolated test pile. Neither is the preliminary testing of a small group of piles ordinarily of sufficient additional value to warrant the expense of placing the required weight of loading material.

Figure 21 shows a very approximate comparison of pressure bulbs for a test pile, typical pile footing, and four footings comprising the cross-section of a complete building foundation. Although both the shape and the depth of the soil volume, which receives an appreciable increment of stress from the pile loads, depend upon the physical characteristics of the soil and many other variables, the drawing has significance in illustrating the far deeper distribution of load below a complete pile foundation than below a single footing. The inadequacy of a loading test as a means of determining the sustaining value of the lower substrata upon which the support of the complete foundation depends is also indicated.

The different effects produced in the physical characteristics of the soil by driving a single pile and driving the many necessary for the support of a building may alone be sufficient to invalidate any definite numerical comparison, particularly where piles obtain their support by skin friction in cohesive soils. Results are more dependable when piles are driven through sand or gravel. The following brief description of making a loading test is quoted from "Pile Foundations and Pile Structures," *Manual of Engineering Practice No.* 27, American Society of Civil Engineers, 1946.

A test pile is one on which known loads are placed in order to determine its load-bearing capacity and settlement rate under various loads. The purpose of the test may be (*a*) to guide the engineer in the selection of a proper type of pile and its load-bearing capacity; or (*b*) to confirm his assumptions in a design already prepared and to check the quality of the work. In the first case, the test piles are specially driven and tested well in advance of the actual construction to serve as a basis for the design. In the second case, the engineer, having already selected the type of pile and the assumed design load, selects certain piles for load-test purposes from those driven on the actual construction work.

The usual method of applying a test load to a pile is to build a suitable test platform on top of the pile and to load it with sand bags to some other measured load. The test pile should be supported laterally to prevent sway. In some cases, anchor piles are driven on each side of the pile to be tested, and the load is applied to the test pile by means of a hydraulic jack reacting against a beam fastened to the anchor piles. In such a test, the anchor piles should be at least 5 ft from the test pile.

Load should be applied in increments of 5 to 10 tons, and settlement readings should be made for a period of time at each load increment. When the full design load is reached, it should be allowed to remain until there is no settlement for a 24-hour period. The load should then be increased 50 per cent and maintained until the pile has again come to rest for a 24-hour period. As the pile is unloaded, rebound readings should be made at intervals, with a final rebound reading after all load has been removed.

The amount of settlement that may be acceptable under a given test load depends on several factors, such as the character of the structure to be supported; the nature of the design load, which may be steady or intermittent; and the amount of live load, due to wind or other causes, which may have been included in the design load. Some building codes contain the requirement that the allowable design load shall be considered as two-thirds of the test load, if the total net settlement after deduction of rebound does not exceed 0.01 in. per ton of test load applied to the pile. Although this simple rule has given satisfactory results, the determination of allowable settlements of test piles and the selection of an allowable design load are problems requiring mature judgment and experience.

Article 8. Concrete Piers

Concrete piers are used to carry the column loads of steel- and reinforced-concrete-framed buildings where it is desired to obtain support by passing through a material of low bearing value down to rock, hardpan, or gravel. Provided that the bearing capacity of the rock or soil is adequate, the design of a plain or reinforced-concrete pier does not present the many uncertain factors that have been discussed in relation to spread foundations and piles. Concrete piers are of professional interest to the architect and architectural engineer only as a means of obtaining adequate structural support. The technical methods employed in field construction, highly developed during the last 30 or 40 years, bear witness to the outstanding ability of our foundation engineers and contractors, but they are not within the scope of this text, as they have little influence upon the choice of structural design.

The chief problem involved is to choose the most economical method of sinking a shaft of the desired dimensions to the chosen bearing stratum. In building construction, this is usually done by means of open wells unless a considerable depth must be penetrated below ground-water level through a cohesionless soil, for which purpose the pneumatic caisson has often been employed. Except in firm soil, such as hard clay, open excavation usually requires some type of sheathing. For both full-lot excavation and individual pier foundations, steel sheet piling has a broad application. It may often be used in connection with perforated pipes, called "well points," driven 3 or 4 ft apart around the section to be excavated and connected with a header pipe run to a pump, which exerts sufficient suction to draw the water from the soil. Such installations have permitted lowering the ground-water level as much as 30 ft and make it possible to use open wells under conditions where pneumatic caissons were formerly considered necessary.

A well-known system, applicable to open-well excavation through firm clay, is known as the Chicago method because of its particular use in that city. Beneath each column location wells are dug to a depth of 3 to 6 ft, depending upon the stability of the soil. This height is then sheathed with 2-in. or 3-in. tongued and grooved boards maintained in place by metal rings. The same procedure is repeated, increasing the depth of the well, until the required level is reached. If the soil is not sufficiently firm to permit excavating ahead of the sheathing, this method is obviously impracticable, and either wood or steel sheet-piling, usually steel, may be driven by means of an air or steam hammer. Piling of considerable length has a very definite use when it is necessary to excavate through water-bearing strata of cohesionless soil underlain with clay. In this case the tips of the piles are sunk into the clay, thereby sealing the bottom of the shaft, which can then be excavated as an open well. In some types of soil both wood cylinders and open steel shells have been sunk by jacking.

The system used for either full-lot or open-well excavation is determined by the character of the soil, the amount of ground water, the required depth,

FIG. 22. The Gow Caisson Pile. Courtesy, Raymond Concrete Pile Company.

and the necessity of avoiding injury to adjacent structures, as well as other considerations which must be evaluated by the foundation engineer for each individual operation. As on work of this nature it is often necessary to maintain the stability of adjoining buildings, the problem merges into underpinning.[18]

The Gow caisson, Fig. 22, has its particular application when concrete piers are supported by rock or soil of suitable bearing capacity lying at moderate depths below grade or below an open excavation. The shell is

[18] See *Underpinning*, by E. A. Prentis and Lazarus White, Columbia University Press, 1931.

composed of telescoping steel cylinders, power-driven successively and withdrawn in reverse order after filling with concrete. When supported by soil, the base is excavated as shown to form a pedestal or "bell." For the successful installation of a Gow caisson of bell type, it is essential that: (*a*) the ground water be sealed above the level of the bell by the lowest cylinder; (*b*) the character of the soil permit excavating for the bell and filling it with concrete without forming; and (*c*) there be sufficient depth of soil to permit the bell design.

Pneumatic caissons are used where piers must be carried to bedrock through water-bearing material under conditions which do not permit the less expensive open-well methods. This system has been extensively employed for the foundations of the higher buildings in congested districts, such as lower Manhattan in New York City. An interesting description of this and other foundation methods will be found in *Building Construction*, by Whitney C. Huntington, Second Edition, John Wiley & Sons, Inc., 1941.

INDEX

(Numbers refer to pages)